Grades 2-4 Supplement

Mathematical Reasoning™ Series

Beginning 1 · Beginning 2
Level A · Level B · Level C · Level D
Level E · Level F · Level G
Understanding Geometry
Grades 2-4 Supplement · Grades 4-6 Supplement
Middle School Supplement (Grades 7-9)

Written by
Warren Hill
Ronald Edwards

Cover Design by
Scott Slyter

THE CRITICAL THINKING CO.™
www.CriticalThinking.com
Phone: 800-458-4849 • Fax: 831-393-3277
P.O. Box 1610 • Seaside • CA 93955-1610
ISBN 978-1-60144-414-1

Printed in the United States of America by McNaughton & Gunn, Inc., Saline, MI (July 2013)

TABLE OF CONTENTS

ABOUT THE AUTHORS iv
INTRODUCTION v

NUMBER AND NUMERATION
Counting Dots and Letters 1
Counting Sequences of Letters 7
Counting Sequences of Numbers 11
Completing Number Sequences 15
Properties of Sets of Numbers 21
Comparing Lengths 23
Comparing Sets 25
Comparing Regions 29
Using the Number Line 33
Comparing Numbers 41
Place Value 47

GEOMETRY
Estimating Lengths 63
Comparing Lengths 69
Classifying by Shape 77
Symmetry 83
Geometric Motions 89
Congruent Figures 95
Similar Figures 101
Combining Shapes 105
Matching and Finding Shapes 111
Dividing Figures 115

OPERATIONS
Counting to Ten 117
Sums Using Coins 123
Sums to Ten 127
Grouping by Tens 131
Using Basic Facts (Sums) 133
Equal Lengths and Regions 139
Missing Addends / Differences 143
Equal Sets of Coins 149
Grouping Using Arrays 153
Products / Missing Factors 157
Multiple Operations 161
Rounding / Estimating 165
Multiples of 10 and 100 169

MEASUREMENT
Finding Lengths by Counting 171
Finding Lengths Using Sums 175
Drawing Paths: Equal / Longer / Shorter 179
Comparing Paths: Equal / Longer / Shorter 185
Distance Around Figures 189
Area by Counting 201
Computing Area 211
Estimating Area 219
Area / Distance Around 221

RELATIONS
Comparing Numbers 223
Using the Order Relations 225
Number Sentences 233
Sequences of Numbers 237
Using Number Machines / Pairing Numbers 241
Multiples of 2, 3, and 5 249
Dividing Using 2, 3, and 5 251
Basic Facts Using 1, 2, 3, and 5 253

TABLES AND GRAPHS
Reading and Making Tables 255
Reading and Making Bar Graphs 261
Reading Charts 267
Reading and Drawing Line Graphs 275

ANSWERS 283

ABOUT THE AUTHORS

Dr. Warren H. Hill has been a Professor of Mathematics at Westfield State College (Massachusetts) for 20 years. He is a graduate of Peabody College for Teachers and holds doctorates in both mathematics and psychology. Dr. Hill has taught college-level mathematics and teacher-training courses for many years and prior to that had several years of high school-level teaching experience. He is a frequent speaker at both national and international conferences on reading, math, and thinking skills and regularly serves as a consultant and workshop teacher for school districts across the United States. Dr. Hill is the author of several books and numerous articles on mathematics.

Dr. Ronald R. Edwards has been a Professor of Mathematics at Westfield State College (Massachusetts) for 19 years. He holds an A.B. degree from Brown University, an M.A.T. from Wesleyan University, and a Ph.D. from the University of Connecticut. Dr. Edwards currently teaches college-level mathematics, computer science, and teacher training courses and has had several years of high school level teaching experience. He presents national workshops and seminars on computer science and mathematics and is the author of several books and numerous articles on mathematics.

INTRODUCTION

Objective

Mathematical Reasoning™ Grades 2-4 Supplement introduces children in the lower elementary grades to the application of analytical and critical thinking skills within the study of mathematics. The primary goal of the book is not to teach students a set of arithmetic skills, but to encourage them to develop analytical and reasoning skills applicable to a wide range of mathematical concepts. This is achieved through activities that are compatible with the standards developed by the National Council of Teachers of Mathematics.

These activities encourage students to develop investigative, analytical, and explanatory abilities in a cooperative learning environment. In addition, the activities explore a variety of quantitative and spatial relationships that are an essential part of the foundation of mathematics. The system of whole numbers and elementary geometry are used in the activities as vehicles to promote the development of these numerical and spatial concepts. To this end, there are 1,436 individual exercises on 282 reproducible student activity sheets. After the teacher or parent has *discussed* the example as well as explained any vocabulary new to the students, then students may proceed to work the next few exercises independently or in a small group. As a result of exploring each exercise to the fullest extent, layer by layer, the students should show significant gains in vocabulary development, substantially increase observational skills, and be able to process mathematical concepts on a much higher level.

The activities are arranged in six sections which address six major strands in the elementary mathematics curriculum:

- Number and Numeration
- Geometry
- Operations
- Measurement
- Relations
- Tables and Graphs

The first two sections develop an understanding of basic number and geometric concepts. The remaining four sections build upon these number and spatial understandings and investigate their relationships and applications in problem solving. To be used effectively, the materials should be followed sequentially. The presentation of the activities in each section assumes students have been exposed to the key concepts developed in earlier sections.

Cognitive Model

Many of the activities in *Mathematical Reasoning™ Grades 2-4 Supplement* have their origin in the cognitive development of Jean Piaget. A basic tenet of Piaget's cognitive model is that learning is an *interactive* process. Piaget maintained that the goal of education should be to provide the settings and opportunities for the student to become actively involved in the learning process. In a general sense, Piaget would have maintained that learning and intellectual development are not passive, sporadic activities, but dynamic, ongoing processes. The ability to acquire knowledge is built upon the capacity to organize and structure a concept's key components. Furthermore, this process is based upon the development of logical relationships. Thus, it is necessary, first of all, to identify those logical relationships that serve as the foundation of intellectual development, then provide the settings within an academic discipline that will enable a student to acquire proficiency with these relationships.

The application of logic and analytical skills to numerical and spatial concepts is introduced in this book through activities that are designed to focus student attention on the tasks of examining, discussing, and describing numerical and geometric relationships in terms of logical relations.

These logical relations include:

- analyzing similarities and differences
- recognizing sequences and patterns
- using numerical and spatial concepts for classification
- applying the concept of analogies to relations and functions

In addition, many of the activities stress using inductive reasoning to extend patterns, make predictions based upon available data, and formulate inferences. The role of deductive reasoning is introduced to students through the use of logical connectives, counterexamples, and the application of the process of elimination to derive solutions to numerical and geometric problems.

The presence of multiple solutions to certain exercises encourages students to realize that mathematics does not necessarily restrict itself to a single simple solution or a single strategy to arrive at a solution. The need to share ideas and compare solutions is of paramount importance. Such analysis and verbalizing results in students developing an appreciation that mathematics is indeed a logical discipline with recognizable patterns, order, and structure.

The Roles of the Teacher and the Student

The activities in *Mathematical Reasoning™ Grades 2-4 Supplement* provide teachers with an opportunity to teach students to *think mathematically*. The teacher's role is changed from simply reciting or explaining mathematical concepts to encouraging learners to explore and interact with these concepts. The teacher is encouraged to employ questioning techniques and discussion strategies that help learners move in a desired direction instead of providing a set of correct answers. The role of the teacher becomes one of developing questioning techniques that allow students to "wrestle" with the task of explaining their reasoning - and providing ample opportunities to do so. This is necessary because a student's understanding of the role of logical relations in mathematics is dependent upon his or her ability to verbalize and explain an underlying mathematical process rather than providing a simple response to an exercise. To achieve the objective of thinking mathematically, students must become active participants in the learning process.

As a corollary to questioning techniques, the teacher must also develop acute listening skills. When an inappropriate response is given, it is often a delicate task to "hear" a student's reasoning and then redirect it toward an appropriate response. The teacher must continually be aware that there may be more than one correct response in some situations. In fact, it may be more appropriate in many cases to think in terms of a "best" response rather than a correct or incorrect response. Unanimous agreement on the best answer is not crucial. What is crucial, however, is that each person understands and appreciates the other's reasoning.

In the case of an unexpected response, the teacher should focus on the student's verbalized explanation or rationale for the answer before discussing its correctness. For example, a typical teacher reaction to an unexpected response might be, "Why did you choose that answer?"

In sum, the role of the teacher is not to put forth a body of information but to serve as a catalyst between the student's intuitive responses and the student's ability to offer a verbal rationale for his or her conclusions. At the same time, the role of the student is not to be passive but to be an active participant in the learning process by applying analysis and reasoning to mathematics and by discussing the reasoning used in solving the activities.

HOW MANY DOTS?

Draw lines to match the pictures of dots with the numbers.

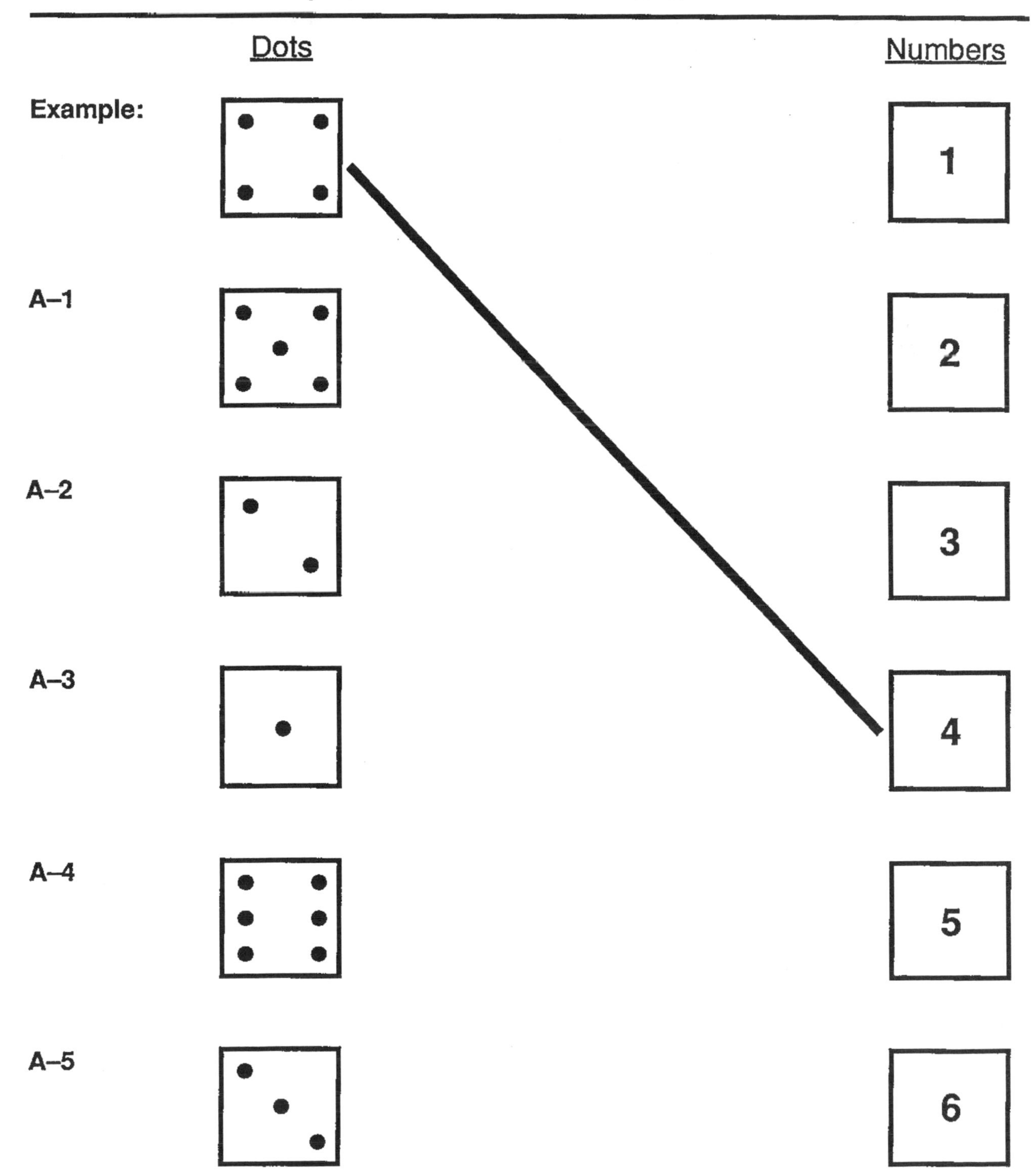

HOW MANY LETTERS?

Find the number of letters in each box.
Write the answer in the circle.

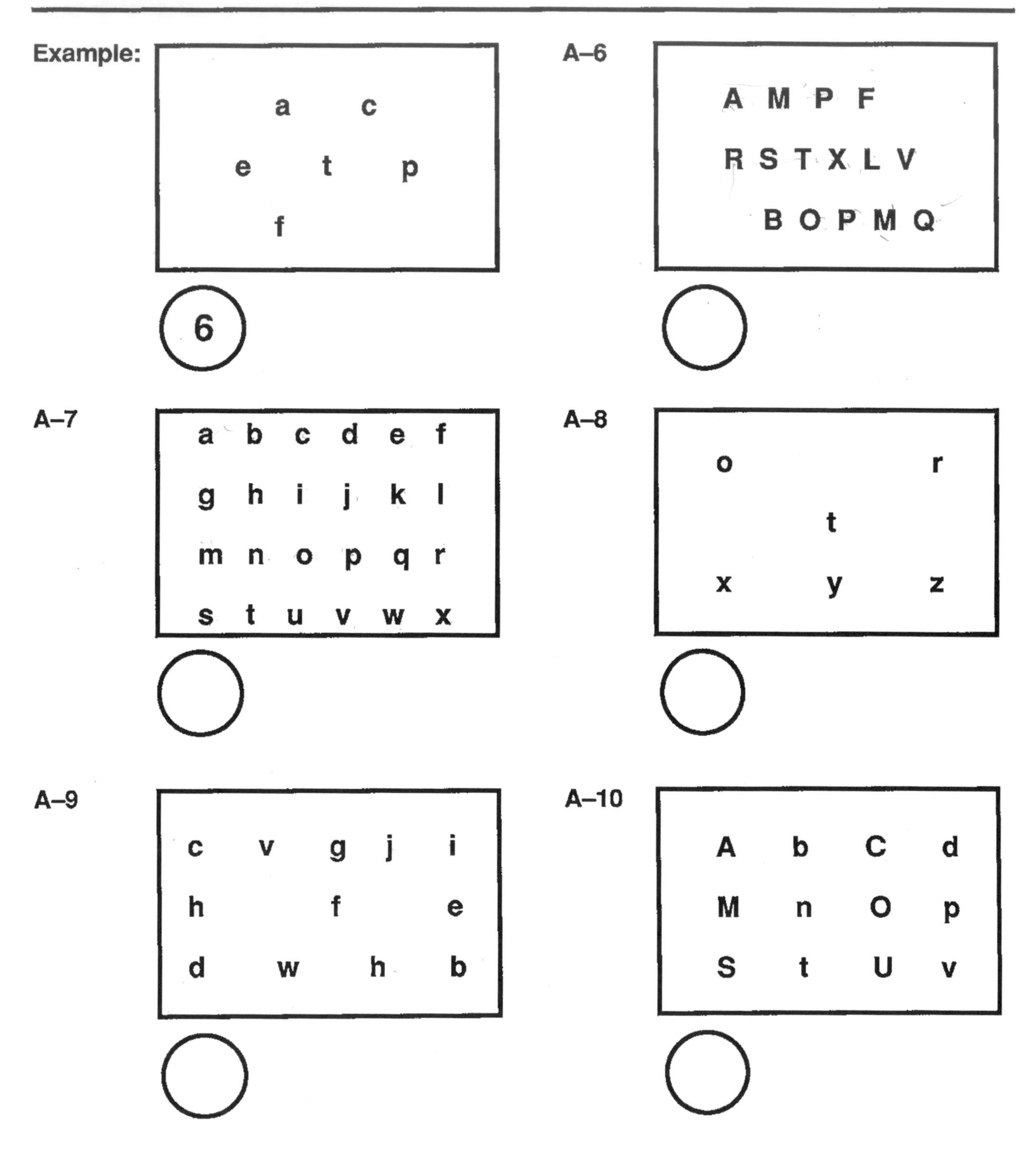

HOW MANY DOTS?

Each box contains pictures of four sets of dots.
Count the total number of dots in the box.
Write the answer in the circle.

Example:

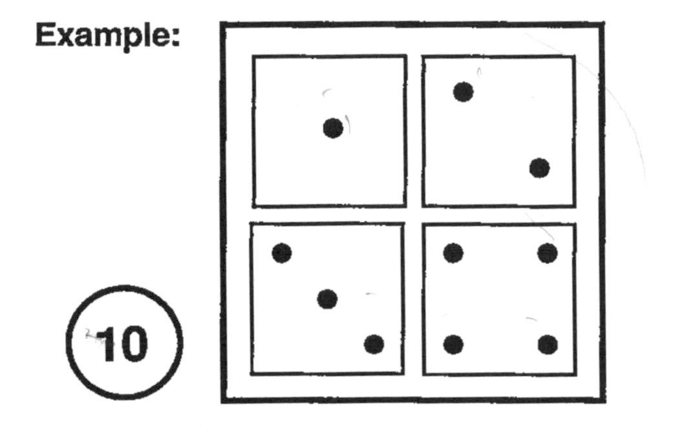

A–11

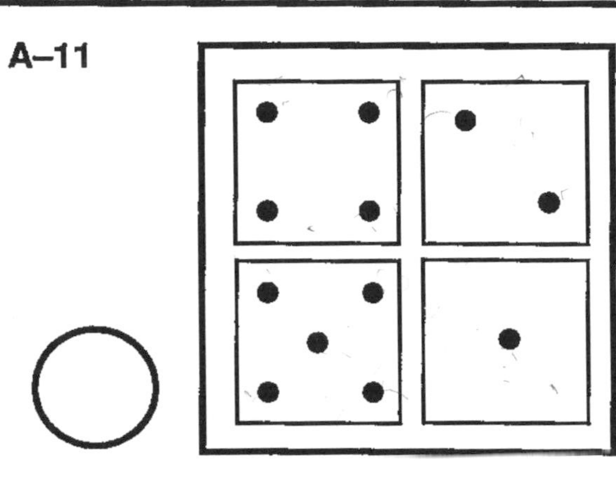

A–12

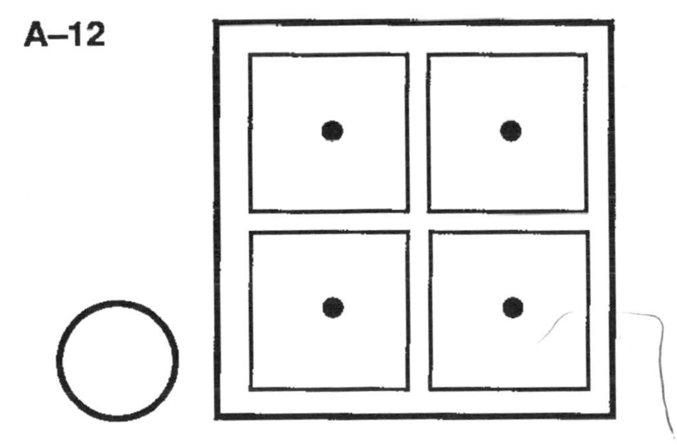

A–13

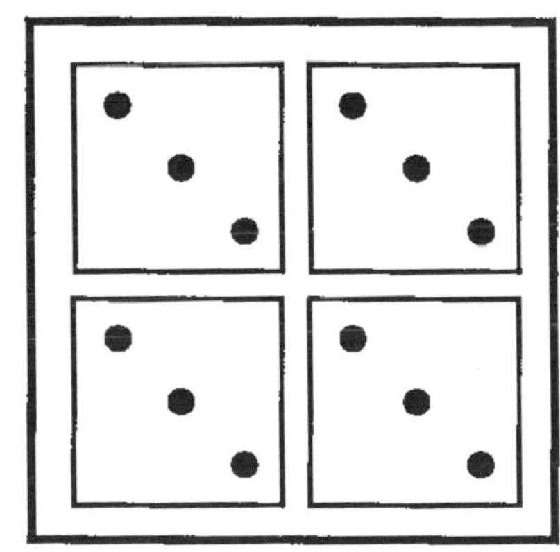

A–14

A–15

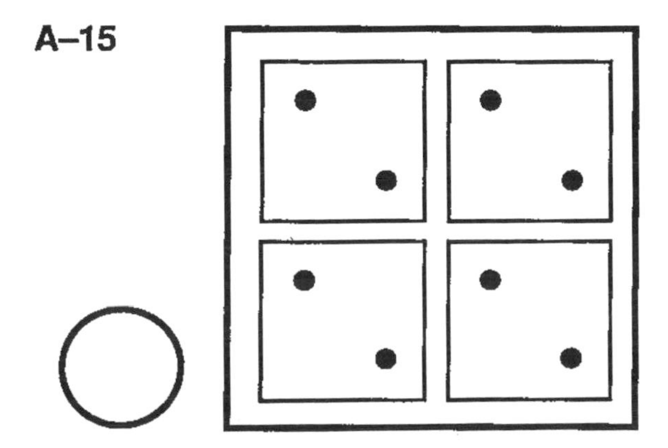

HOW MANY LETTERS?

Find the number of letters in each box.
Write the answer in the circle.

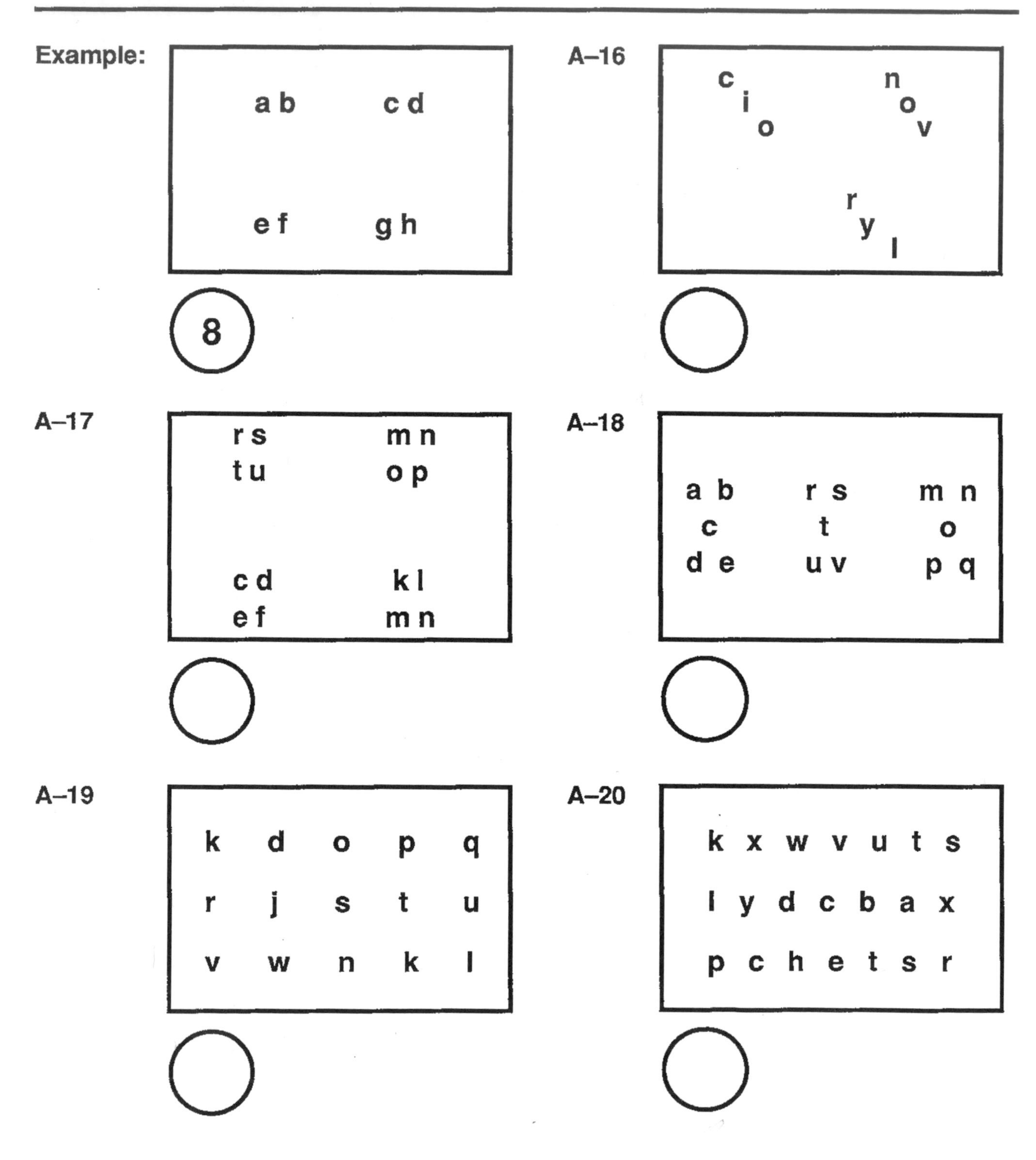

HOW MANY LETTERS?

Find the number of letters in each box. Count the letters only.
Write the answer in the circle.

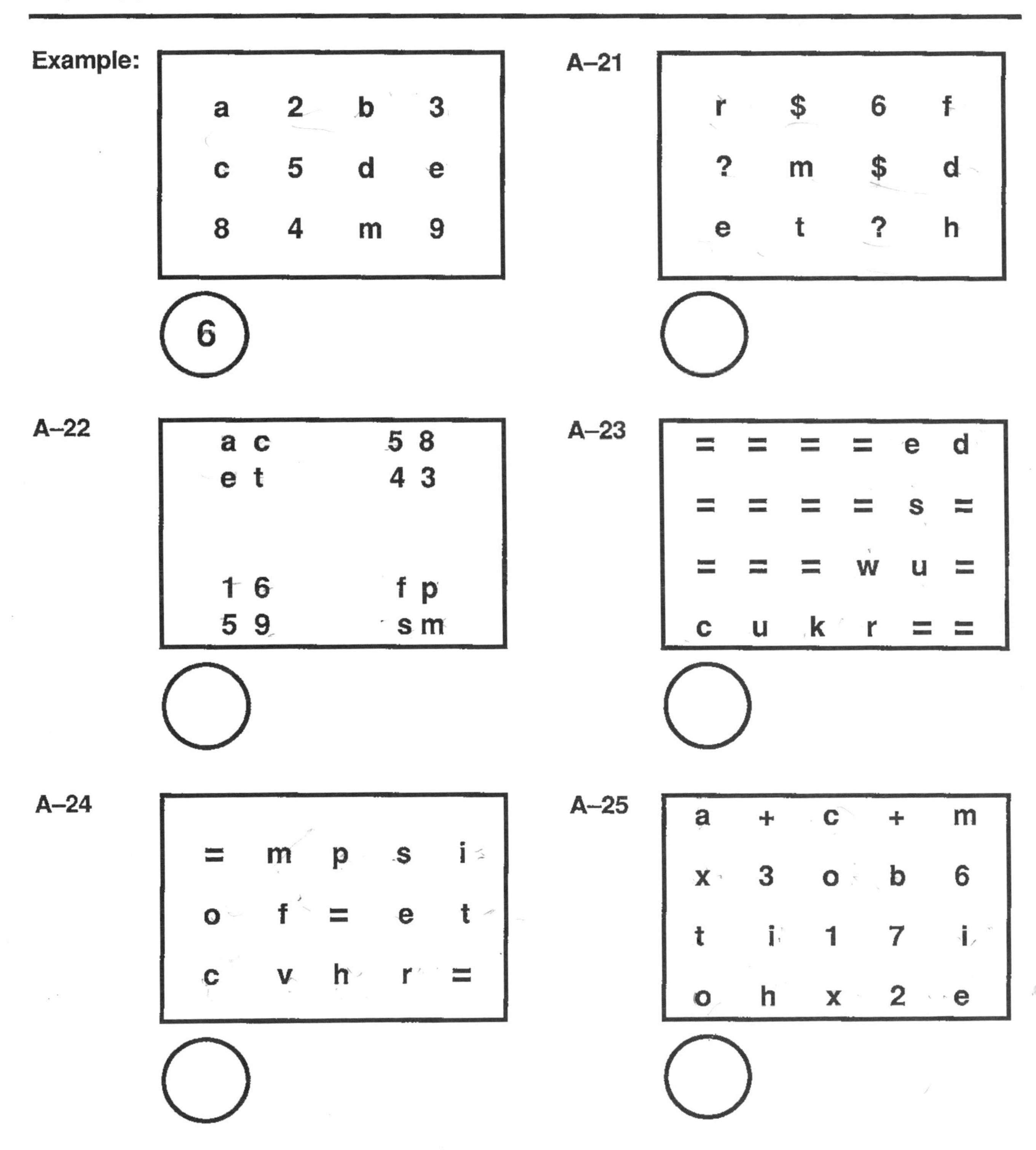

HOW MANY DIFFERENT LETTERS?

Look at the boxes below. Each box contains a mixture of letters.
Find the number of different letters in each box.
Write the answer in the circle.

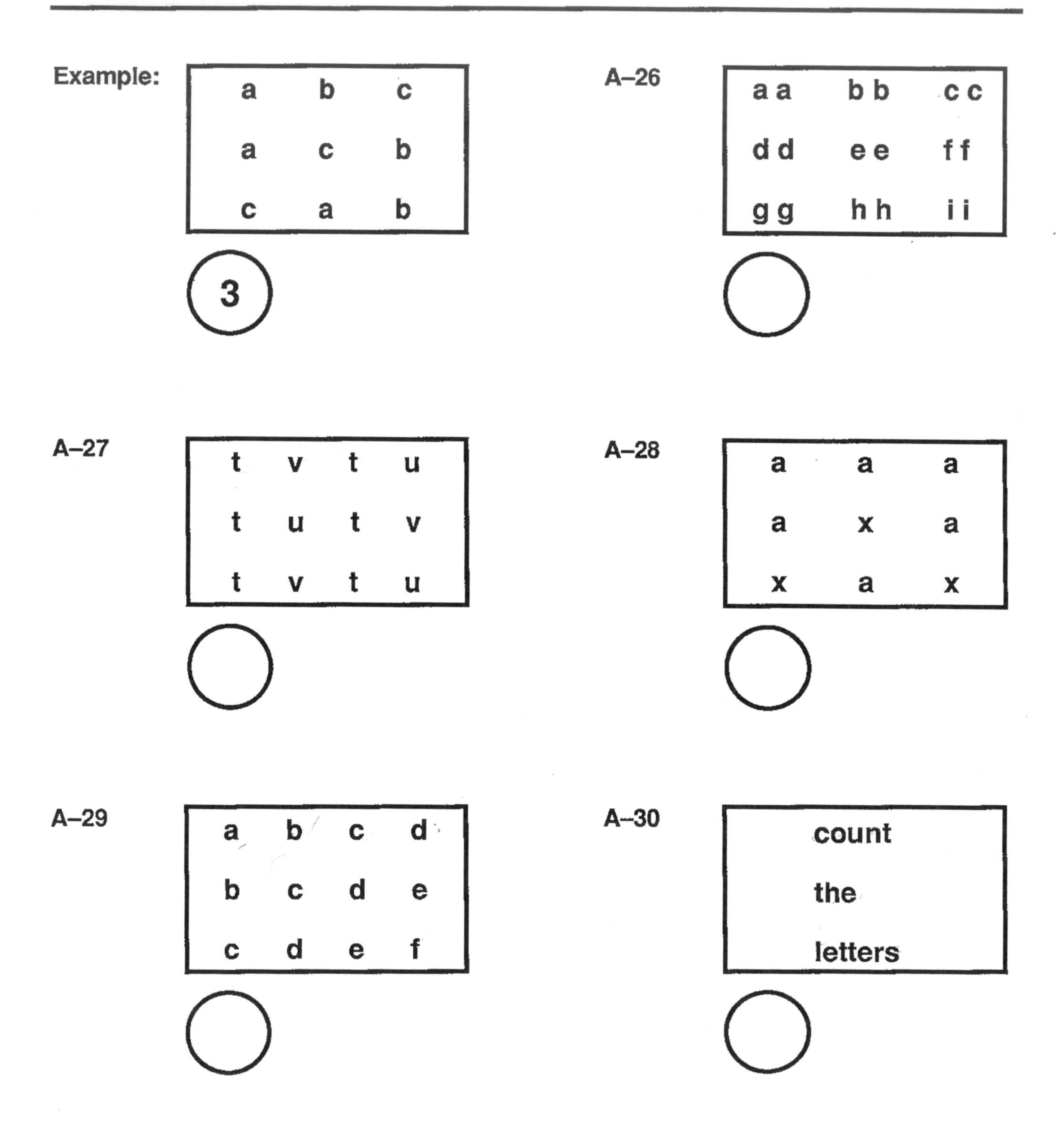

HOW MANY LETTERS IN A LIST?

Each list below is part of the alphabet. The lists have missing letters.
Put the missing letters in the boxes.
Count the number of letters in each list and write the answer in the circle.

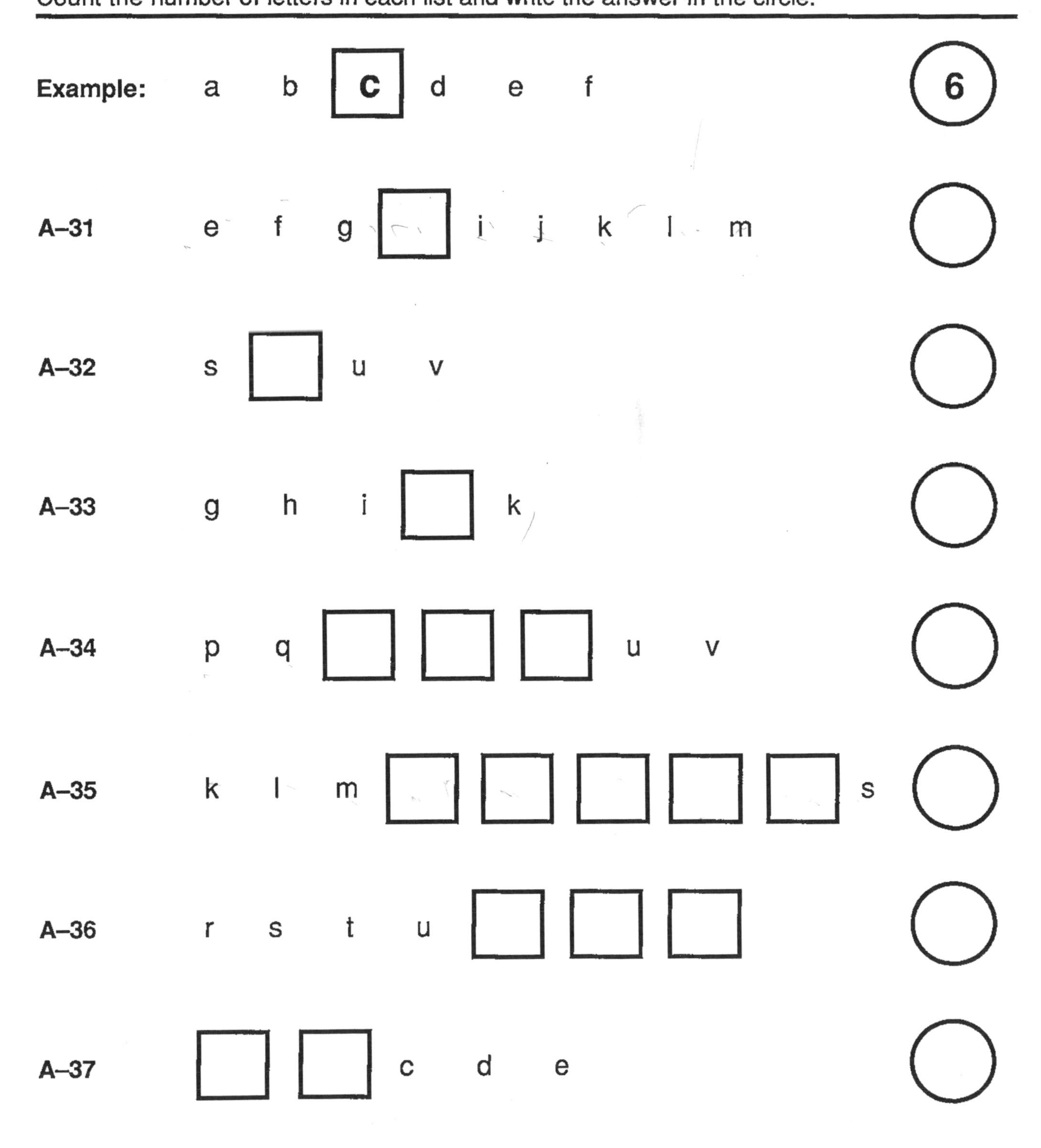

HOW MANY LETTERS IN A LIST?

Each list below is part of the alphabet. The lists have missing letters.
Put the missing letters in the boxes.
Count the number of letters in each list and write the answer in the circle.

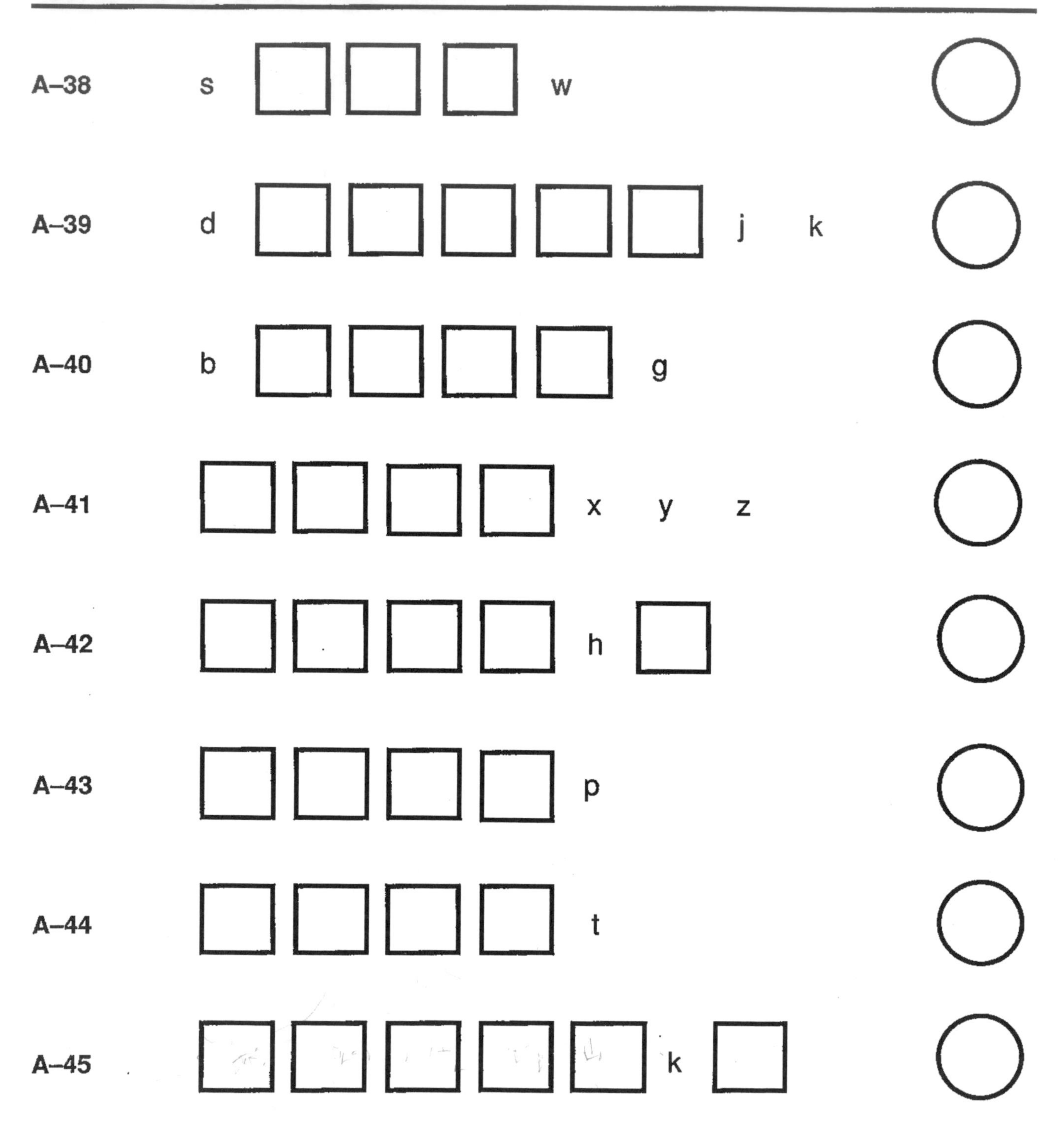

HOW MANY LETTERS IN A LIST?

Three dots means a list continues.

a b c • • • j	means	**a b c d e f g h i j**

This list has 10 letters.
Write the missing letters in each list in the boxes.
Write the number of letters in the list in the circle.

Example: a b c • • • f

a b c [**d**] [**e**] f (**6**)

A–46 c d e • • • j

c d e [ ] [ ] [ ] [ ] j ( )

A–47 p q r • • • v

p q r [ ] [ ] [ ] v ( )

A–48 m n • • • t

m n [ ] [ ] [ ] [ ] [ ] t ( )

A–49 k l • • • s

k l [ ] [ ] [ ] [ ] [ ] [ ] s ( )

HOW MANY LETTERS IN A LIST?

Three dots means a list continues.
Find the number of letters in each list below.
Write the answer in the circle.

Example: r s t • • • z (9)

A–50 p q • • • t ( )

A–51 e f • • • n ( )

A–52 f • • • o ( )

A–53 a b c • • • z ( )

A–54 a b c • • • x ( )

A–55 c d e • • • z ( )

A–56 c • • • x ( )

HOW MANY NUMBERS IN A LIST?

The lists below have missing numbers.
Put the missing numbers in the boxes.
Count the numbers in each list and write the answer in the circle.

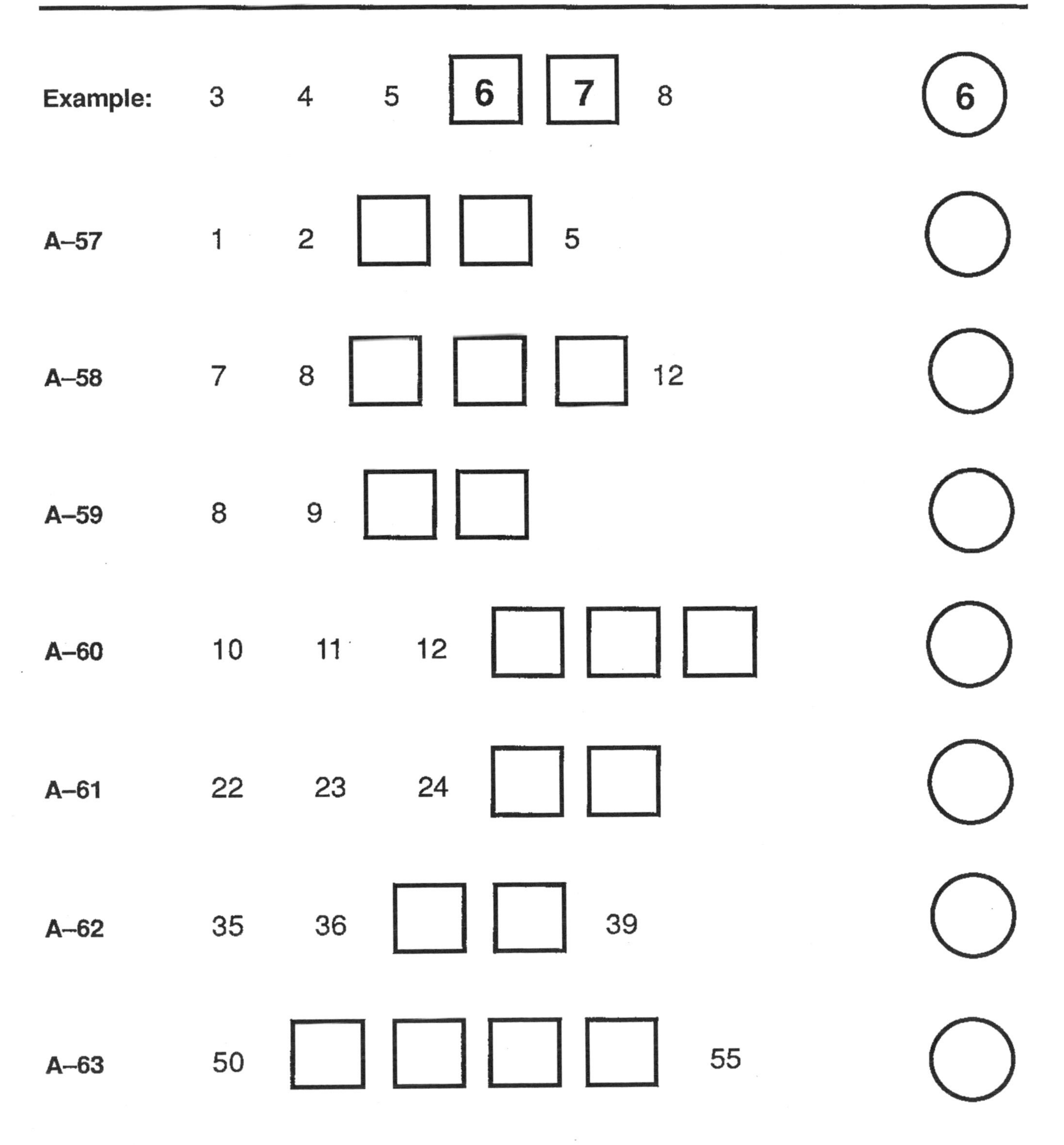

Example:	3	4	5	**6**	**7**	8		**6**
A–57	1	2	☐	☐	5			◯
A–58	7	8	☐	☐	☐	12		◯
A–59	8	9	☐	☐				◯
A–60	10	11	12	☐	☐	☐		◯
A–61	22	23	24	☐	☐			◯
A–62	35	36	☐	☐	39			◯
A–63	50	☐	☐	☐	☐	55		◯

HOW MANY NUMBERS IN A LIST?

The lists below have missing numbers.
Put the missing numbers in the boxes.
Count the numbers in each list and write the answer in the circle.

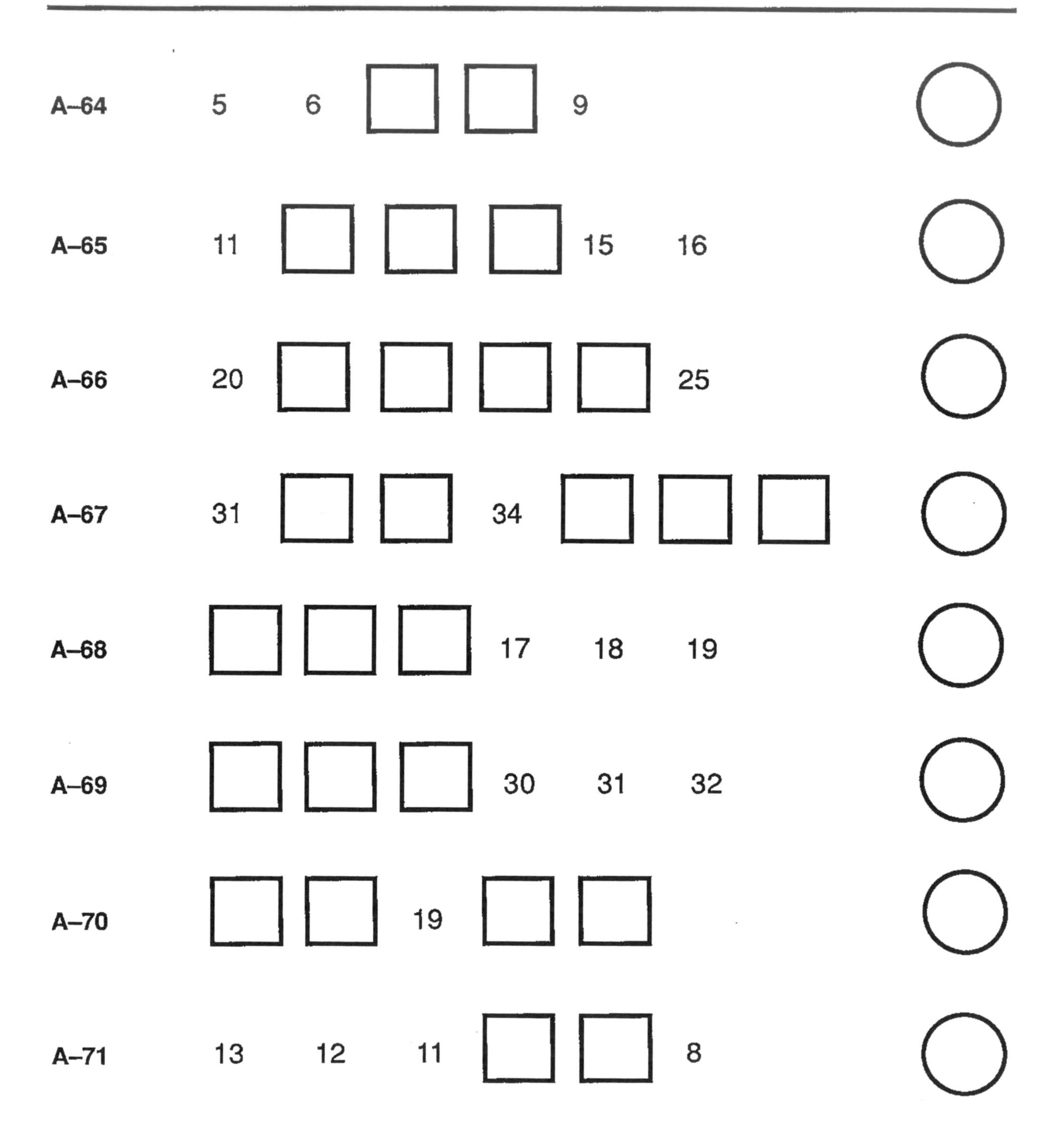

HOW MANY NUMBERS IN A LIST?

Three dots means a list continues.

2 3 4 • • • 9 10 means **2 3 4 5 6 7 8 9 10**

This list has 9 numbers.
Write the missing numbers in the boxes.
Count the numbers in each list and write the answer in the circle.

Example: 1 2 3 • • • 6

1 2 3 [4] [5] 6

(6)

A–72 3 4 5 • • • 9

3 4 5 [ ] [ ] [ ] 9

( )

A–73 11 12 13 • • • 18

11 12 13 [ ] [ ] [ ] [ ] 18

( )

A–74 30 31 • • • 38

30 31 [ ] [ ] [ ] [ ] [ ] [ ] 38

( )

A–75 50 51 • • • 58

50 51 [ ] [ ] [ ] [ ] [ ] [ ] 58

( )

HOW MANY NUMBERS IN A LIST?

Three dots means a list continues.
The circle shows how many numbers are in each list.
Find the last number in each list and write it in the box.

							Last Number	Number in List
Example:	4	5	6	•	•	•	9	6
A–76	1	2	3	•	•	•		6
A–77	10	11	12	•	•	•		8
A–78	21	22	23	•	•	•		5
A–79	9	10	11	•	•	•		7
A–80	1	2	3	•	•	•		9
A–81	1	2	3	•	•	•		20

SEQUENCES OF NUMBERS

Place numbers in the blank spaces to continue the sequence.

Example: 9 10 11 12 __13__ __14__ __15__ __16__

A–82 17 18 19 ____ ____ ____

A–83 15 16 17 18 ____ ____ ____ ____

A–84 51 52 53 ____ ____ ____

A–85 90 91 92 ____ ____ ____ ____

A–86 64 65 66 ____ ____ ____

A–87 7 8 ____ ____ ____ ____

A–88 30 31 ____ ____ ____ ____

SEQUENCES OF NUMBERS

Place numbers in the blank spaces to continue the sequence.

A–89 14 13 12 11 _____ _____ _____

A–90 20 19 18 _____ _____ _____

A–91 93 92 91 _____ _____ _____ _____

A–92 34 33 32 _____ _____ _____

A–93 42 41 40 _____ _____ _____ _____

A–94 9 8 _____ _____ _____

A–95 59 58 _____ _____ _____ _____

A–96 62 61 _____ _____ _____

COMPLETING THE SEQUENCE

Place numbers in the blank spaces to complete the sequence.

Example:	1	2	3	4	5	6	7
A–97	4	____	6	____	8	____	10
A–98	____	84	85	____	____	88	
A–99	____	19	____	____	22	23	24
A–100	55	____	____	58	59	____	____
A–101	____	____	13	14	15	____	
A–102	____	30	____	____	33	____	35
A–103	____	____	17	____	____	20	

COMPLETING THE SEQUENCE

Place numbers in the blank spaces to complete the sequence.

A–104 _____ _____ 93 92 91 _____ _____

A–105 _____ 84 85 _____ _____ 88 _____

A–106 24 23 22 _____ _____ 19

A–107 17 _____ 15 _____ 13 _____ 11

A–108 9 _____ _____ _____ 5 4 _____

A–109 10 _____ 8 _____ 6 _____ _____

A–110 _____ _____ 47 48 _____ _____ _____

A–111 72 _____ _____ _____ 68 _____ _____

CONTINUING THE SEQUENCE

Place numbers in the blank spaces to continue the sequence.

Example:	12	14	16	18	20	22	24
A–112	2	4	6	____	____	____	____
A–113	3	6	9	12	____	____	____
A–114	5	10	15	____	____	____	____
A–115	24	26	28	30	____	____	____
A–116	40	50	60	____	____	____	
A–117	30	35	40	____	____	____	____
A–118	30	33	36	____	____	____	____

COMPLETING THE SEQUENCE

Place numbers in the blank spaces to complete the sequence.

Example: 8 __10__ 12 14 16 __18__ __20__

A–119 3 ____ 9 12 ____ 18

A–120 5 10 ____ ____ 25 ____ ____

A–121 ____ ____ ____ 30 ____ 40 45 50

A–122 2 ____ 6 ____ 10 ____ 14 16

A–123 ____ ____ 19 ____ ____ 22 23 24

A–124 ____ 16 14 ____ 10 ____ 6 4

A–125 55 50 ____ ____ 35 ____ ____

WHICH NUMBER BELONGS?

Each set contains five numbers.
The numbers have something in common.
Circle another number that belongs to the set.

Example: { 10, 30, 40, 20, 60 }

a. 45 b. 8
c. (50) d. 17

A–126 { 5, 25, 10, 15, 20 }

a. 18 b. 30
c. 12 d. 1

A–127 { 64, 68, 63, 65, 60 }

a. 70 b. 6
c. 67 d. 54

A–128 { 8, 18, 14, 6, 12 }

a. 19 b. 4
c. 5 d. 21

A–129 { 3, 2, 9, 5, 6 }

a. 10 b. 7
c. 12 d. 23

WHICH NUMBER DOES NOT BELONG?

Each set contains five numbers.
Four of the numbers have something in common.
Circle the number in each set that does not belong.

Example: { 2, 6, 4, 7, 8 }

A–130 { 10, 30, 46, 20, 50 }

A–131 { 25, 15, 45, 21, 35 }

A–132 { 75, 74, 71, 33, 79 }

A–133 { 12, 49, 32, 62, 42 }

A–134 { 33, 44, 21, 77, 55 }

A–135 { 1, 6, 3, 9, 7 }

A–136 { 5, 1, 2, 64, 6 }

MORE THAN

Shade all the rectangles that have more than 10 squares.

Example:

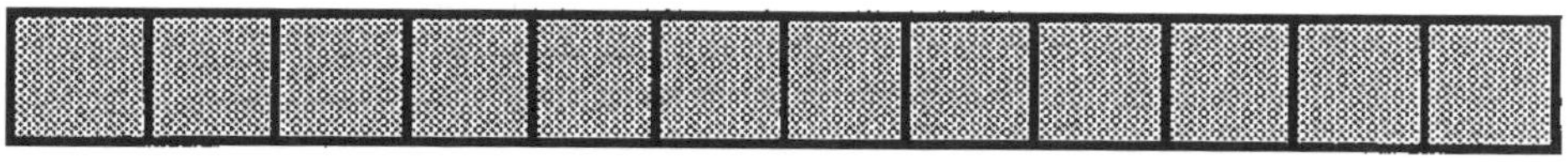

A–137

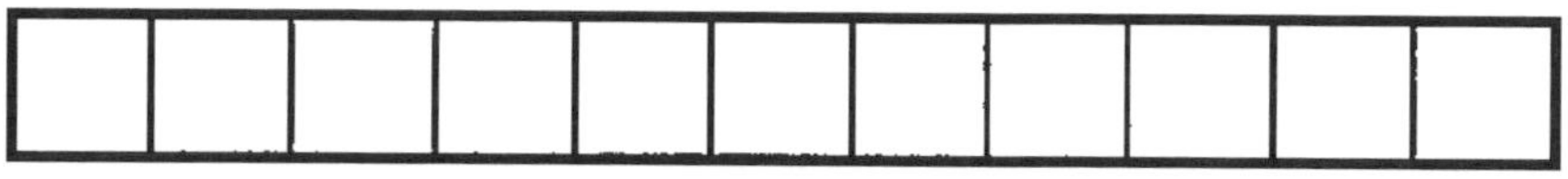

A–138

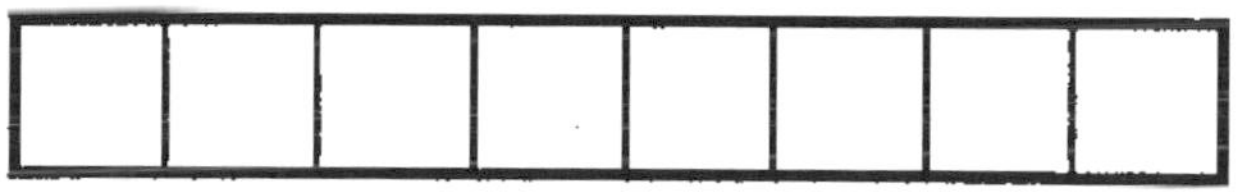

A–139

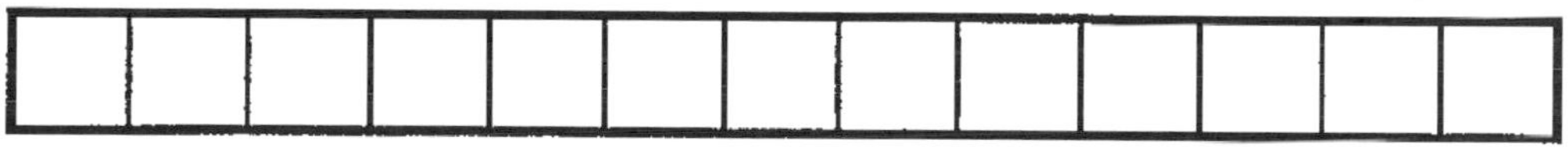

A–140

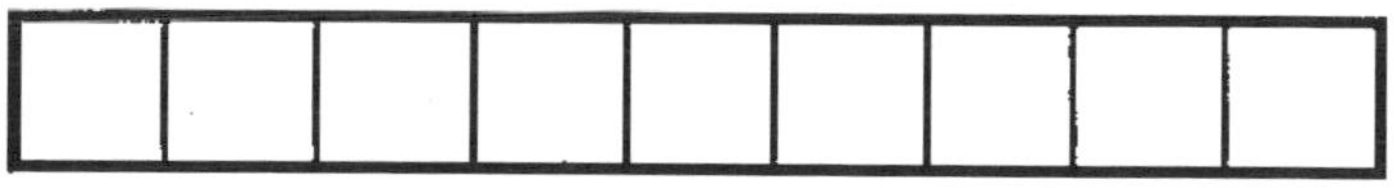

A–141

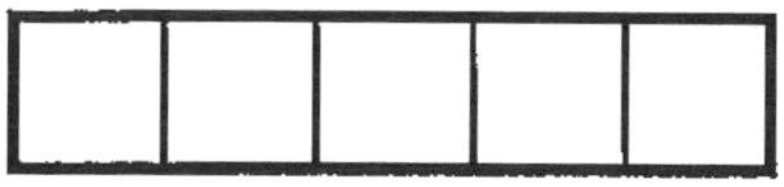

A–142

A–143

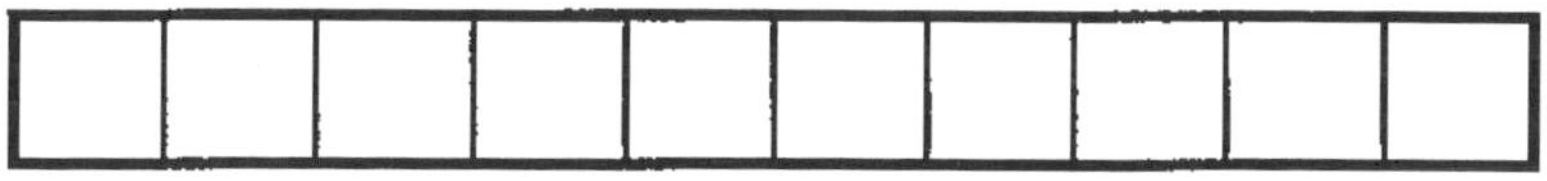

LESS THAN

Shade all the rectangles that have less than 10 squares.

Example:

A–144

A–145

A–146

A–147

A–148

A–149

A–150

COMPARING SIZES OF SETS

Compare set A with set B.
Circle the set that contains more dots.

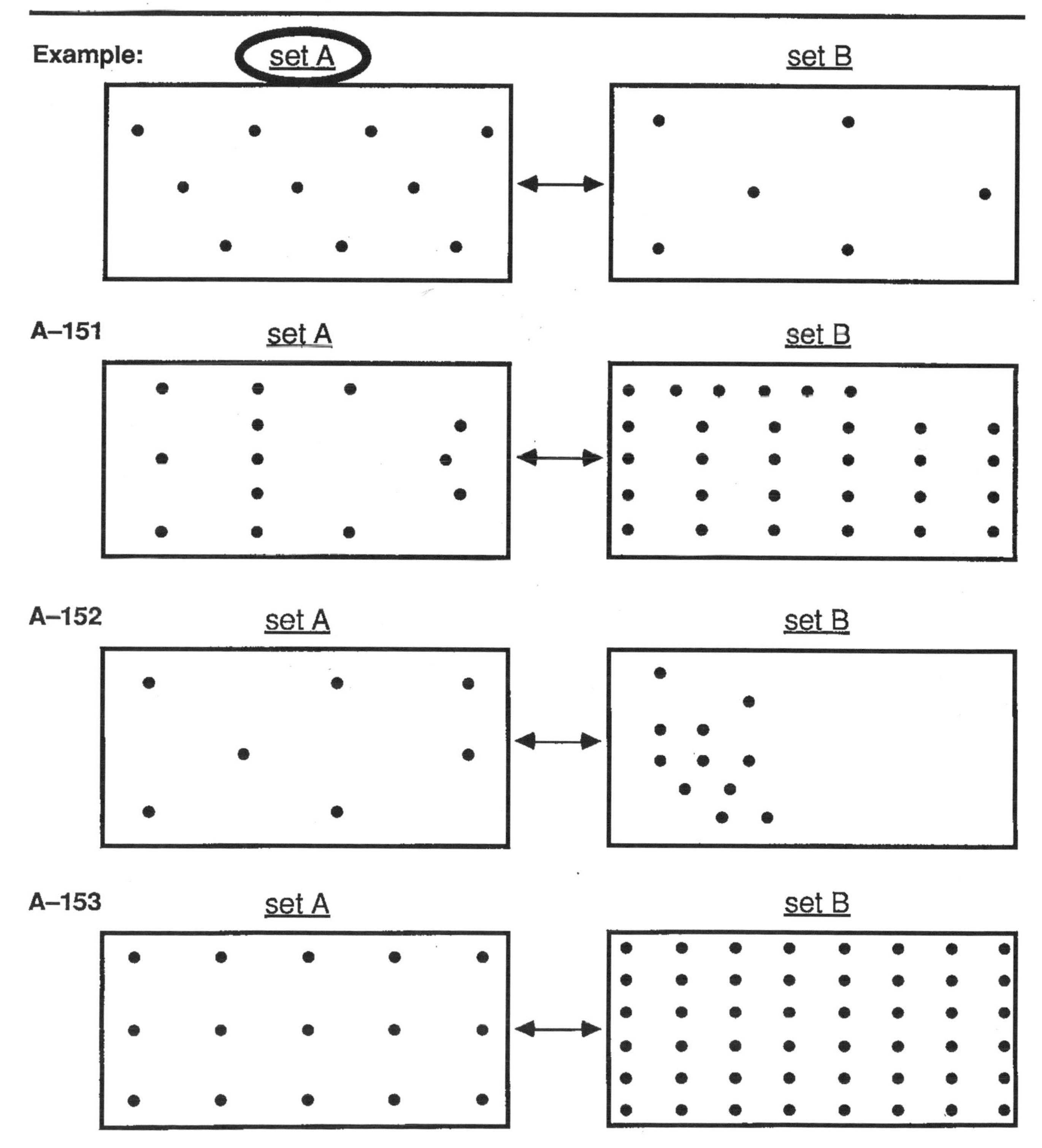

COMPARING SIZES OF SETS

Compare set A with set B.
Circle the set that contains more dots.

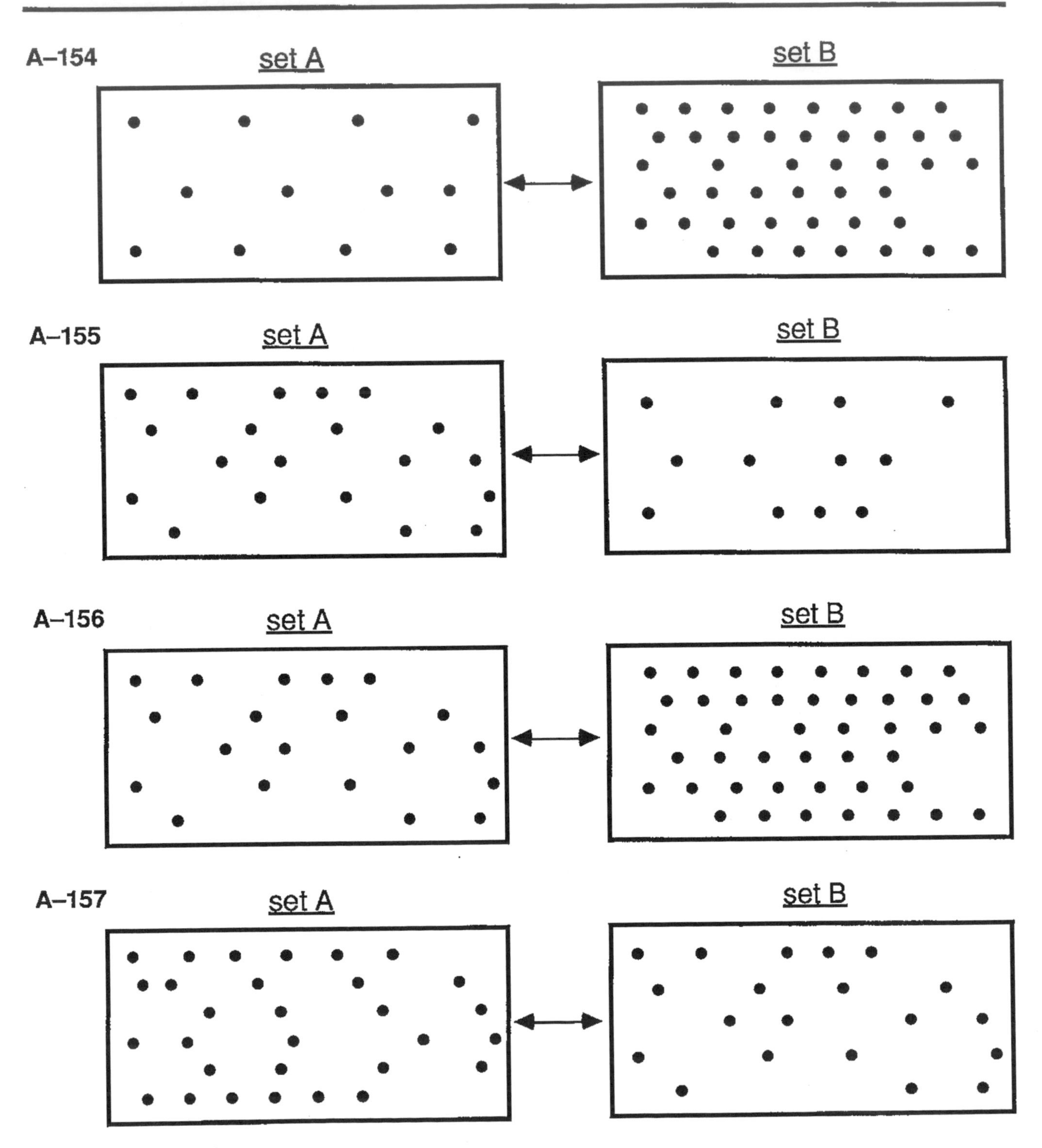

COMPARING SIZES OF SETS

Match the sets that have the same number of dots.

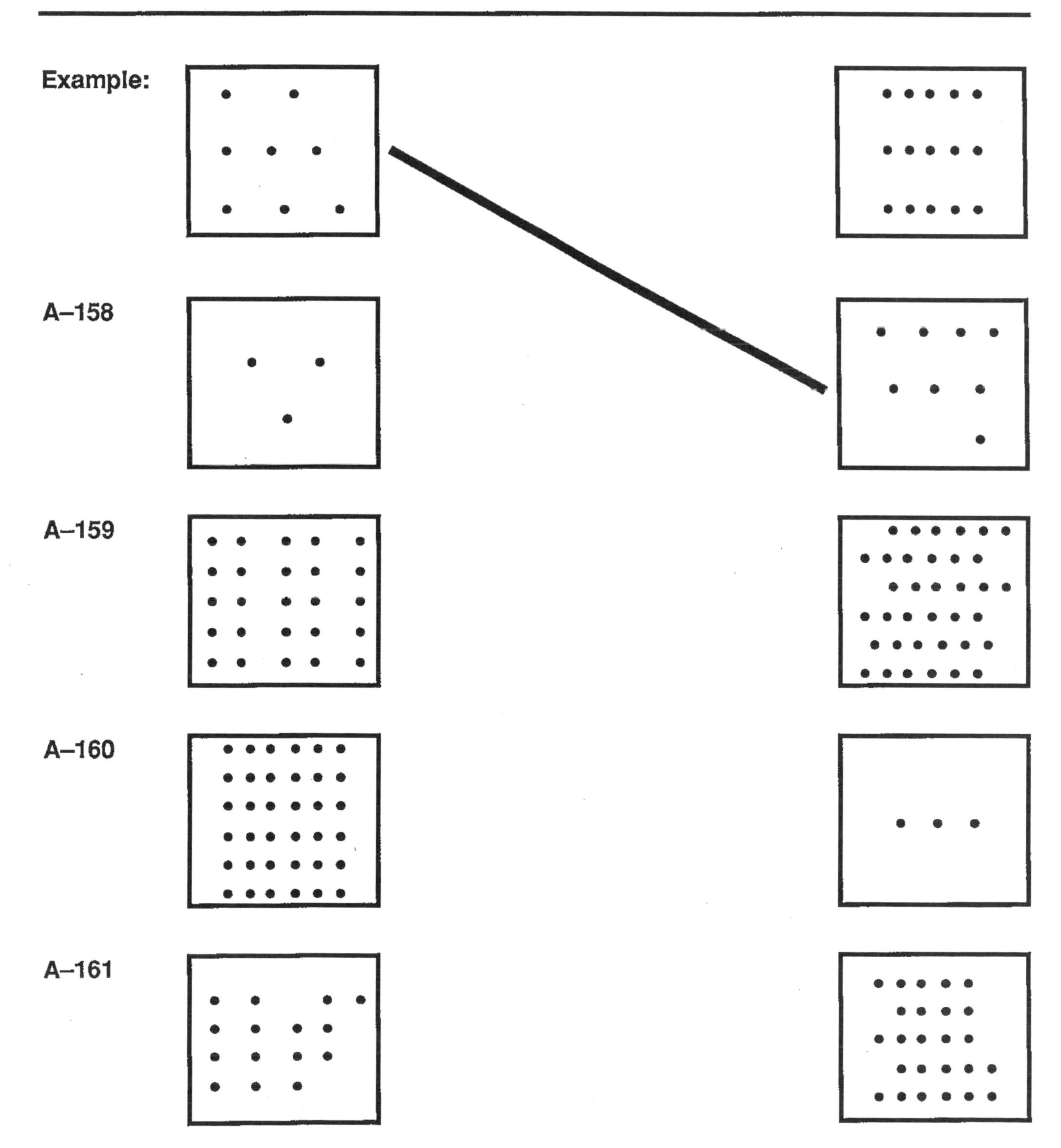

COMPARING SIZES OF SETS

Match the sets that have almost the same number of dots.

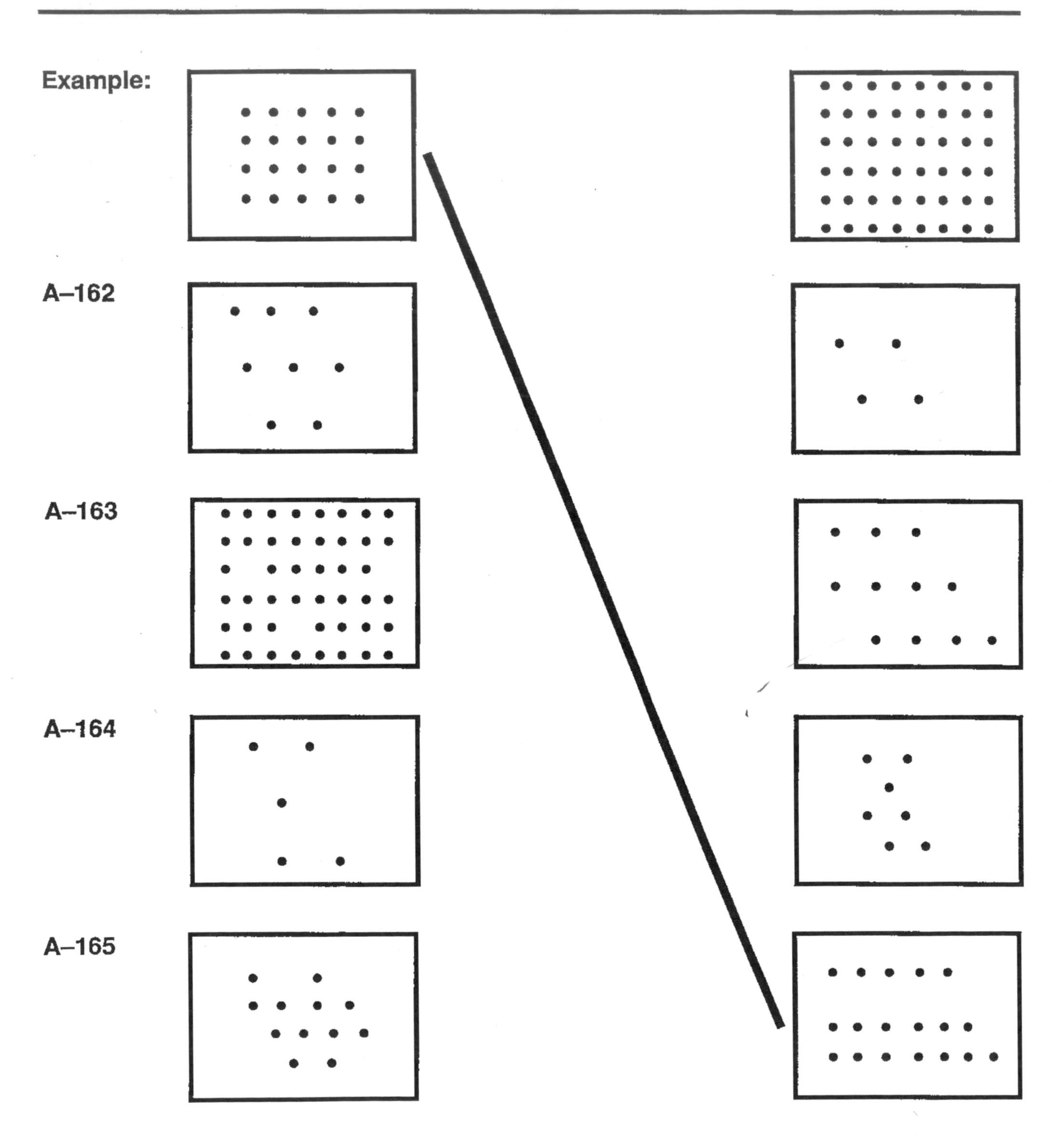

COUNTING PARTS

Count the number of shaded pieces in each circle.
Count the total number of pieces in each circle.
Write the answers in the boxes.

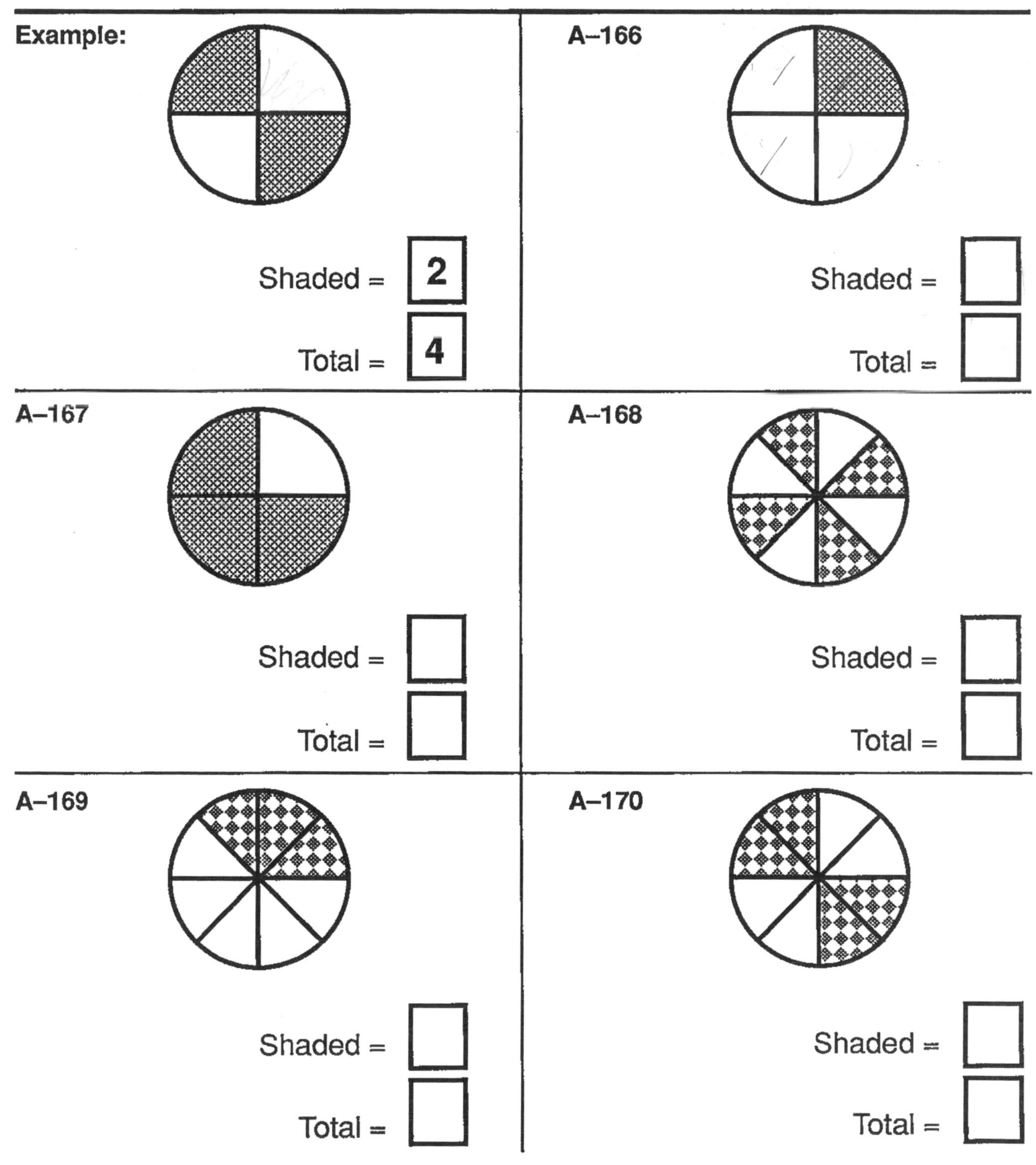

COUNTING PARTS

Count the number of shaded squares in each figure.
Count the total number of squares in each figure.
Write the answers in the boxes.

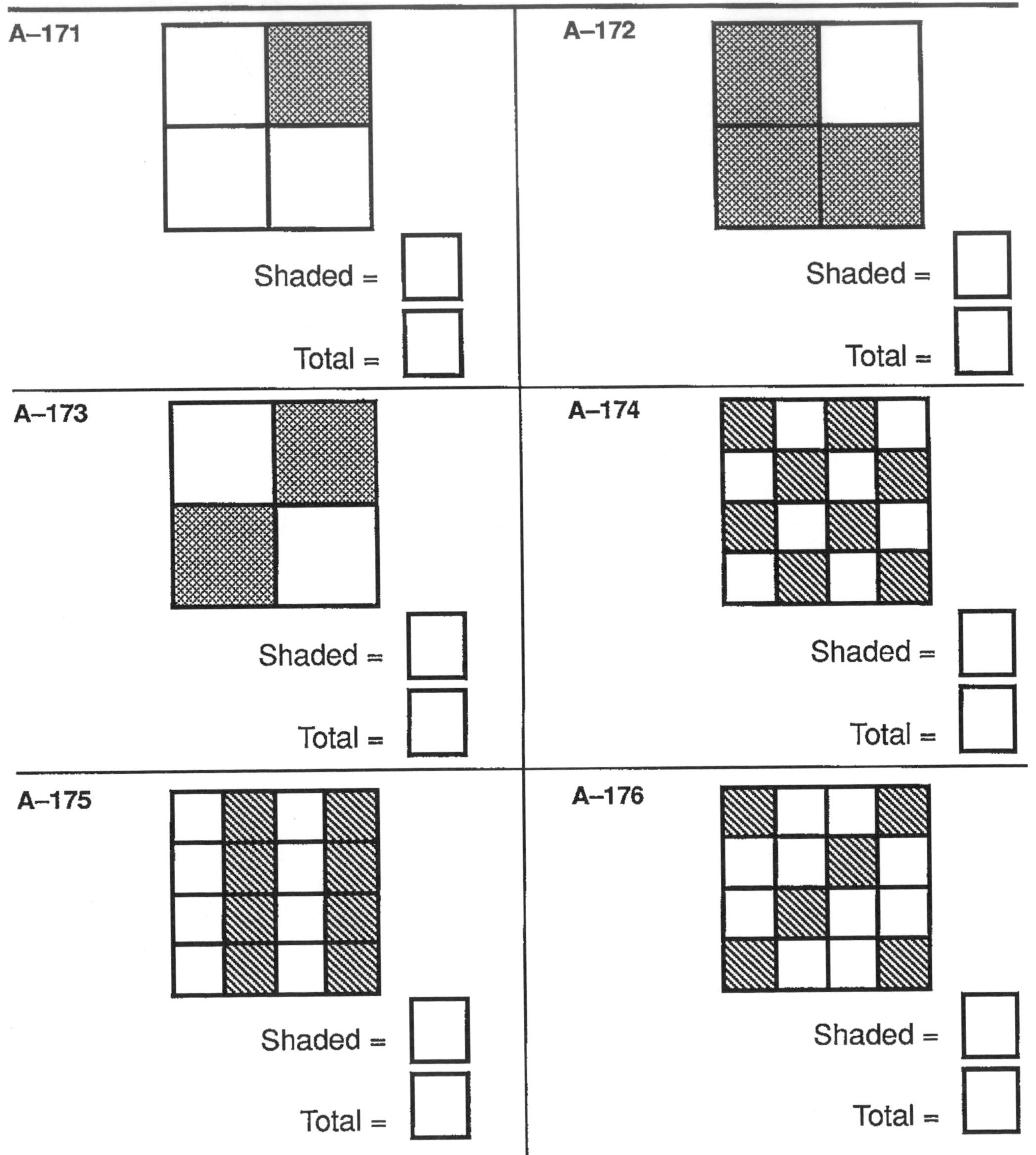

MORE OR LESS THAN 1/2

Look at the shaded pieces in each circle.
If more than 1/2 of the circle is shaded, place an X in the More box.
If less than 1/2 of the circle is shaded, place an X in the Less box.

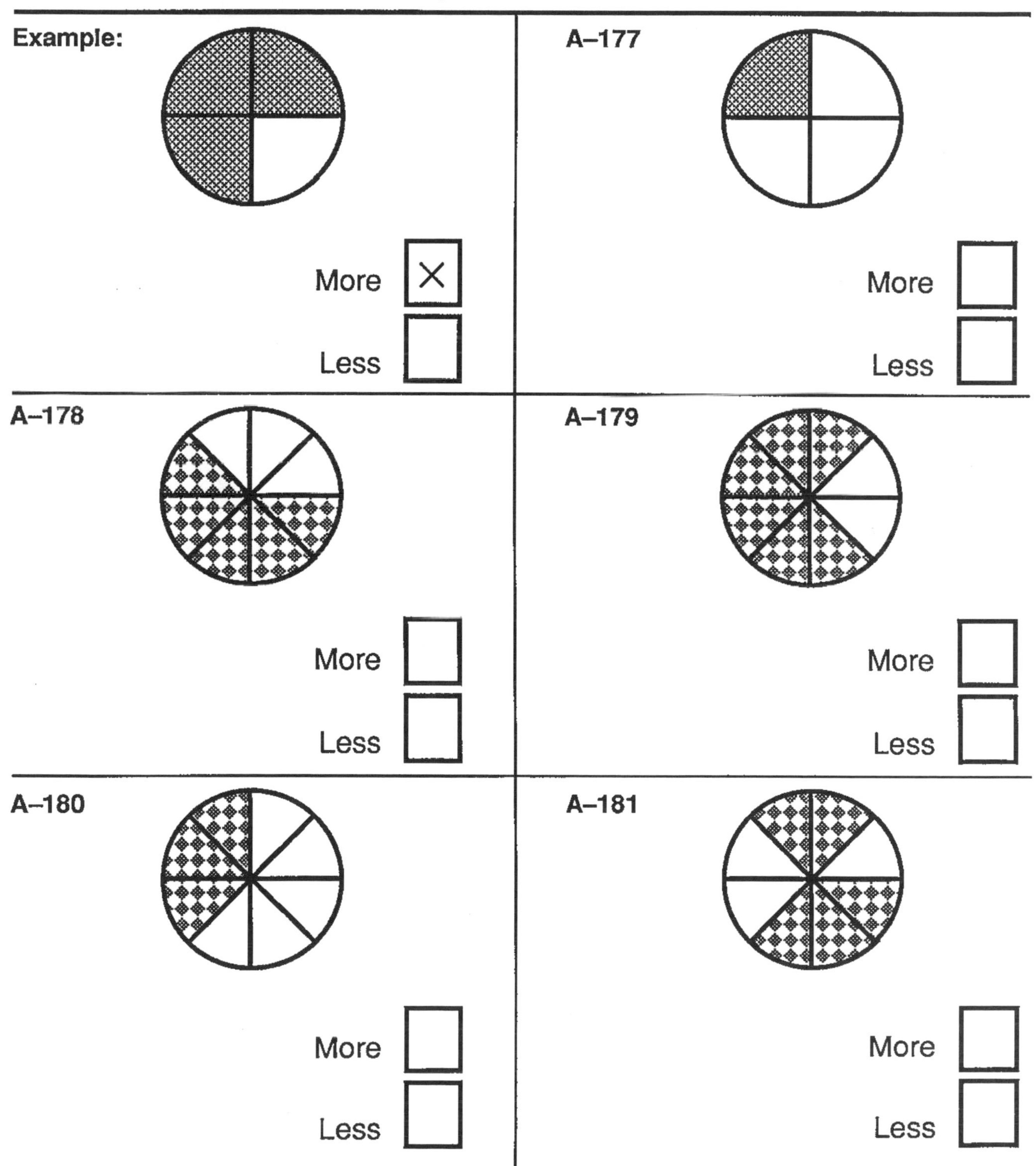

MORE OR LESS THAN 1/2

Look at the shaded part of each circle.
If more than 1/2 of the circle is shaded, place an X in the More box.
If less than 1/2 of the circle is shaded, place an X in the Less box.

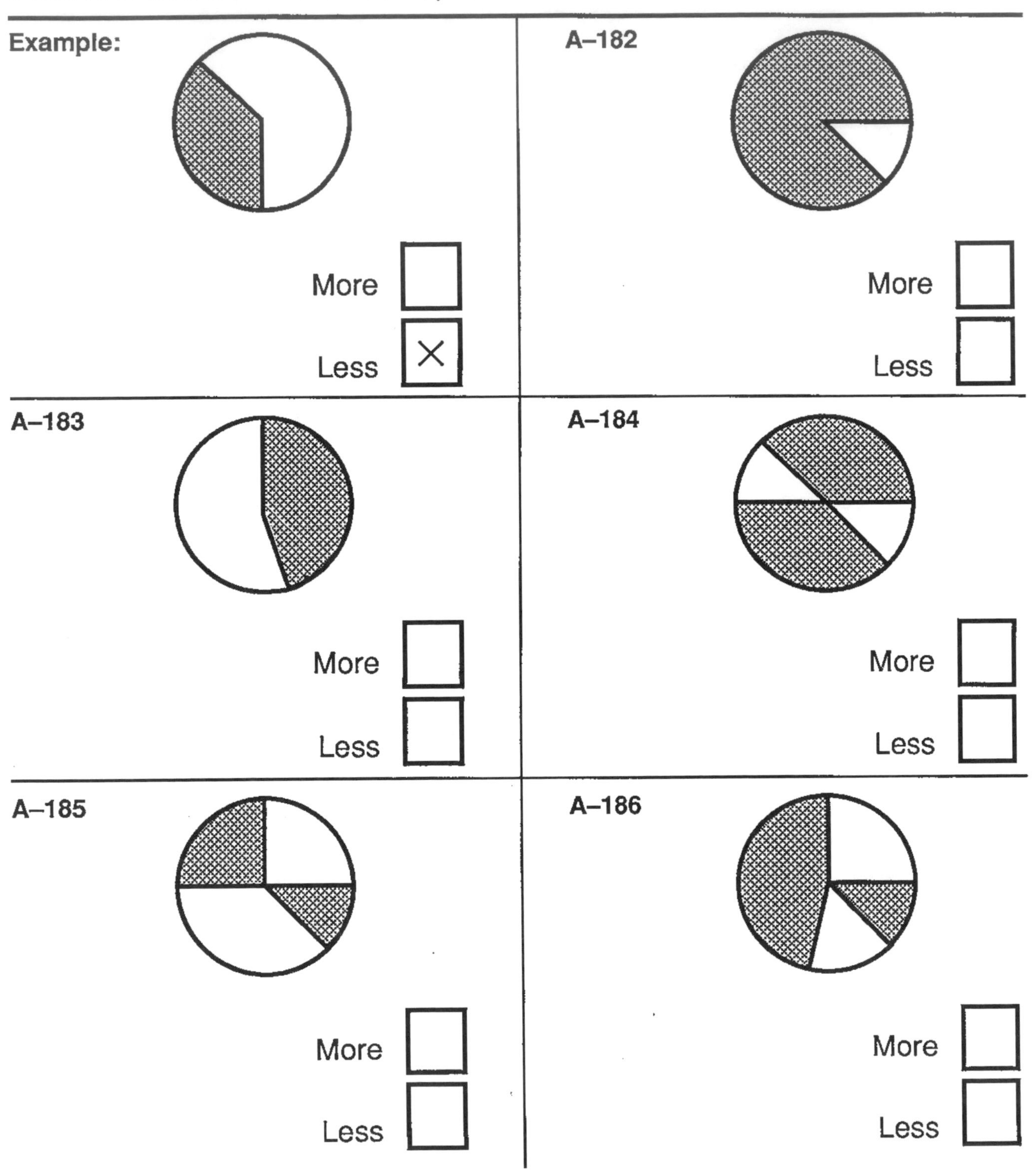

POINTS ON THE NUMBER LINE

Some numbers are missing on each number line.
Write the missing numbers in the boxes.

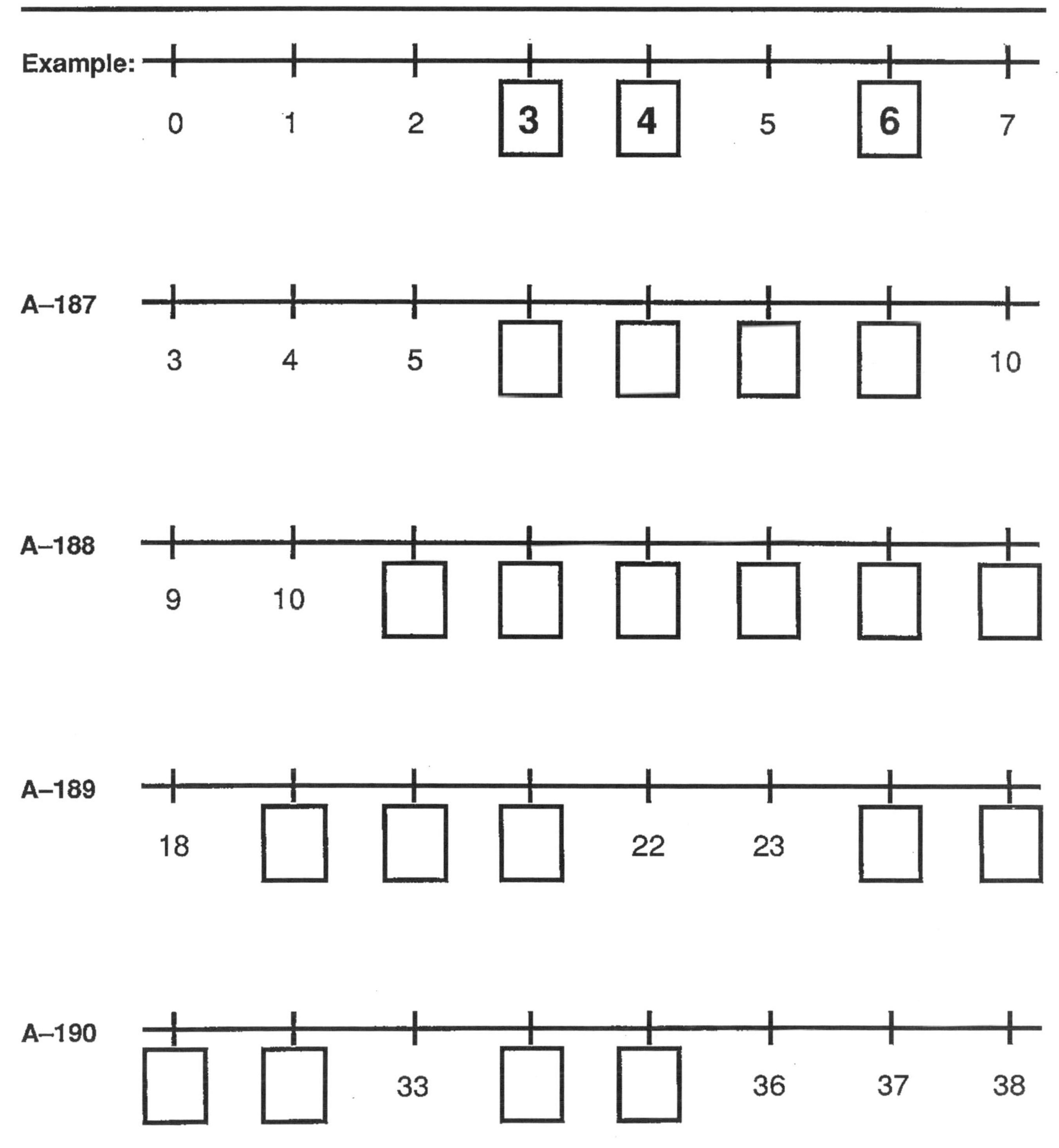

POINTS ON THE NUMBER LINE

Some numbers are missing on each number line.
Write the missing numbers in the boxes.

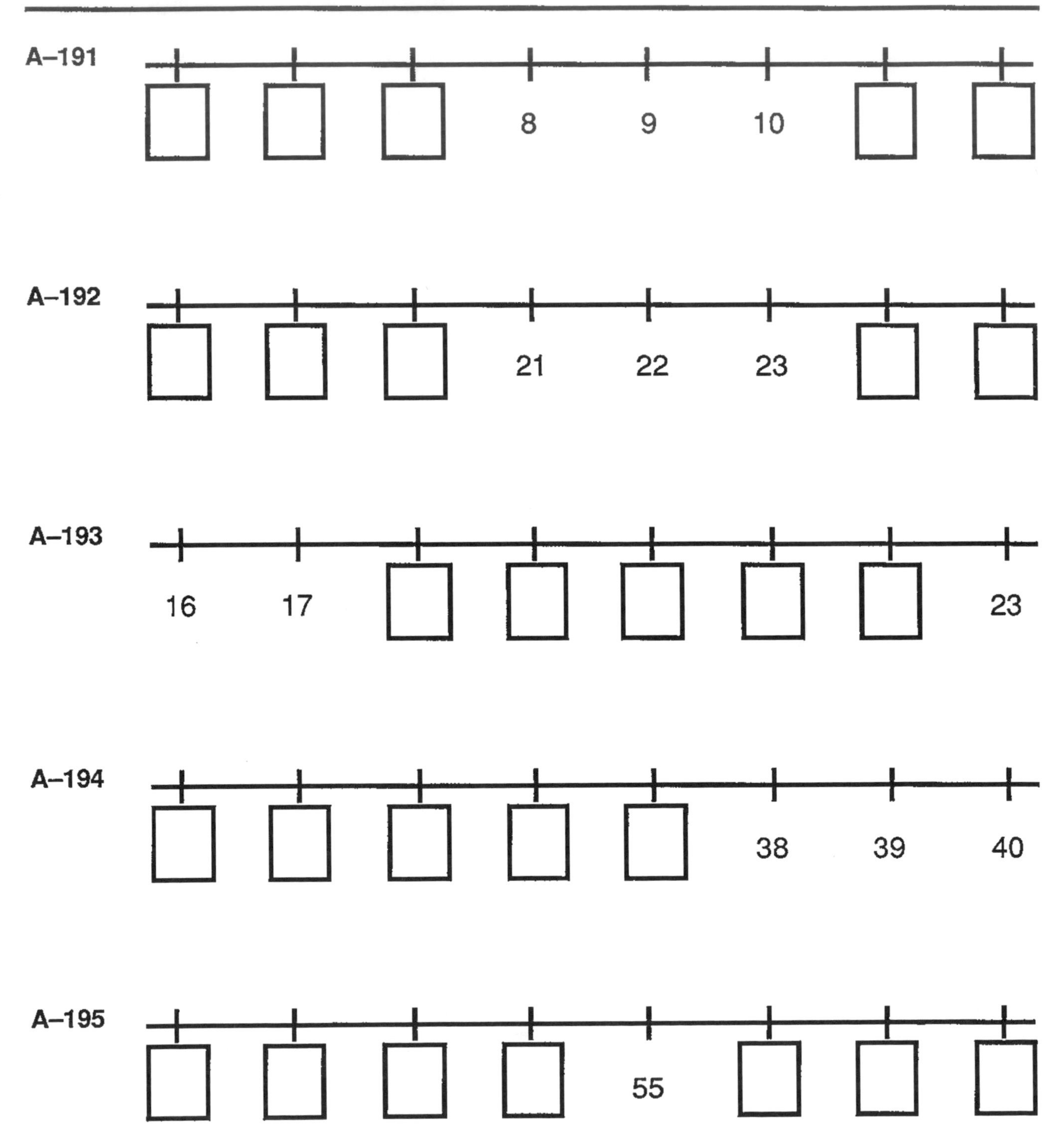

WHAT IS THE NUMBER?

Look at the numbers on the number line.
The arrow is pointing to a missing number.
Write the missing number in the box.

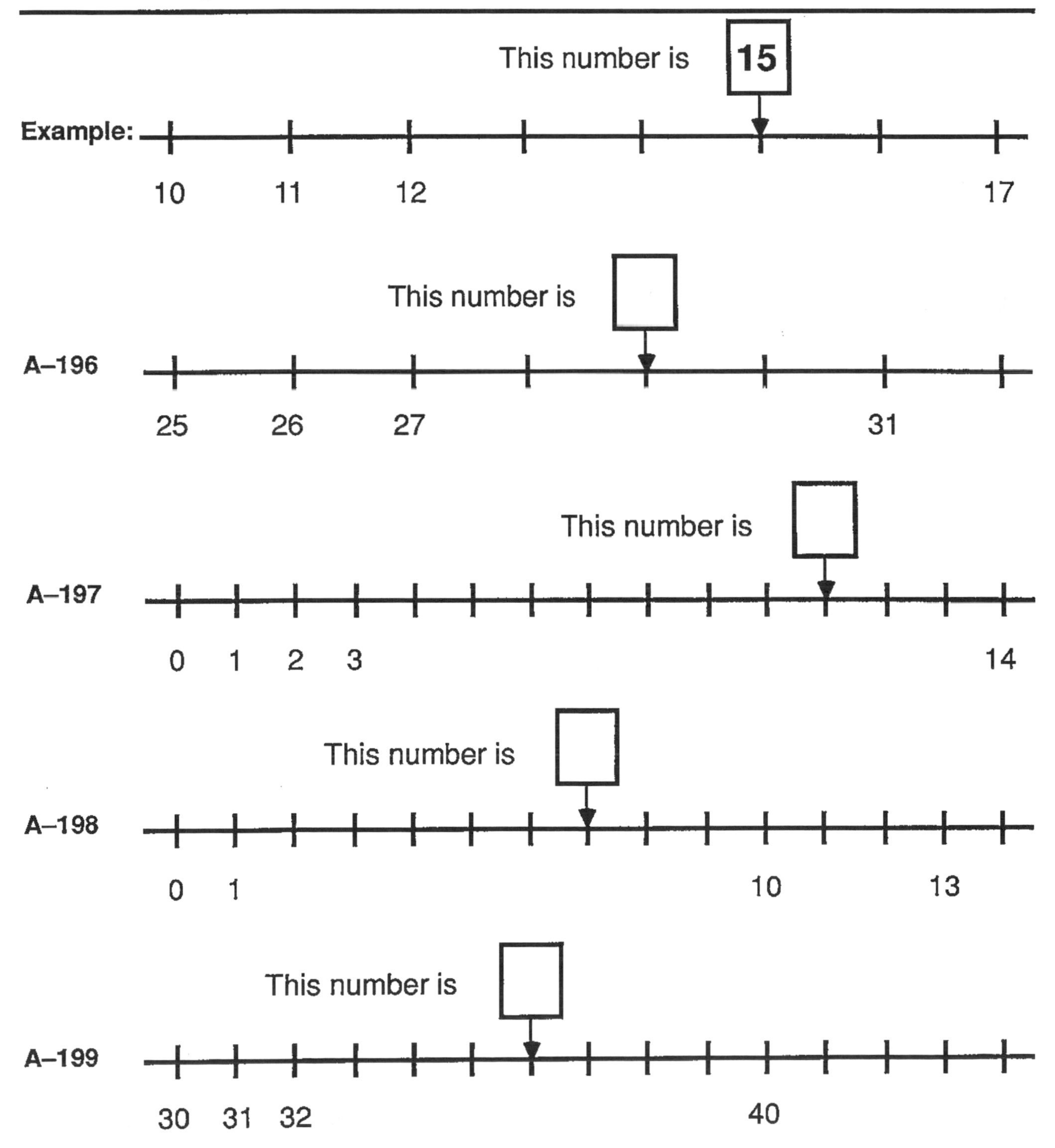

WHAT IS THE NUMBER?

One number is written in a box on each number line.
Write the missing number in the other box.

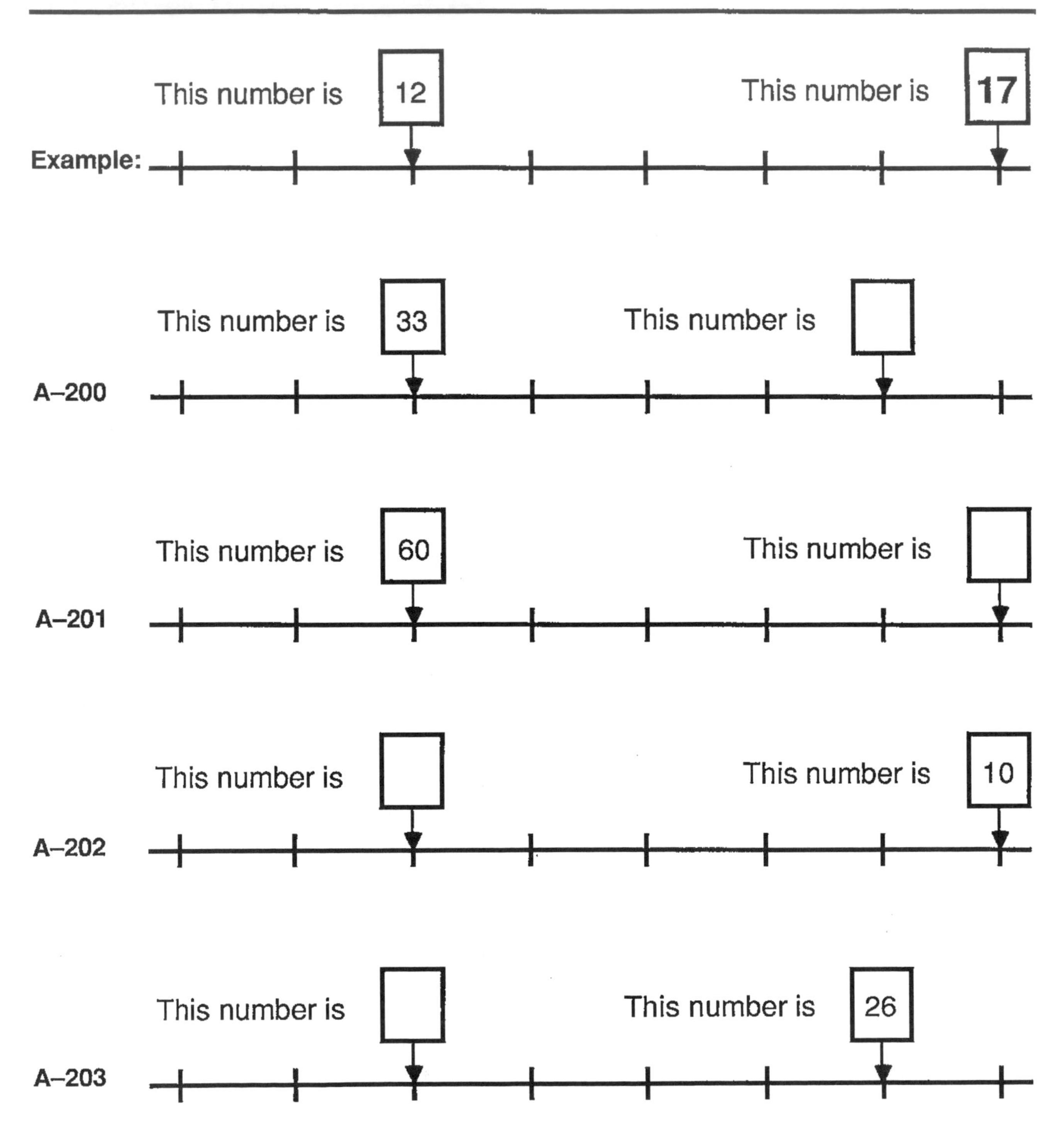

NAMING POINTS ON THE NUMBER LINE

Look at the set of four numbers above each number line.
Write each number in the correct box on the number line.

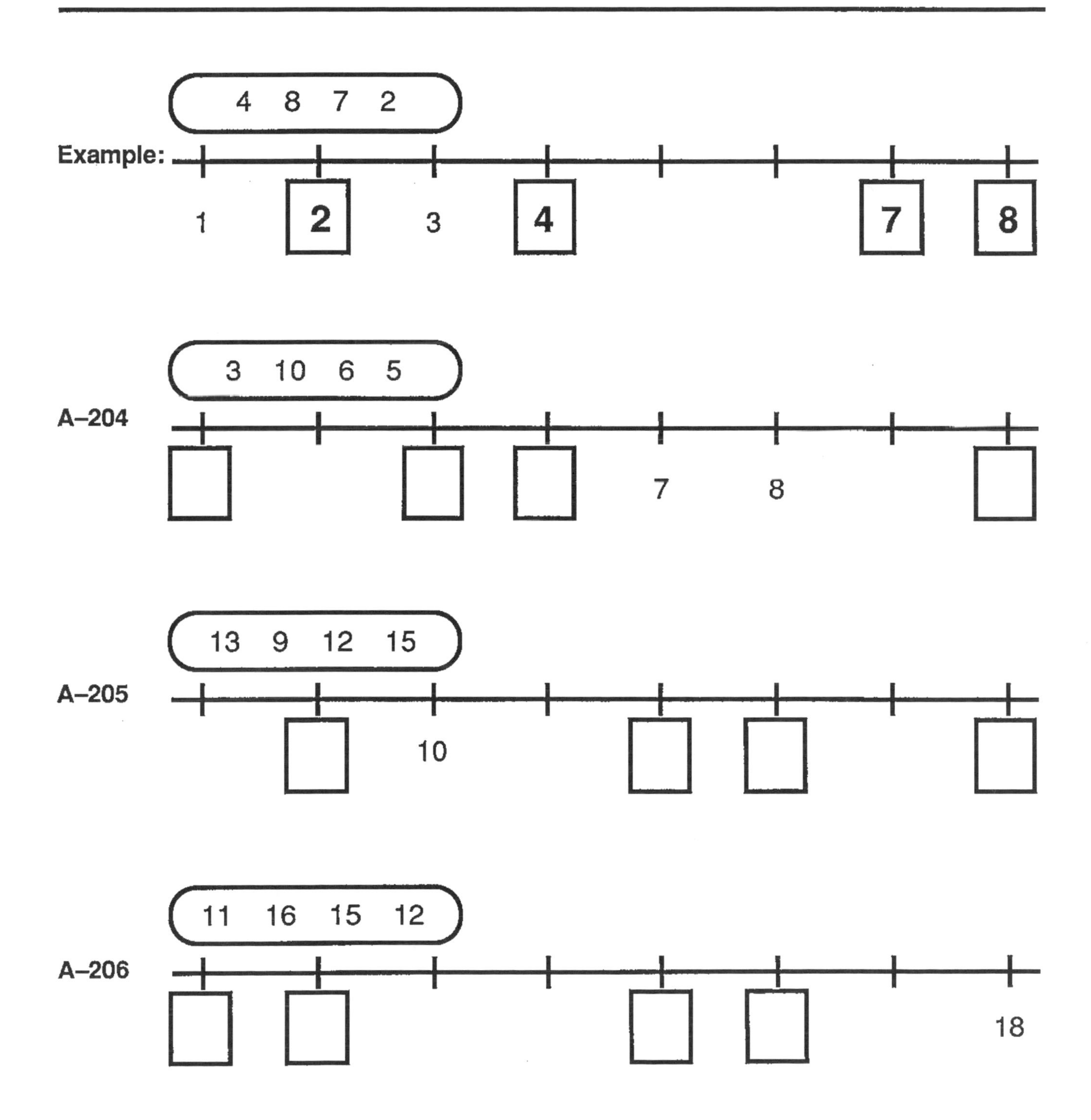

NAMING POINTS ON THE NUMBER LINE

Look at the set of four numbers above each number line.
Write each number in the correct box on the number line.

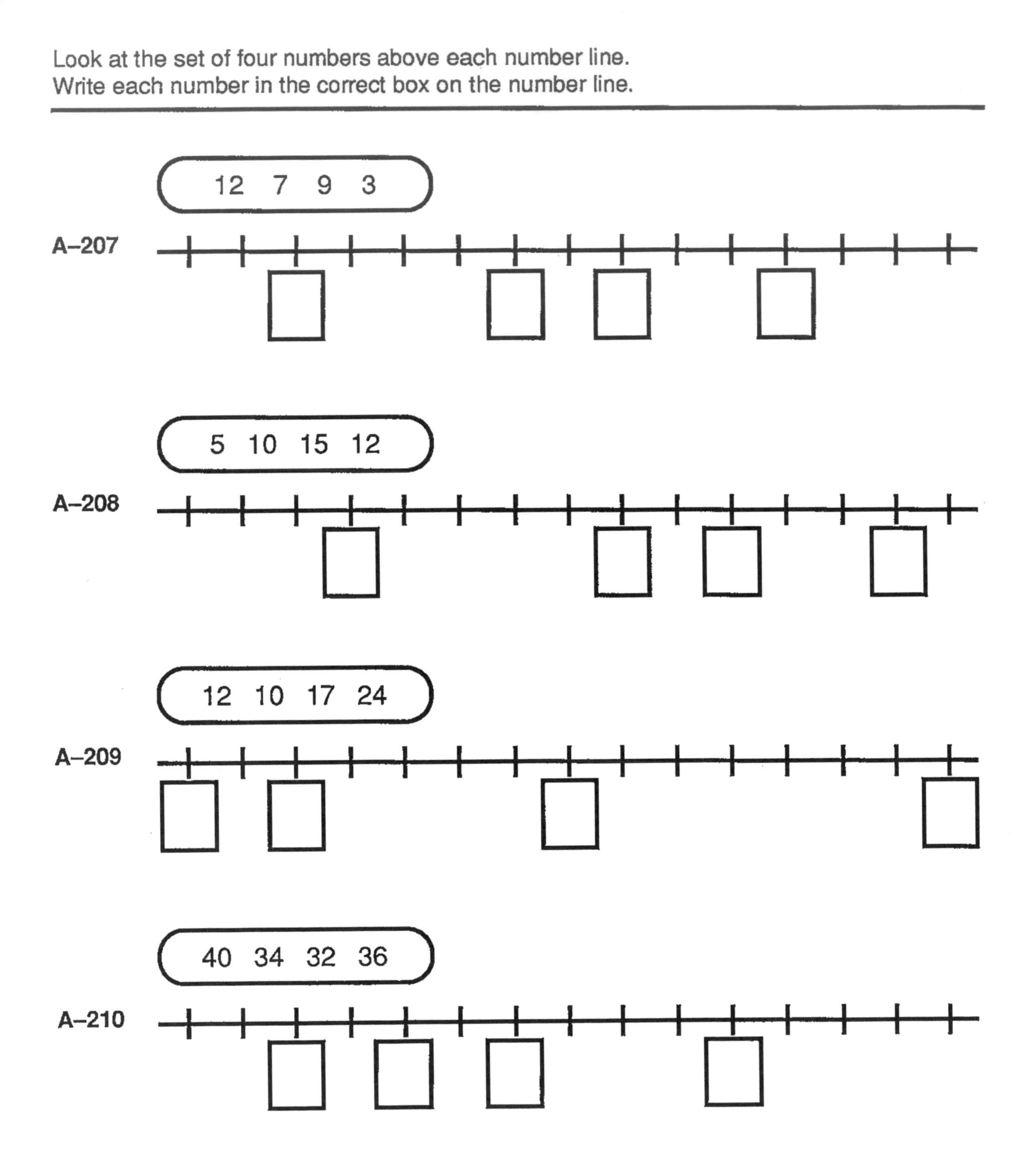

WHICH NUMBER DOES NOT FIT?

A part of the number line is shown.
Circle the number that does not fit on that part of the number line.

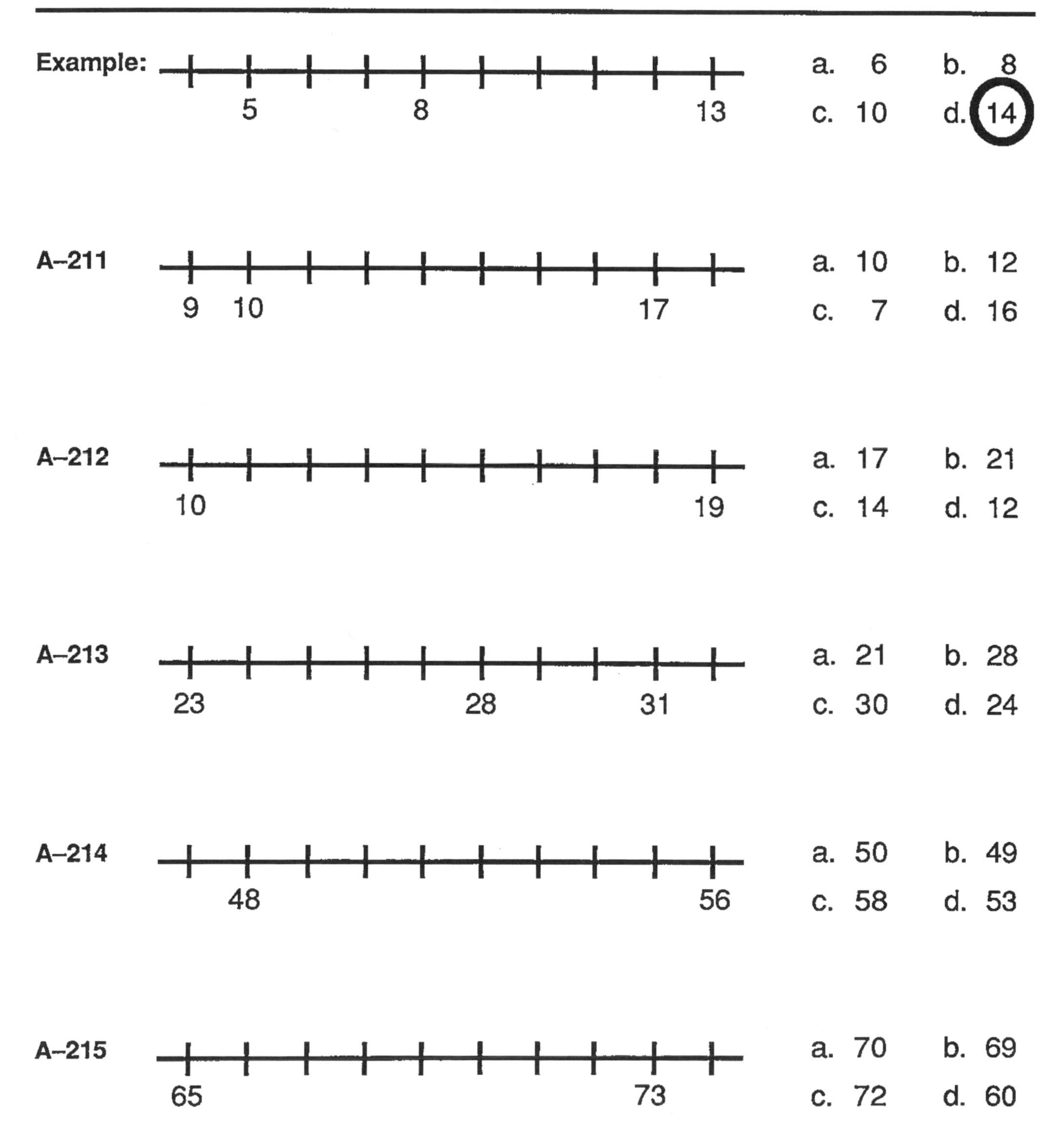

WHICH NUMBER DOES NOT FIT?

A part of the number line is shown.
Circle all the numbers that do not fit on that part of the number line.

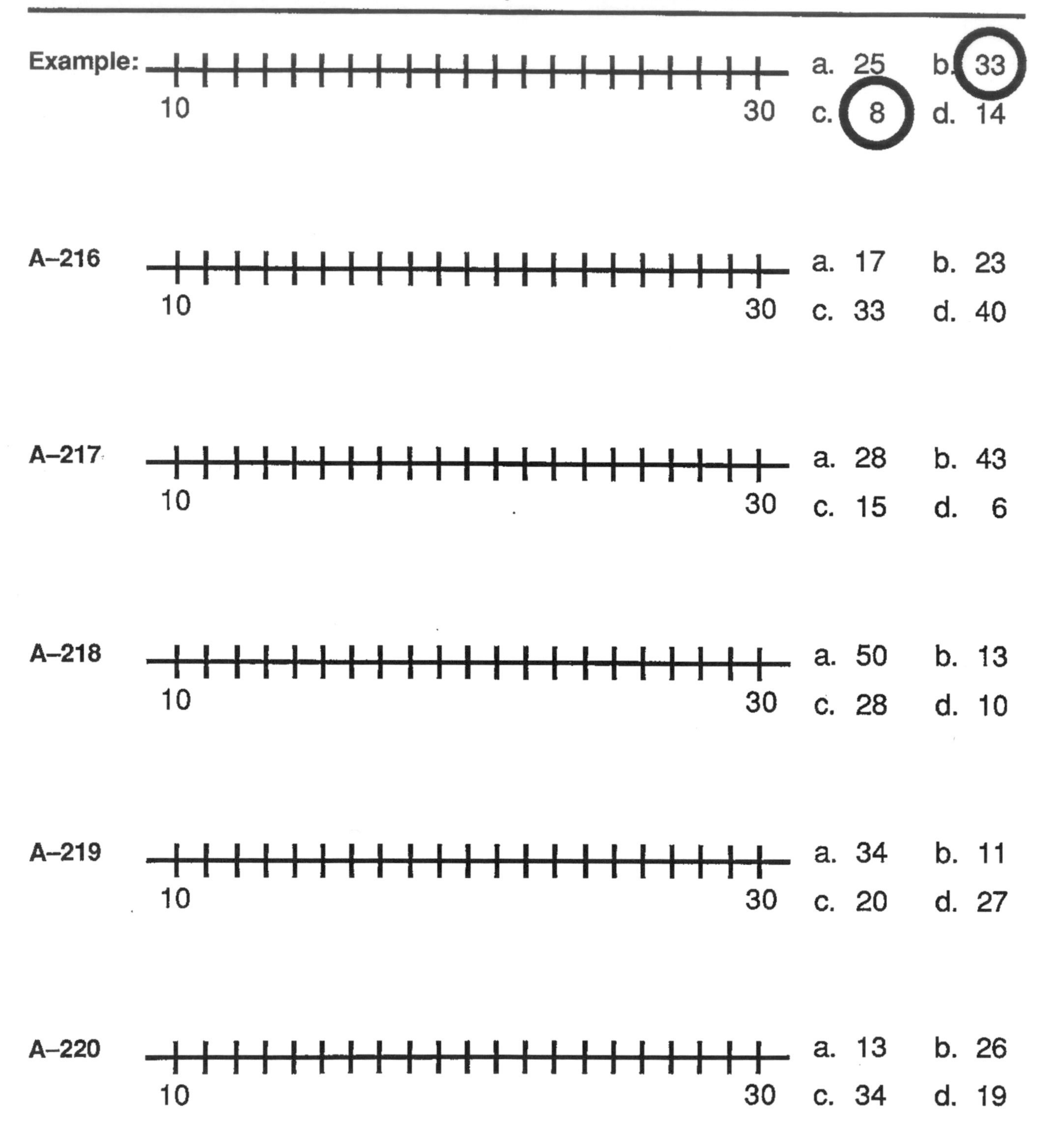

WHICH IS NEAREST?

Look at the number in the box.
Circle the number in the row that is nearest to that number on the number line.

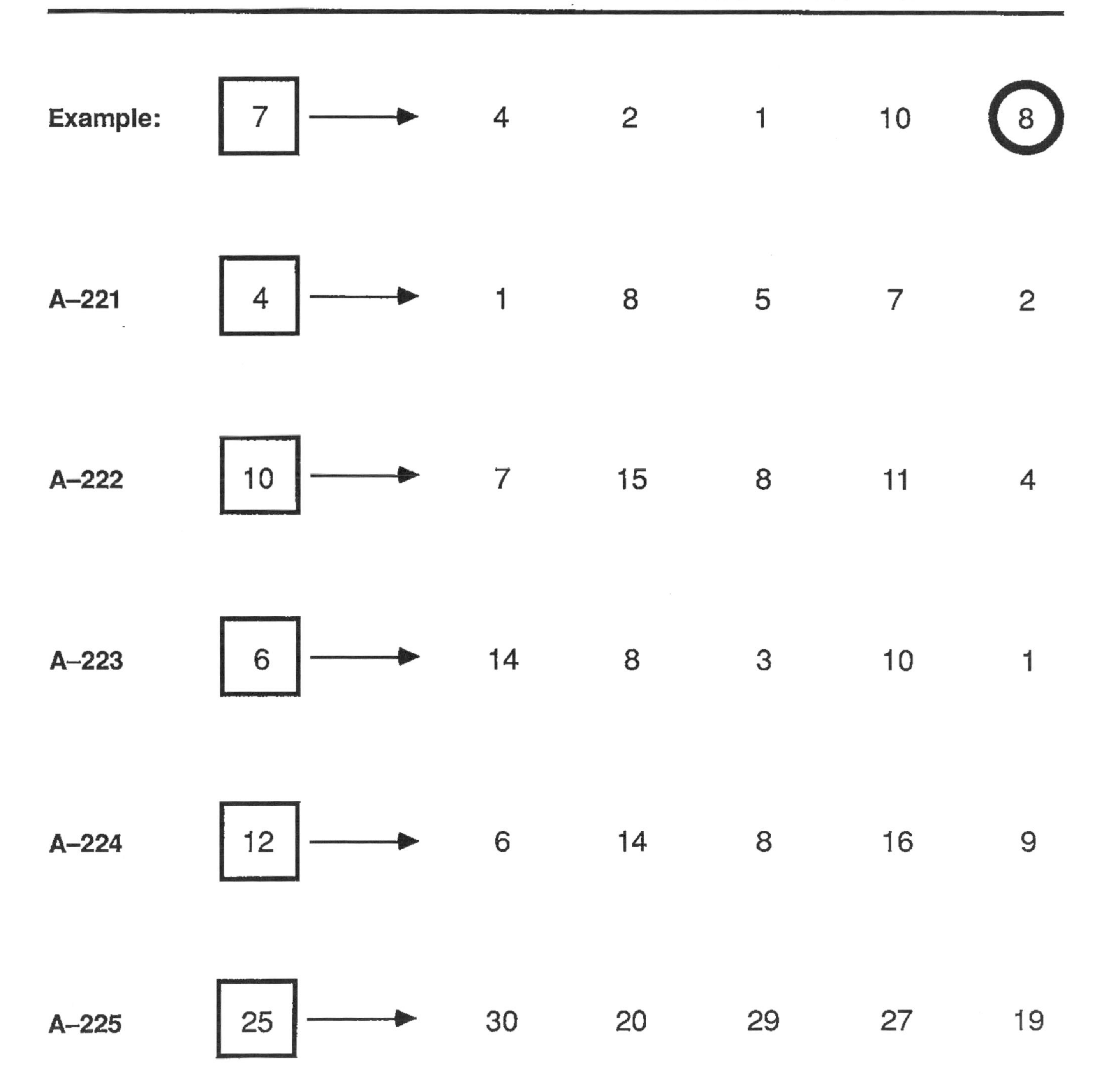

WHICH IS NEAREST?

Look at the number in the box.
Circle the number in the row that is nearest to that number on the number line.

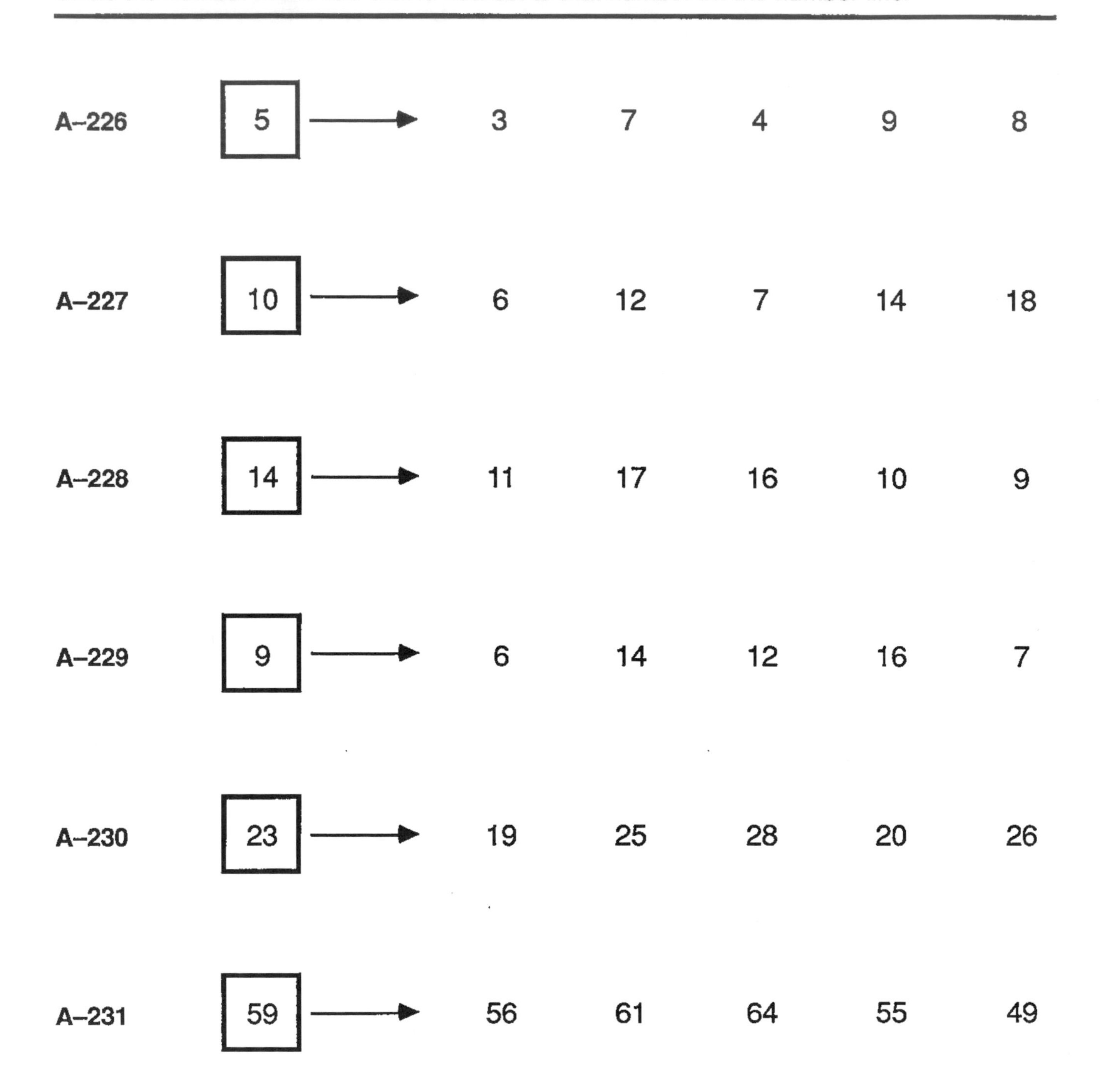

	Box					
A–226	5	3	7	4	9	8
A–227	10	6	12	7	14	18
A–228	14	11	17	16	10	9
A–229	9	6	14	12	16	7
A–230	23	19	25	28	20	26
A–231	59	56	61	64	55	49

GREATER THAN

Circle all the numbers in the box that are greater than the number in the square.
Put an X on the largest number in each box.

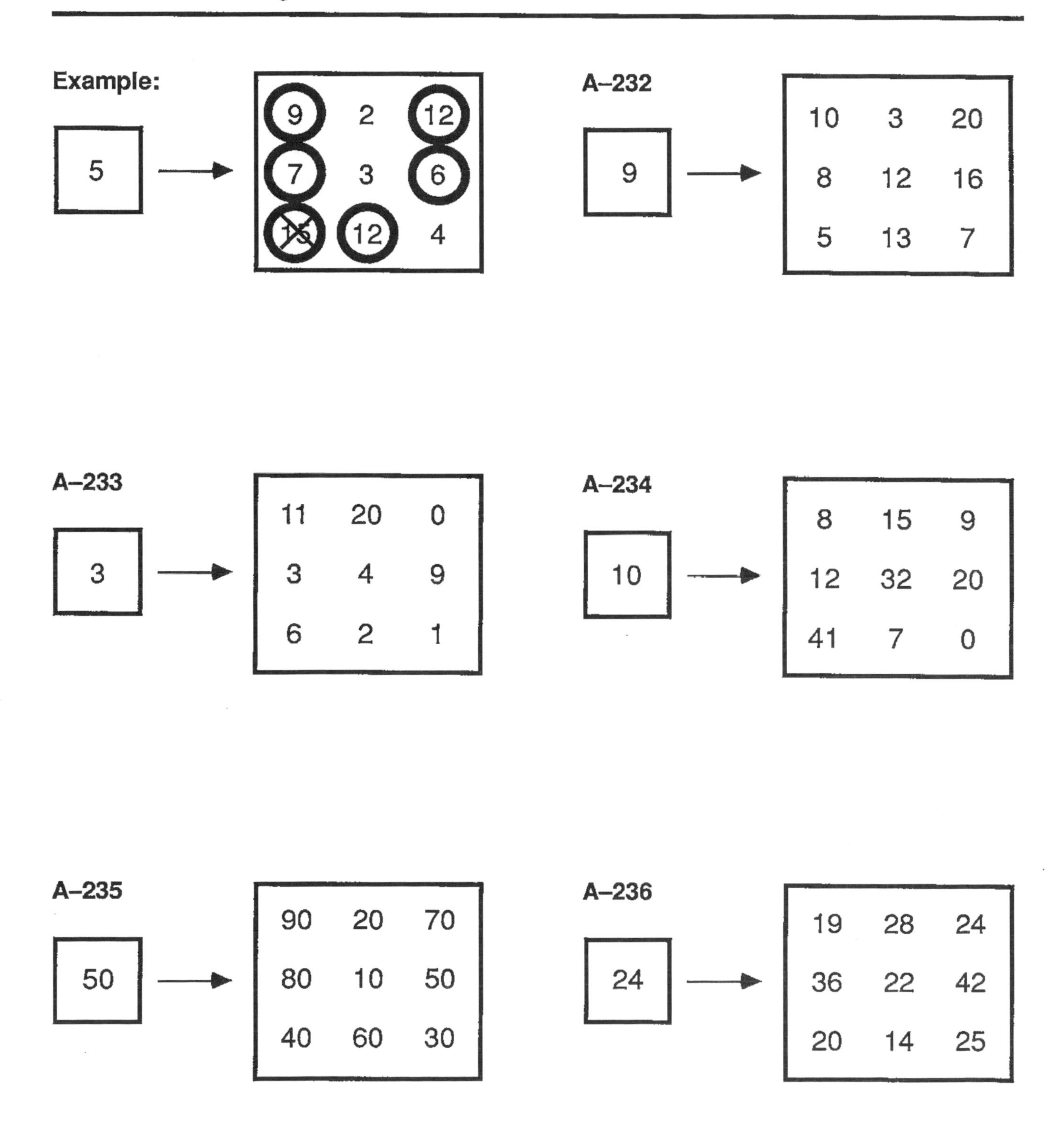

LESS THAN

Circle all the numbers in the box that are less than the number in the square.
Put an X on the smallest number in each box.

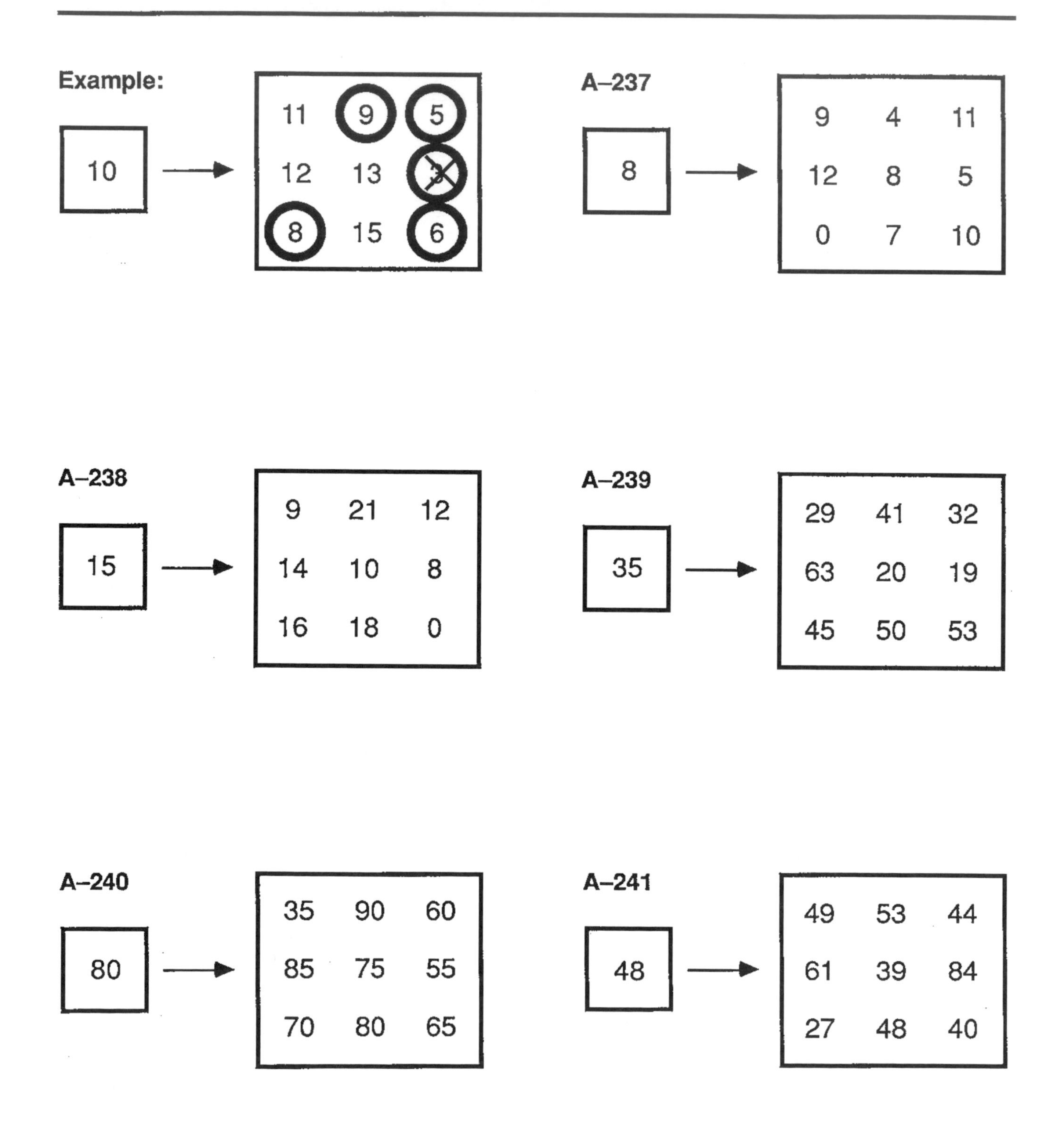

BETWEEN

Circle all the numbers in the box that are between the two numbers above the box.

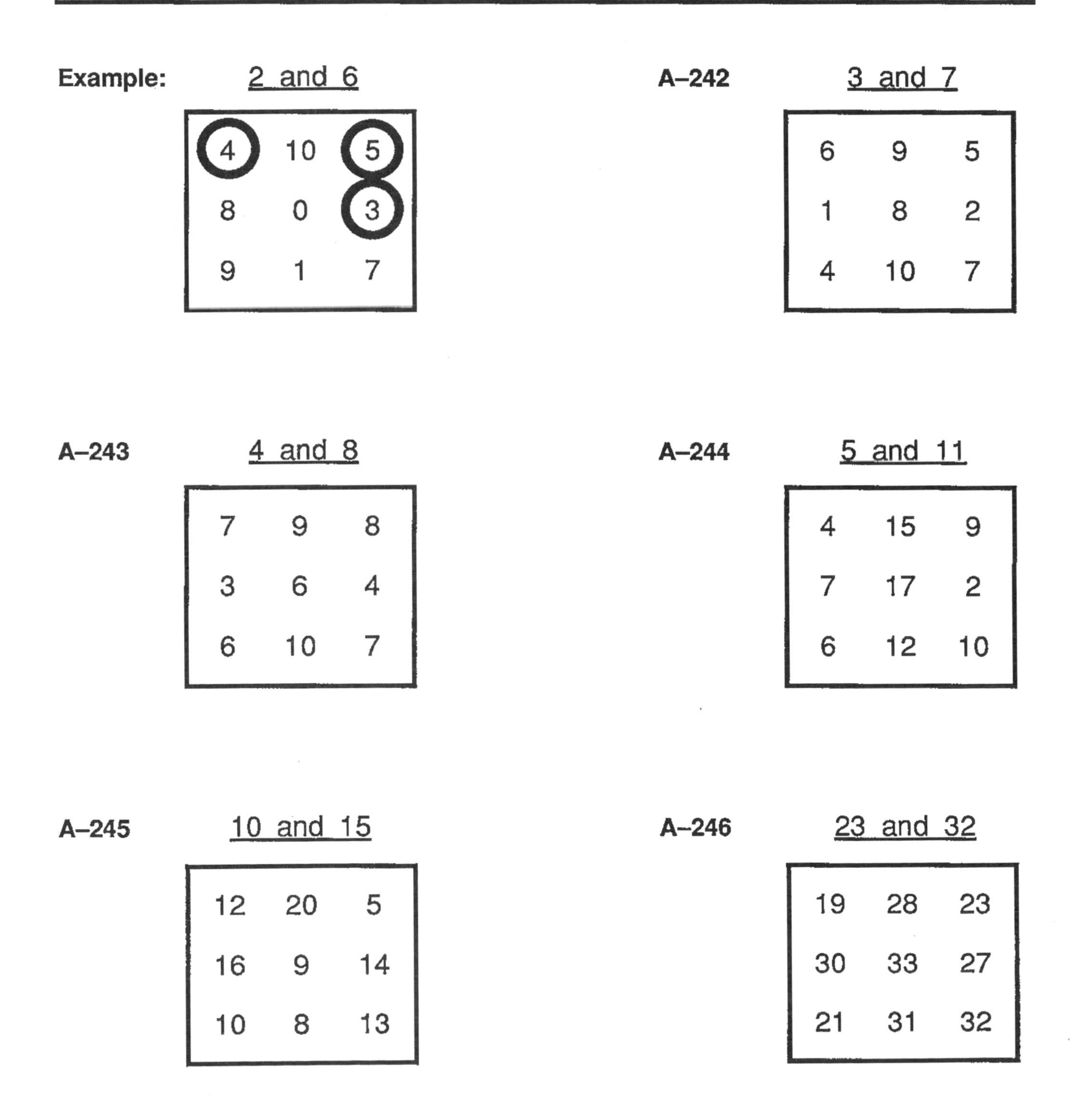

Example: 2 and 6

(4)	10	(5)
8	0	(3)
9	1	7

A–242 3 and 7

6	9	5
1	8	2
4	10	7

A–243 4 and 8

7	9	8
3	6	4
6	10	7

A–244 5 and 11

4	15	9
7	17	2
6	12	10

A–245 10 and 15

12	20	5
16	9	14
10	8	13

A–246 23 and 32

19	28	23
30	33	27
21	31	32

BETWEEN

Circle all the numbers in the box that are between the two numbers above the box.

A–247 13 and 16

10	11	12
13	14	15
16	17	18

A–248 13 and 18

18	16	21
14	12	11
19	17	23

A–249 20 and 30

15	35	10
45	20	30
25	5	40

A–250 15 and 35

65	0	25
15	50	30
60	10	20

A–251 55 and 70

72	49	68
59	71	80
81	54	27

A–252 34 and 45

39	28	46
34	43	54
41	30	35

USING PLACE VALUE TO MATCH SETS

Each rod is made with 10 cubes.
Draw a line around groups of 10 cubes in the sets in the first column.
Match these sets with the same number of cubes in the second column.

Example:

A–253

A–254

A–255

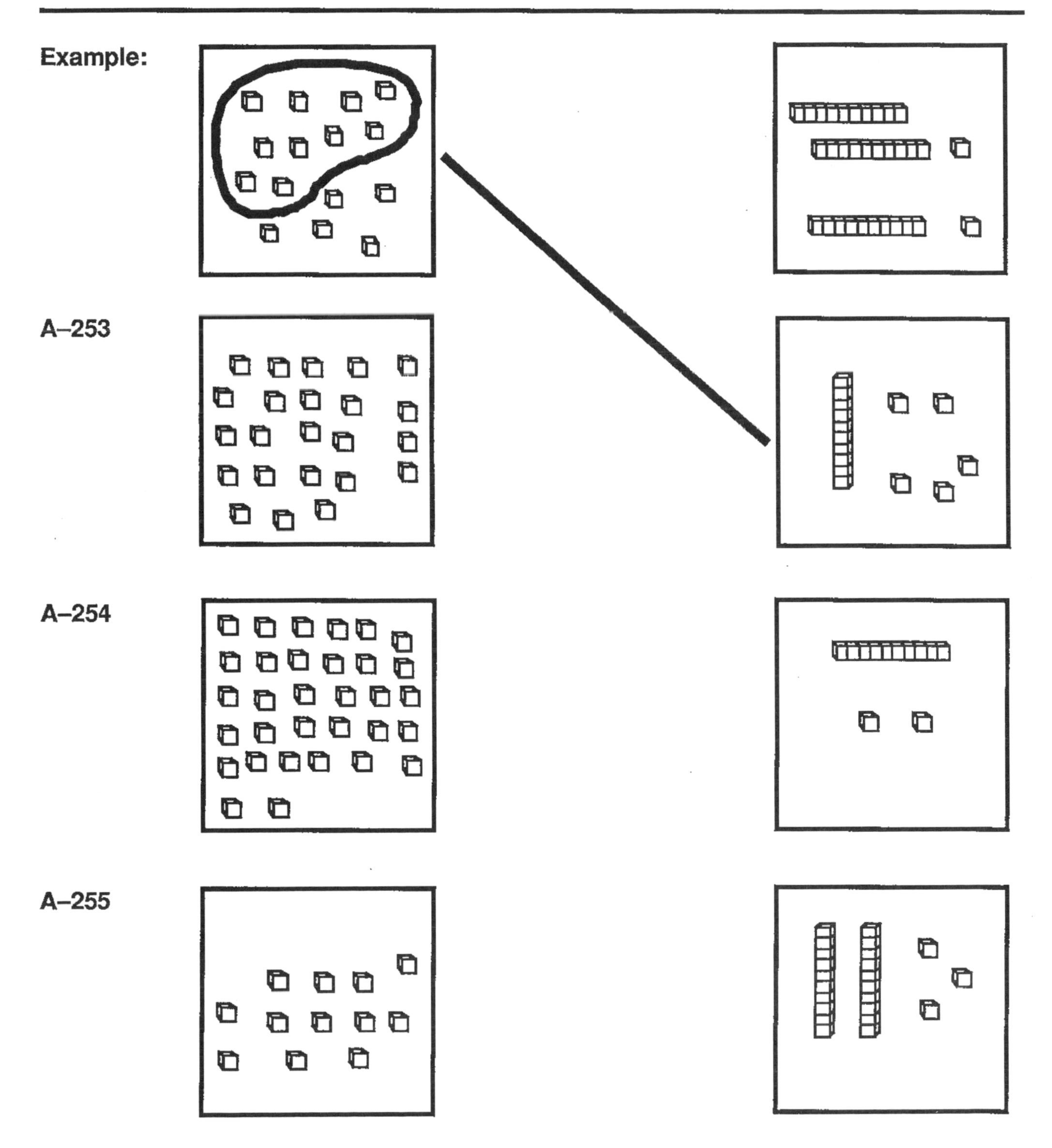

USING PLACE VALUE TO MATCH SETS

Each flat is made with 100 cubes. Each rod is made with 10 cubes.
Draw a line around groups of 10 cubes in the sets in the first column.
Match these sets with the same number of cubes in the second column.

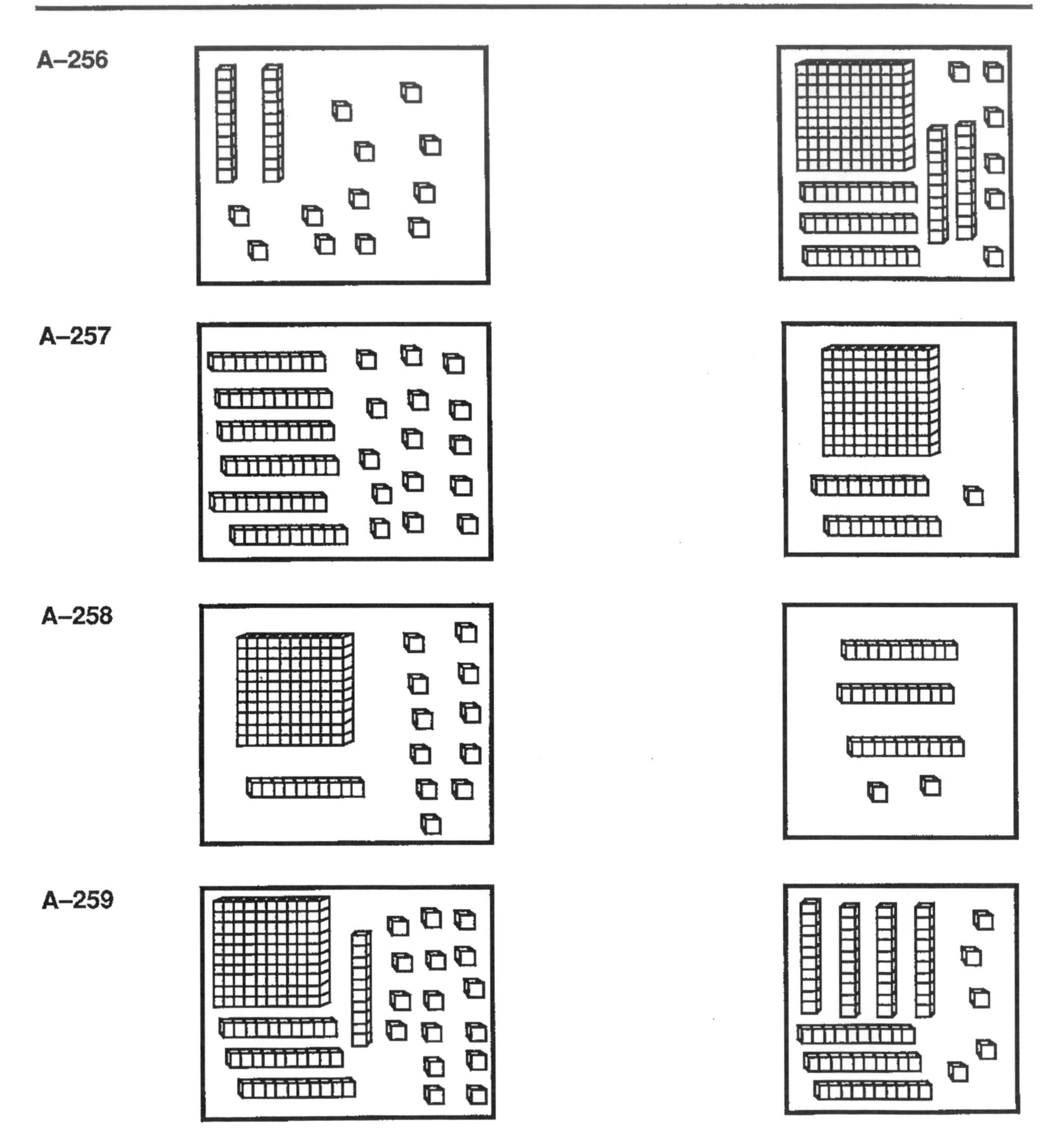

COUNTING RODS AND CUBES

Match each set with the chart that shows how many rods and cubes are in the set.

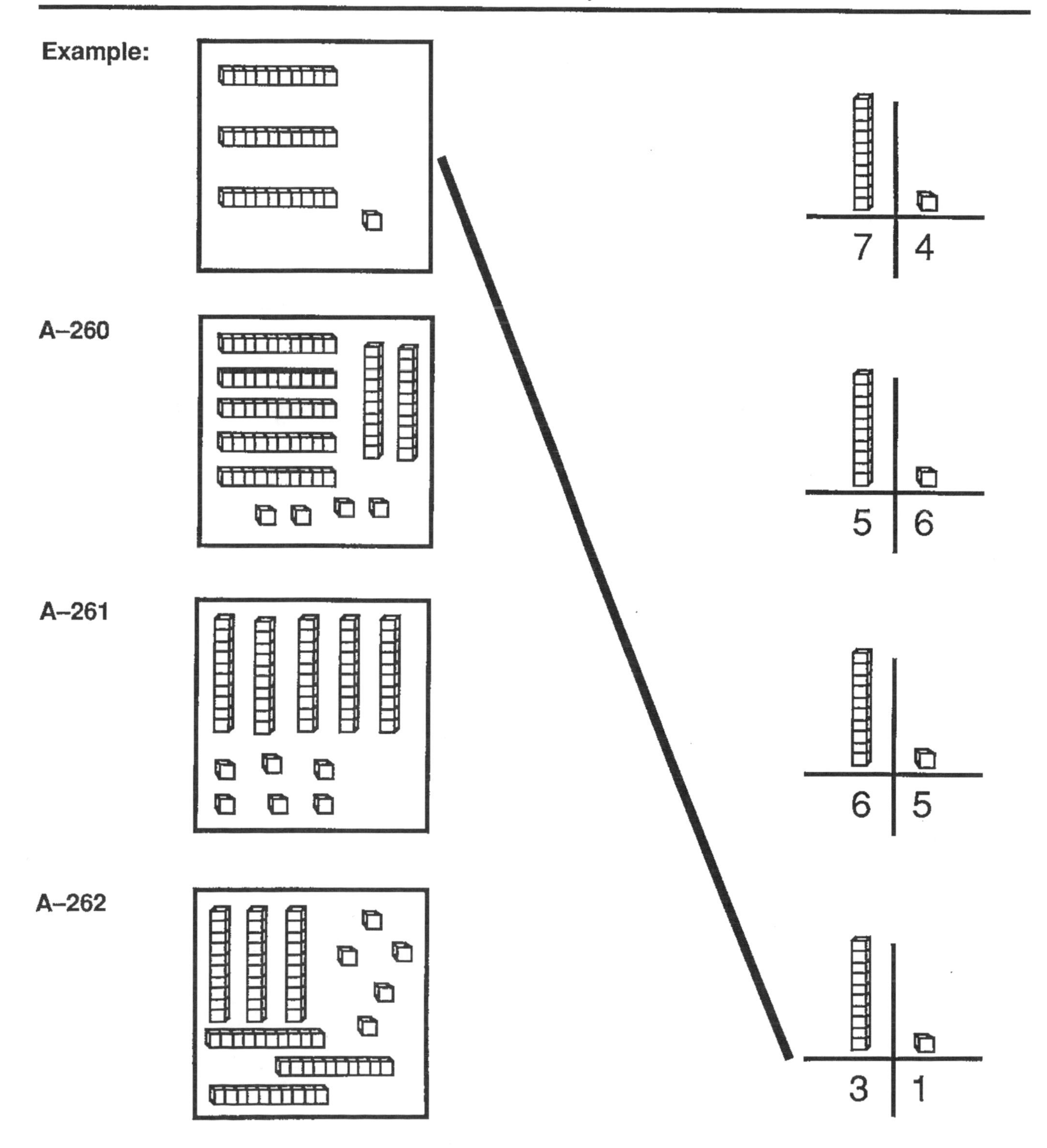

COUNTING FLATS, RODS, AND CUBES

Match each set with the chart that shows how many flats, rods, and cubes are in the set.

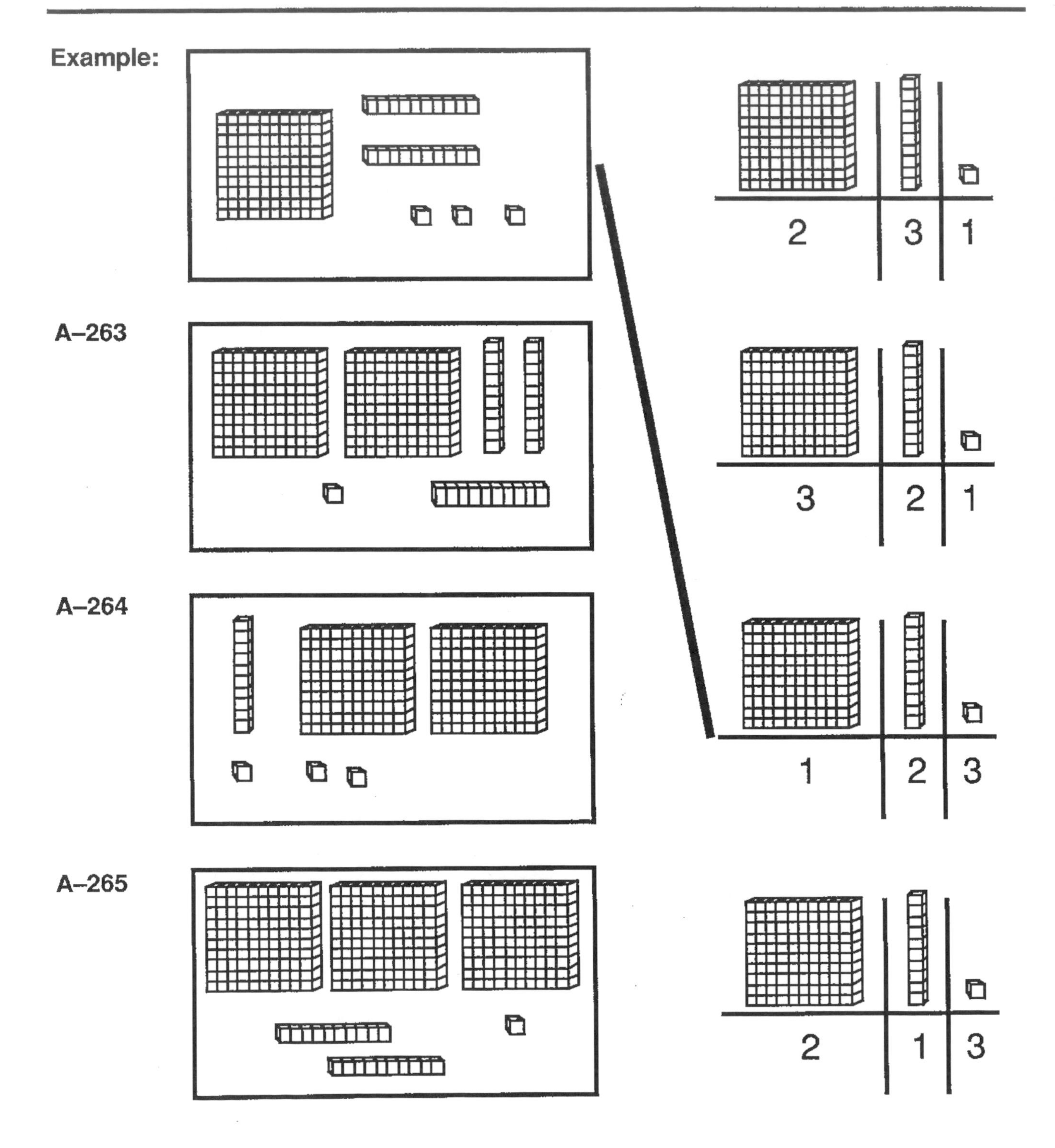

COUNTING RODS AND CUBES

Each rod is made with 10 cubes.
Write the number of rods and cubes in the chart.
Write the total number of cubes in the circle.

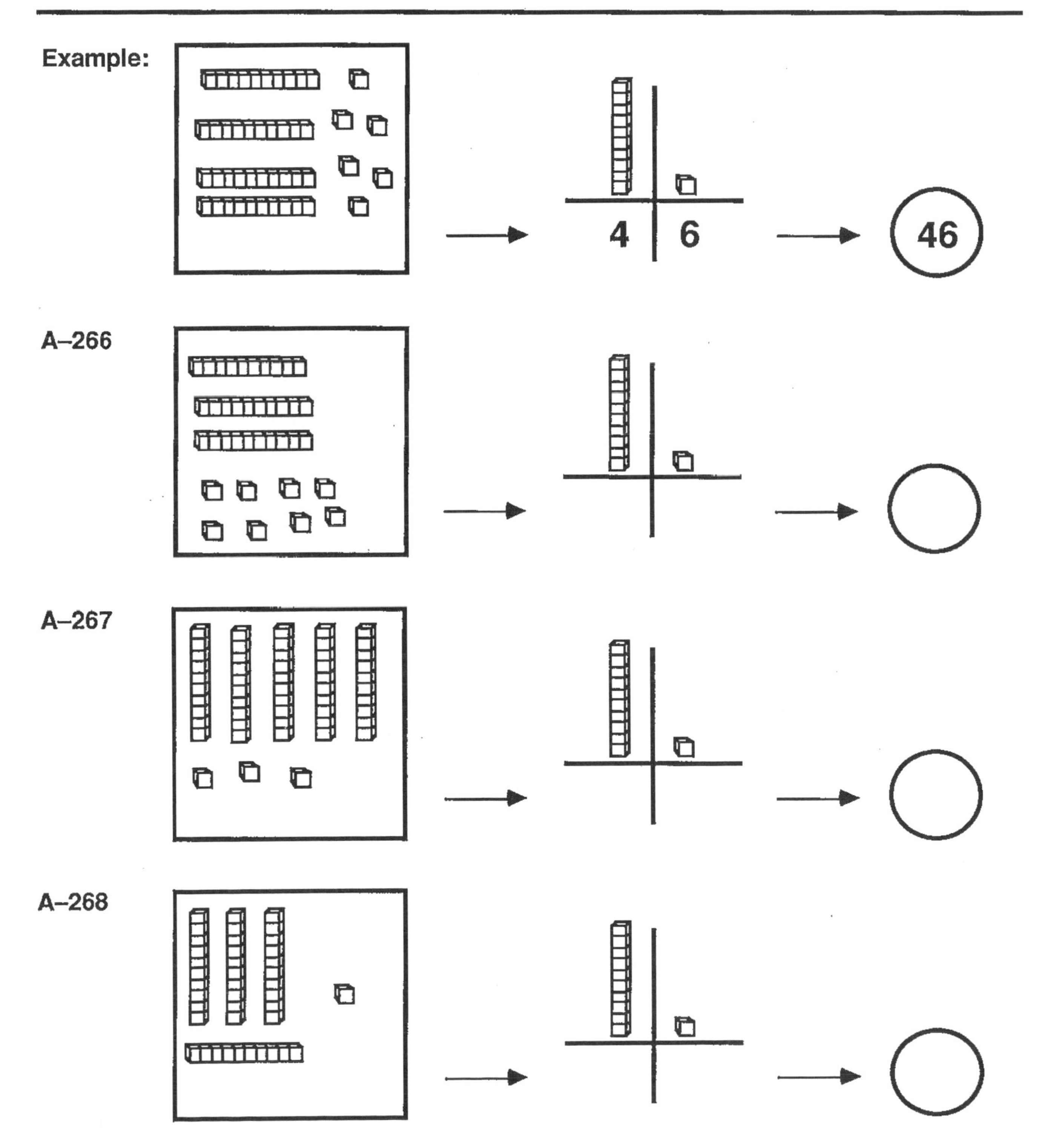

COUNTING FLATS, RODS, AND CUBES

Each flat is made with 100 cubes. Each rod is made with 10 cubes.
Write the number of flats, rods, and cubes in the chart.
Write the total number of cubes in the circle.

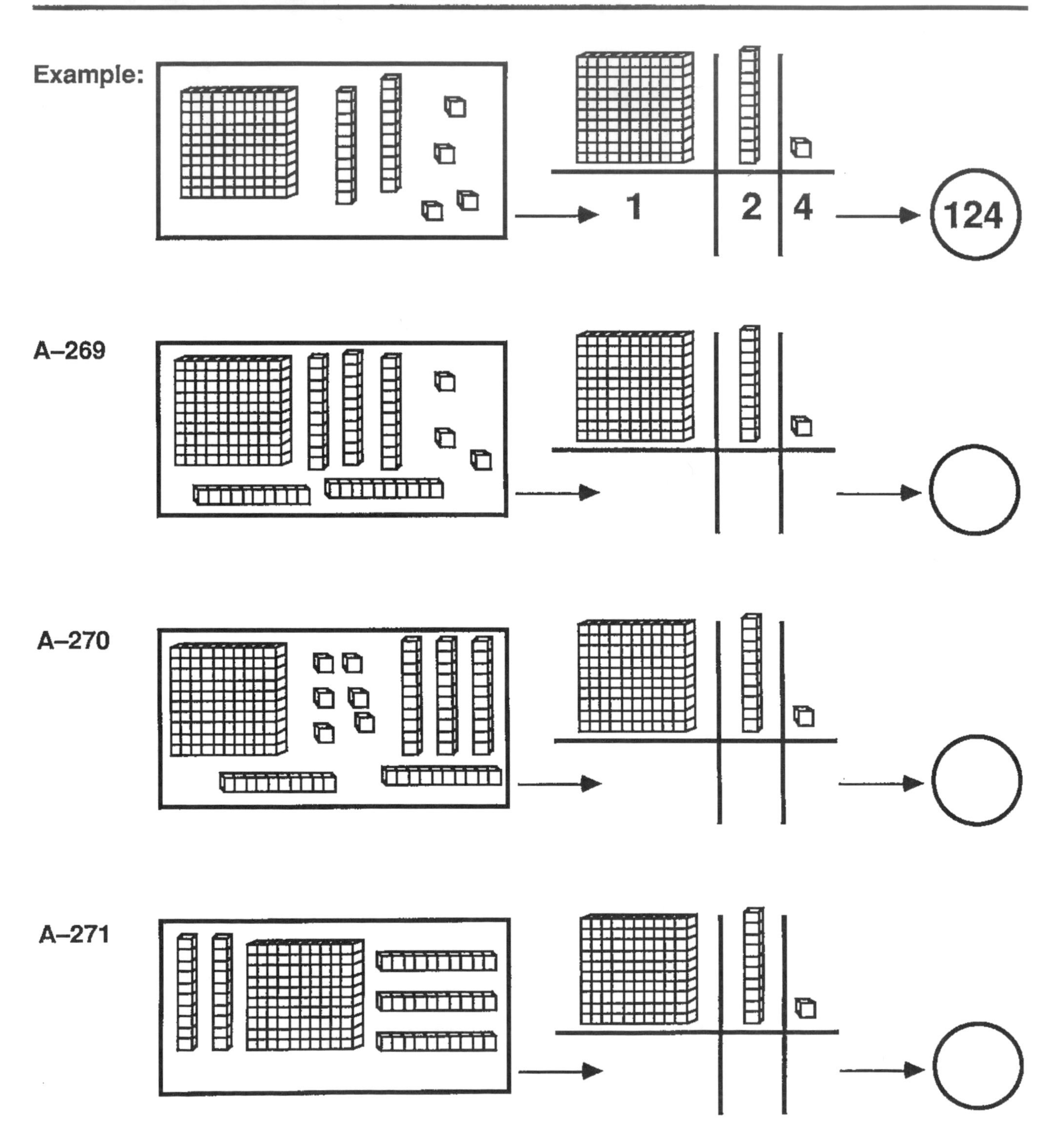

COUNTING RODS AND CUBES

Each rod is made with 10 cubes.
Match each set with the correct number.

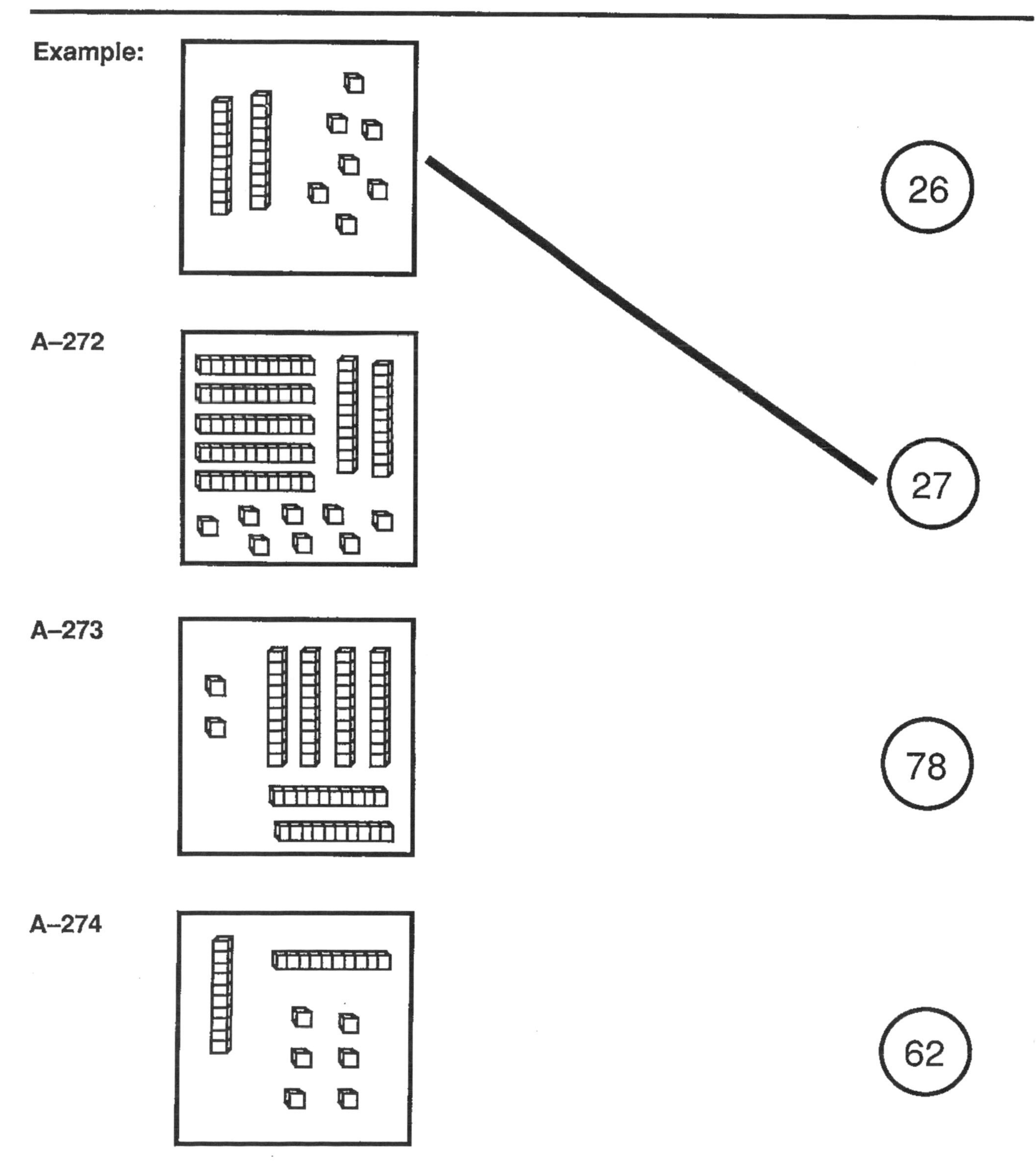

COUNTING FLATS, RODS, AND CUBES

Each flat is made with 100 cubes. Each rod is made with 10 cubes.
Match each set with its correct number.

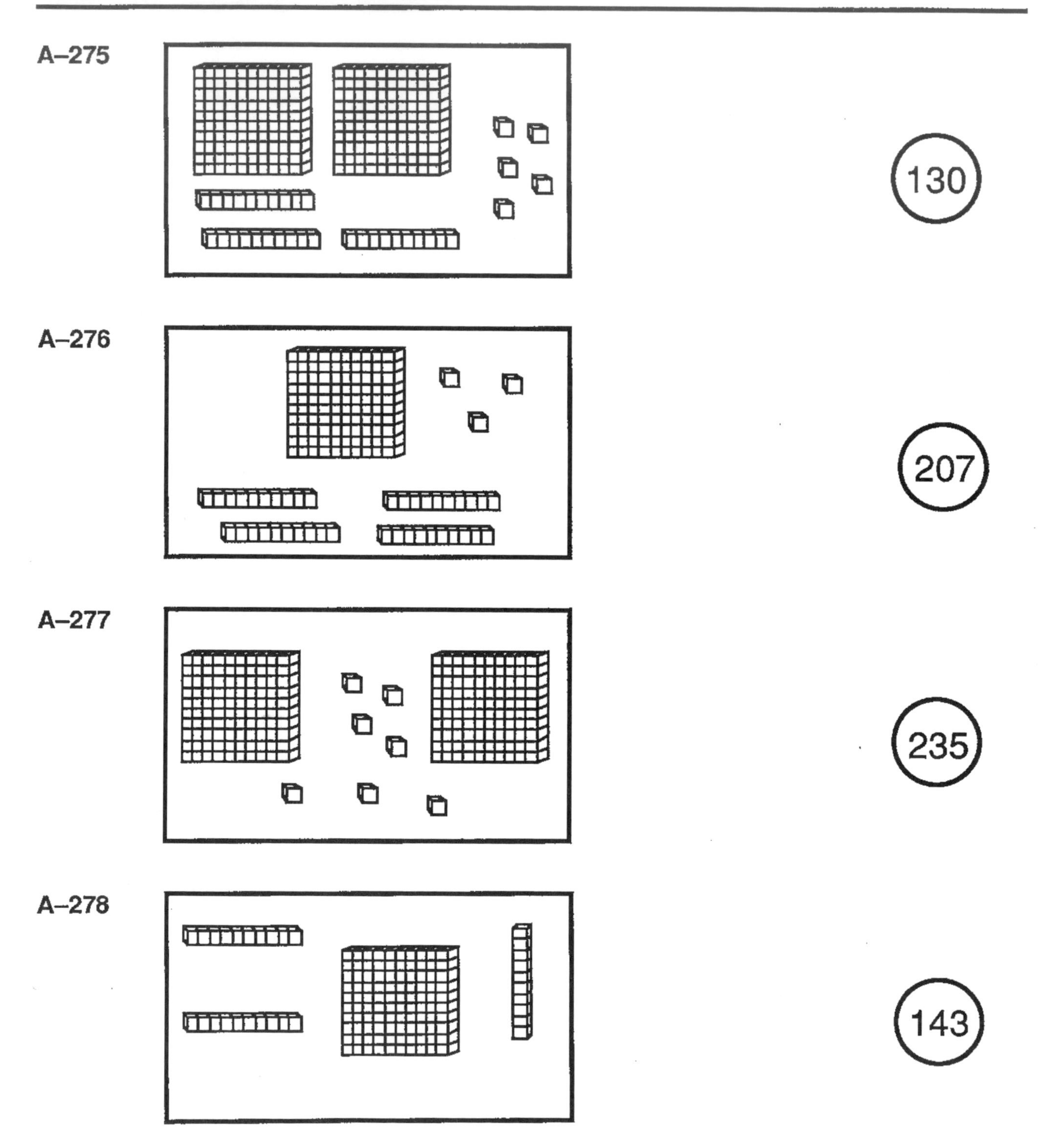

COUNTING RODS AND CUBES

Each rod is made with 10 cubes.
Put an X on the rods and cubes that are needed to make the number in the circle.

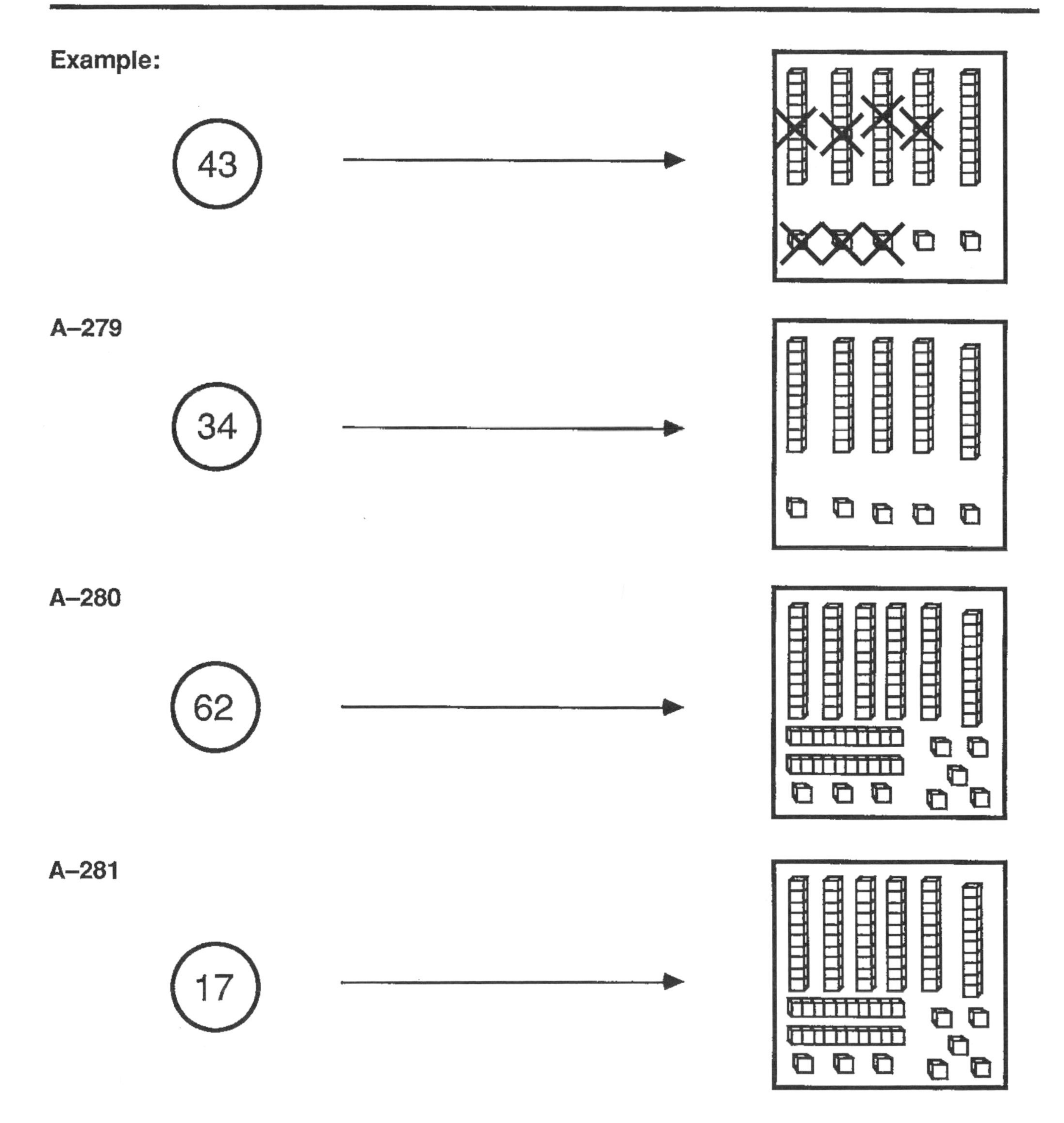

COUNTING FLATS, RODS, AND CUBES

Each flat is made with 100 cubes. Each rod is made with 10 cubes.
Put an X on the flats, rods, and cubes that are needed to make the number in the circle.

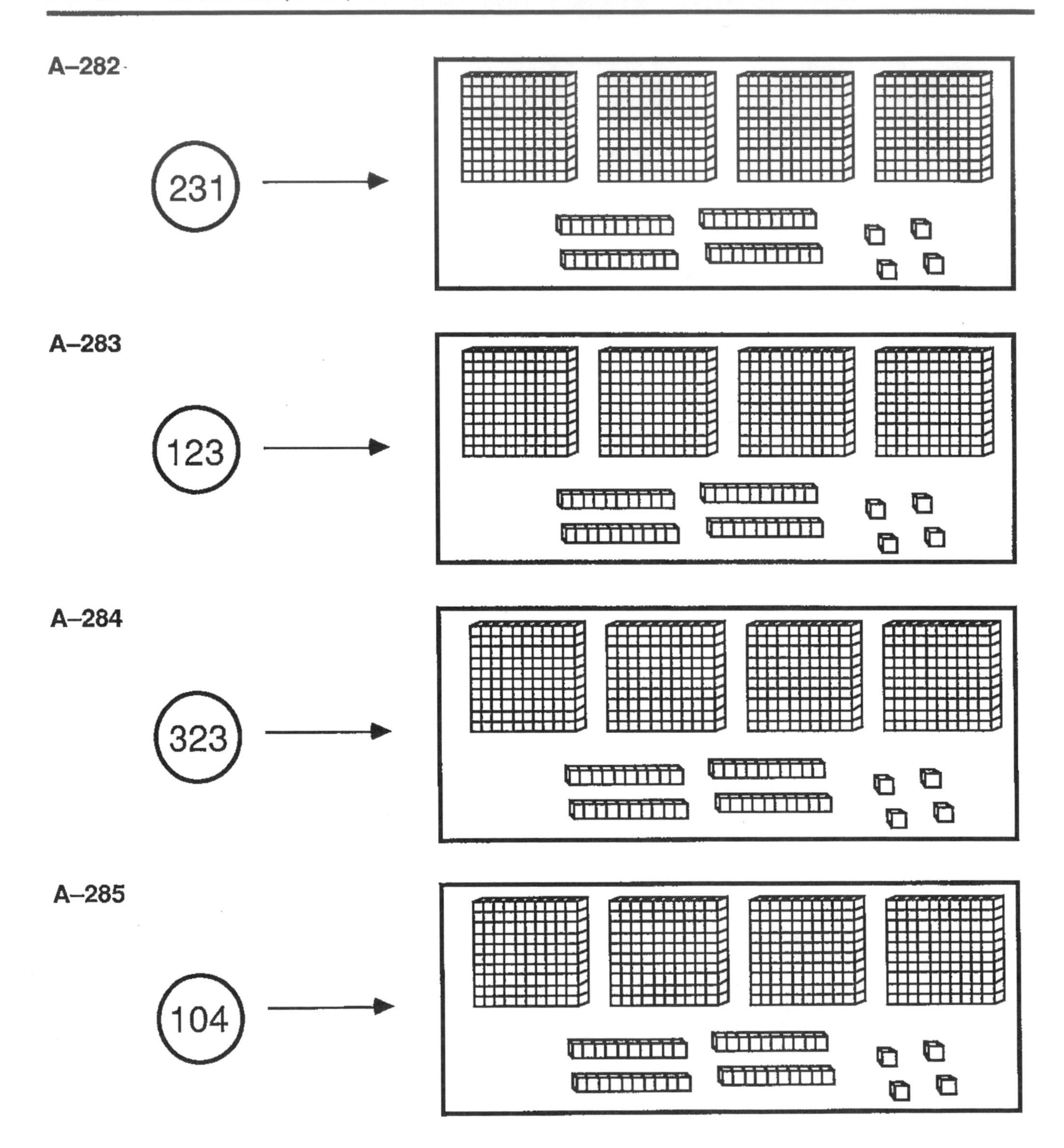

COUNTING RODS AND CUBES

Each rod is made with 10 cubes.
Write the number of rods and cubes in the chart.
Write the total number of cubes in the circle.

Example:

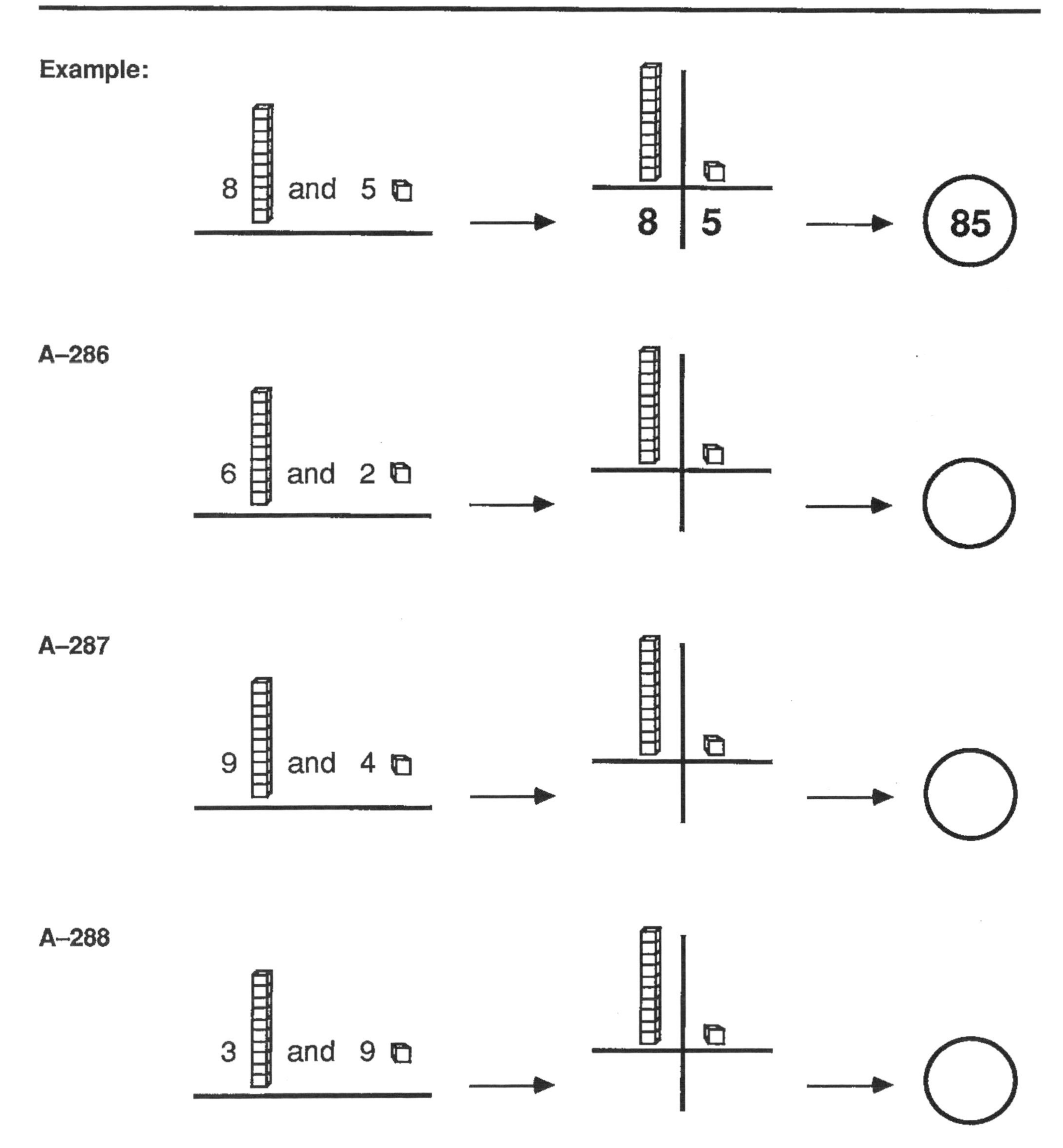

COUNTING FLATS, RODS, AND CUBES

Each flat is made with 100 cubes. Each rod is made with 10 cubes.
Write the number of flats, rods, and cubes in the chart.
Write the total number of cubes in the circle.

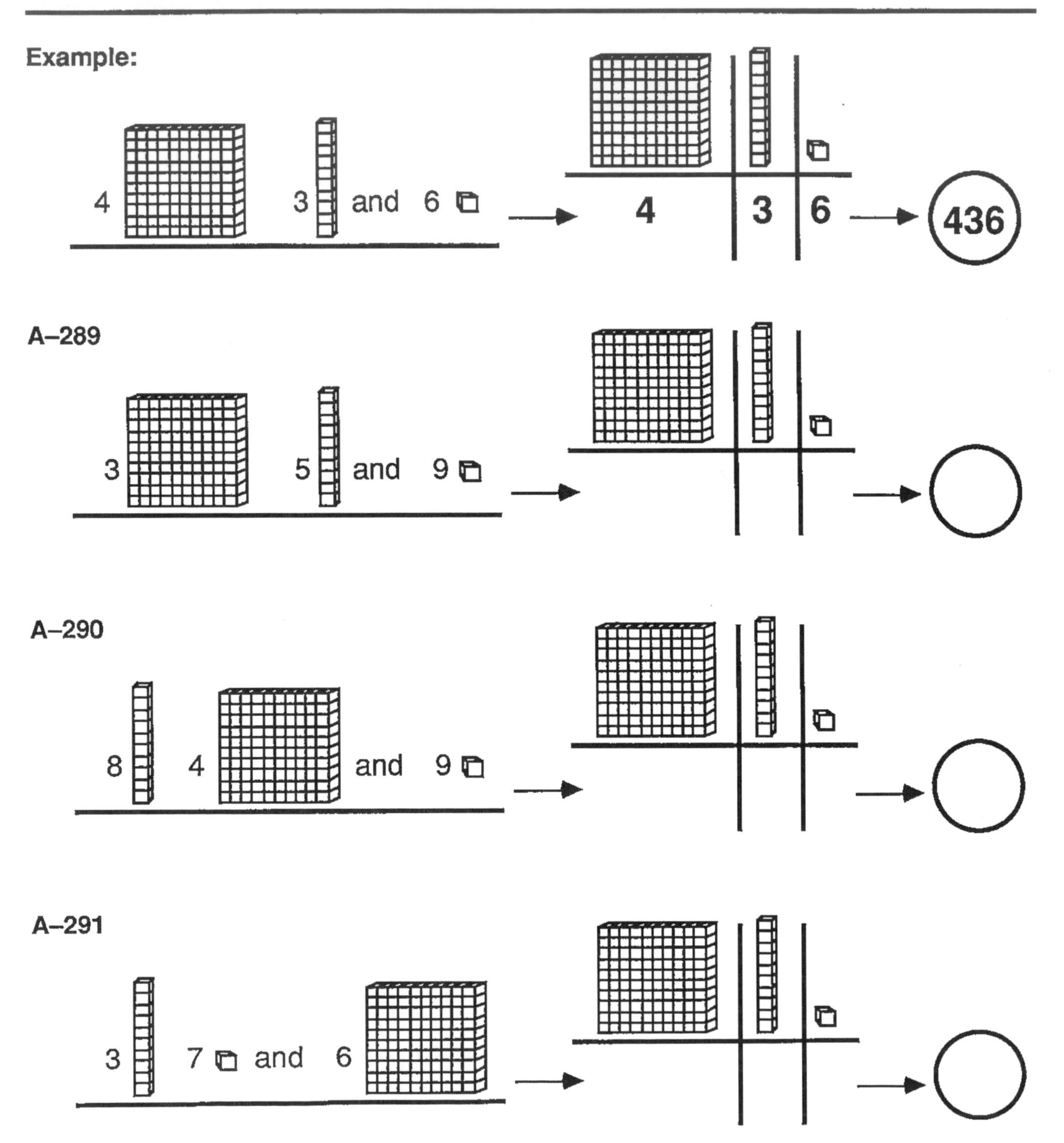

COUNTING RODS AND CUBES

Each rod is made with 10 cubes.
Circle the number that shows the total number of cubes in each group.

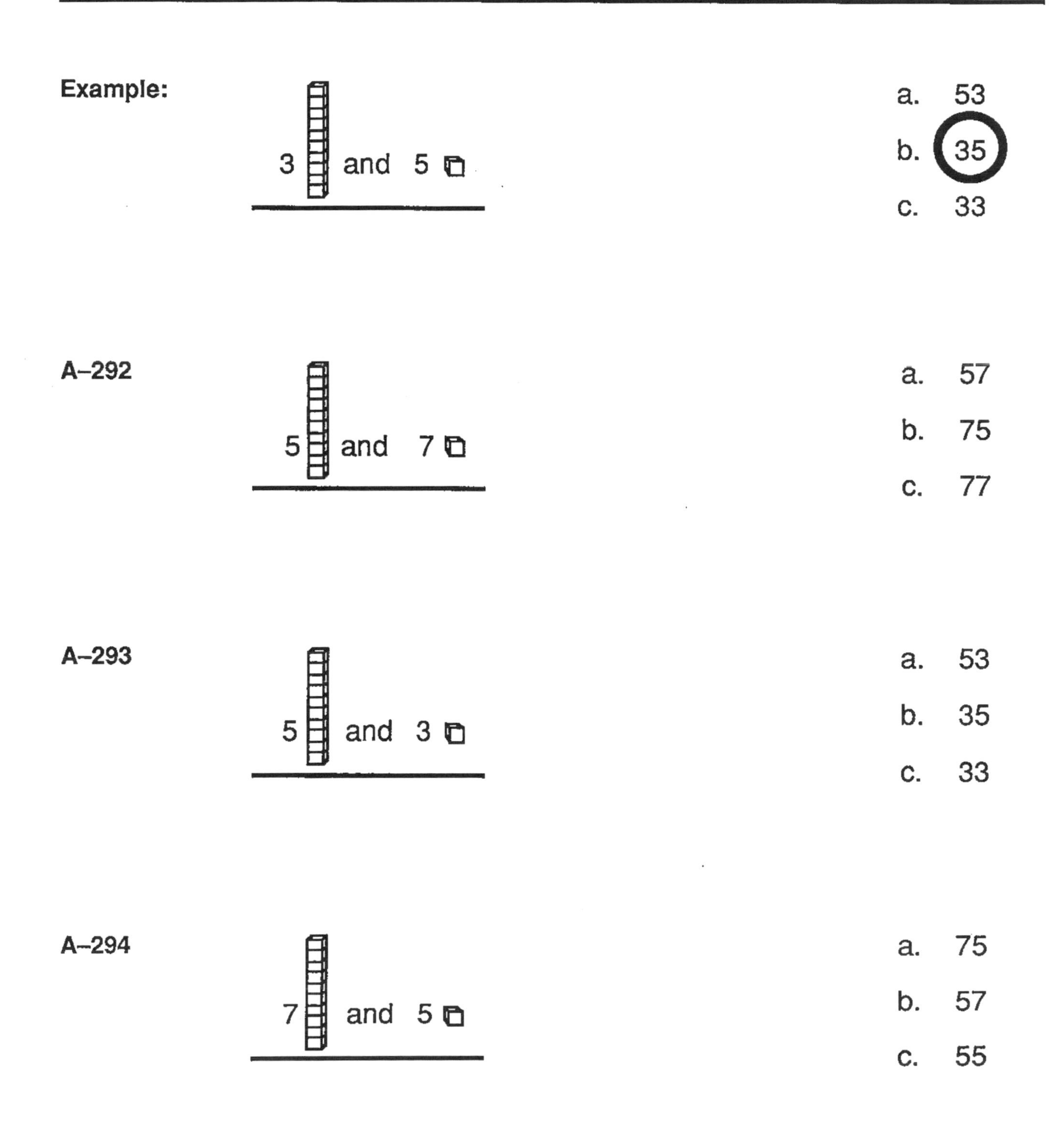

Example:

3 and 5

a. 53
b. 35
c. 33

A–292

5 and 7

a. 57
b. 75
c. 77

A–293

5 and 3

a. 53
b. 35
c. 33

A–294

7 and 5

a. 75
b. 57
c. 55

COUNTING FLATS, RODS, AND CUBES

Each flat is made with 100 cubes. Each rod is made with 10 cubes.
Circle the number that shows the total number of cubes in each group.

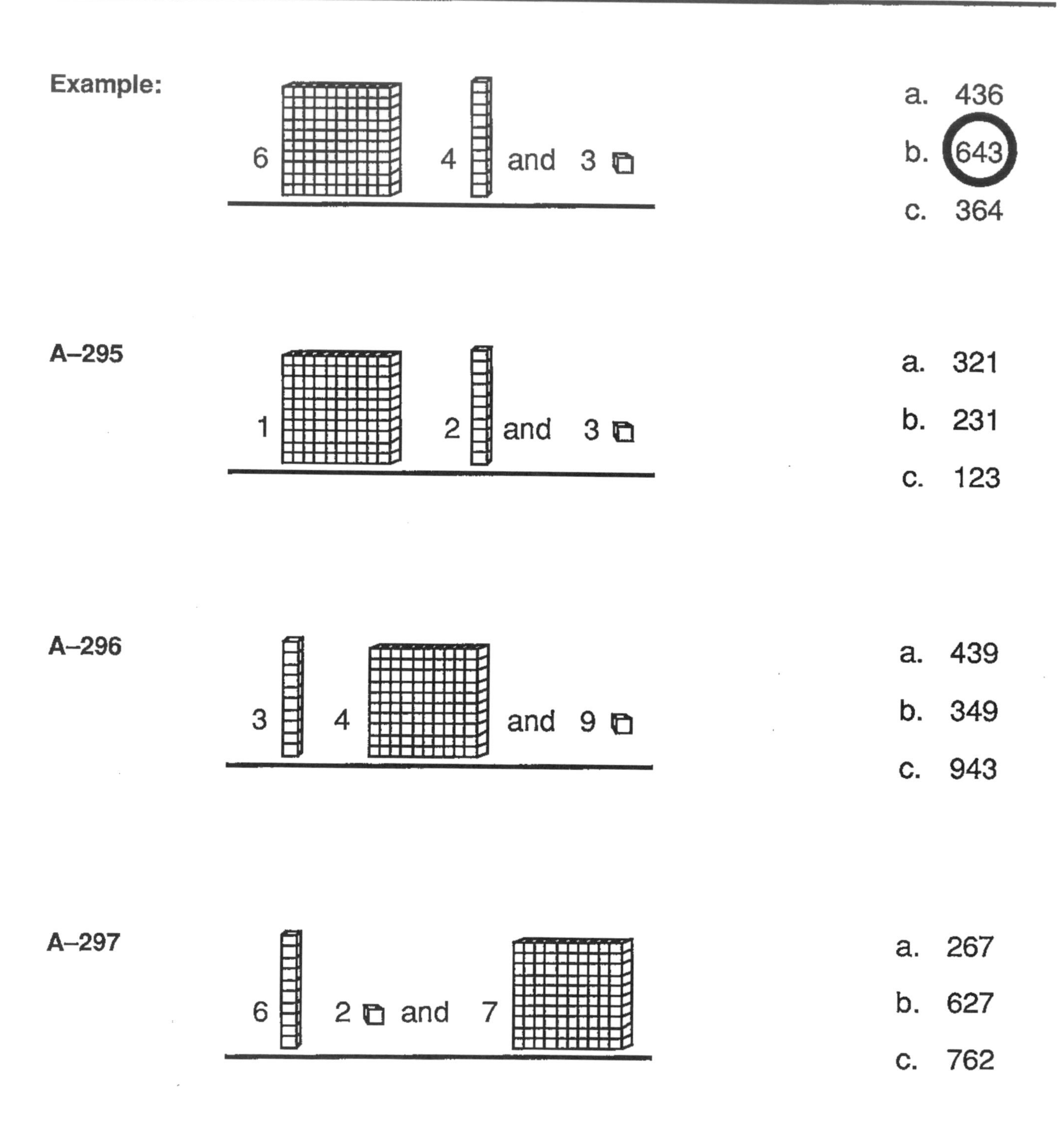

Example:

a. 436
b. 643
c. 364

A–295

a. 321
b. 231
c. 123

A–296

a. 439
b. 349
c. 943

A–297

a. 267
b. 627
c. 762

COUNTING RODS AND CUBES

Each rod is made with 10 cubes.
Look at the number in each box.
Fill in the blanks to show how many rods and cubes are needed to make the number.

Example:

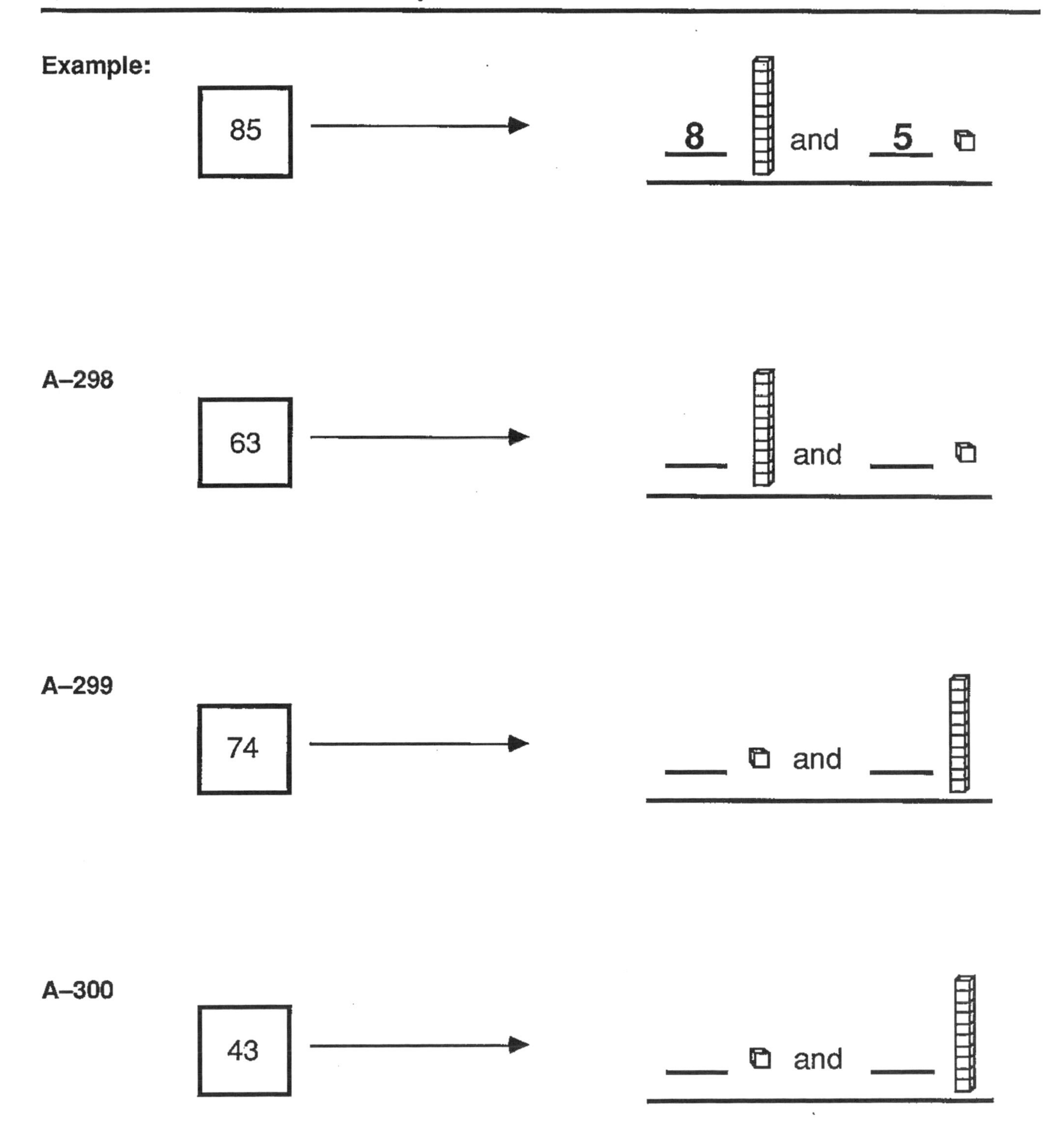

A–298

A–299

A–300

COUNTING FLATS, RODS, AND CUBES

Each flat is made with 100 cubes. Each rod is made with 10 cubes.
Look at the number in the box.
Fill in the blanks to show how many flats, rods, and cubes are needed to make the number.

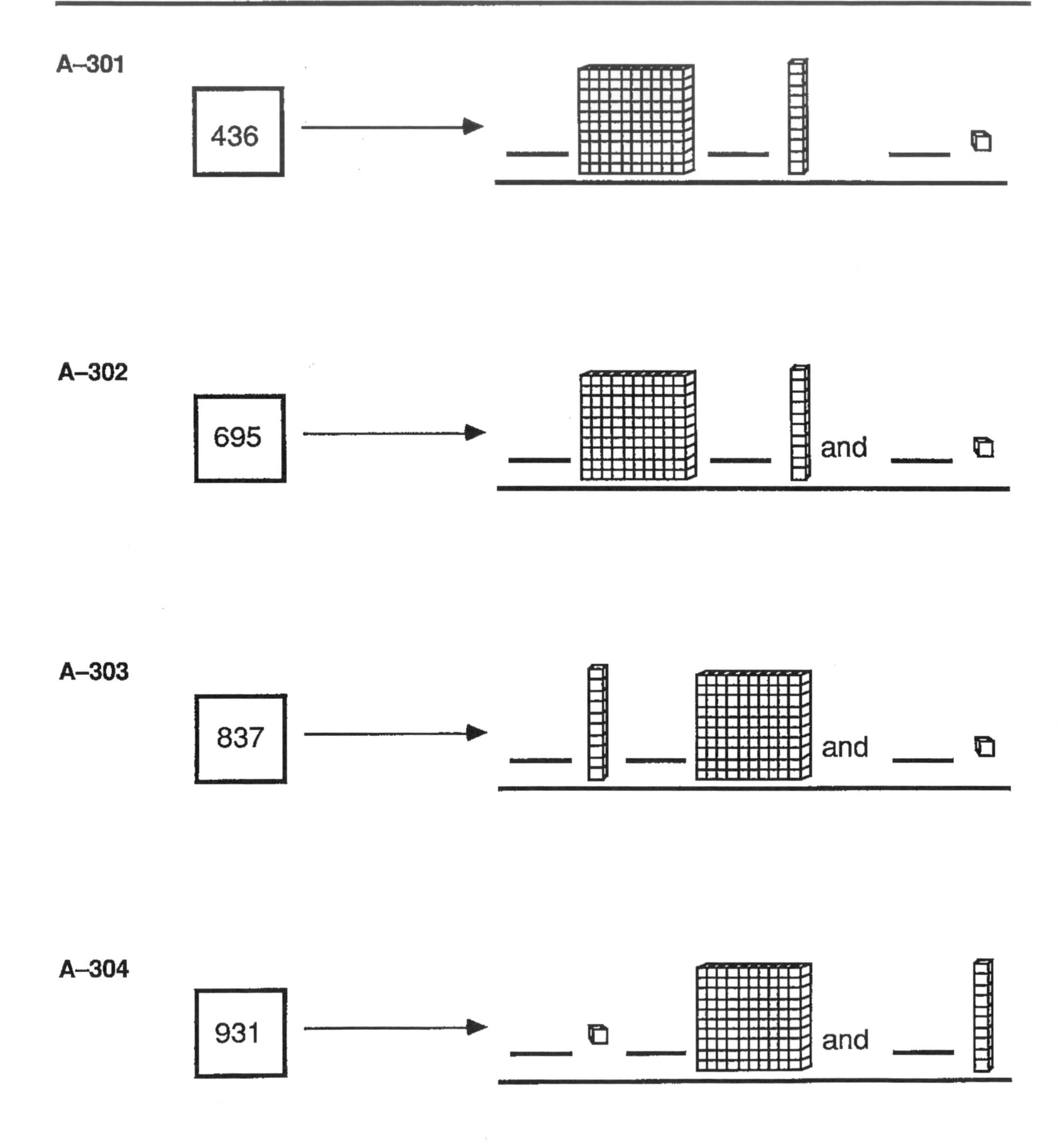

ESTIMATING LENGTH—LESS THAN

The shaded rectangle is 10 centimeters long.

Shade all the rectangles with lengths less than 10 centimeters.

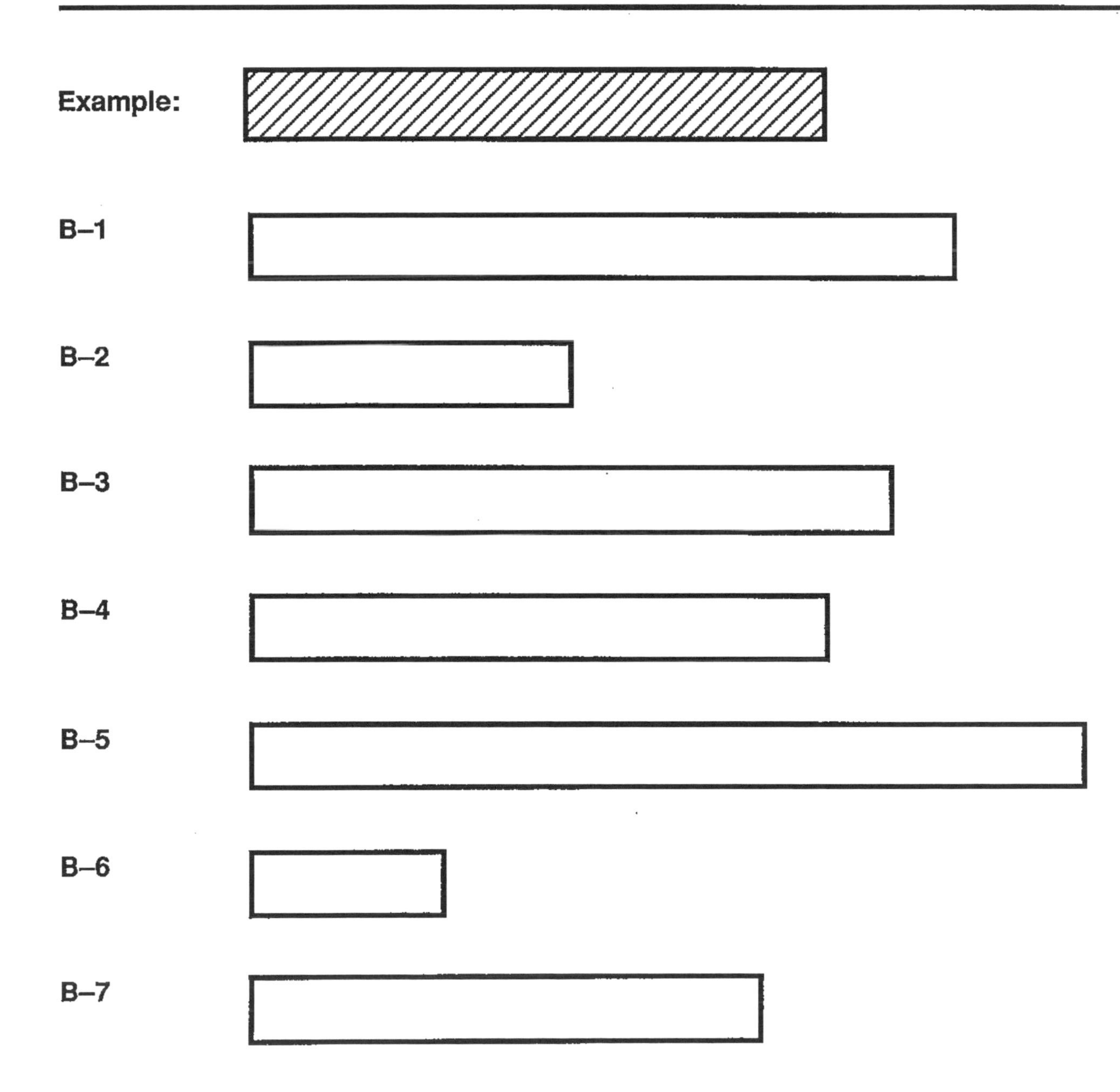

ESTIMATING LENGTH—LESS THAN

The shaded rectangle is 10 centimeters long.

Shade all the rectangles with lengths less than 10 centimeters.

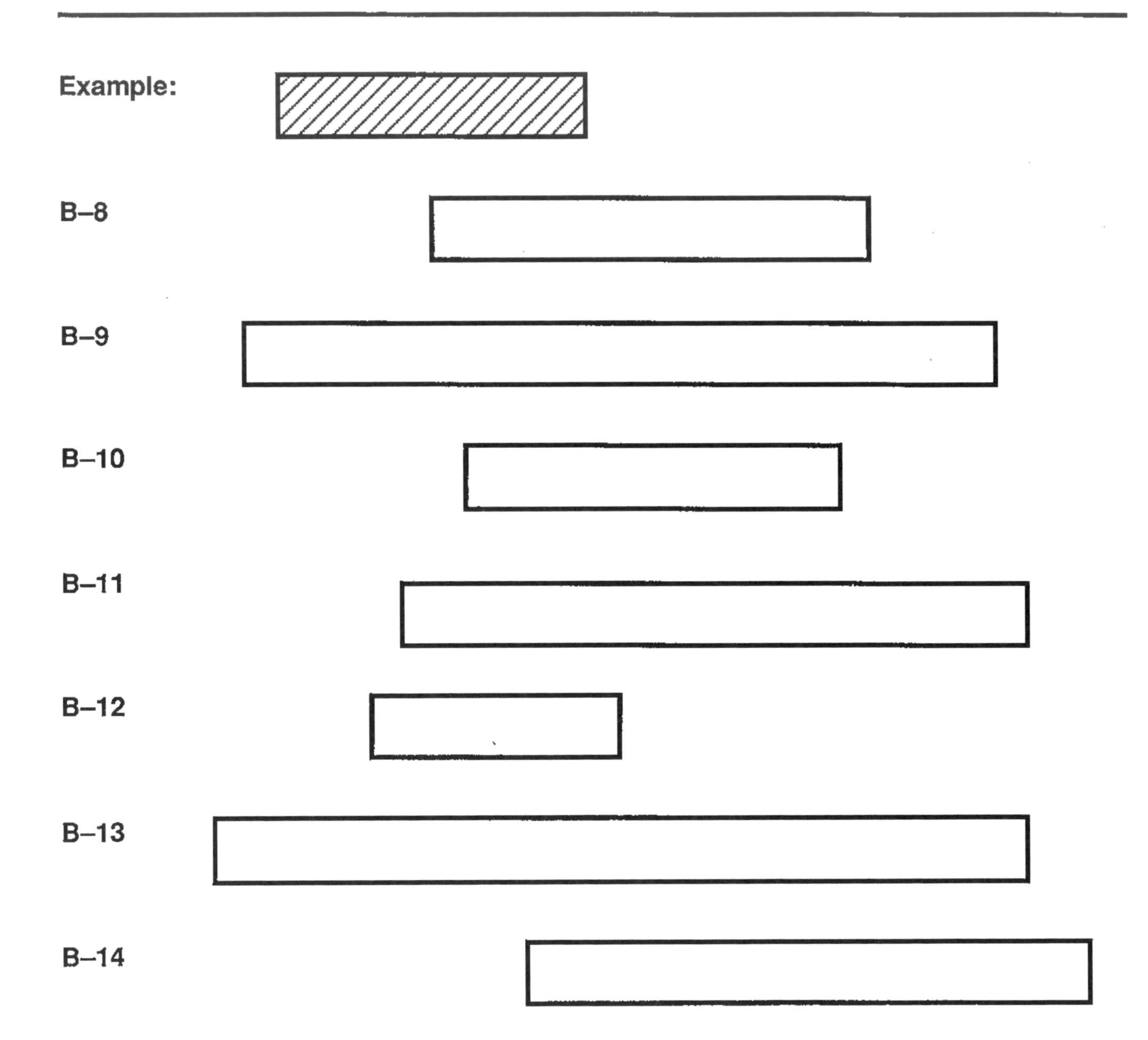

ESTIMATING LENGTH—GREATER THAN

The shaded rectangle is 5 centimeters long.

Shade all the rectangles with lengths greater than 5 centimeters.

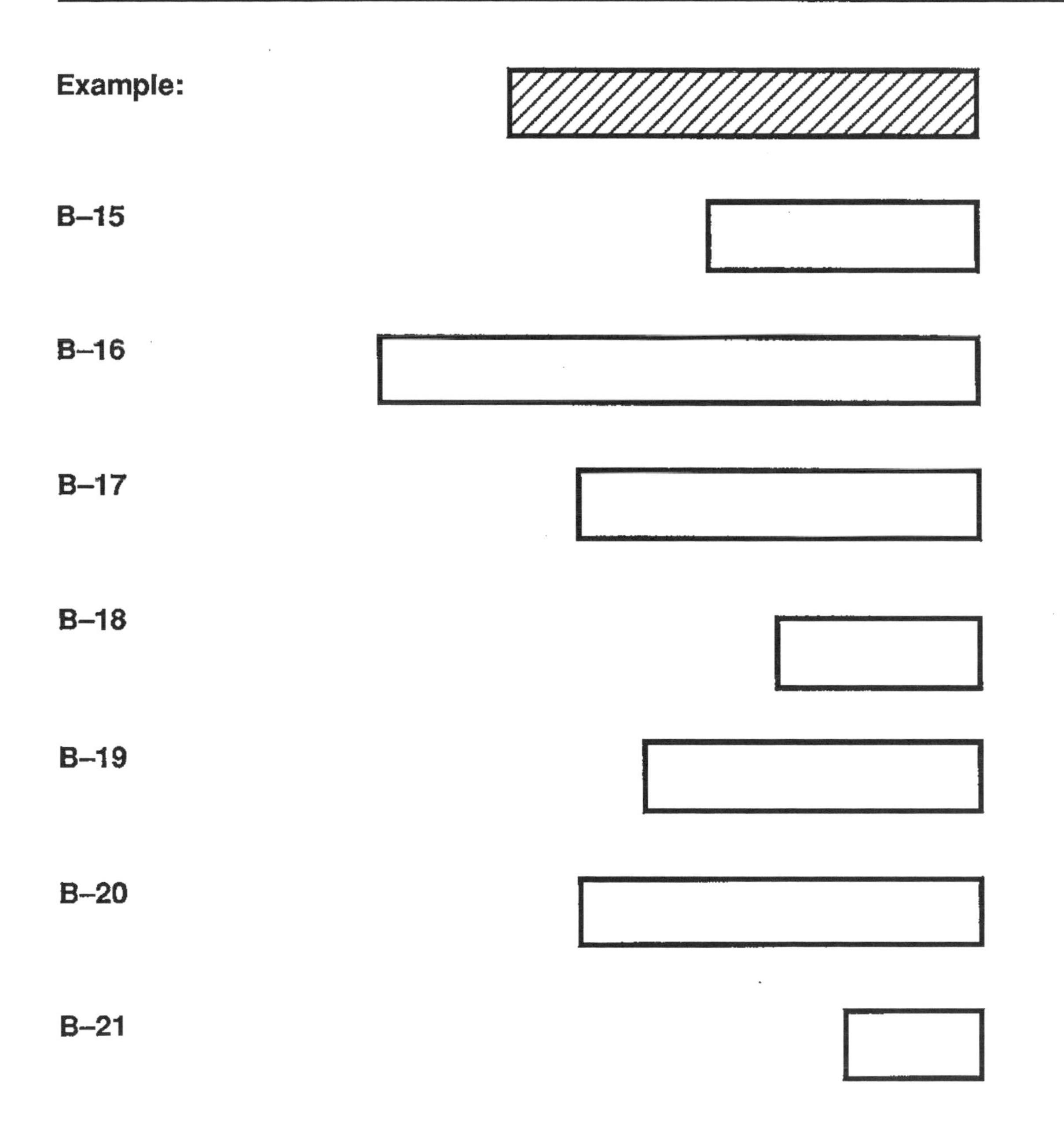

ESTIMATING LENGTH—GREATER THAN

The shaded rectangle is 5 centimeters long.

Shade all the rectangles with lengths greater than 5 centimeters.

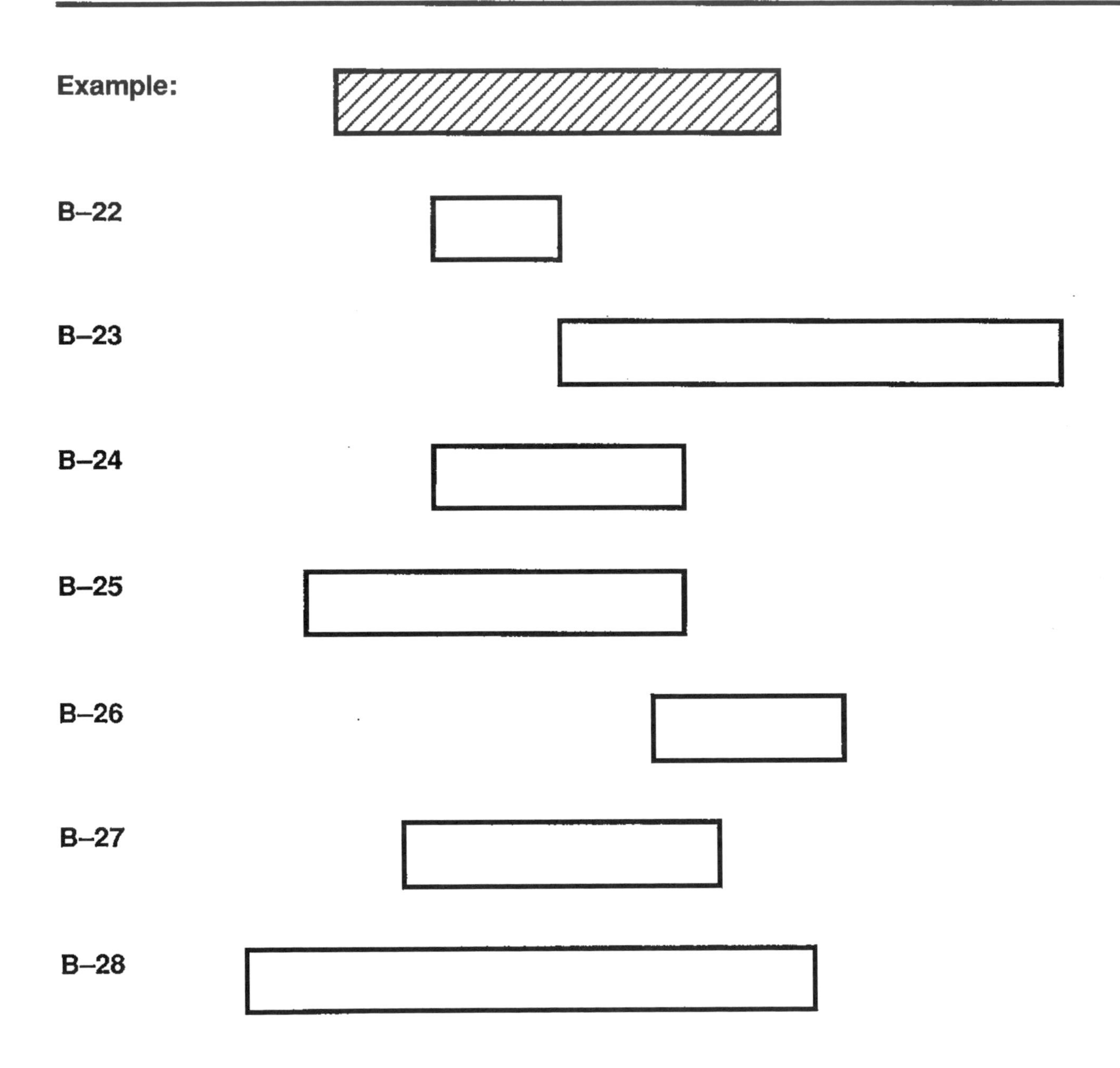

ESTIMATING LENGTH—BETWEEN

The dotted rectangle is 10 centimeters long.
The shaded rectangle is 5 centimeters long.

Shade all the rectangles with lengths between 5 centimeters and 10 centimeters.

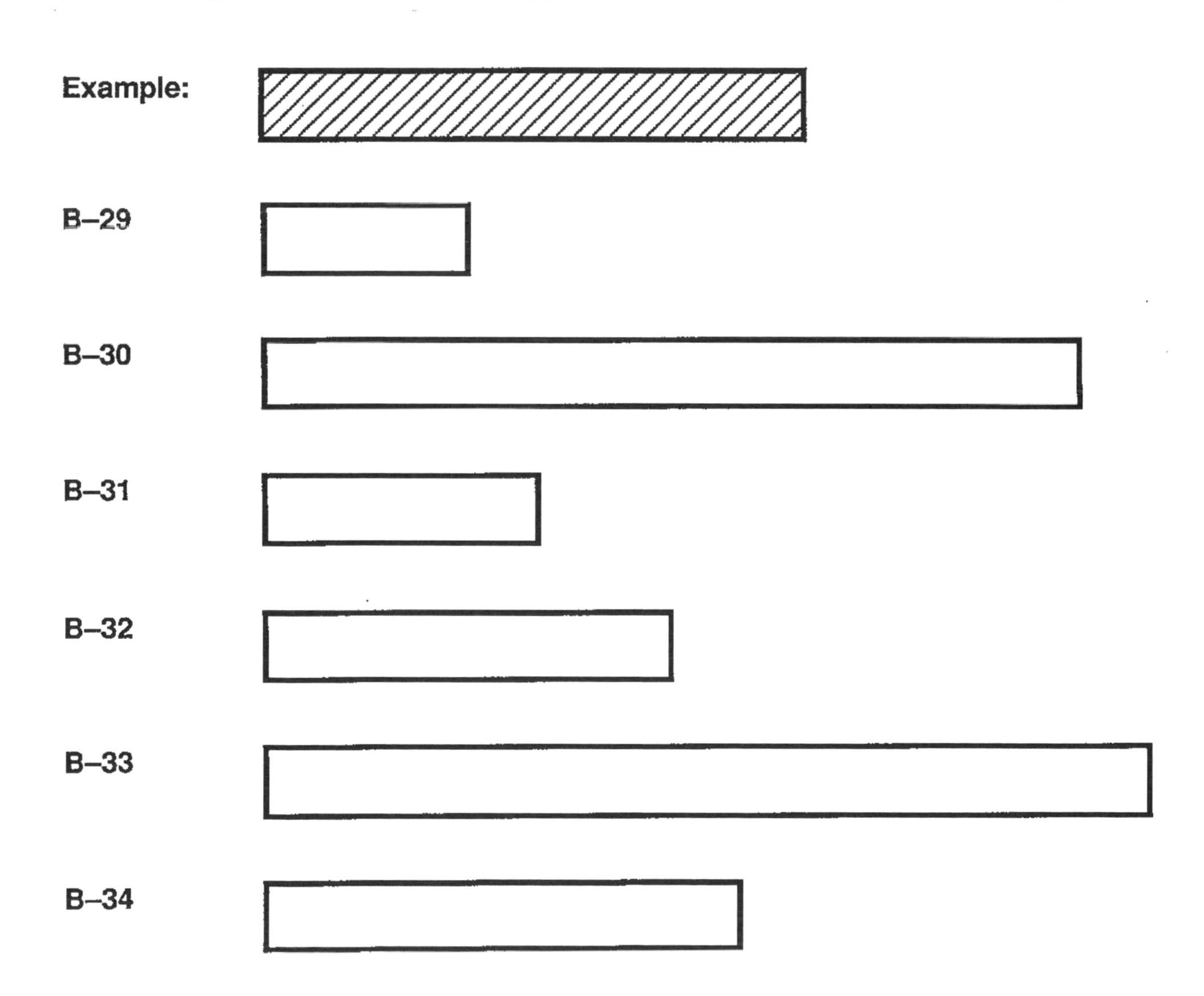

ESTIMATING LENGTH—BETWEEN

The dotted rectangle is 10 centimeters long.
The shaded rectangle is 5 centimeters long.

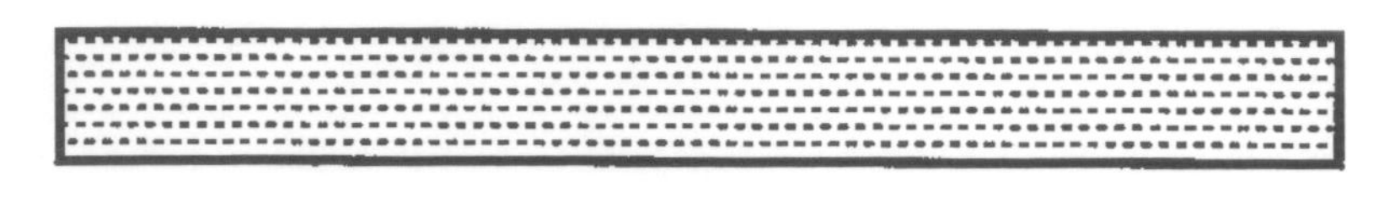

Shade all the rectangles with lengths between 5 centimeters and 10 centimeters.

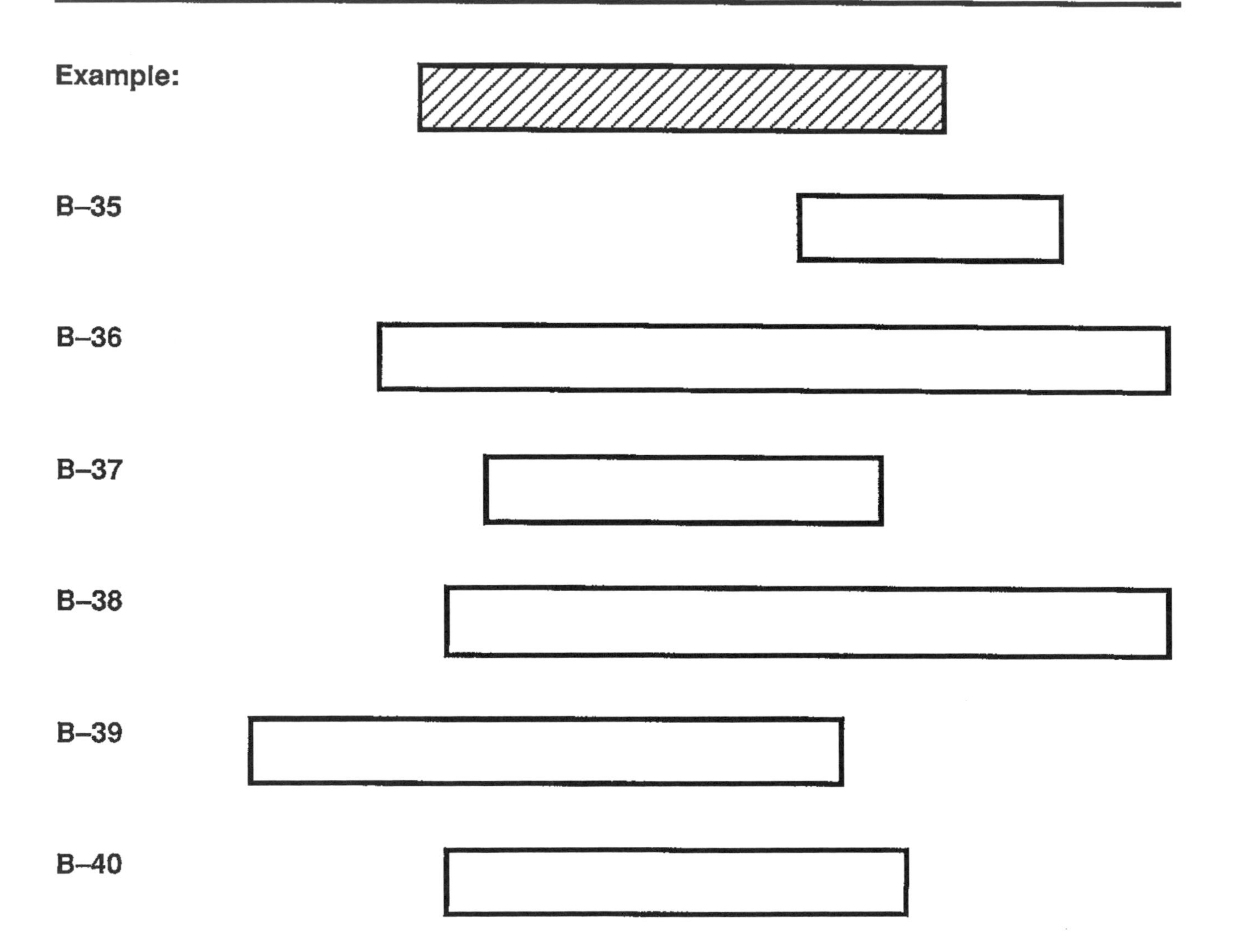

COMPARING LENGTHS

Put an X on the longer line.

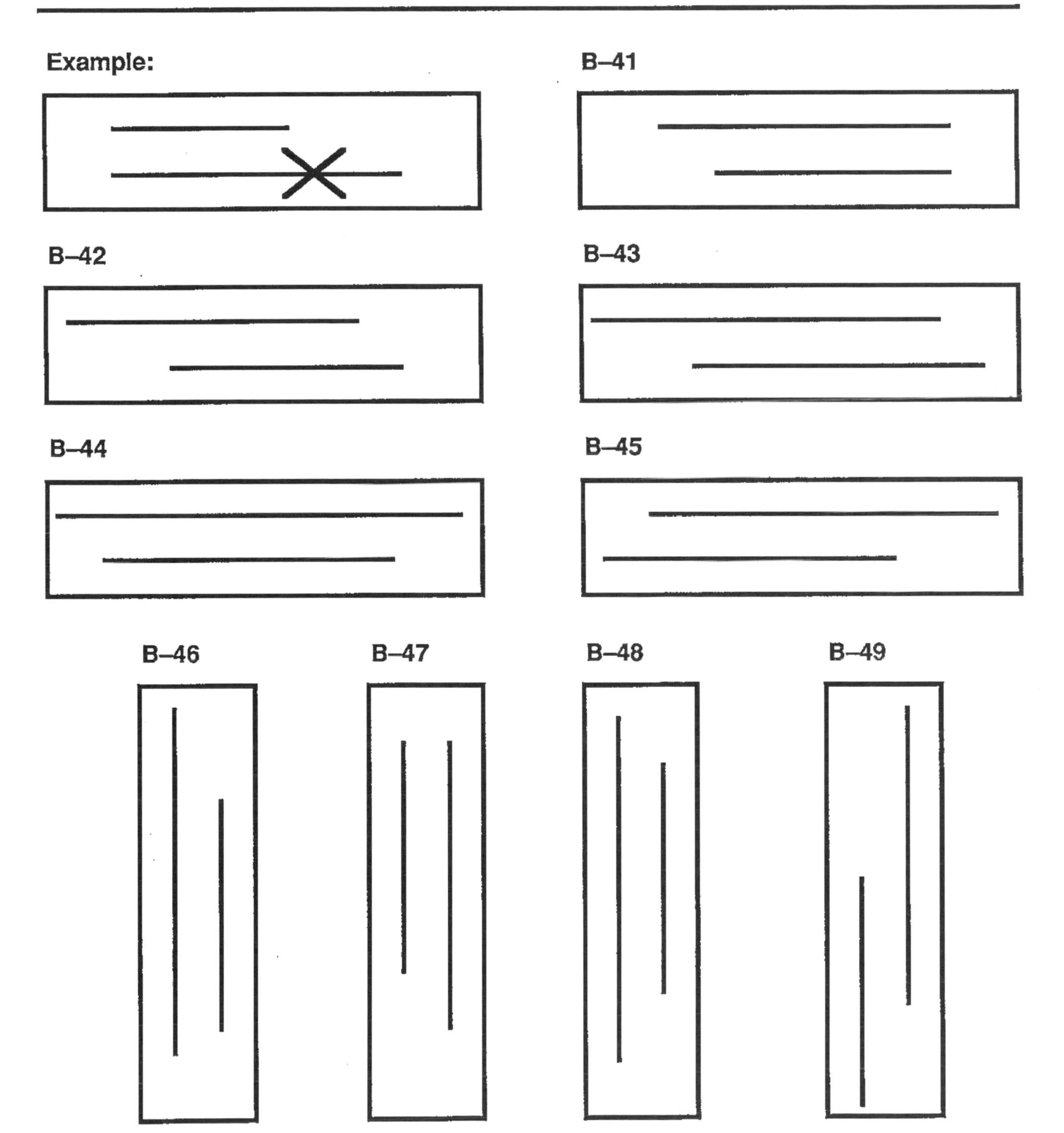

COMPARING LENGTHS

Put an X on the longest line.

Example:

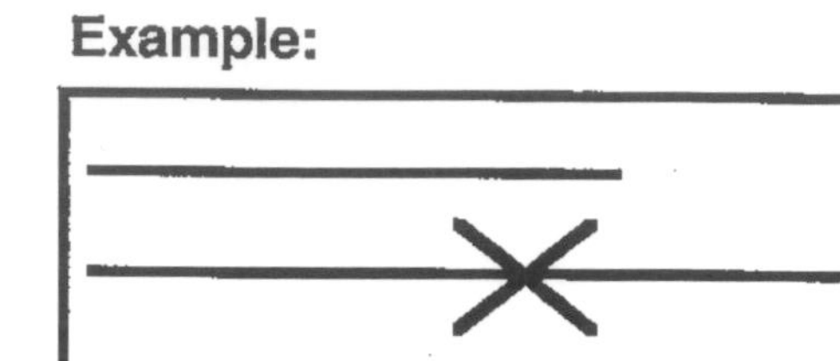

B–50

B–51

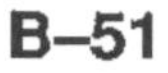

B–52

B–53

B–54

B–55

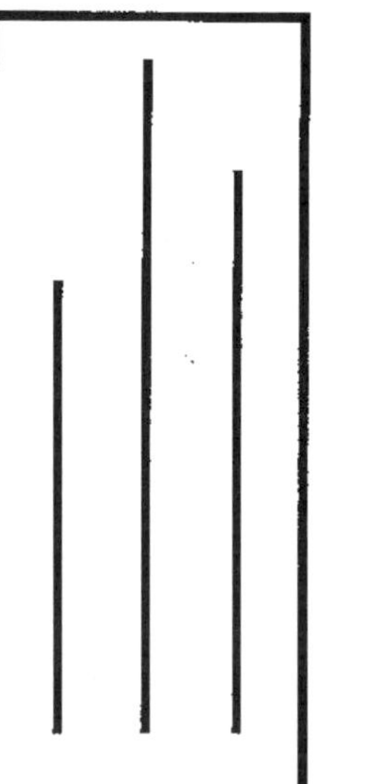

B–56

B–57

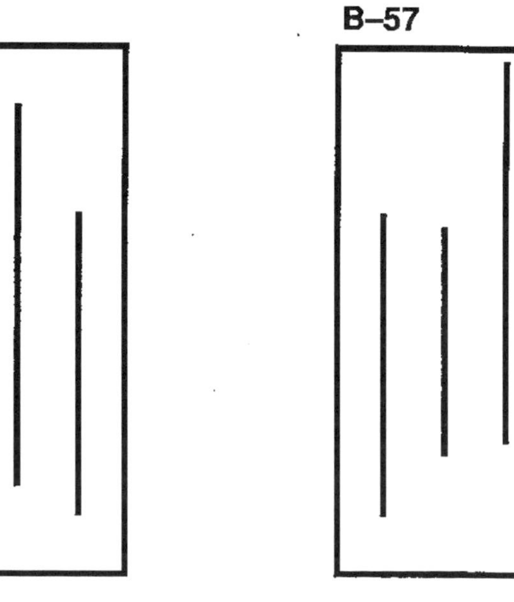

COMPARING LENGTHS

Put an X on the shorter line.

Example:

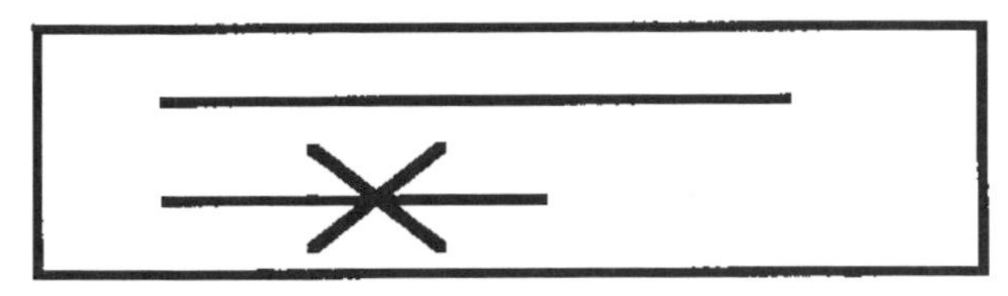

B–58

B–59

B–60

B–61

B–62

B–63 **B–64**

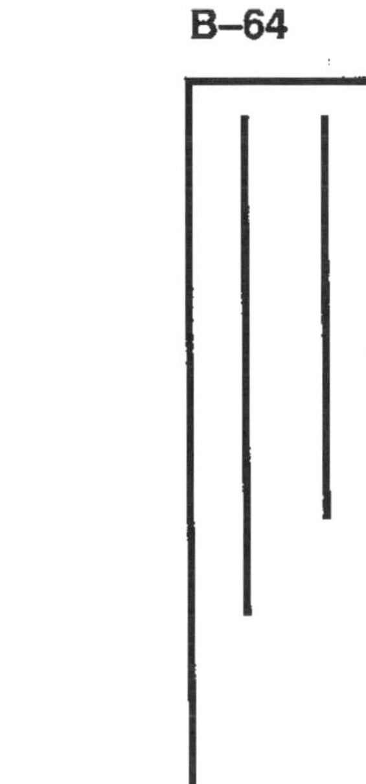

B–65 **B–66**

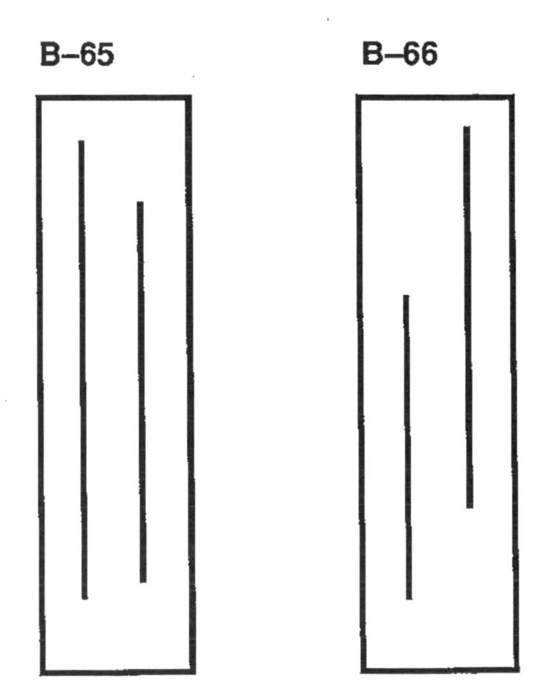

COMPARING LENGTHS

Put an X on the shortest line.

Example:

B–67

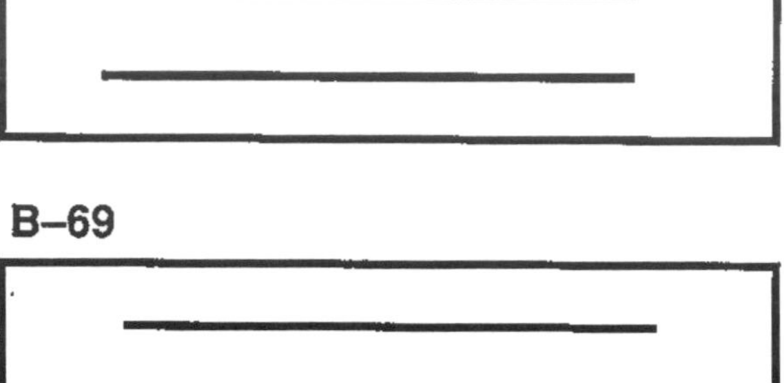

B–68

B–69

B–70

B–71

B–72

B–73

B–74

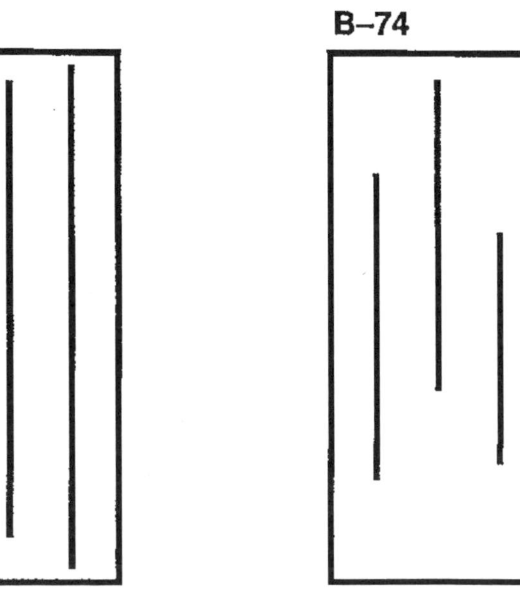

COMPARING LENGTHS

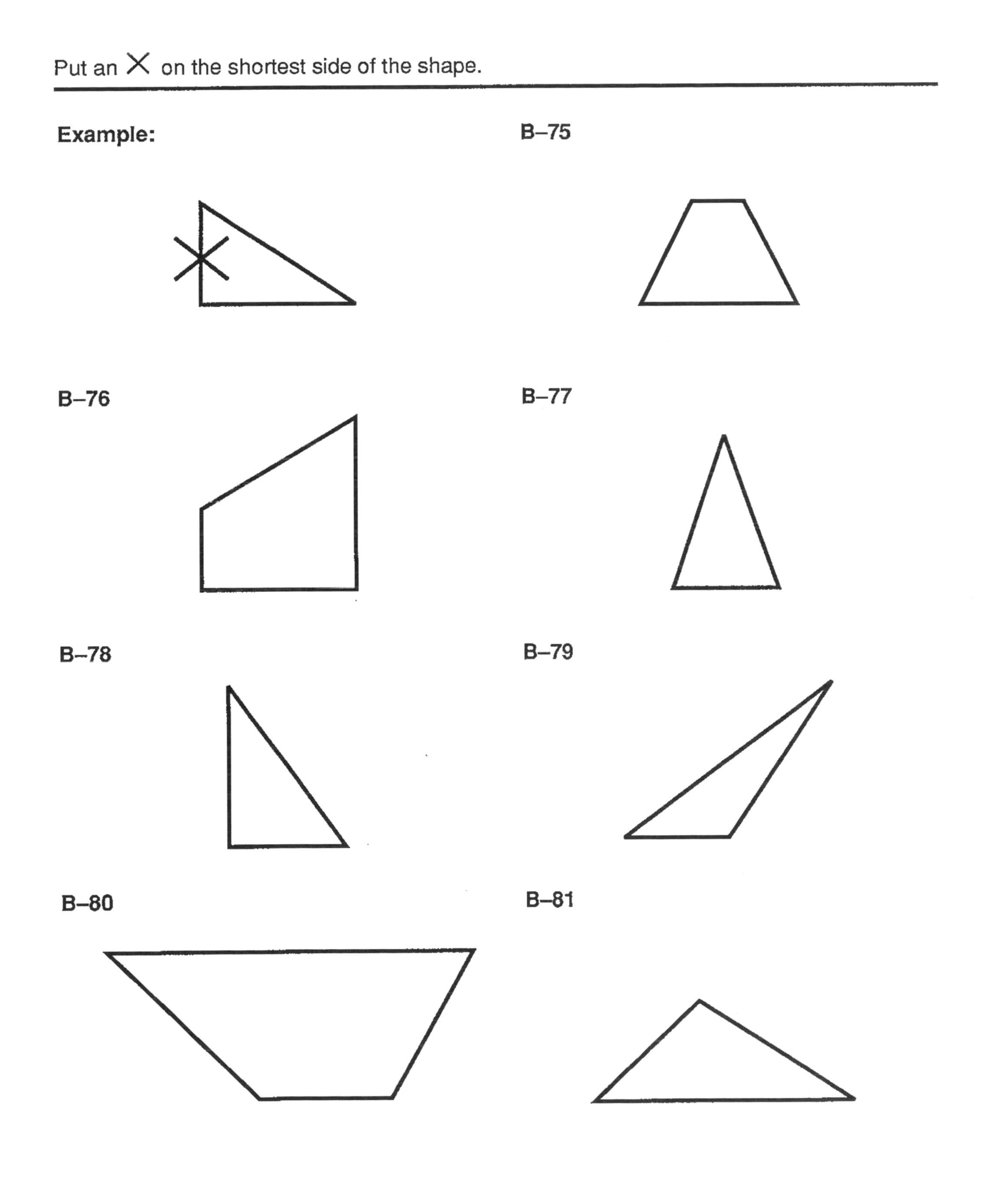

COMPARING LENGTHS

Put an  on the shorter line.

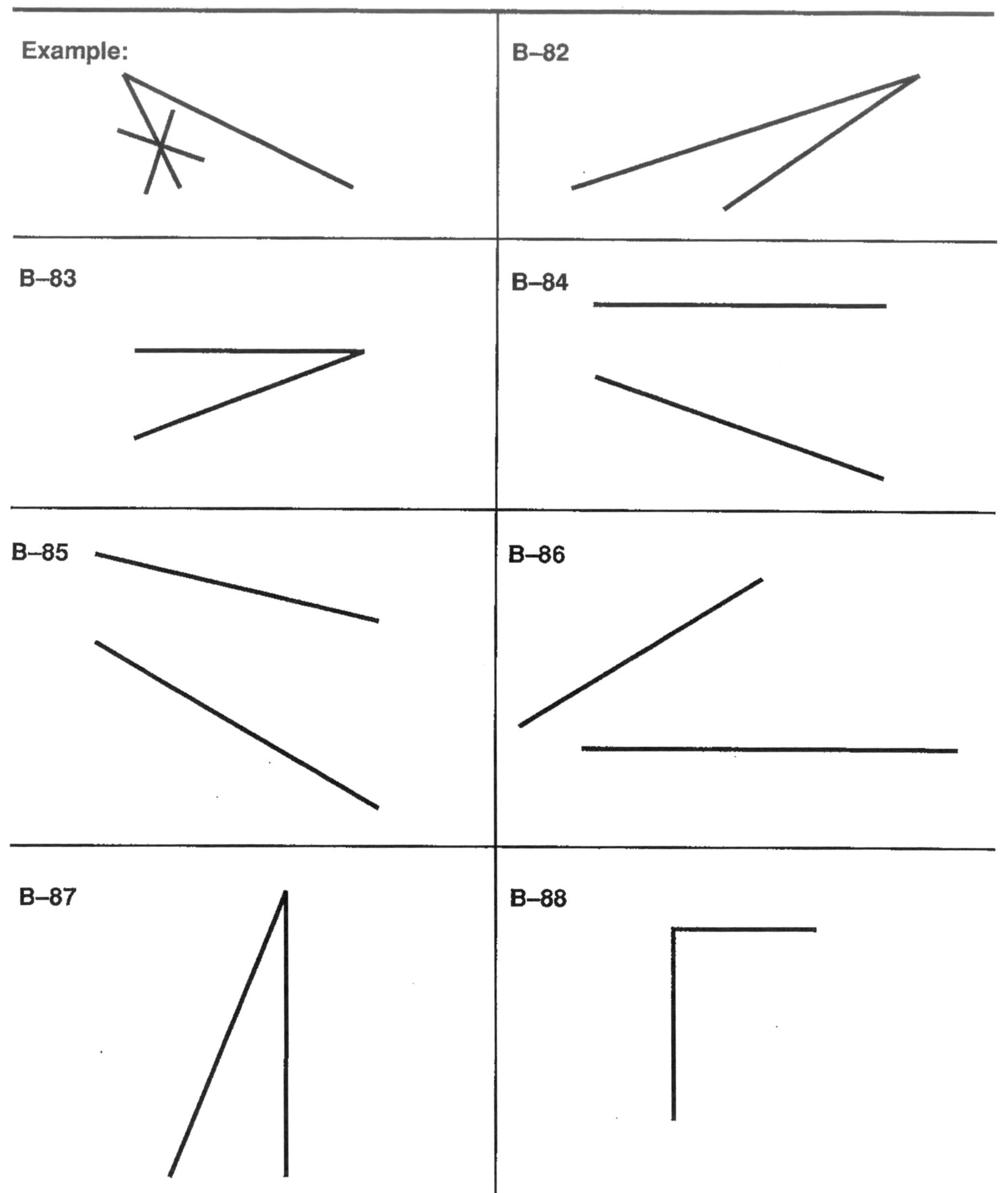

COMPARING LENGTHS

Put an X on the longest side of the shape.

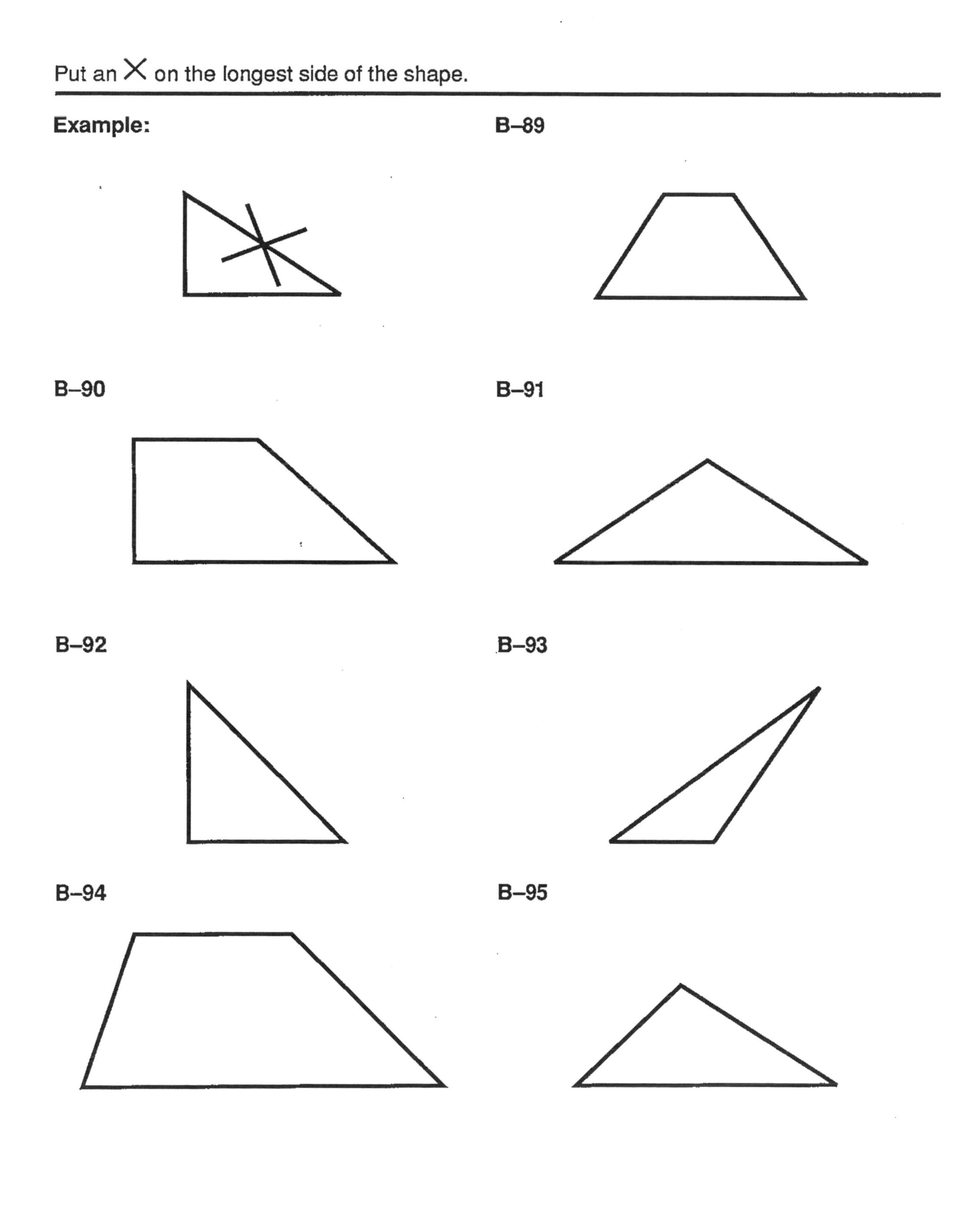

COMPARING LENGTHS

Put an X on the longer line.

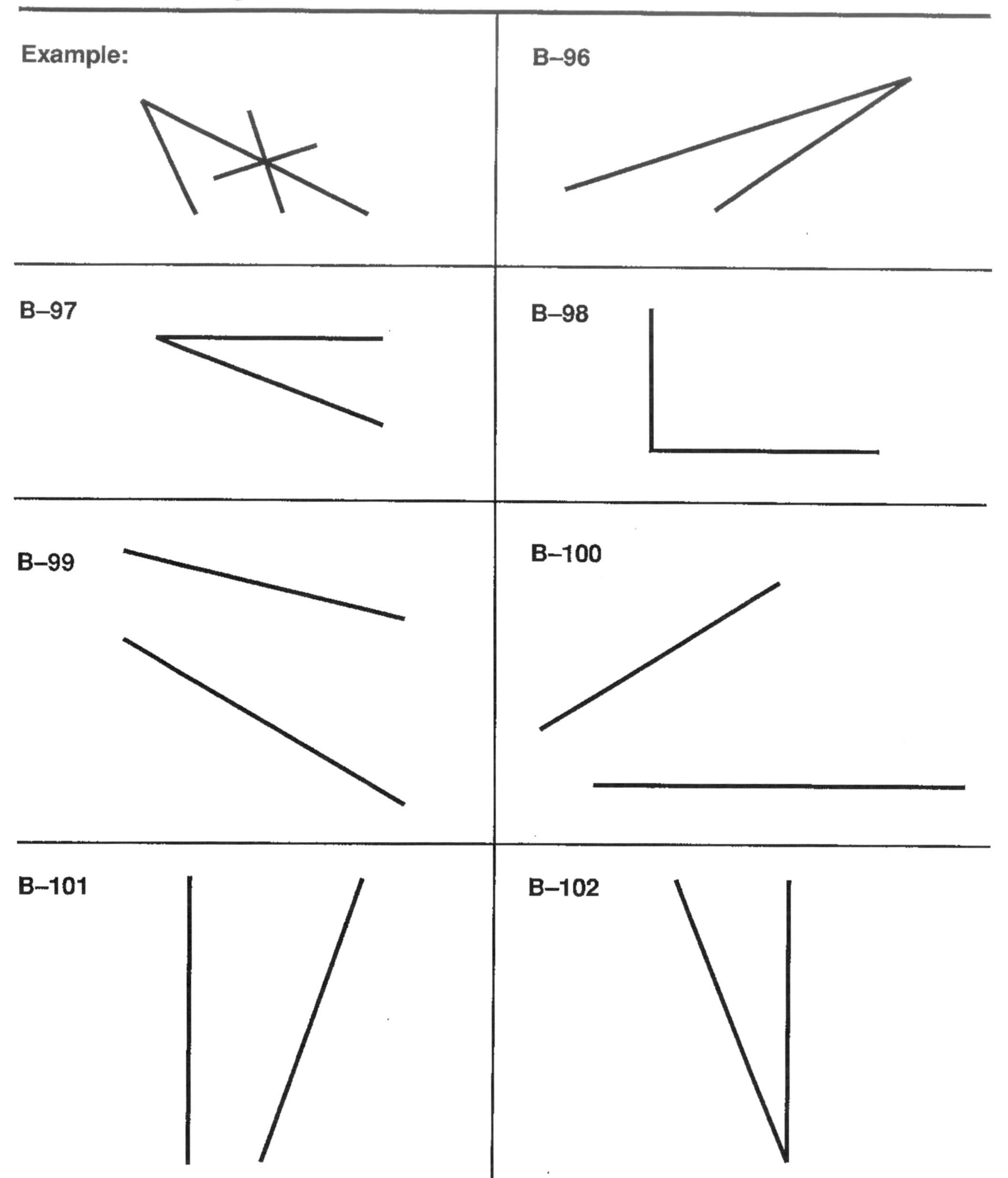

CLASSIFYING BY SHAPE

Put an X on the shapes that have three sides.

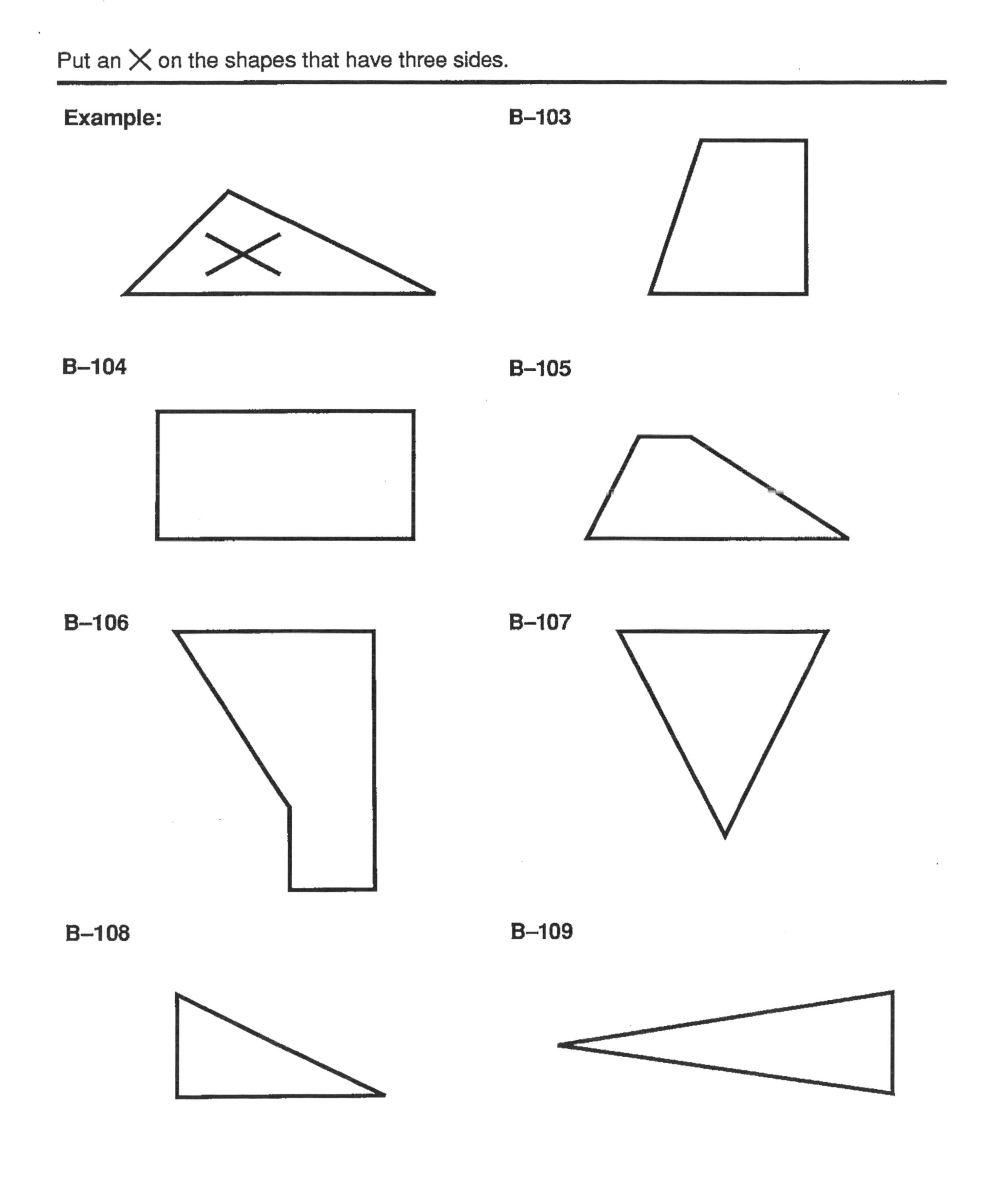

CLASSIFYING BY SHAPE

Put an X on the shapes that have four sides.

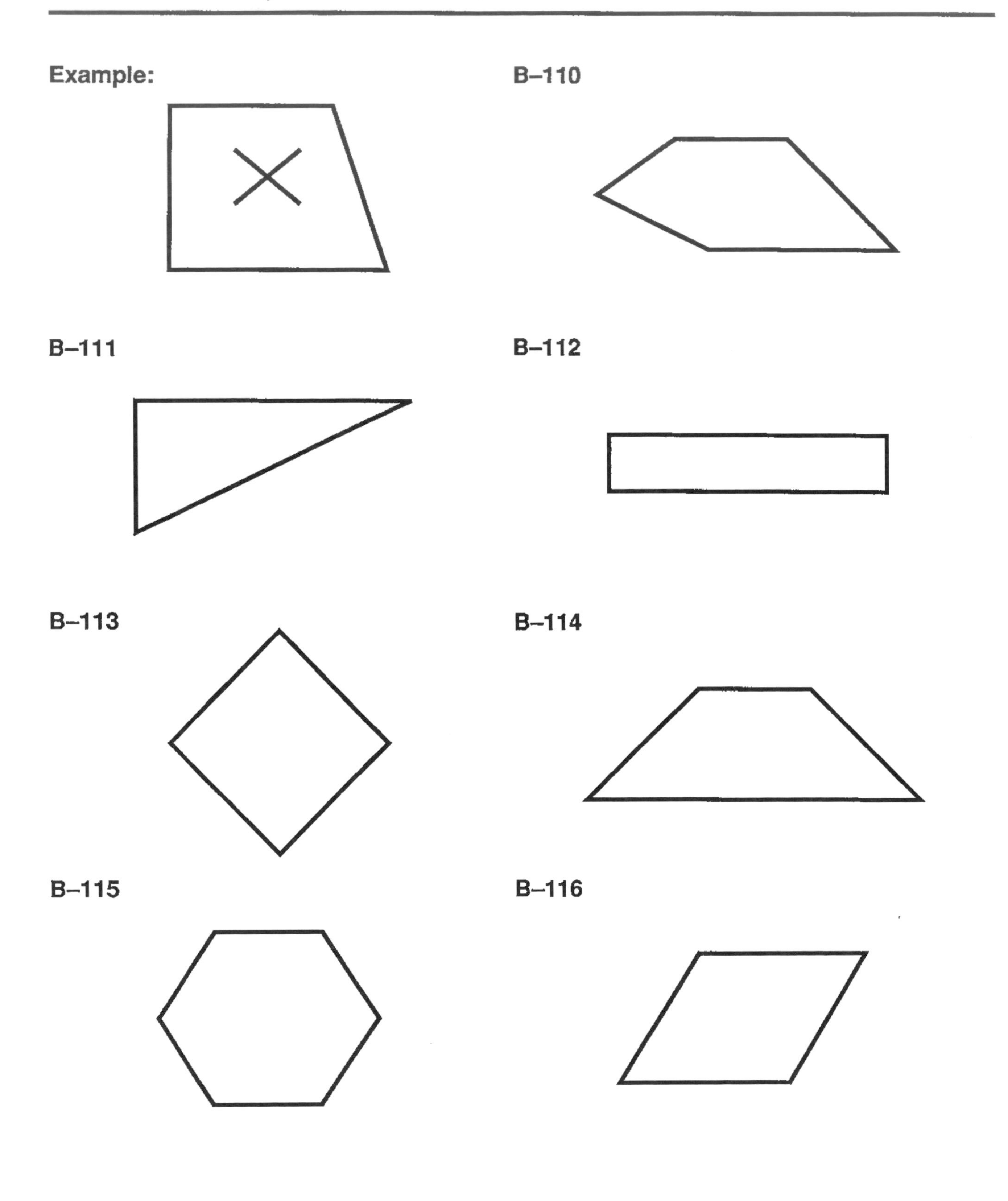

CLASSIFYING BY SHAPE

Put an X on the shapes that have three sides and one square corner.

Example:

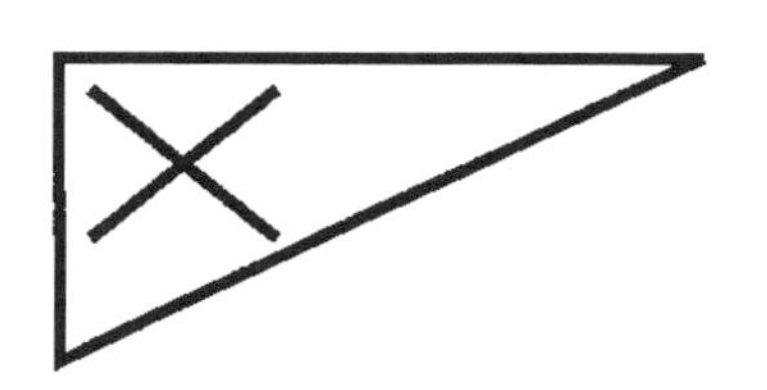

B–117

B–118

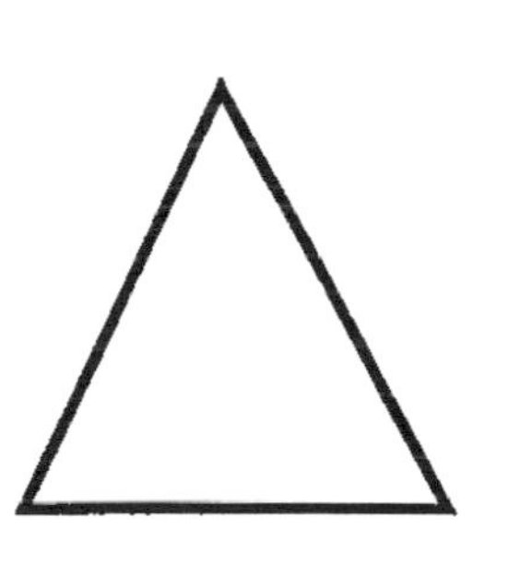

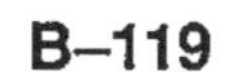

B–119

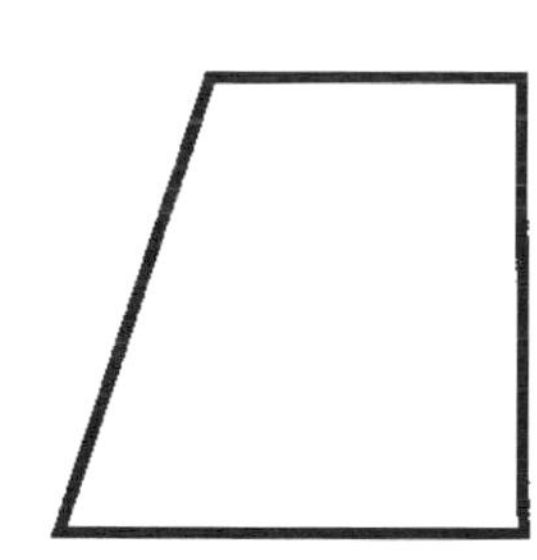

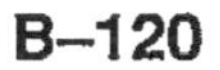

B–120

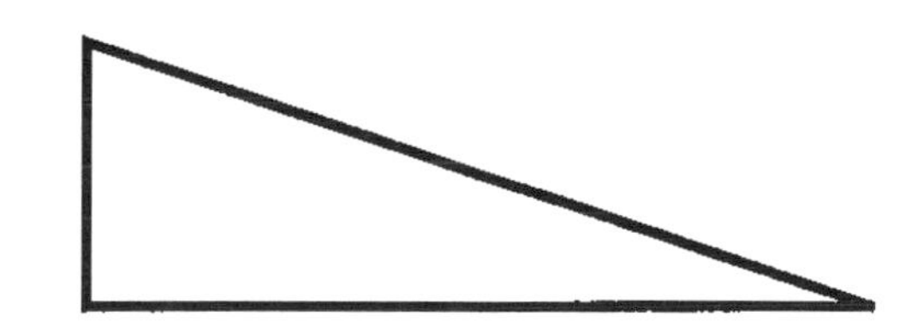

B–121

B–122

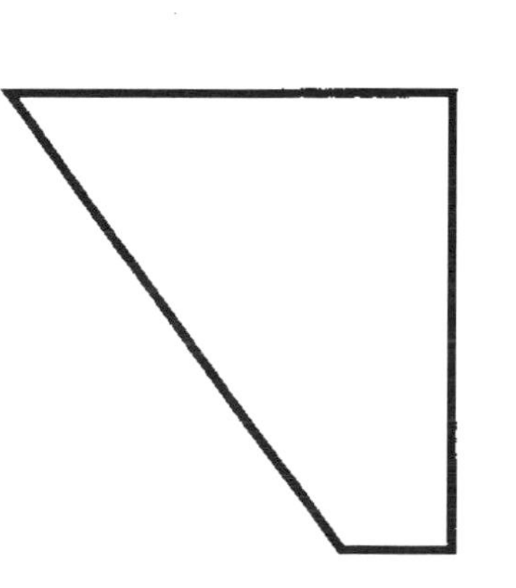

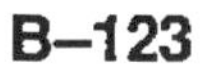

B–123

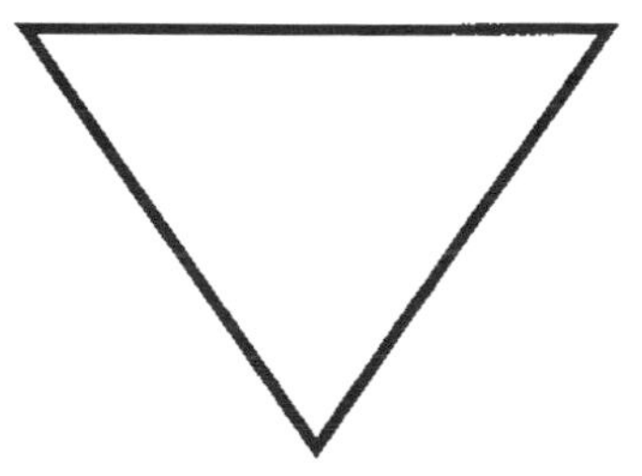

CLASSIFYING BY SHAPE

Put an X on the shapes that have one <u>or</u> more square corners.

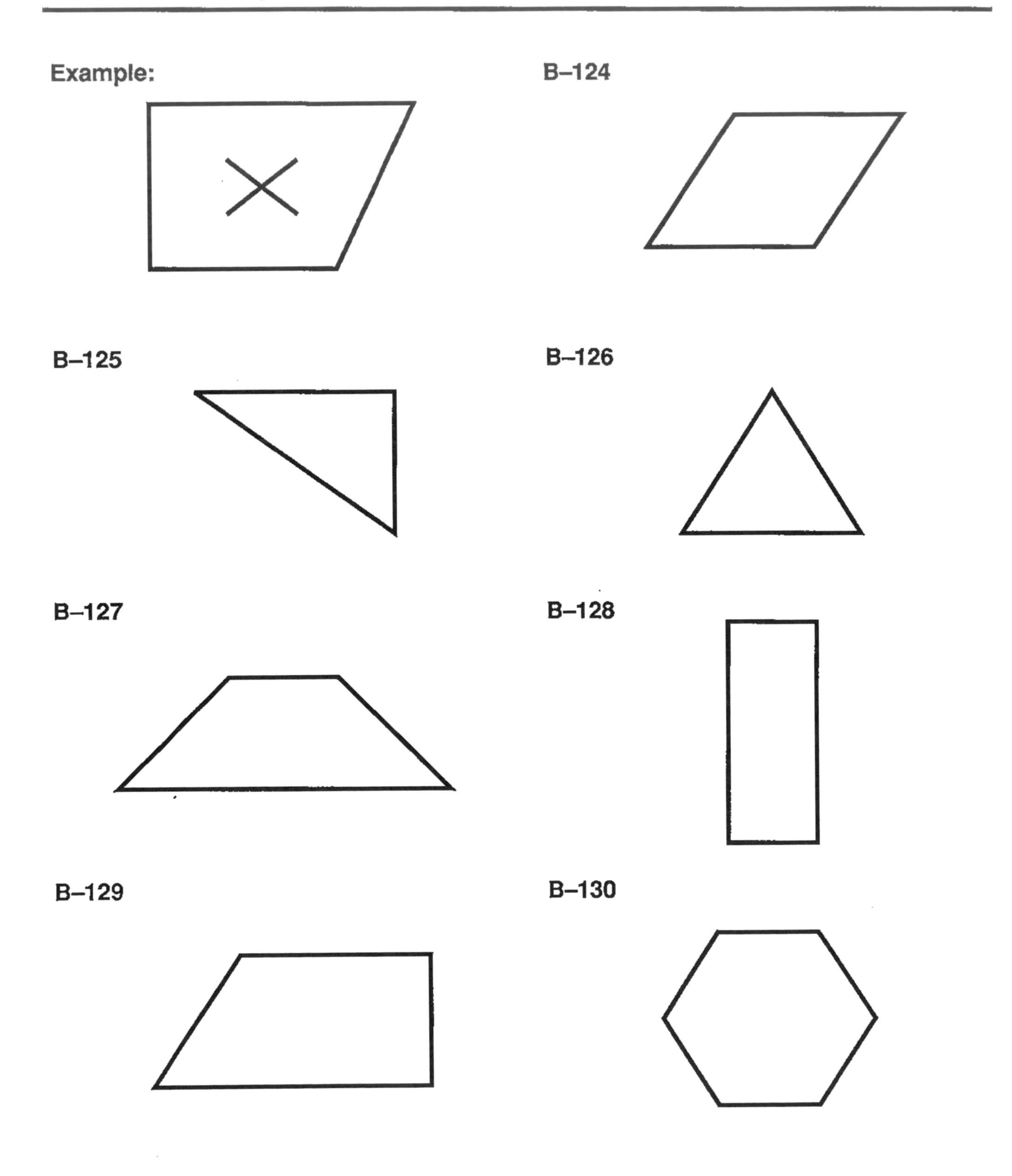

CLASSIFYING BY SHAPE

Put an X on the shape that belongs to the group in the box.

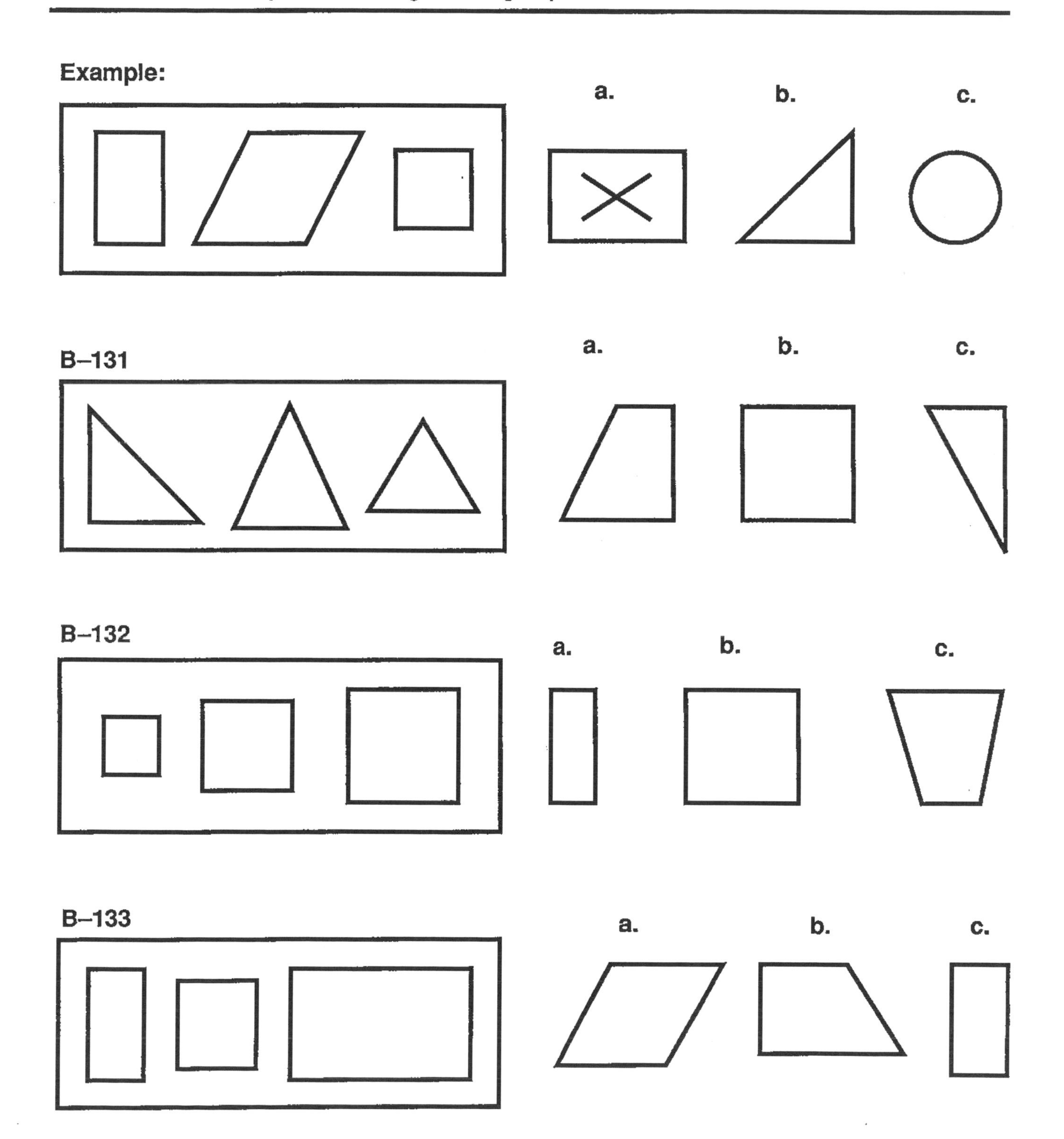

CLASSIFYING BY SHAPE

Put an X on the shape that does not belong to the group in the box.

Example:

B–134

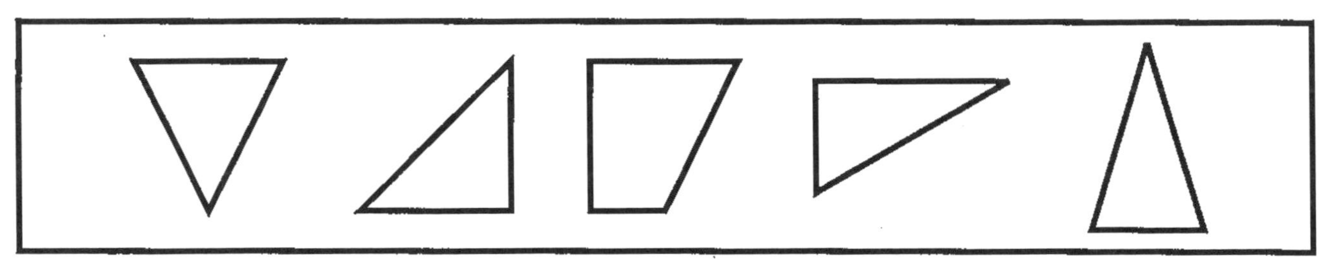

B–135

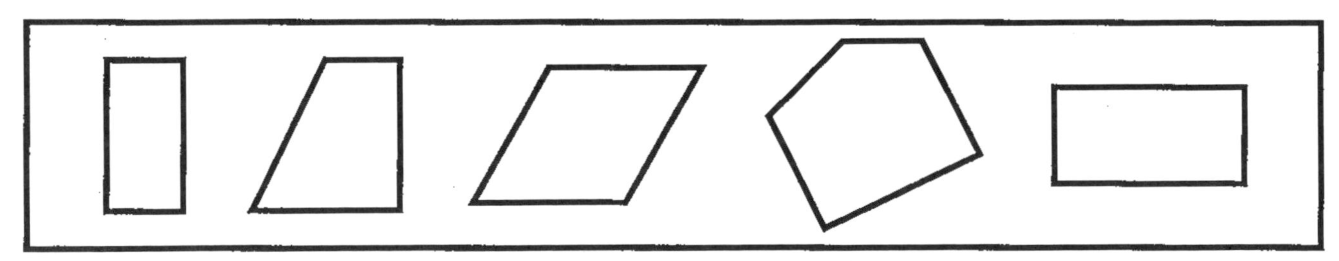

B–136

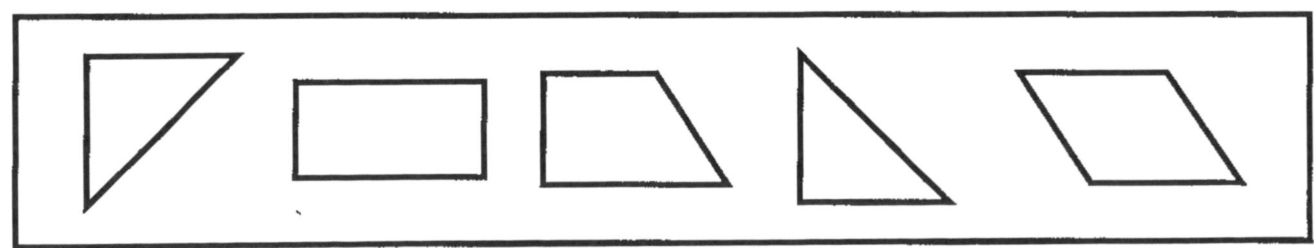

SYMMETRY

A shape is symmetric if you can fold it and the two halves match.
Draw dotted lines to show where to fold these symmetric figures.

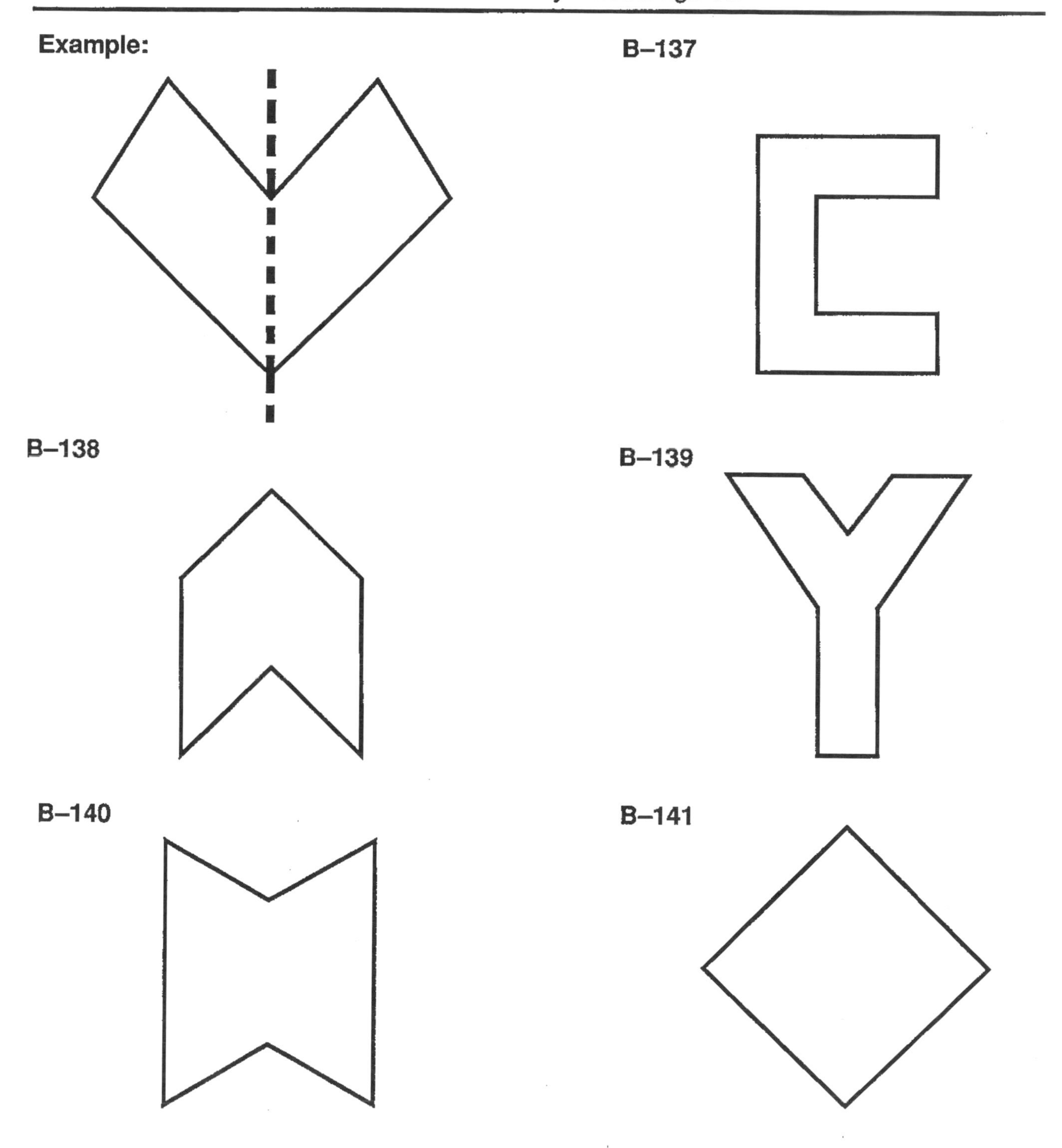

SYMMETRY

Draw a line around the symmetric figures.
Draw dotted lines to show where to fold the symmetric figures.

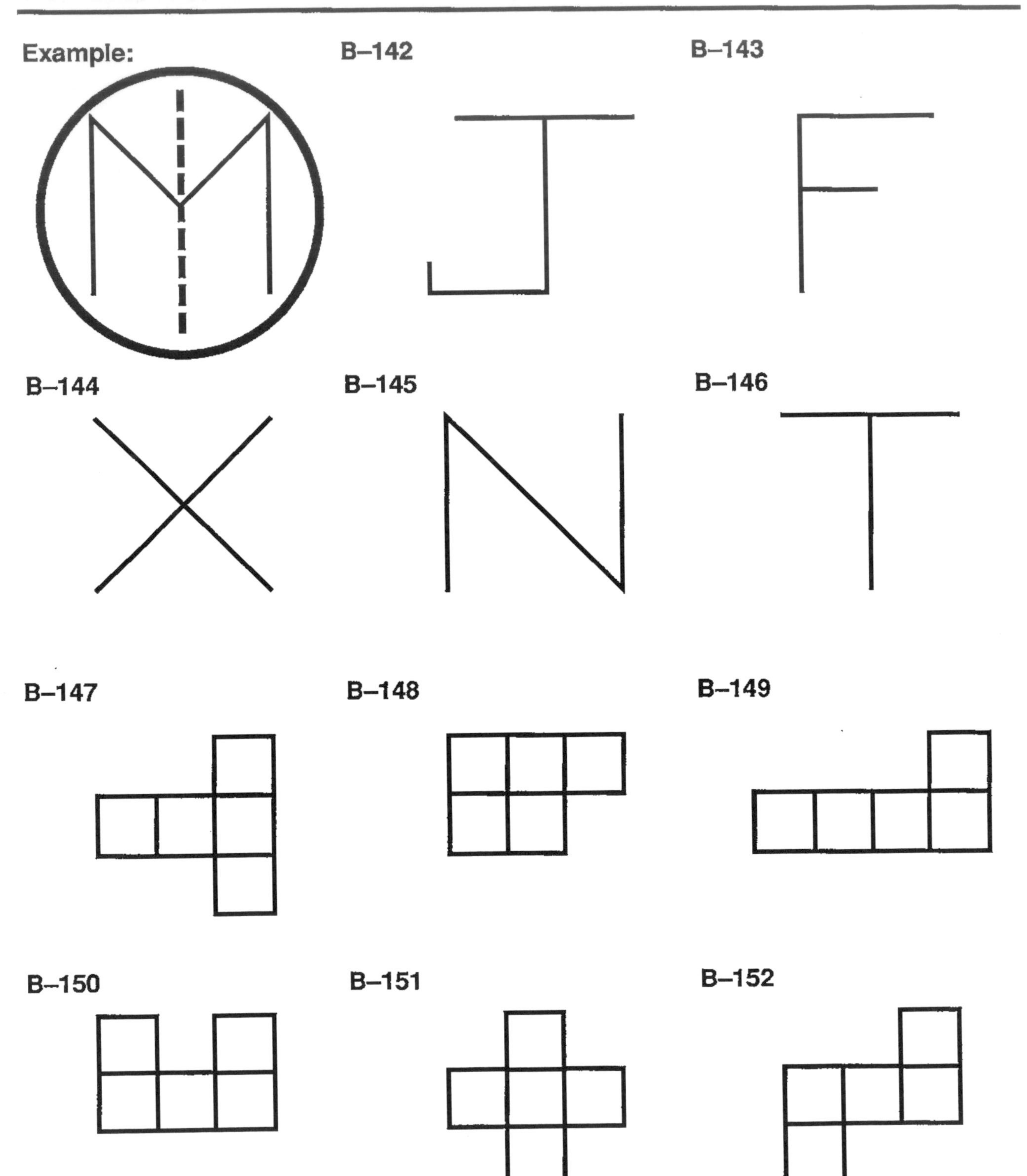

SYMMETRY

The shaded shape is cut from the folded paper.
Draw the shape when the paper is opened.

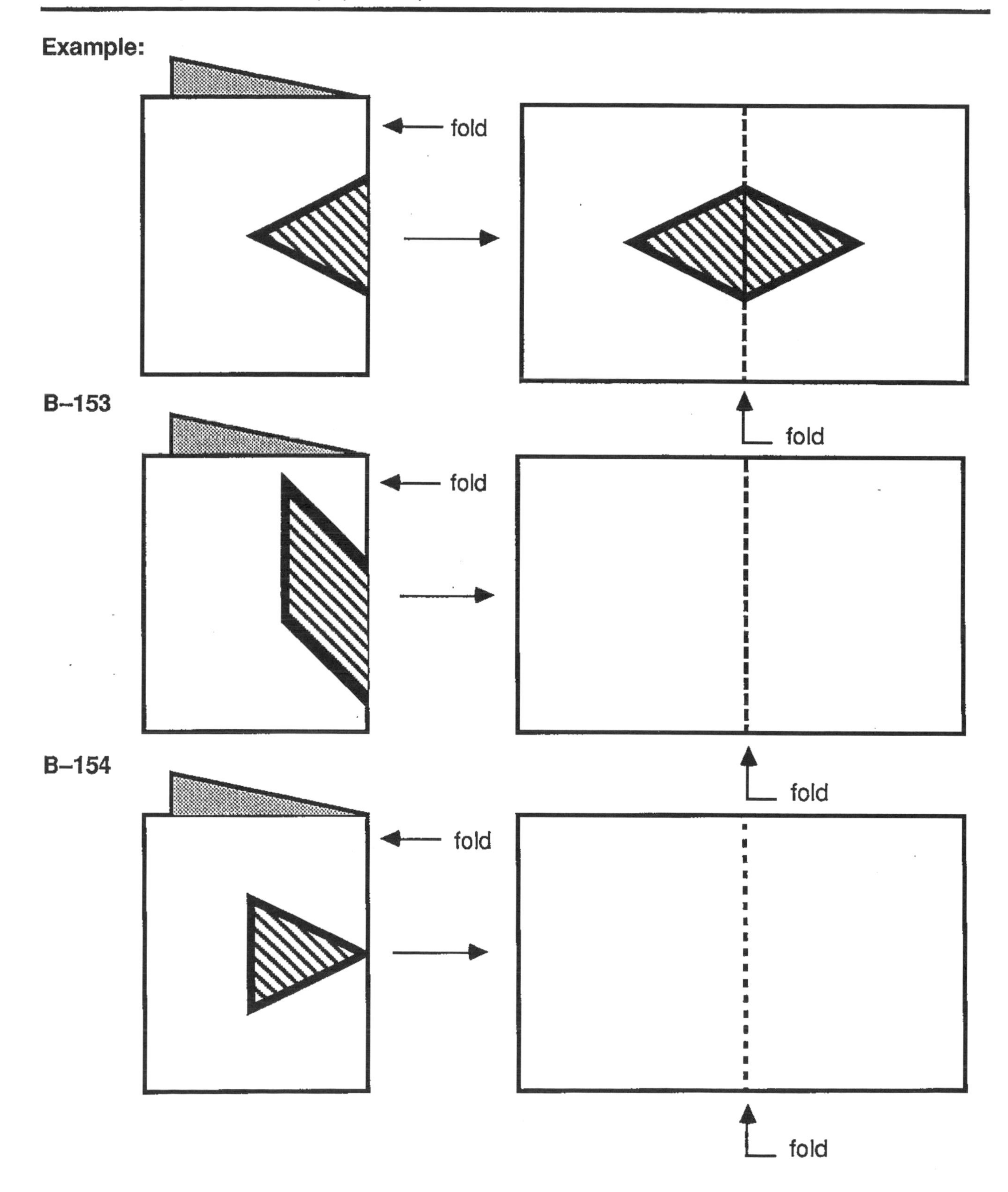

SYMMETRY

The shaded shape is cut from the folded paper.
Draw the letter that is made when the paper is opened.
Use the four letters to spell a word.

Example:

B–155

B–156

B–157

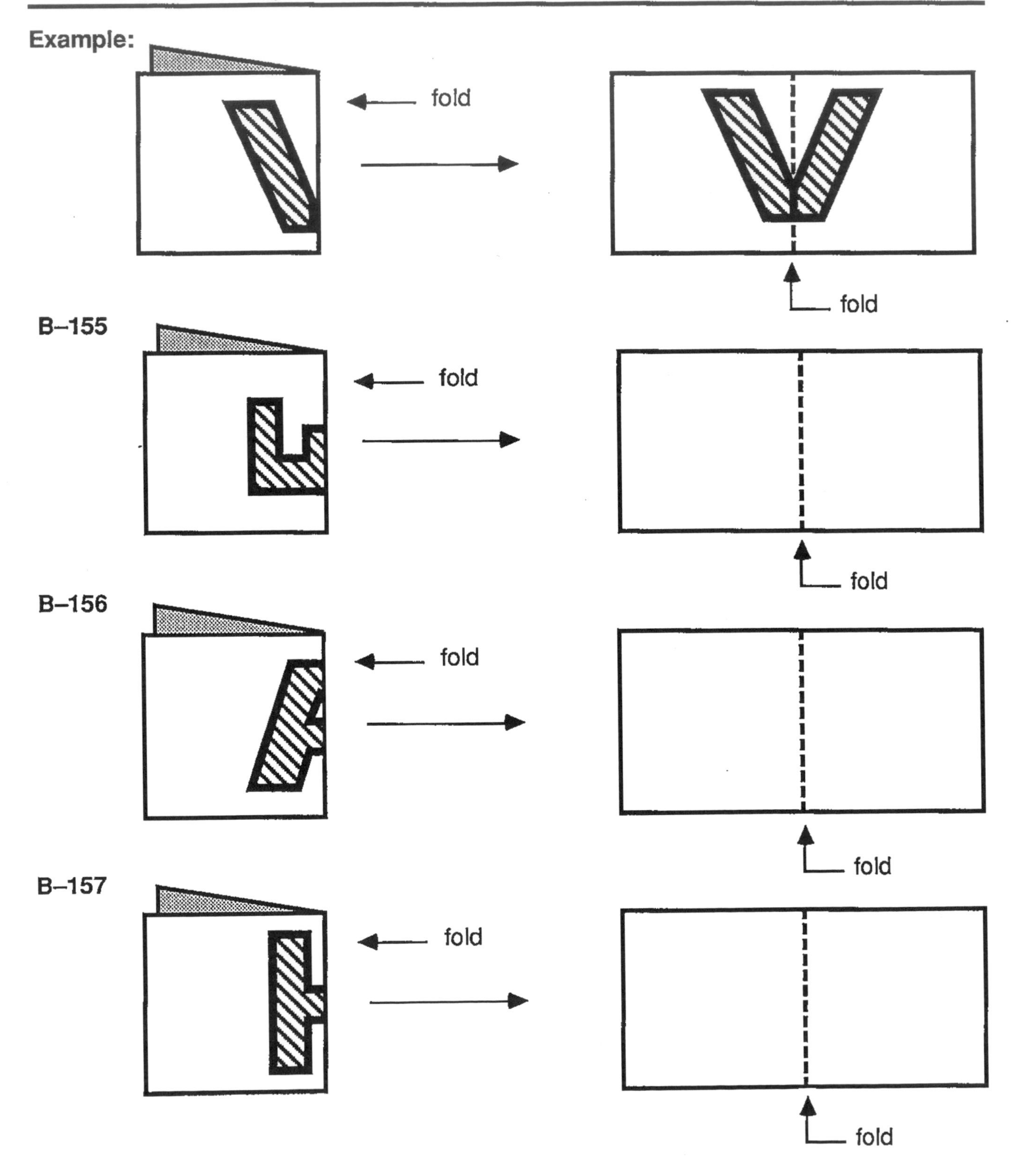

SYMMETRY

Draw a line around the symmetric figures.
Draw a dotted line to show where to fold the symmetric figures.

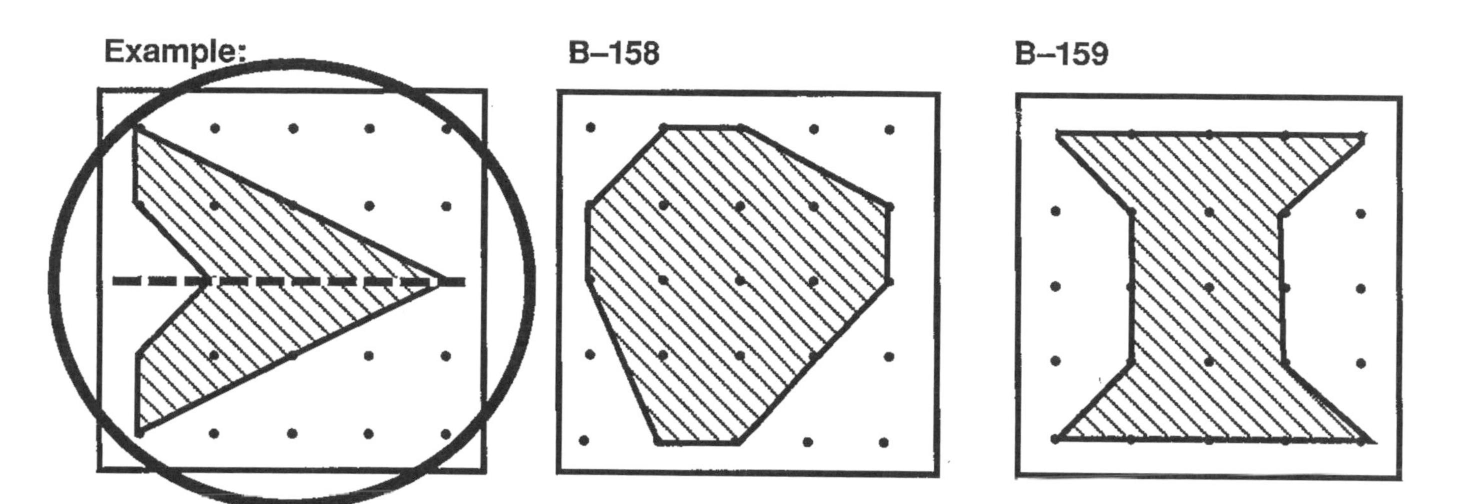

B–160

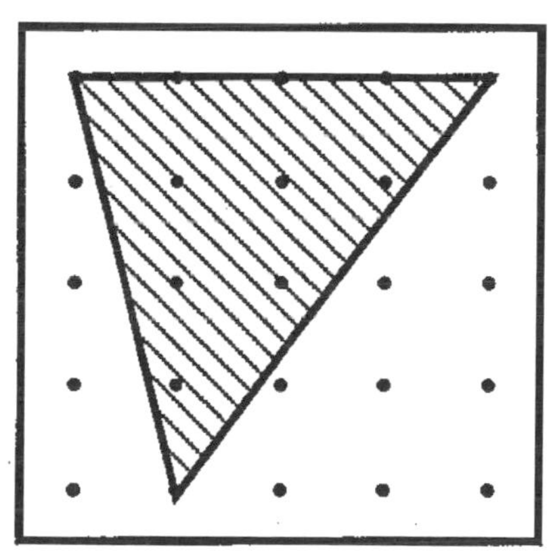

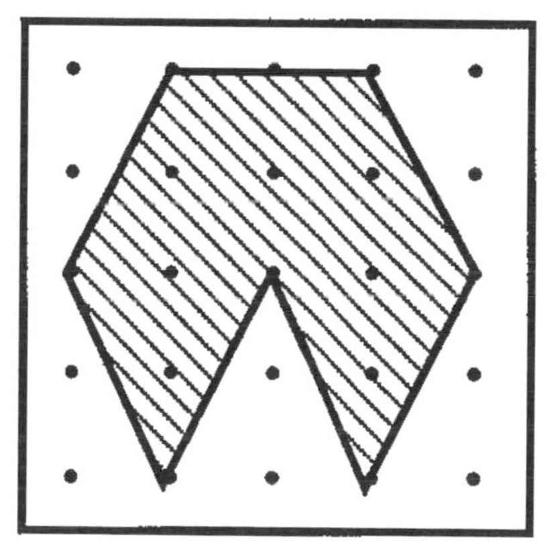

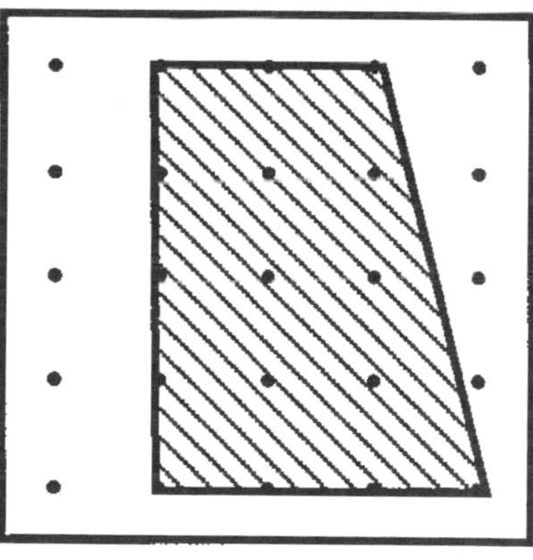

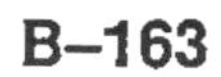

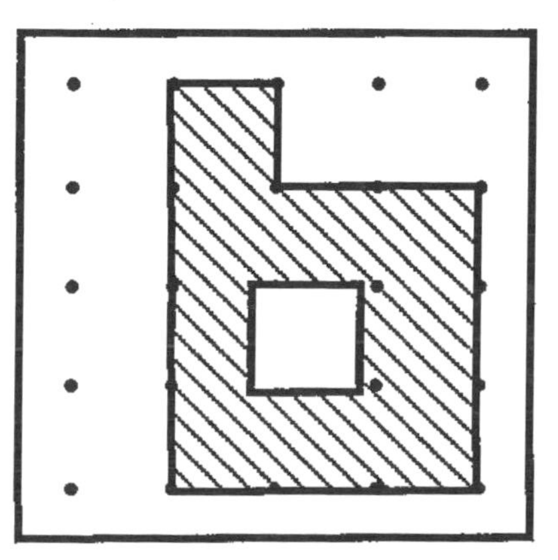

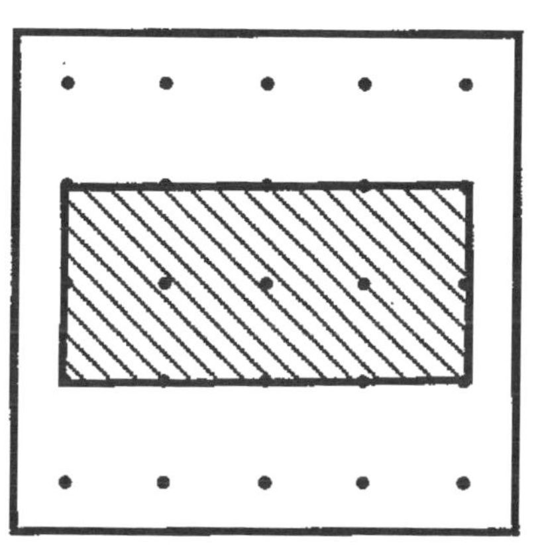

B–165

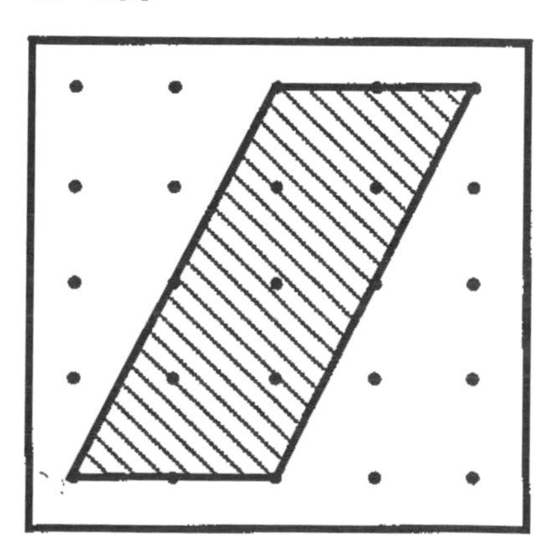

SYMMETRY

The dotted line shows the fold.
Draw the other half of each symmetric figure.

Example:

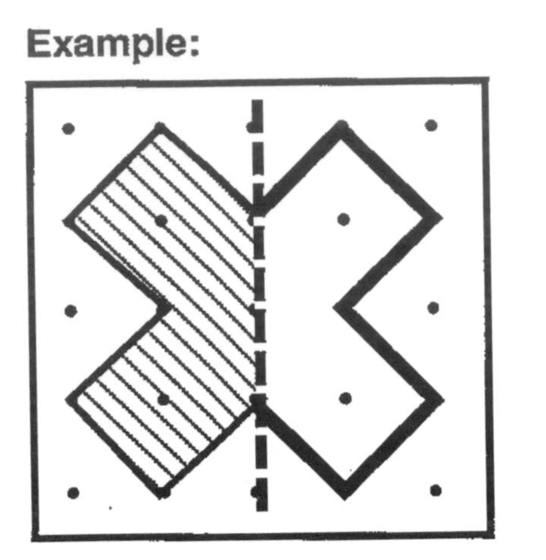

B–166

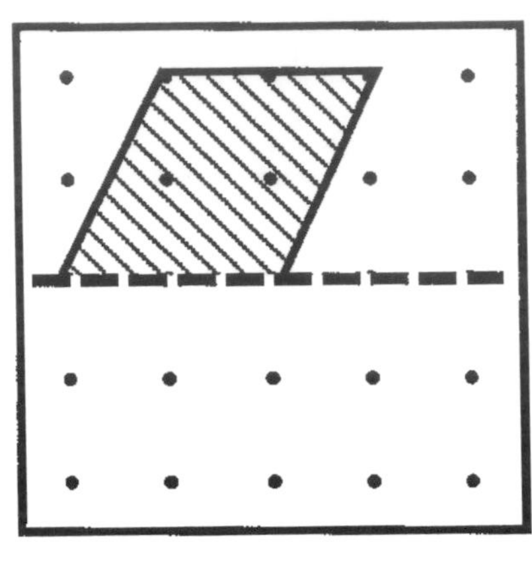

B–167

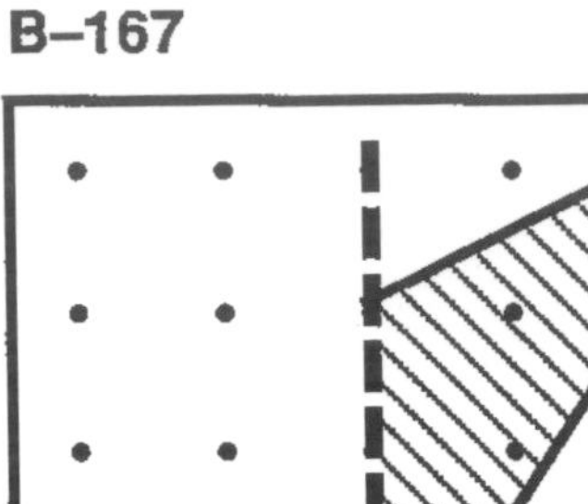

B–168

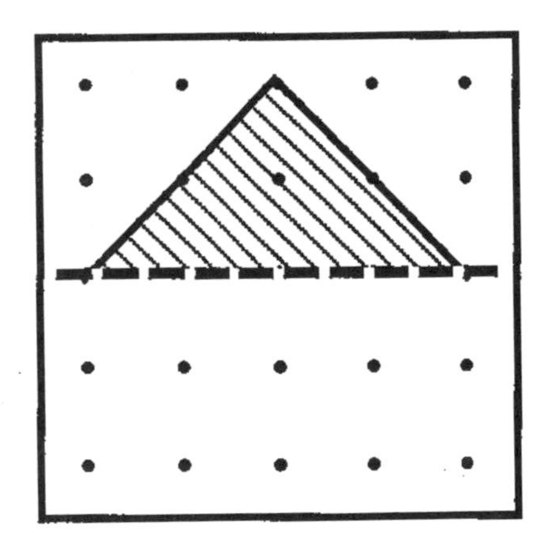

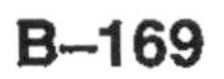
B–169

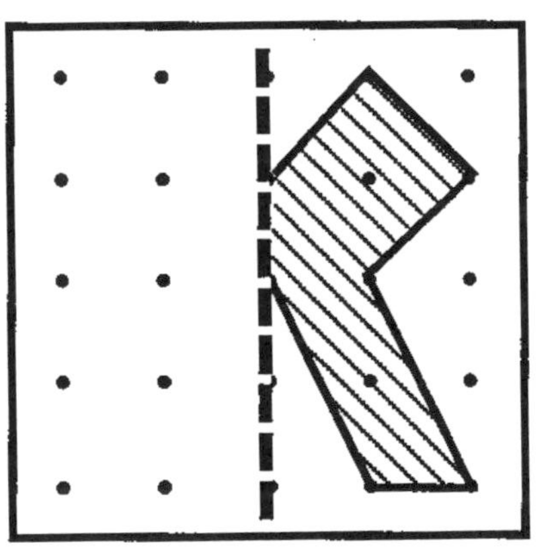

B–170

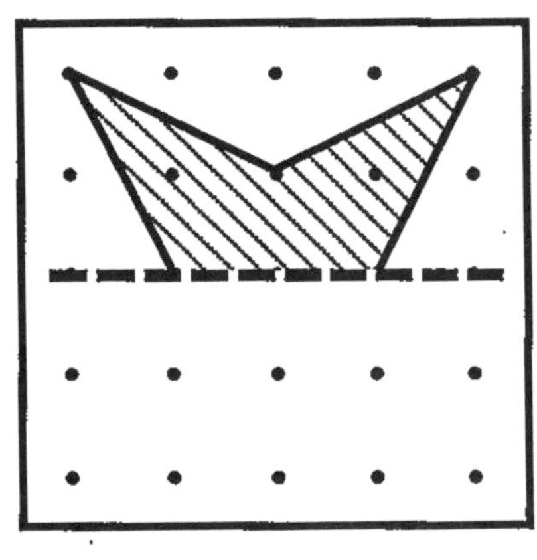

B–171

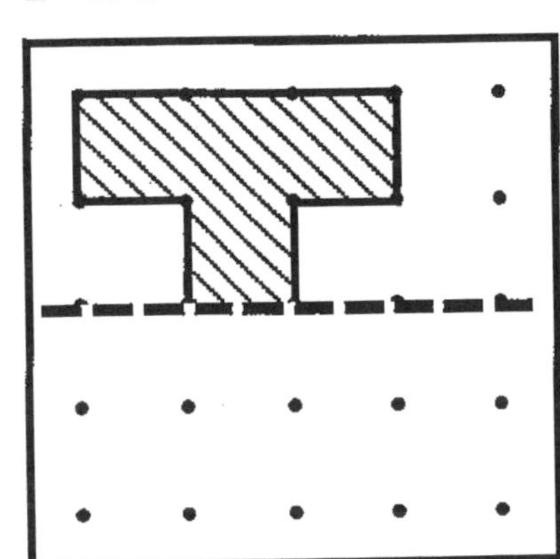

B–172

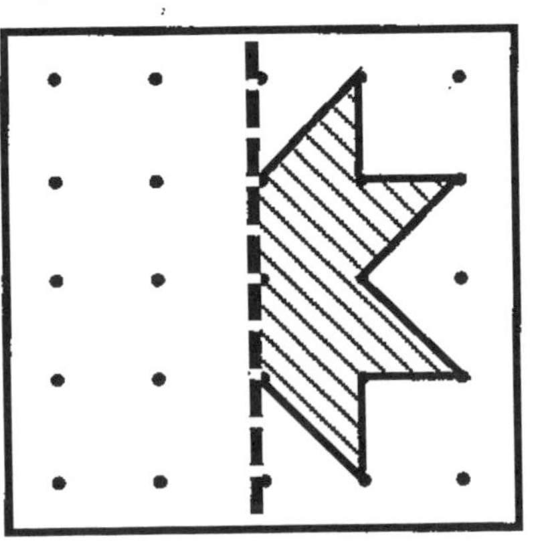

B–173

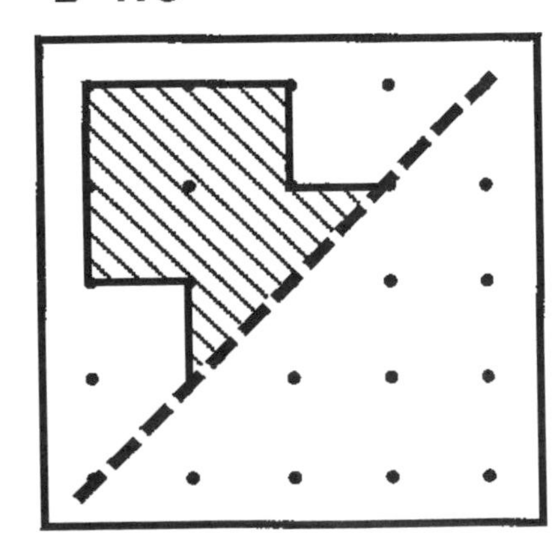

MOTIONS—SLIDES

If you slide triangle 1 across the page you get triangle 2.

Write a 2 in the shape that shows a slide.

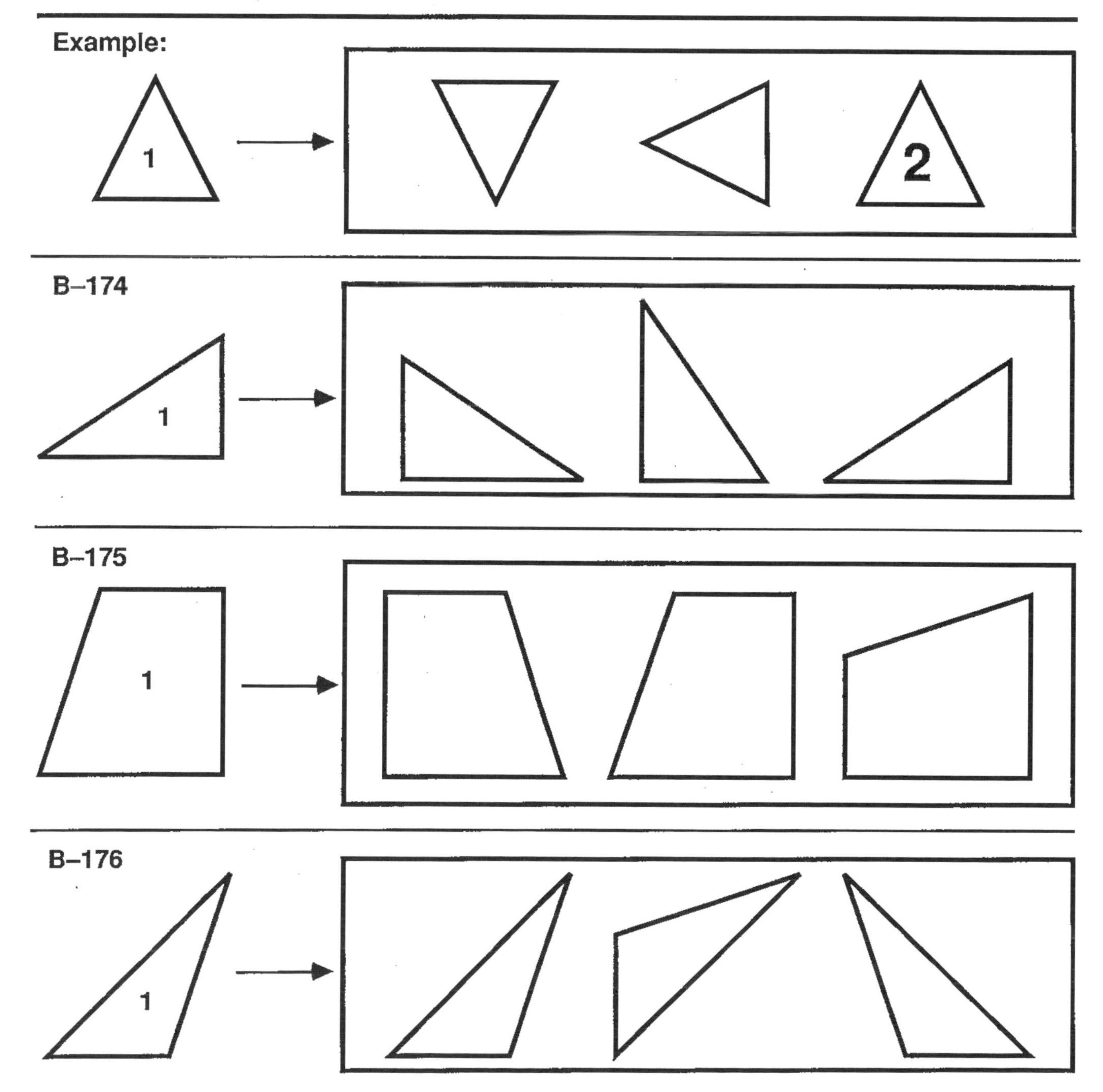

MOTIONS—SLIDES

A figure is pictured before a slide.
The slide is two dots to the right.
Draw the picture after the slide.

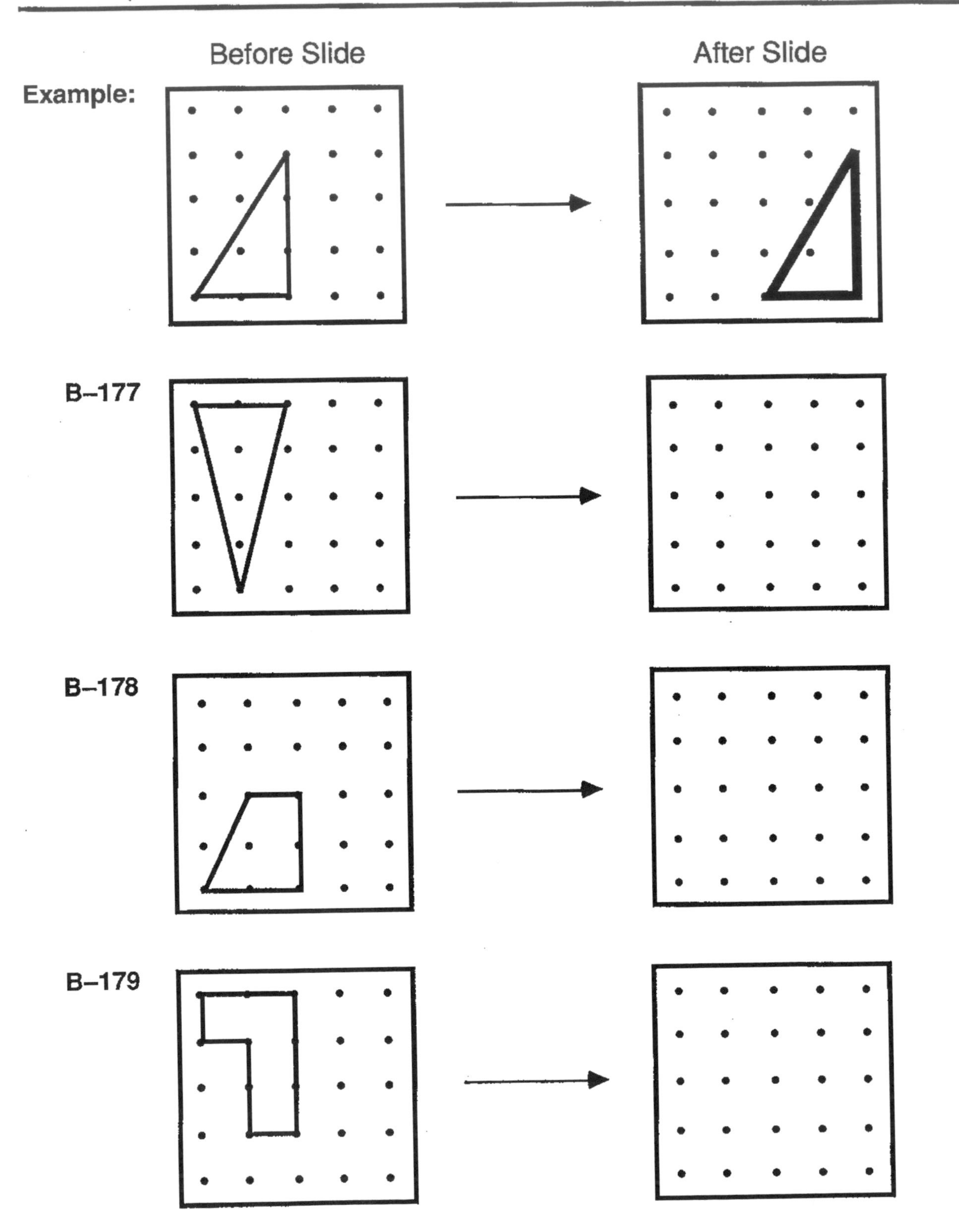

MOTIONS—FLIPS

If you flip over triangle 1 you get triangle 2.

Write a 2 in the shape that shows a flip.

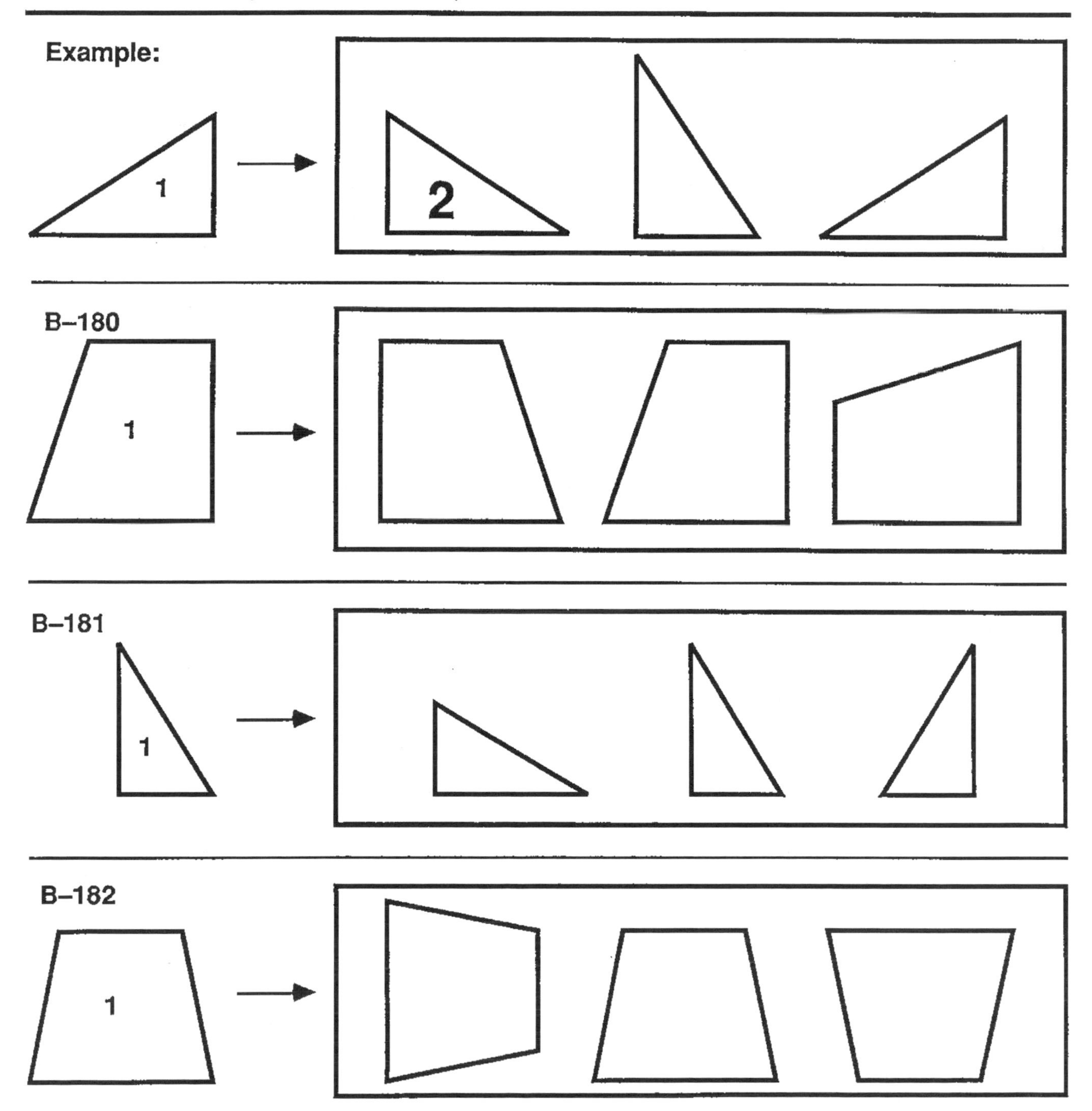

MOTIONS—FLIPS

A figure is pictured before a flip.
Draw the picture after the flip.

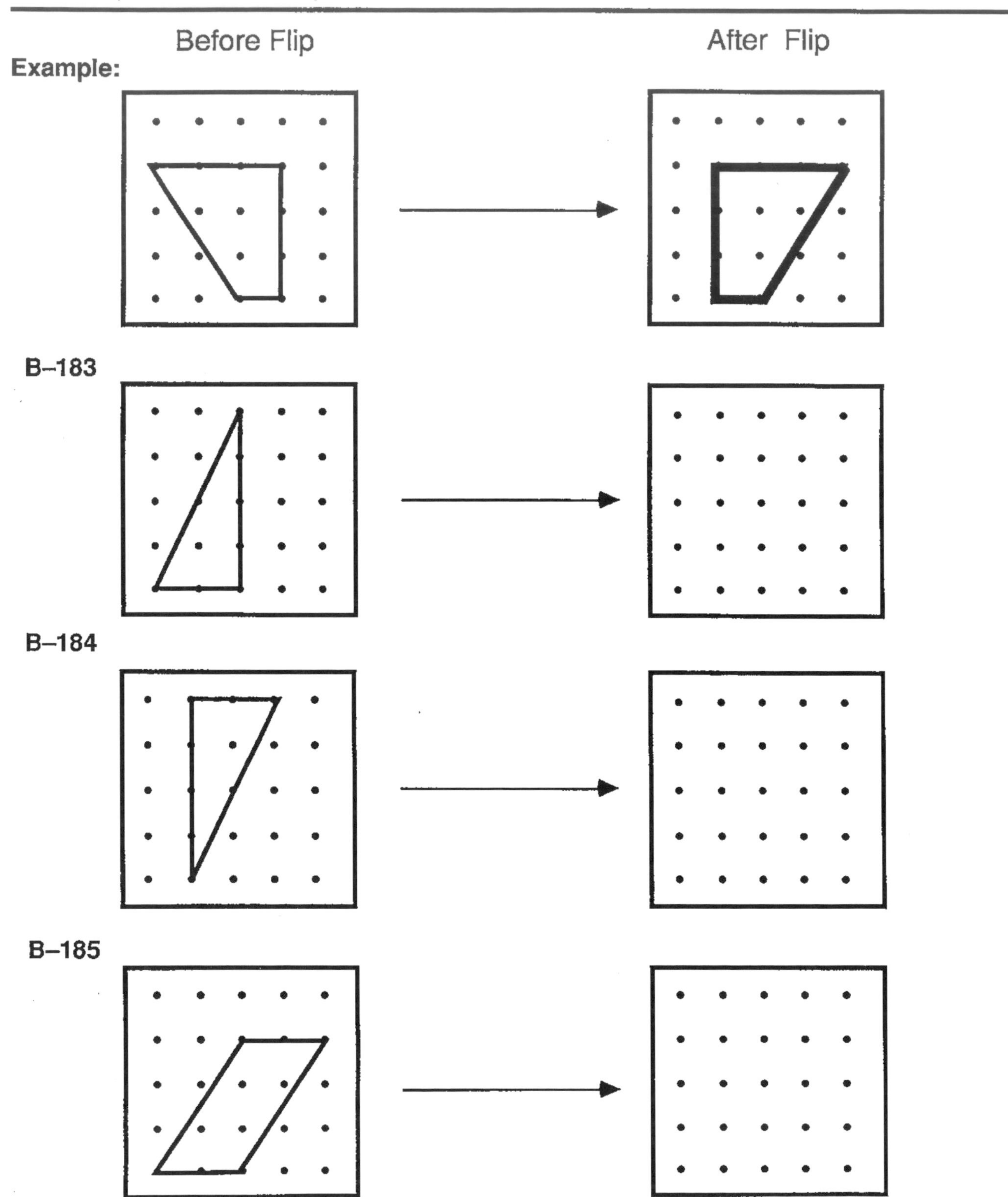

MOTIONS—TURNS

If you turn triangle 1 you get triangle 2.

Write a 2 in the shape that shows a turn.

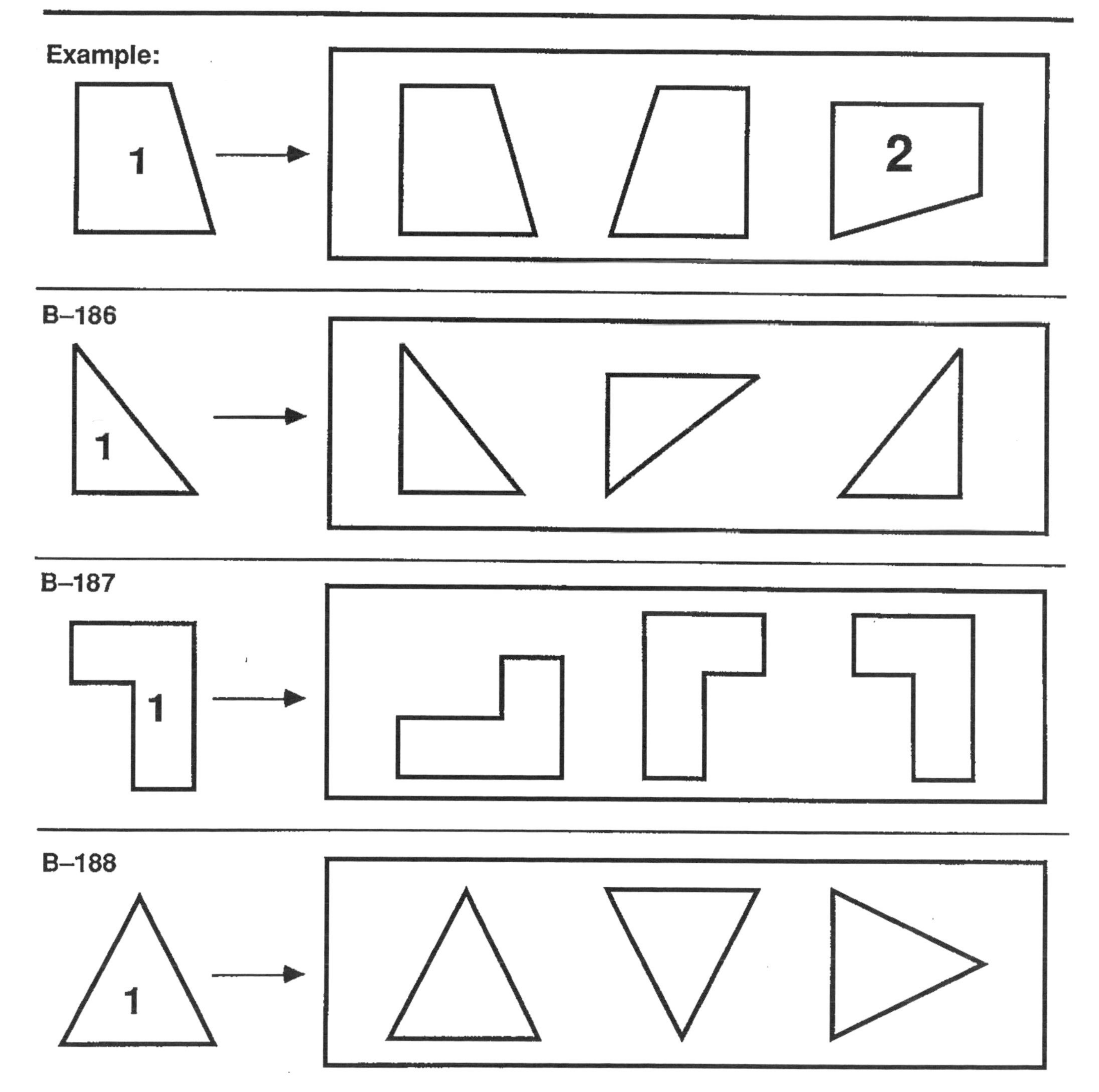

MOTIONS—TURNS

A figure is pictured before a turn.
Draw the picture after the turn.

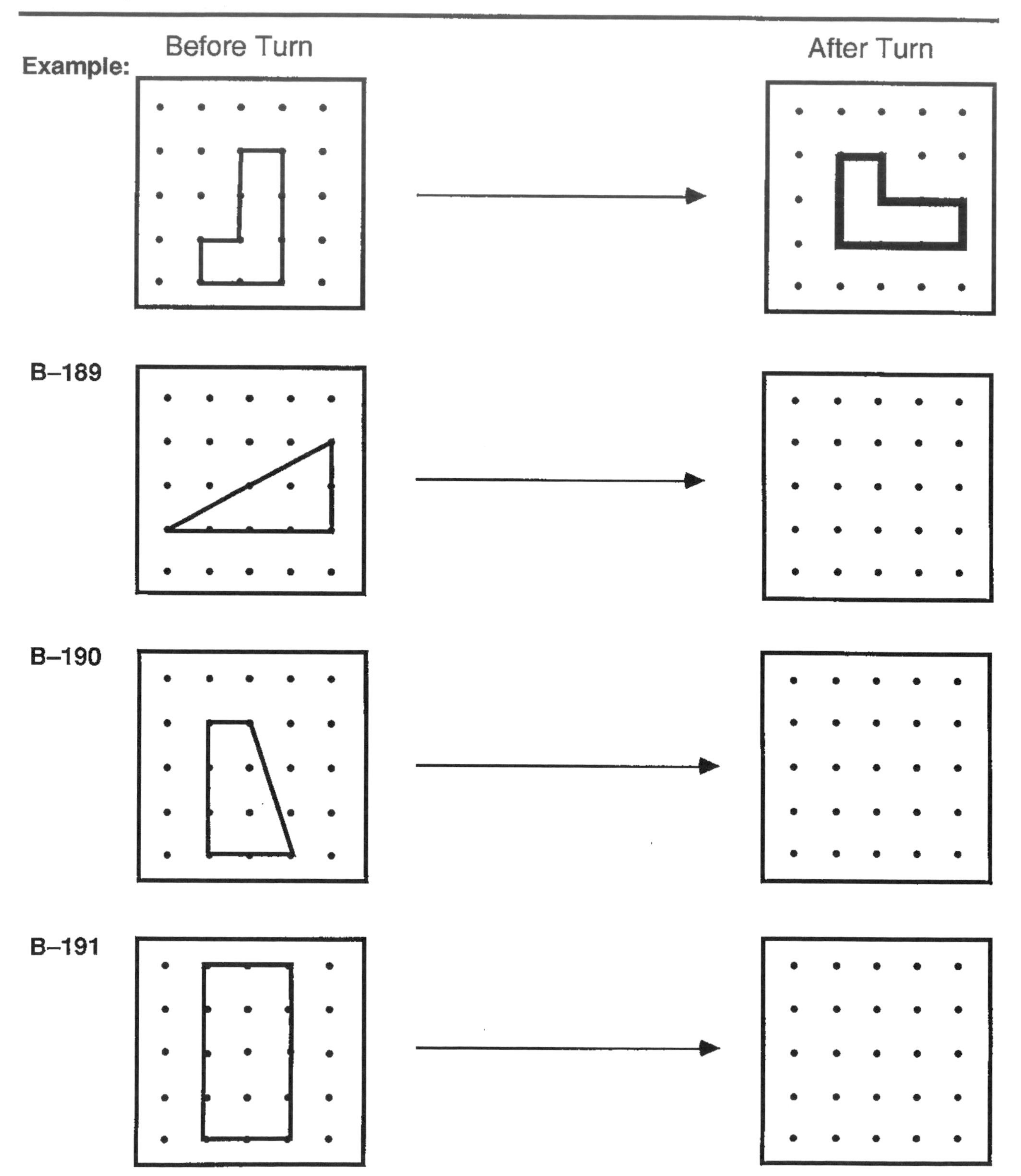

CONGRUENT FIGURES

Congruent figures are the same size and same shape.
Draw a line around the figure that is congruent to the figure in the box.

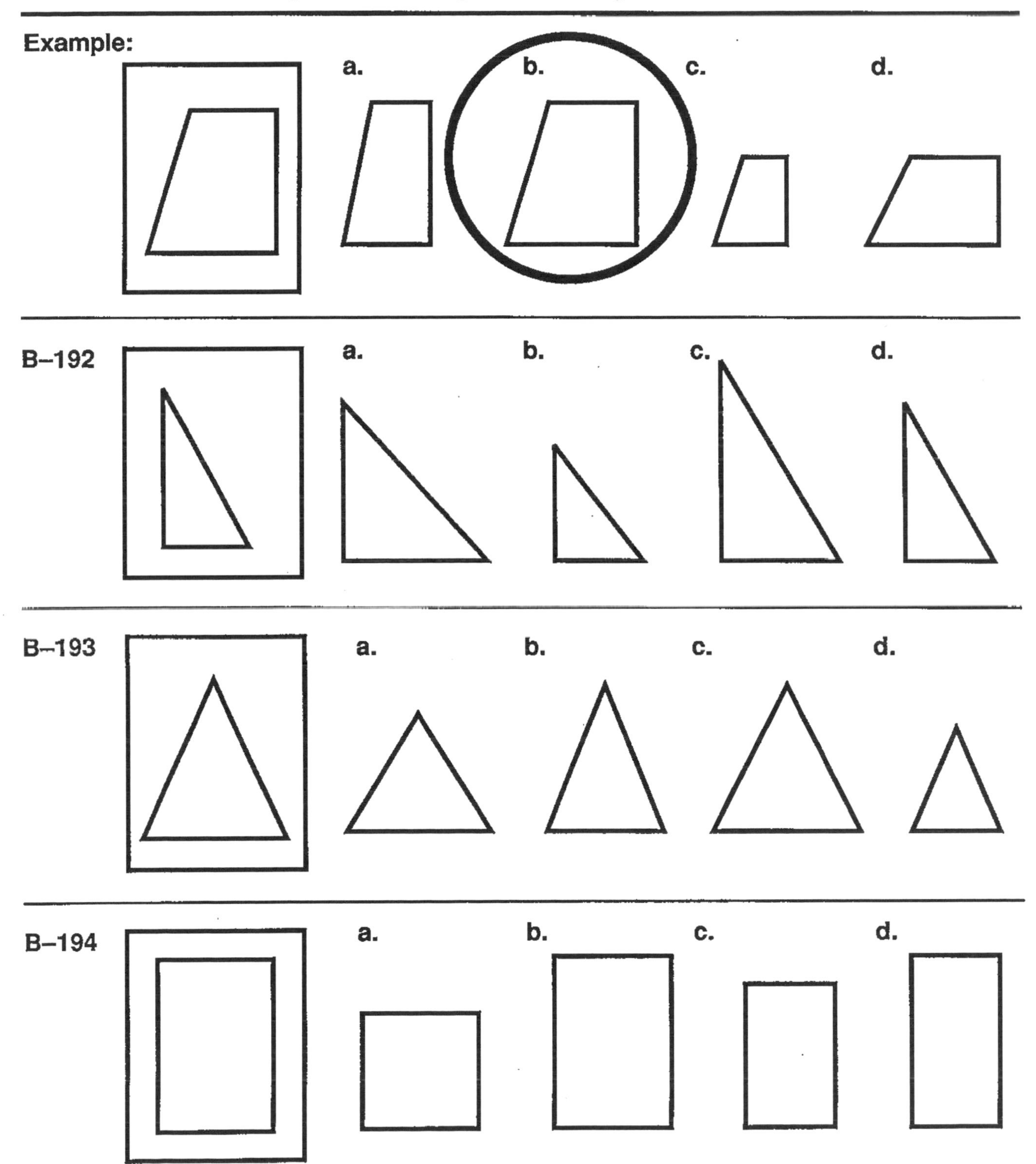

CONGRUENT FIGURES

Congruent figures are the same size and same shape.
Draw a line around the figure that is congruent to the figure in the box.

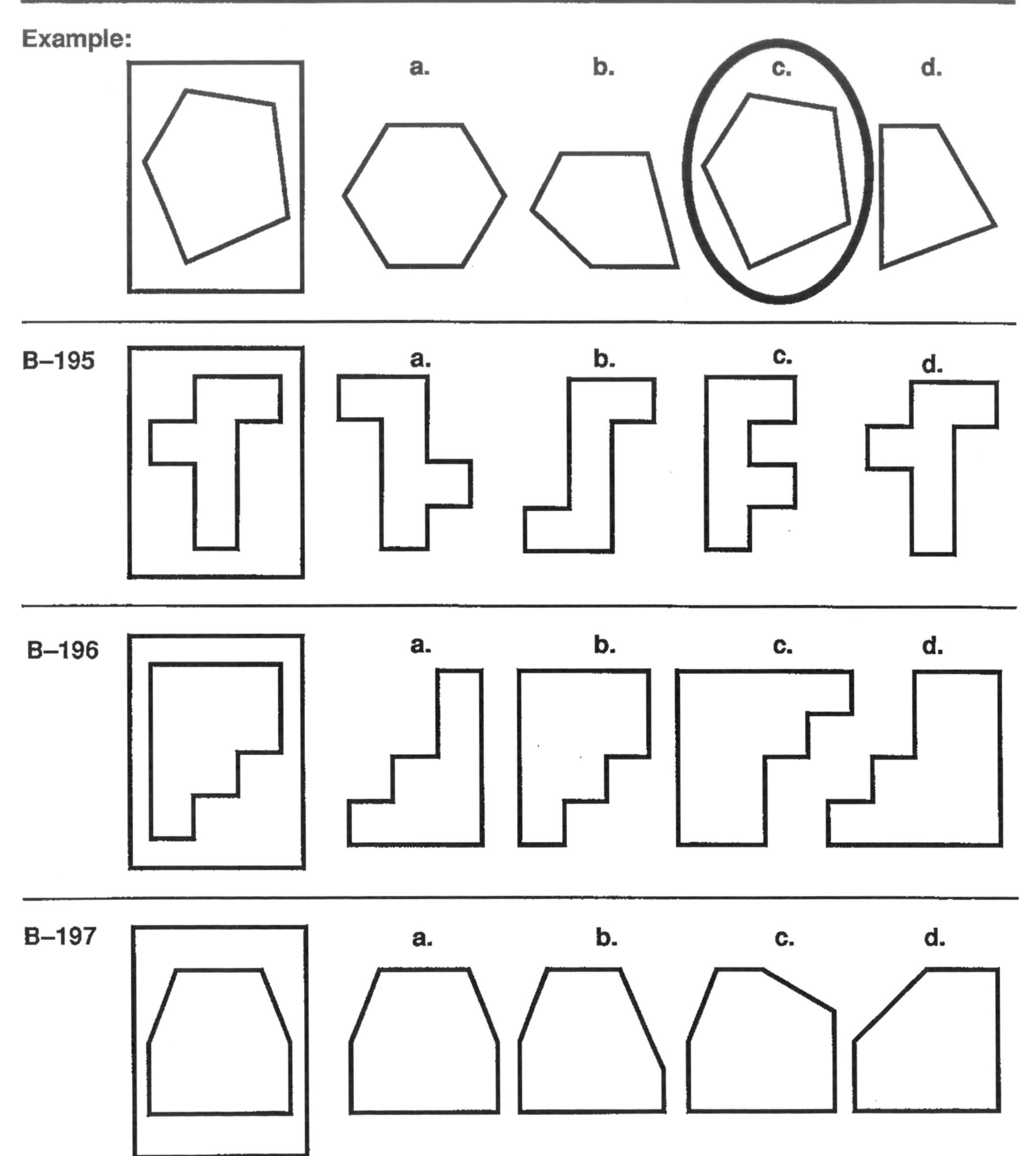

CONGRUENT FIGURES

Congruent figures are the same size and same shape.
Draw a line around the figures that are congruent to the shape in the box.
The matching figure has been flipped.

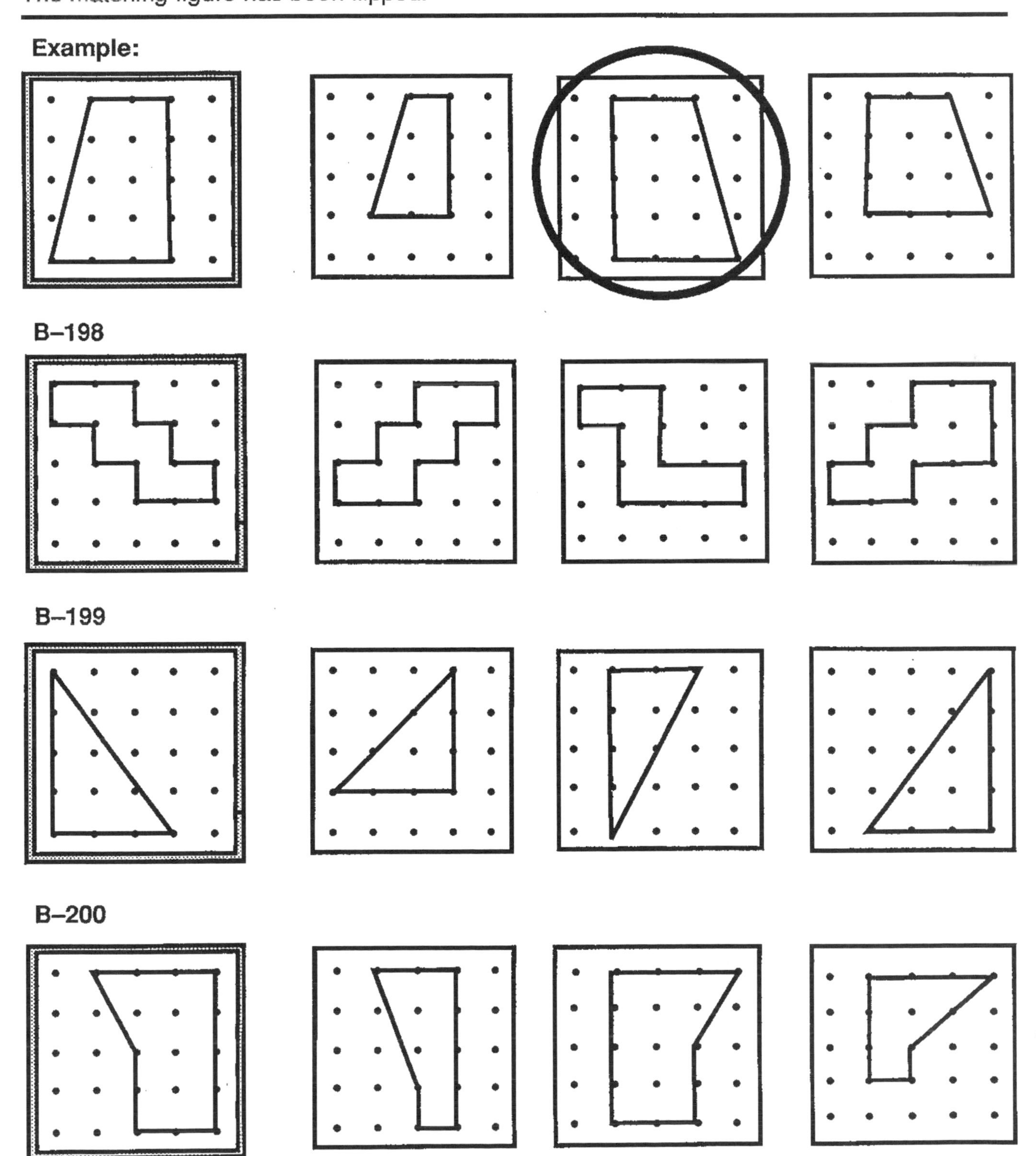

CONGRUENT FIGURES

Congruent figures are the same size and same shape.
Draw a line around the figures that are congruent to the shape in the box.
The matching figure has been turned.

Example:

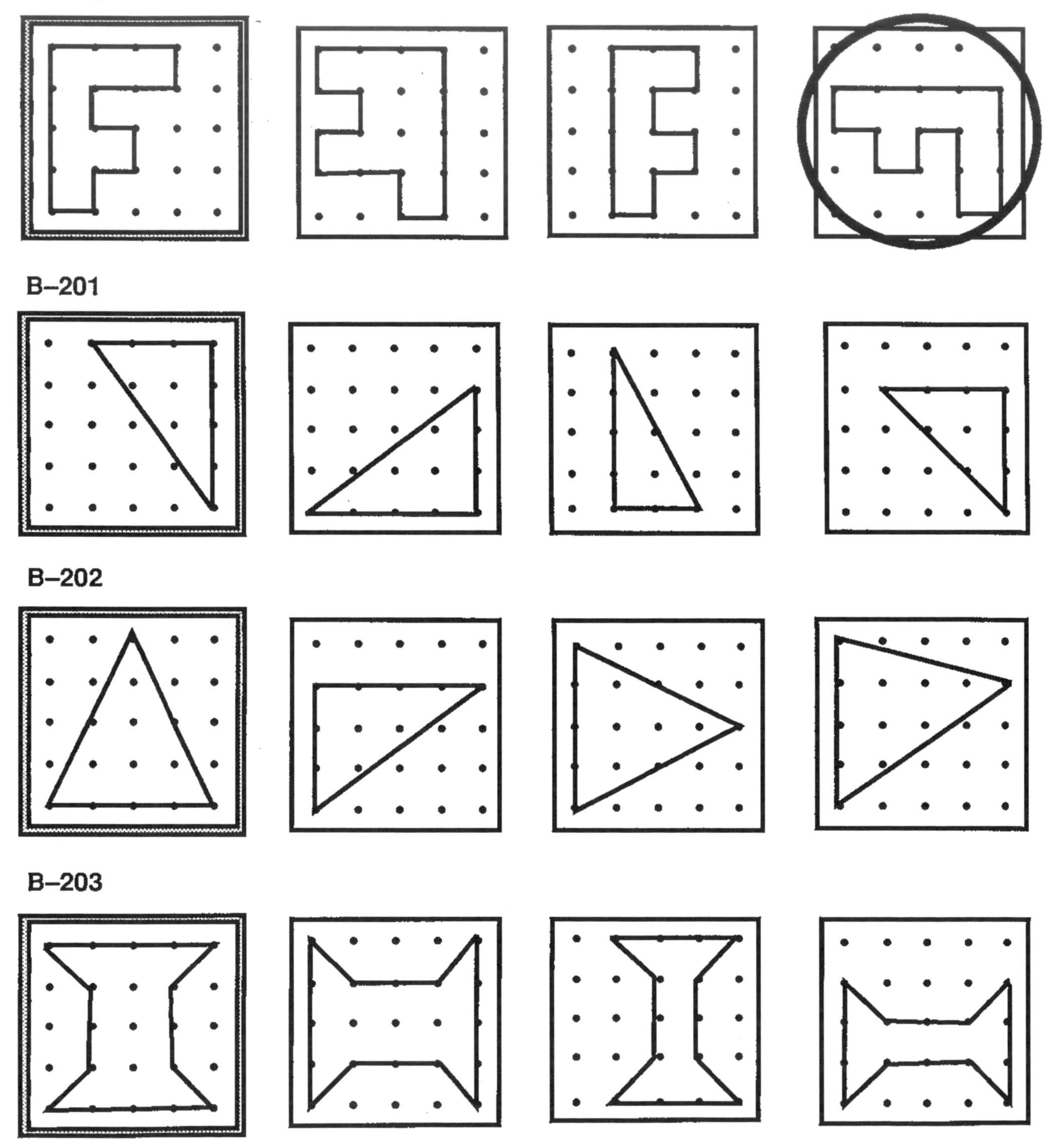

CONGRUENT FIGURES

Draw a congruent figure on the dot paper.

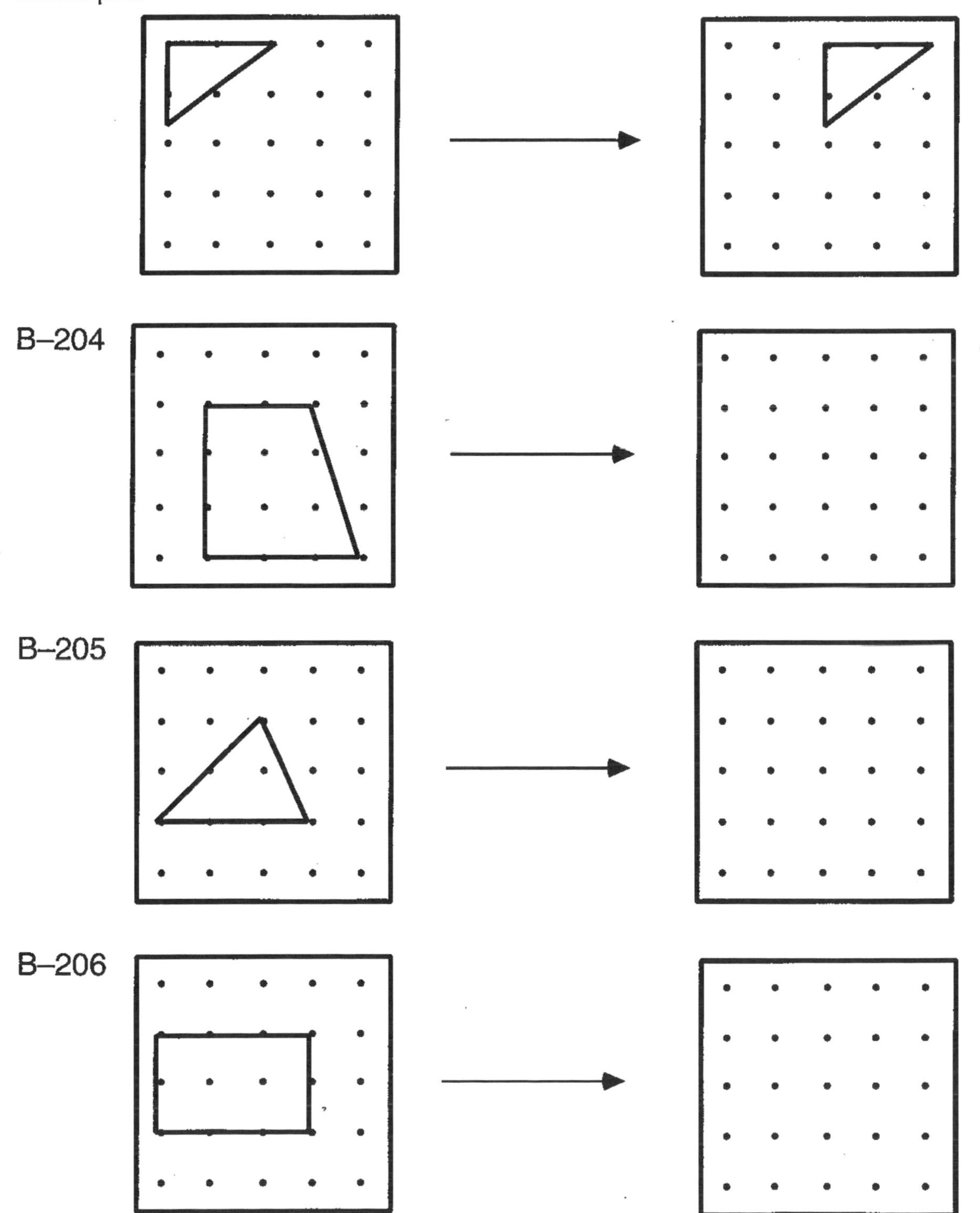

CONGRUENT FIGURES

Draw a congruent figure on the dot paper.

Example:

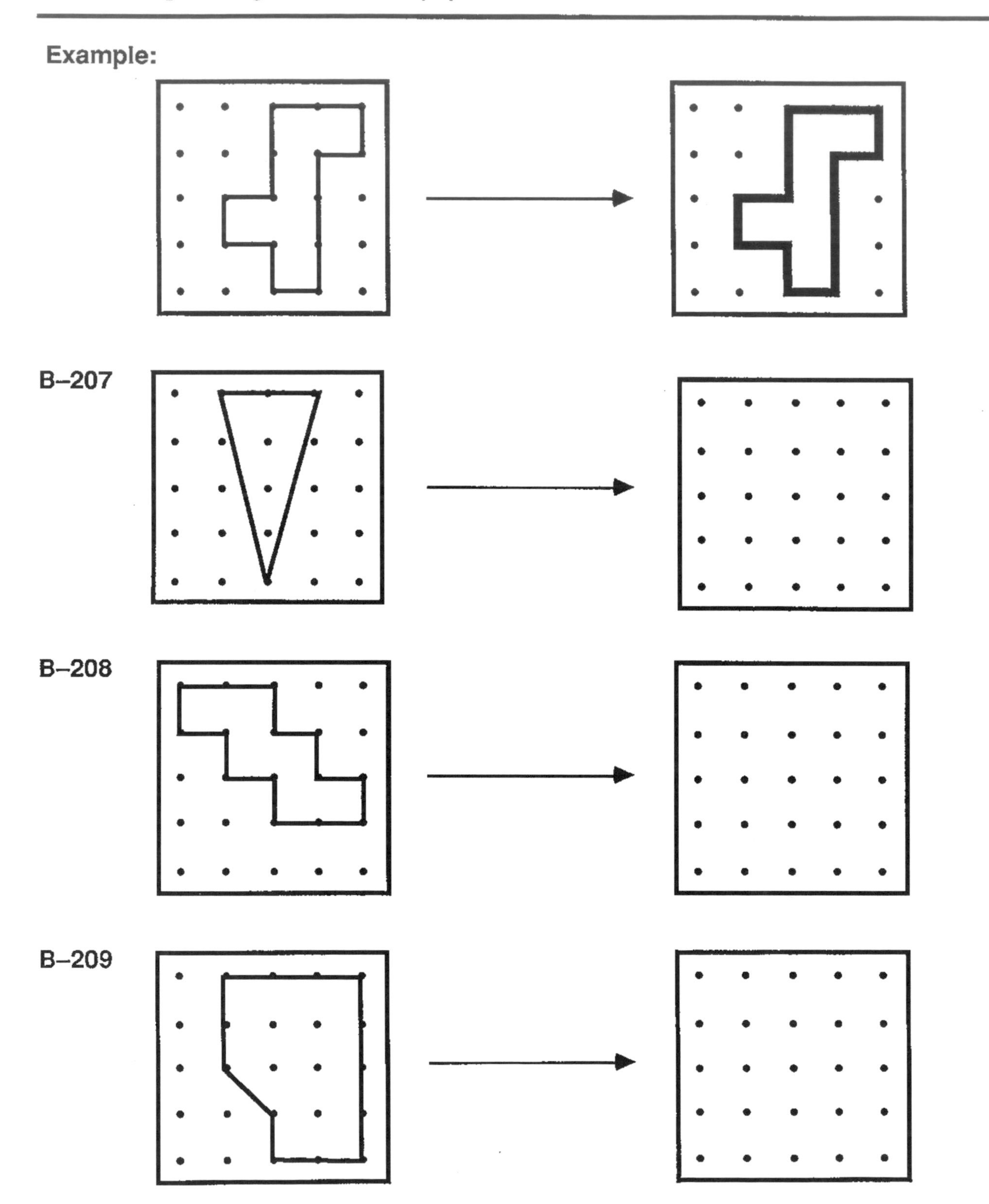

SIMILAR FIGURES

Similar figures have the same shape.
They are not always the same size.
Draw a line around the shape that is similar to the shaded shape.

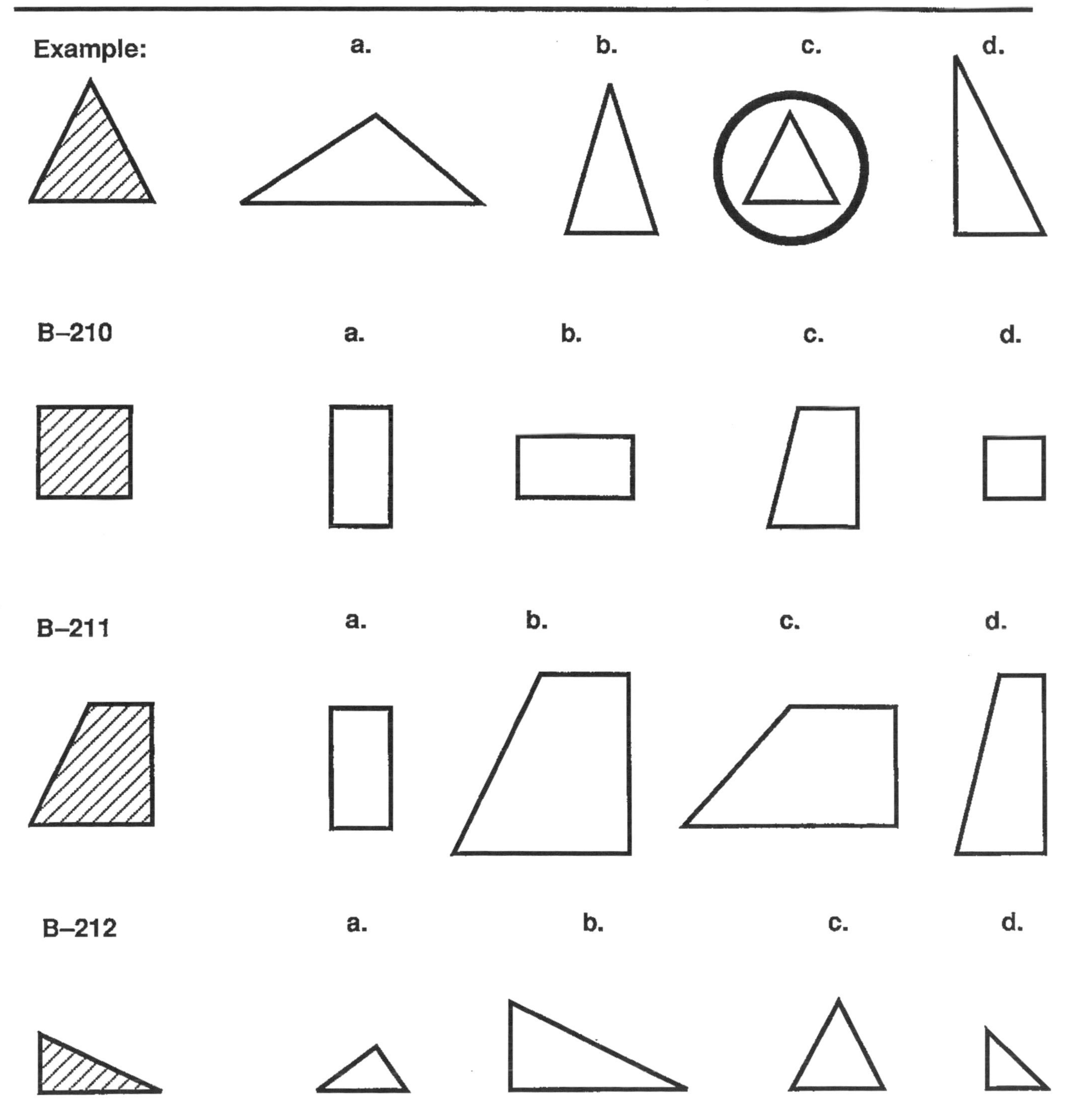

SIMILAR FIGURES

Similar figures have the same shape.
They are not always the same size.
Draw a line around the shape that is similar to the shaded shape.

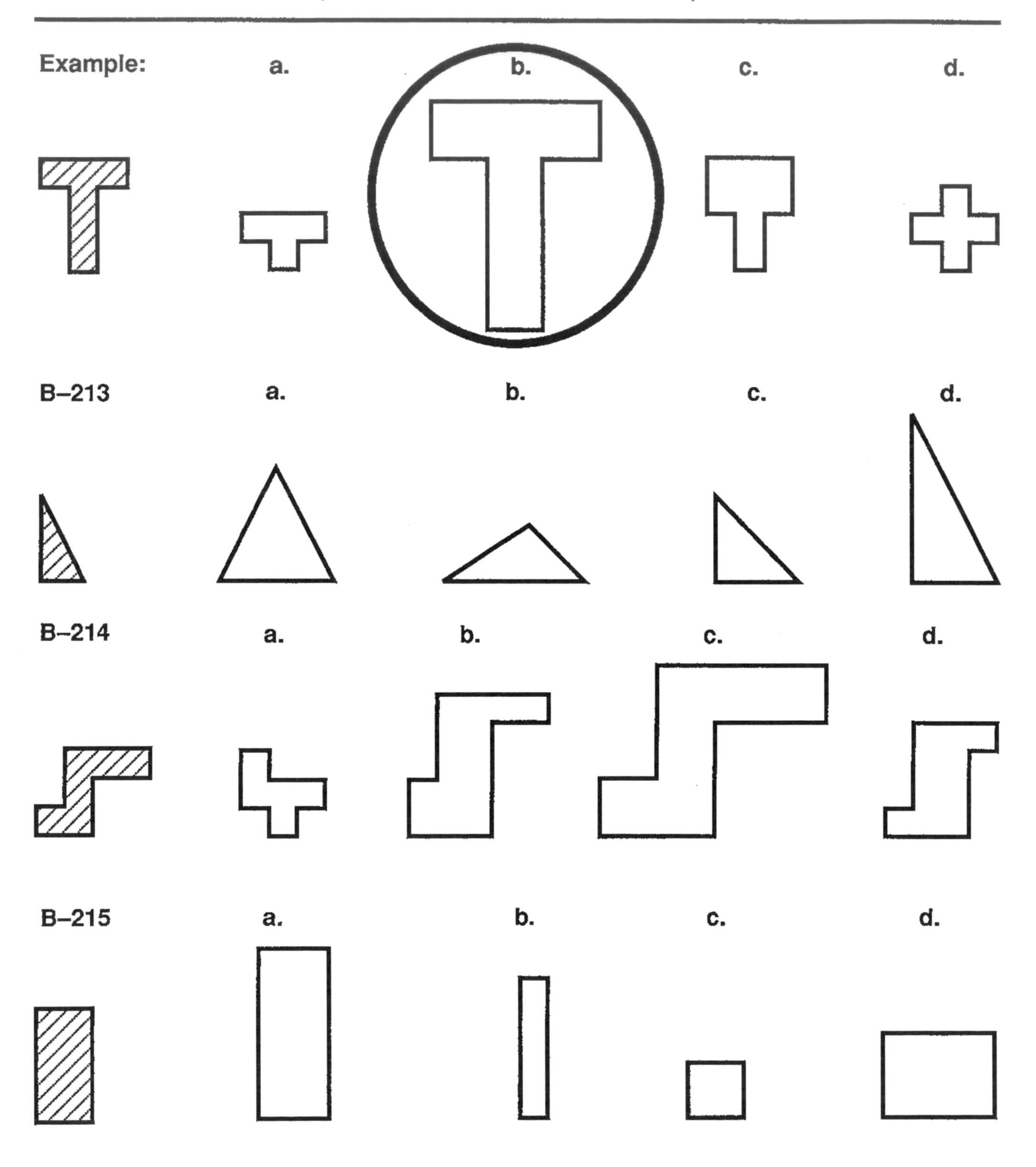

SIMILAR FIGURES

Similar figures have the same shape.
Draw a figure that is similar to the shaded figure.
Make it smaller than the shaded figure.

Example:

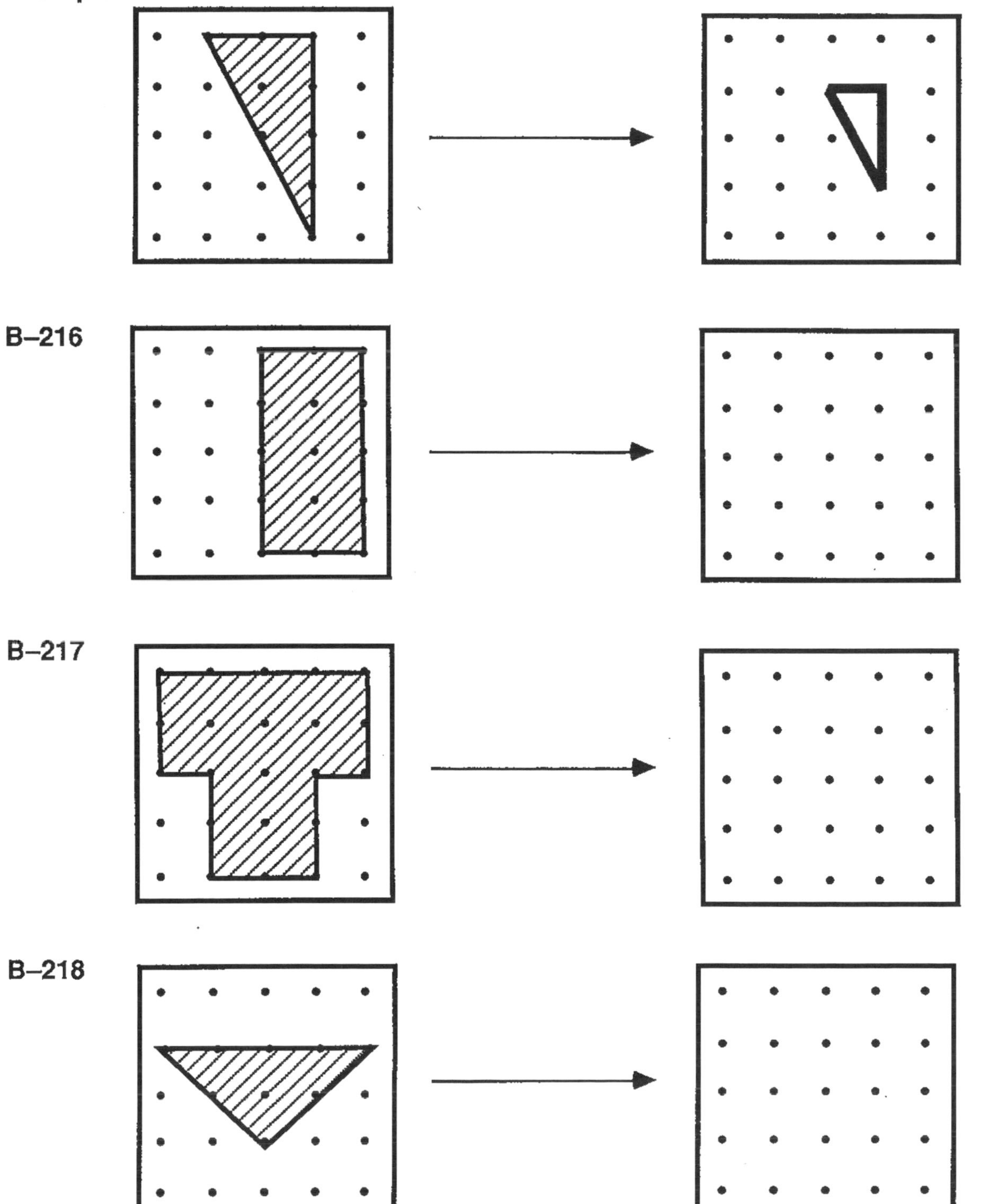

SIMILAR FIGURES

Similar figures have the same shape.
Draw a figure that is similar to the shaded figure.
Make it larger than the shaded figure.

Example:

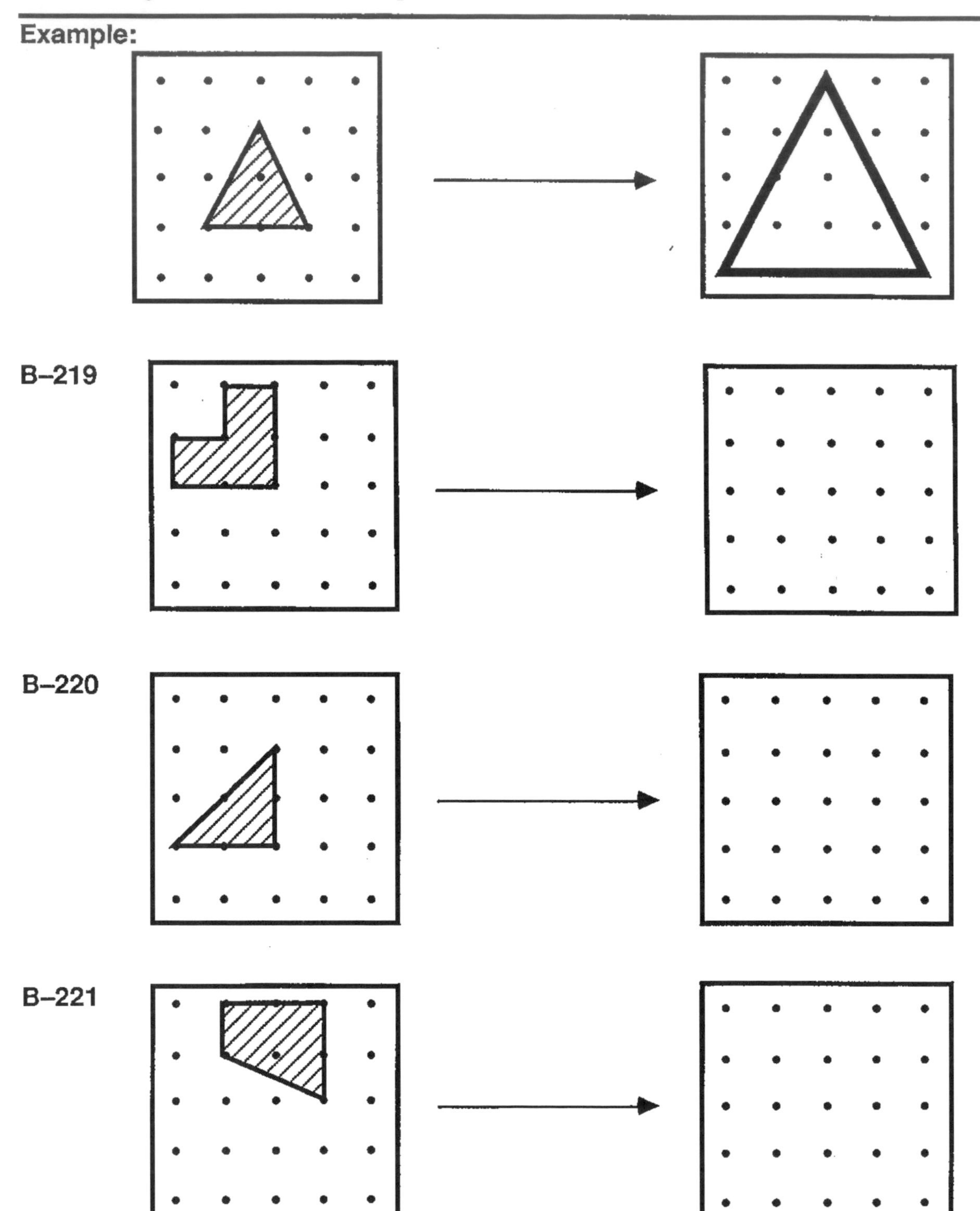

COMBINING SHAPES

Look at the two shaded shapes.

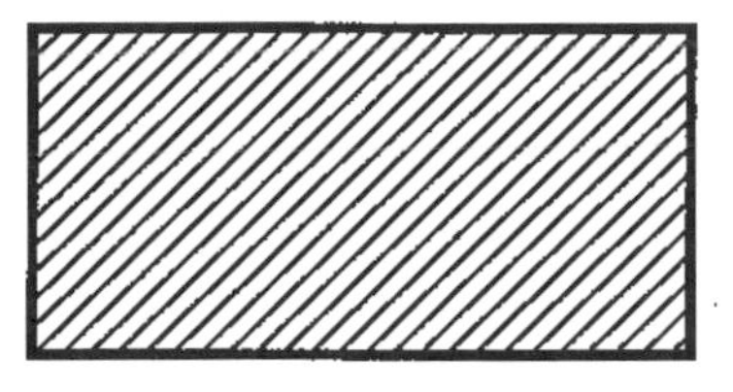

Put an X on all the figures that can be made by combining the two shaded shapes.

Example:

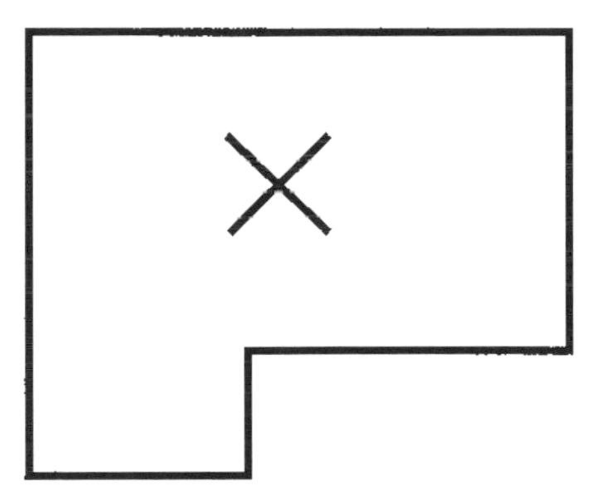

B–222

B–223

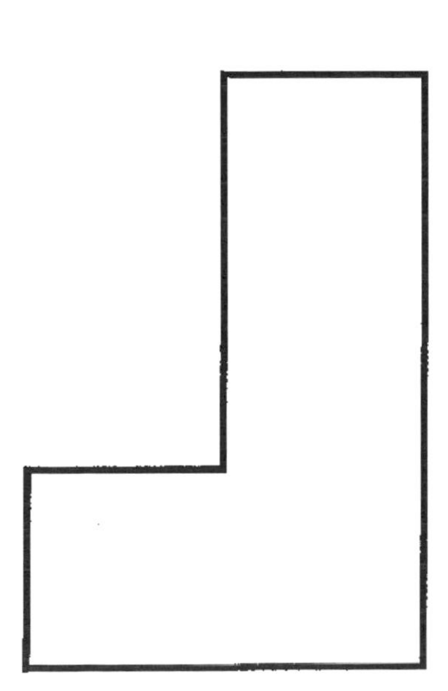

B–224

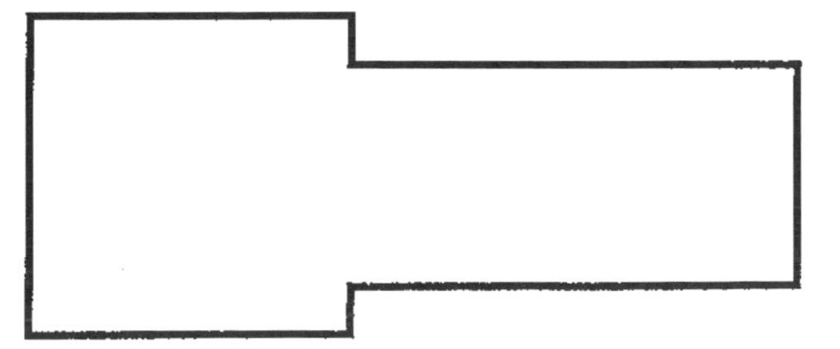

COMBINING SHAPES

Look at the two shaded shapes.

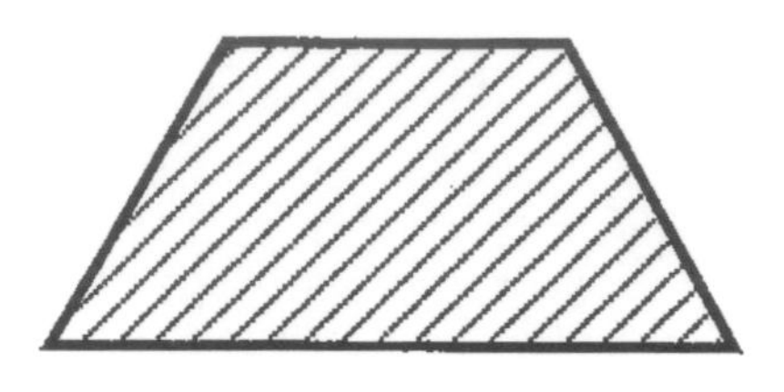

Put an X on all the figures that can be made by combining the two shaded shapes.

Example:

B–225

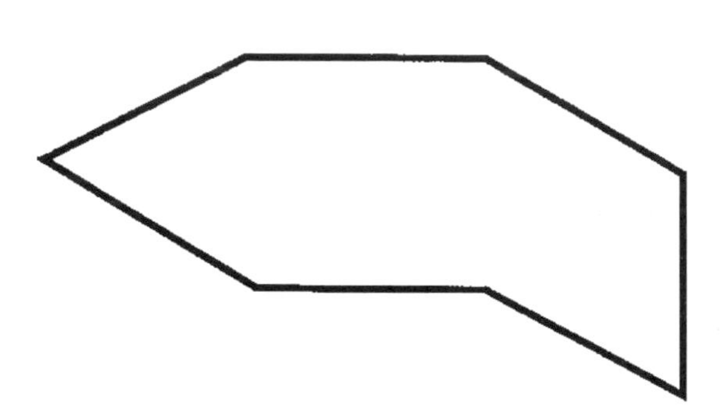

B–226

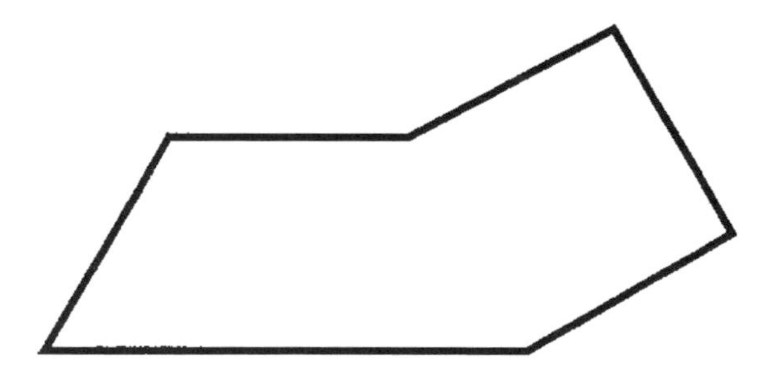

B–227

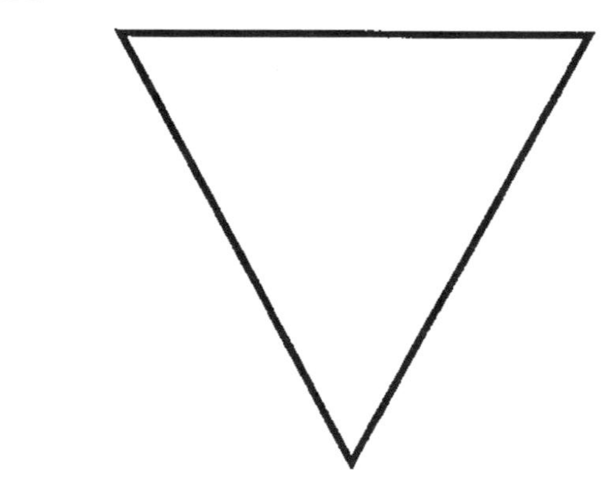

COMBINING SHAPES

Look at the two shaded shapes.

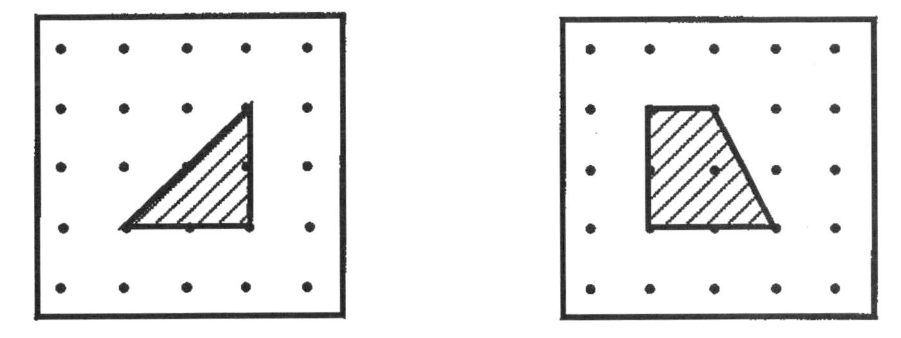

Put an X on all the shapes that can be made by combining the two shaded shapes.

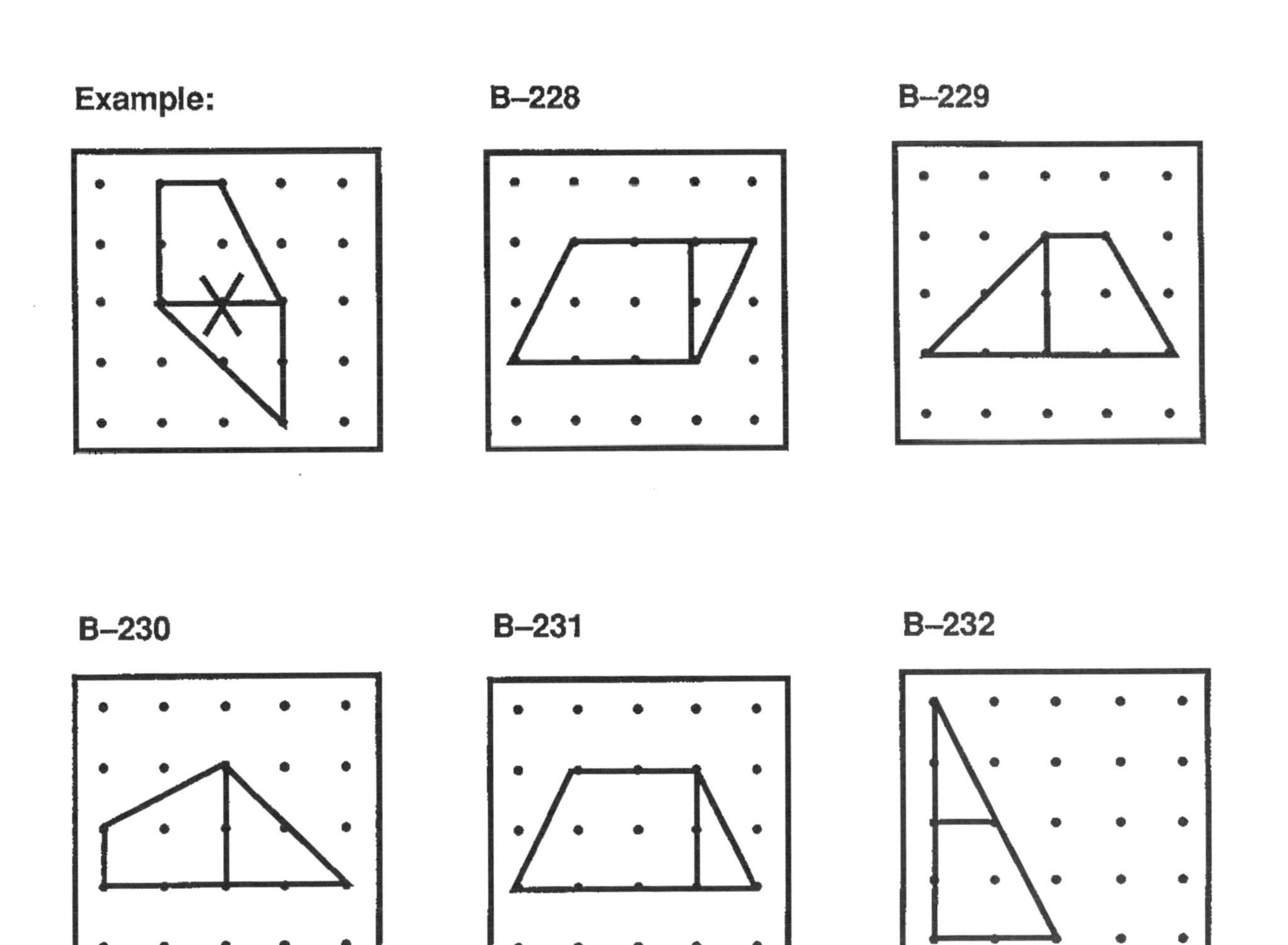

COMBINING SHAPES

Look at the three shaded shapes.

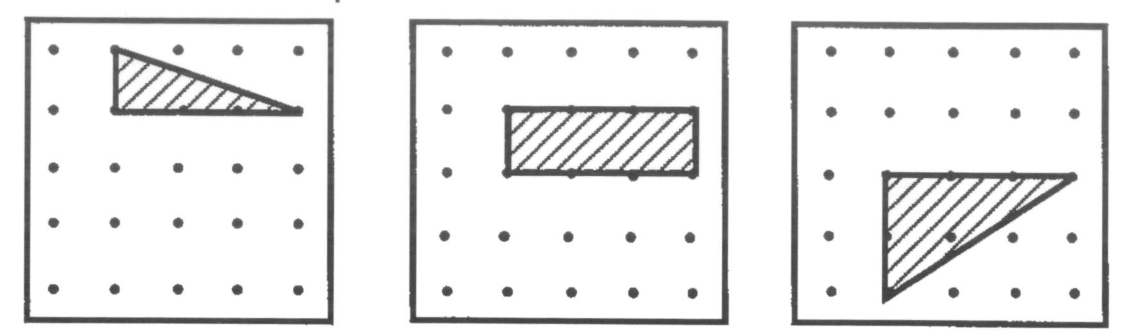

Put an X on all the shapes that can be made by combining the three shaded shapes.

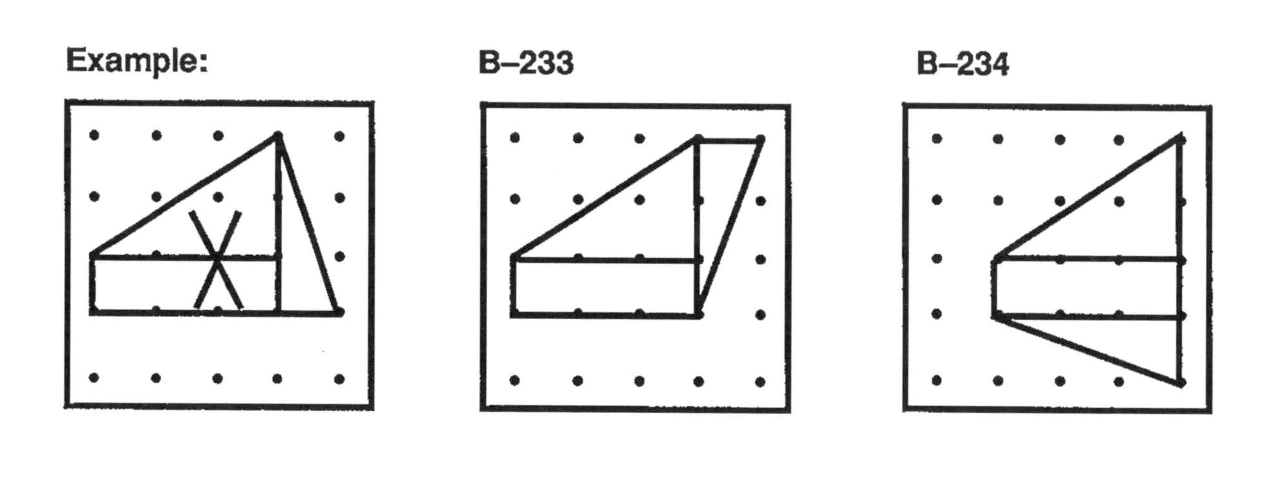

B–235 **B–236** **B–237**

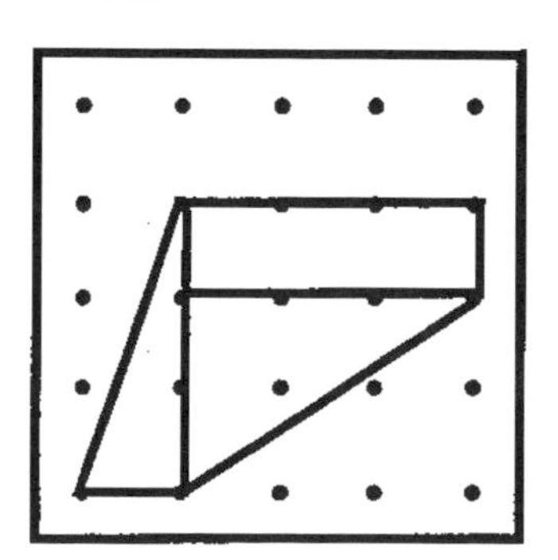

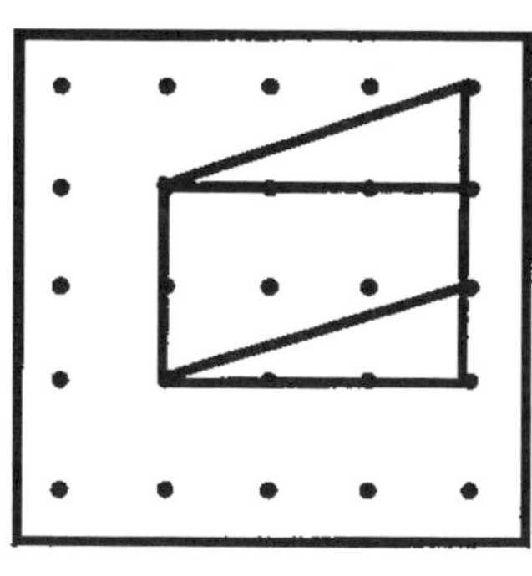

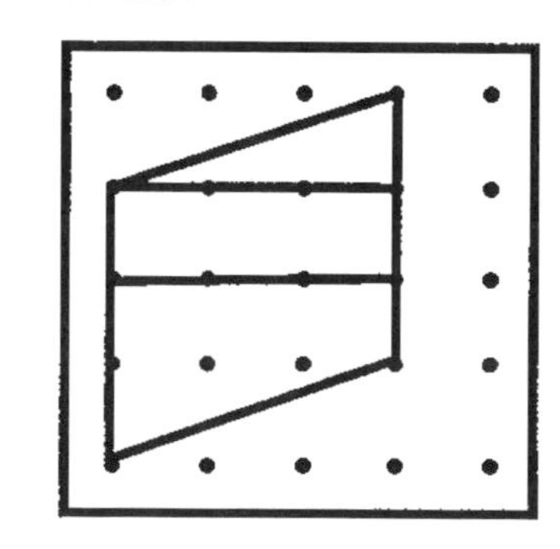

COMBINING SHAPES

Look at the two triangles below.

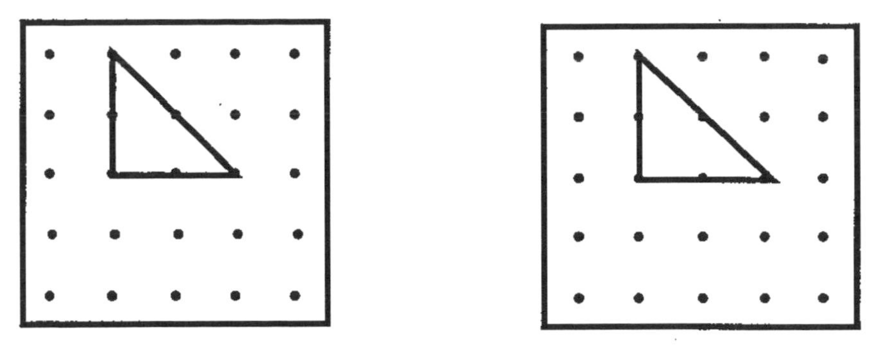

Combine the two triangles above to make a different figure in each box of dots below.

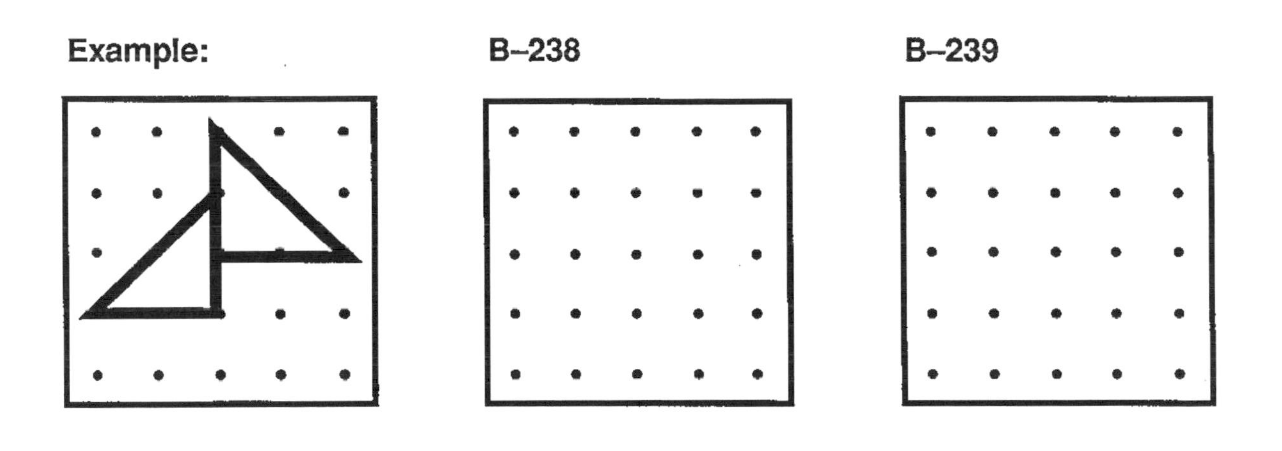

B–240 B–241 B–242

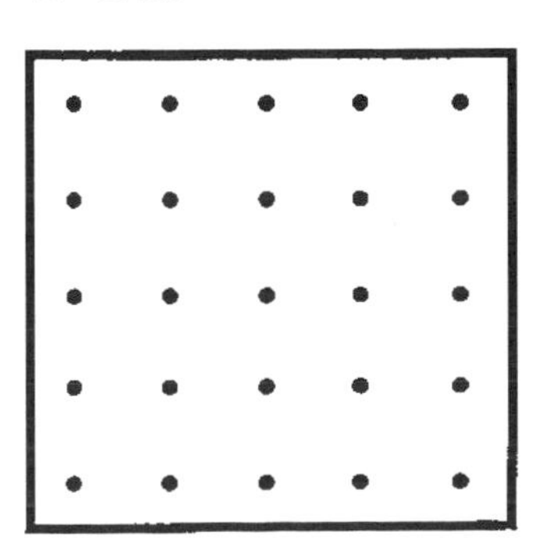
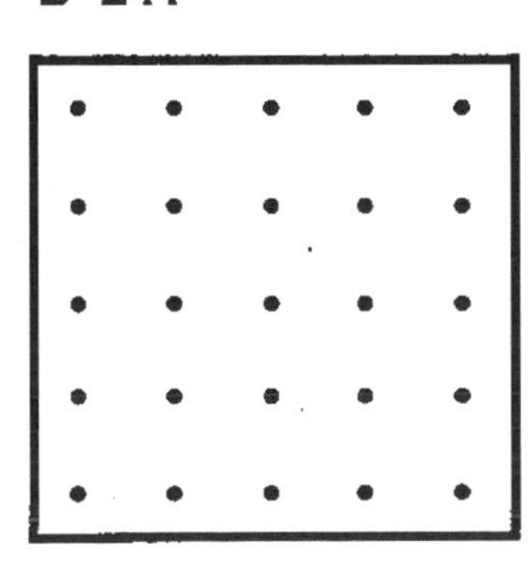
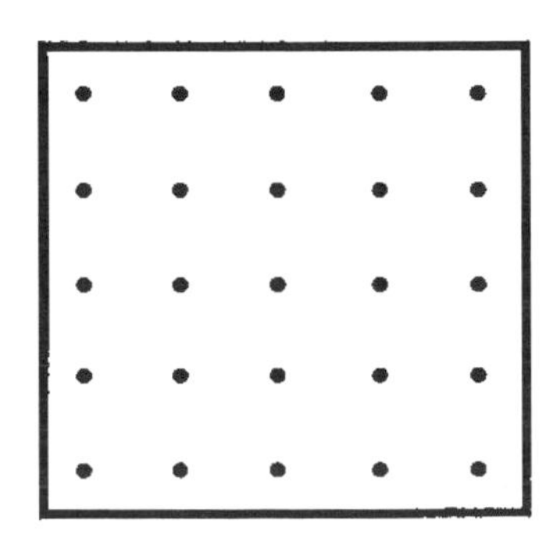

COMBINING SHAPES

Look at the three shapes below.

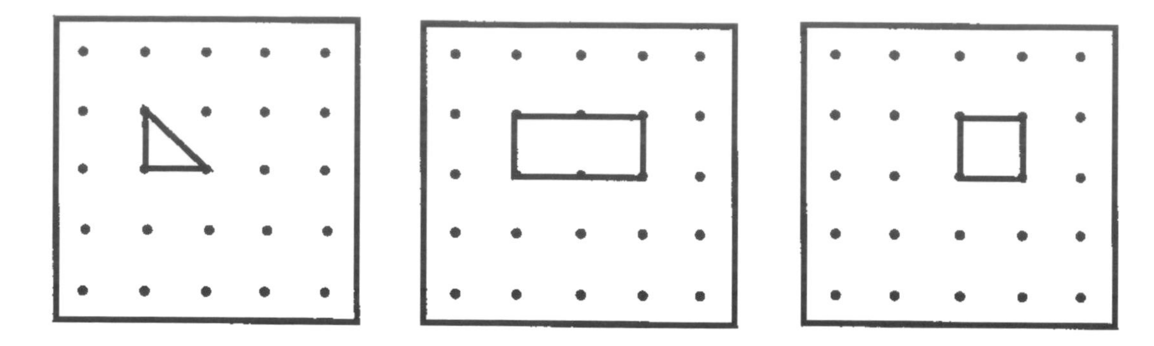

Combine the three shapes above to make a different figure in each box of dots below.

Example: **B–243** **B–244**

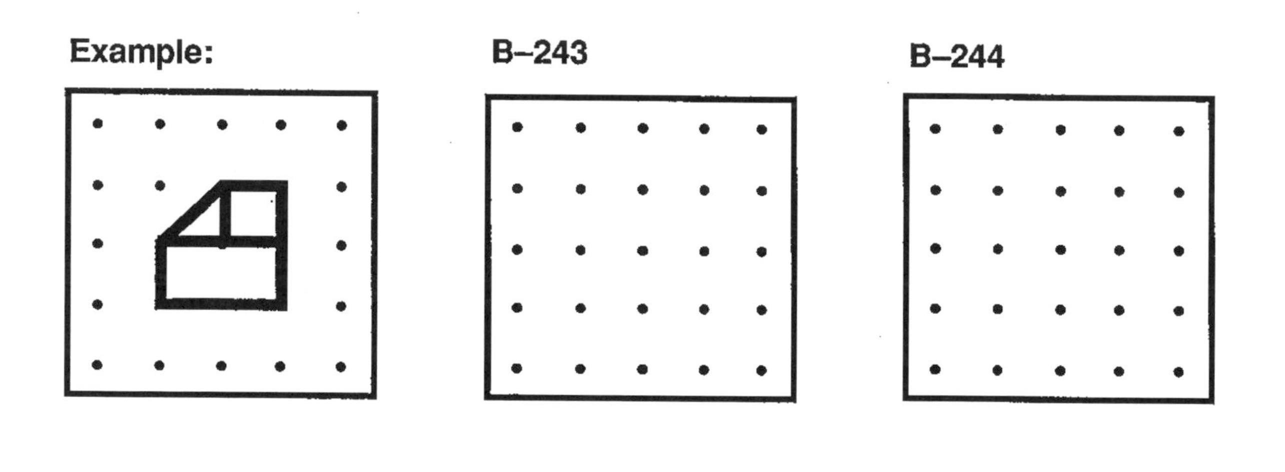

B–245 **B–246** **B–247**

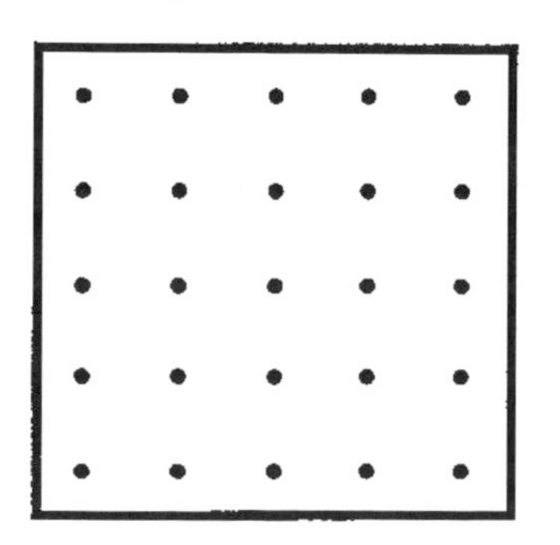

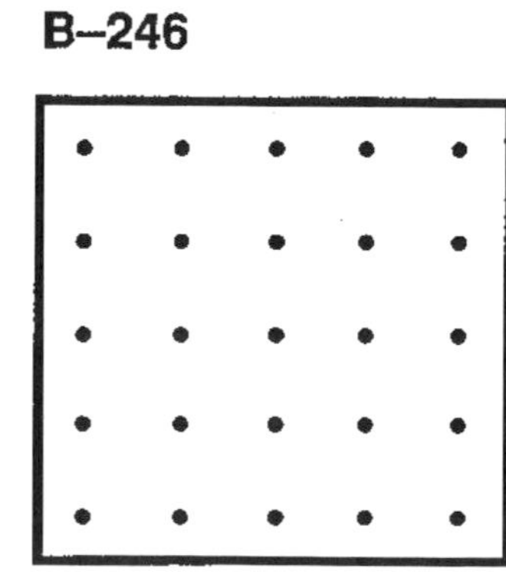

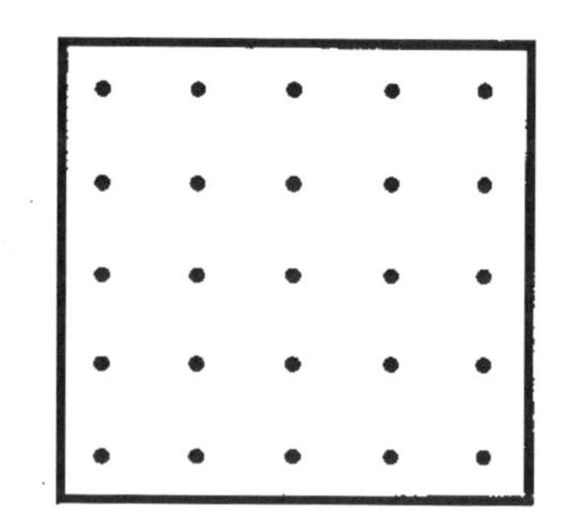

MATCHING SHAPES

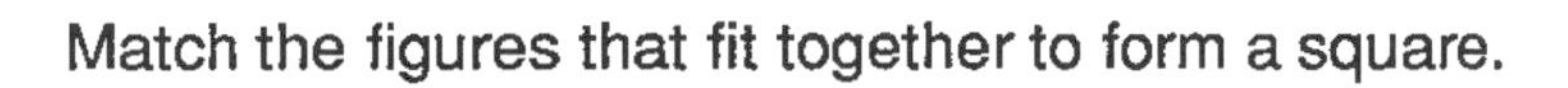

Match the figures that fit together to form a square.

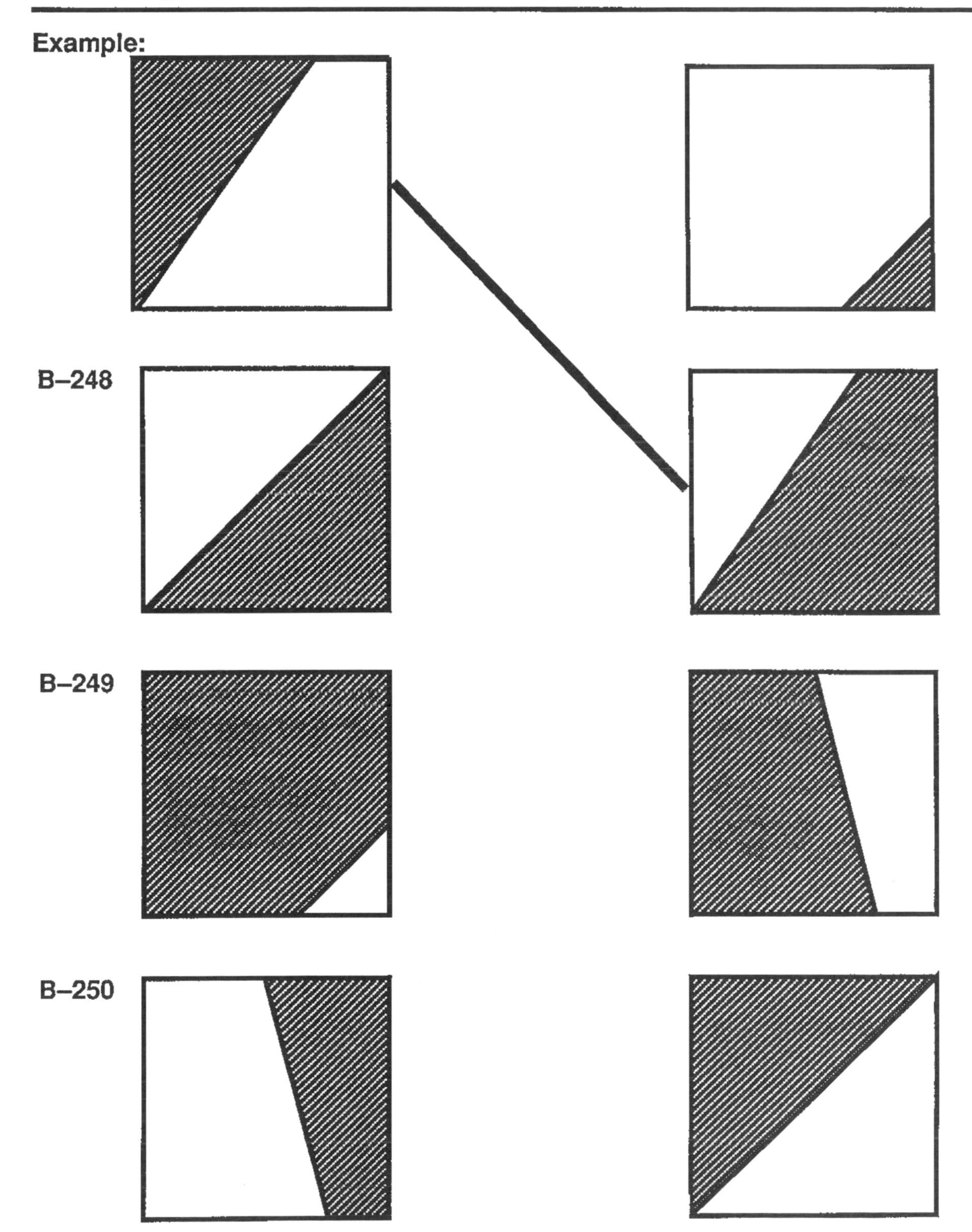

MATCHING SHAPES

Match the figures that fit together to make a circle.

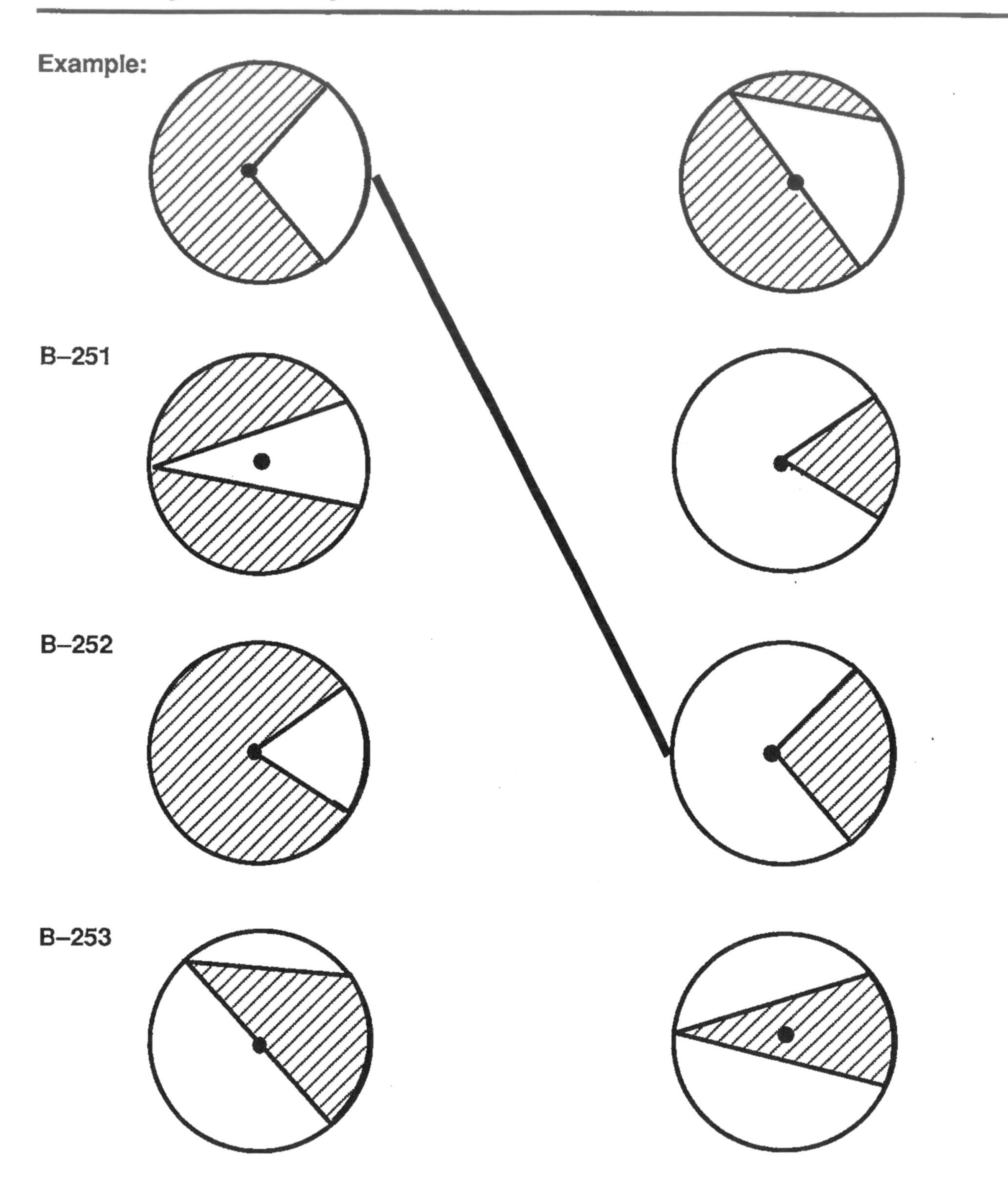

FINDING SHAPES

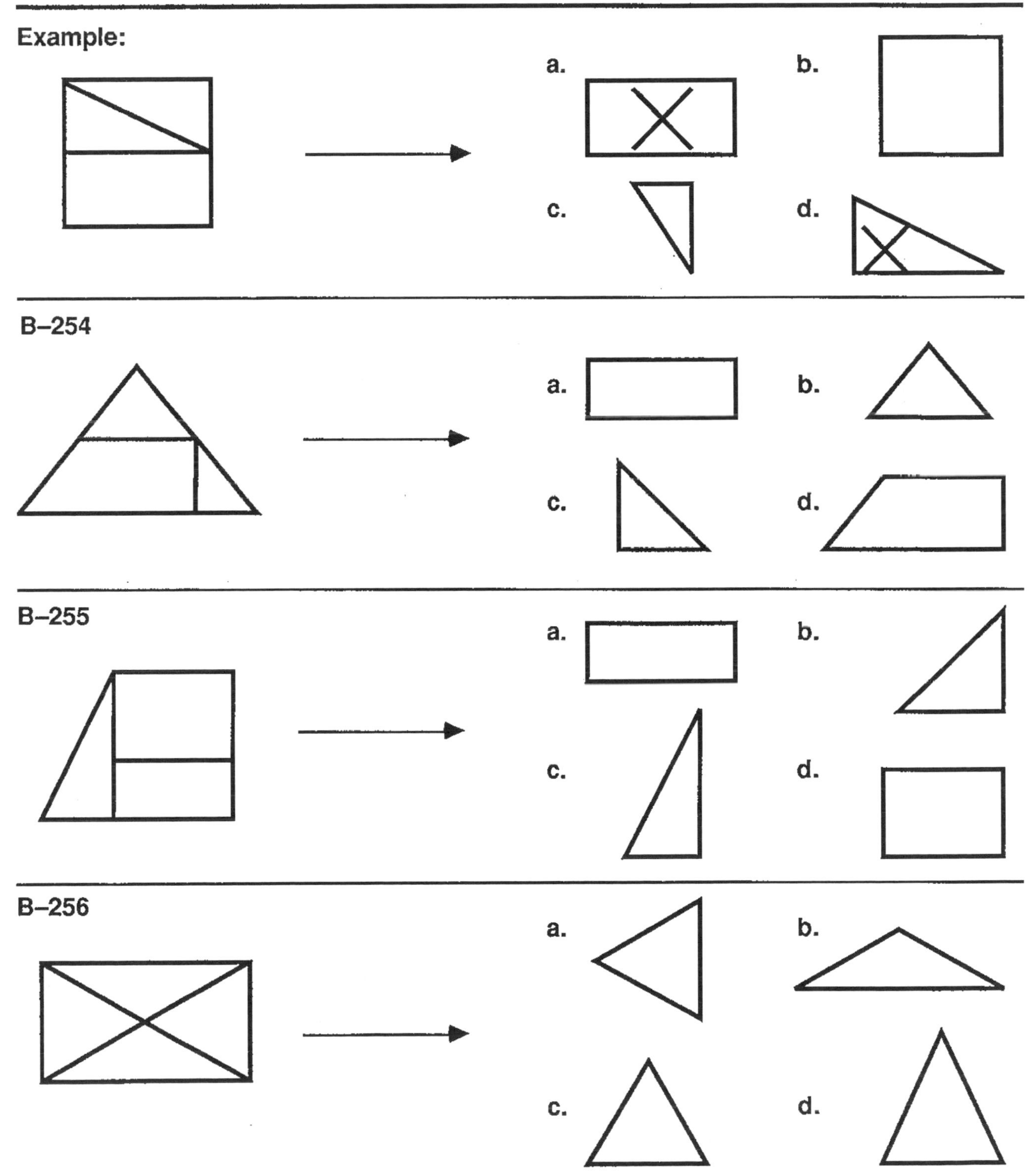

FINDING SHAPES

Put an X on all the shapes you find in the figure.

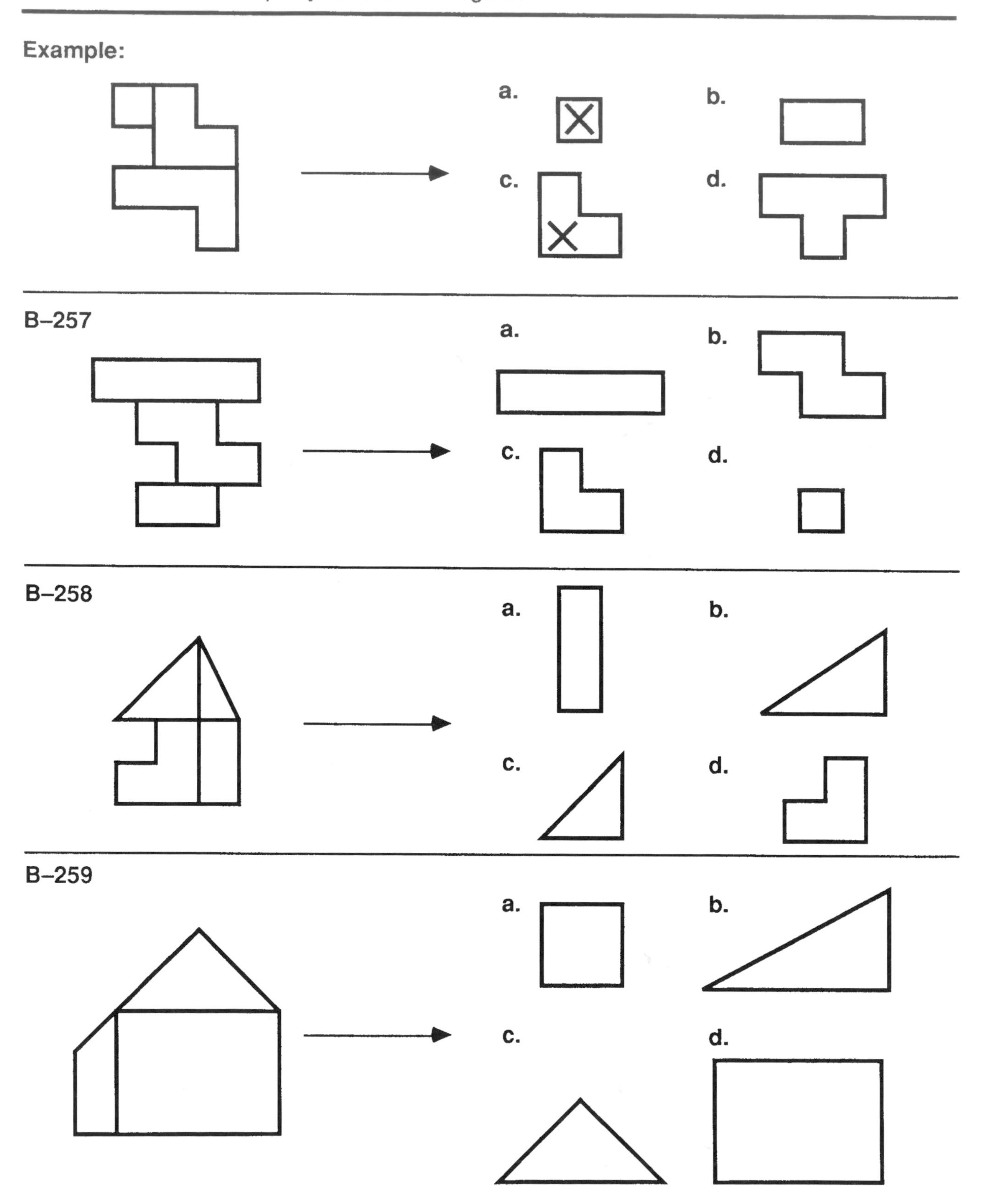

DIVIDING FIGURES

Connect dots to divide the figure into squares and triangles.

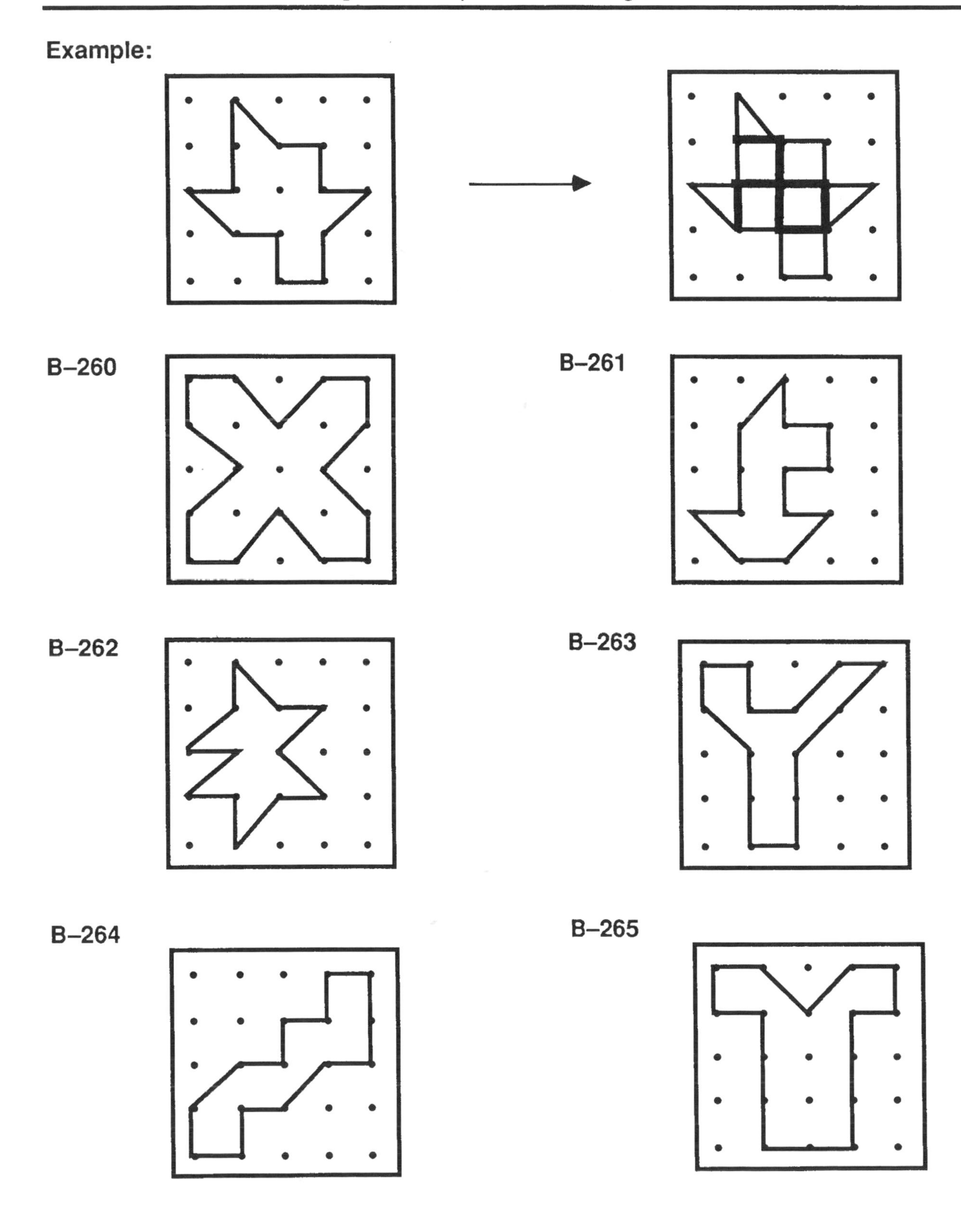

DIVIDING FIGURES

Connect dots to divide the figure into squares and triangles.

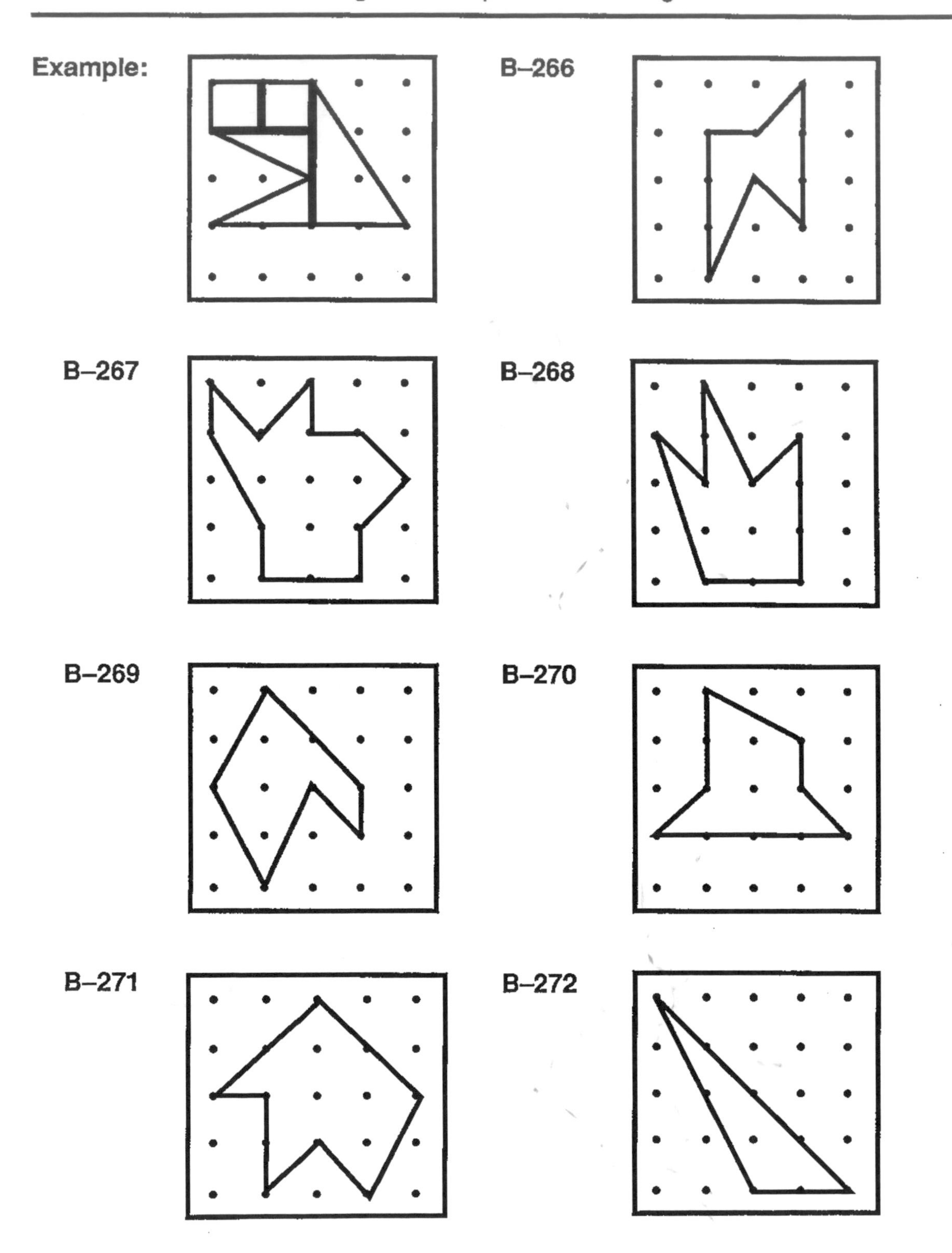

SETS OF FIVE

Match the sets that make a total of five dots.

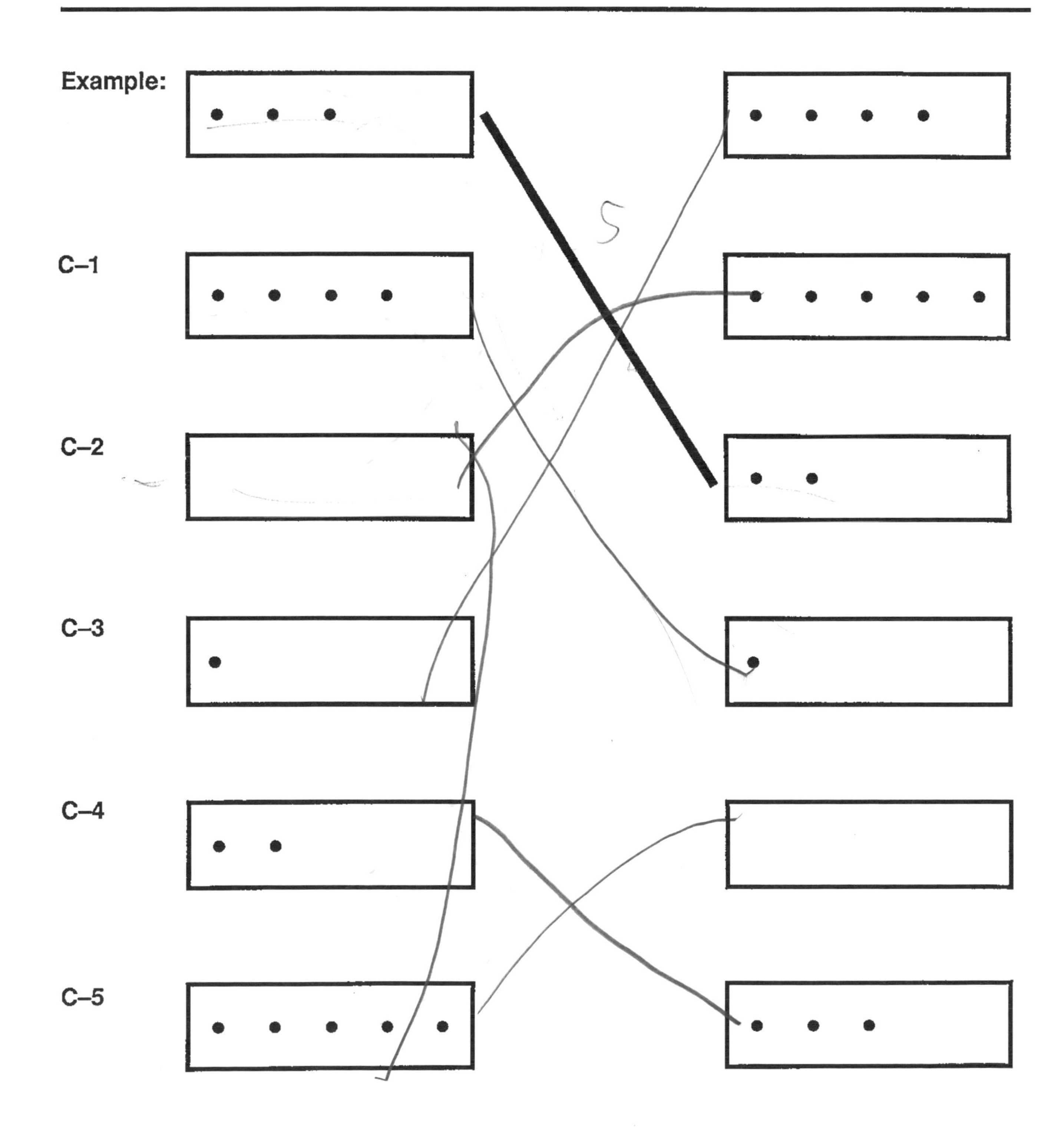

SETS OF SIX

Match the sets that make a total of six dots.

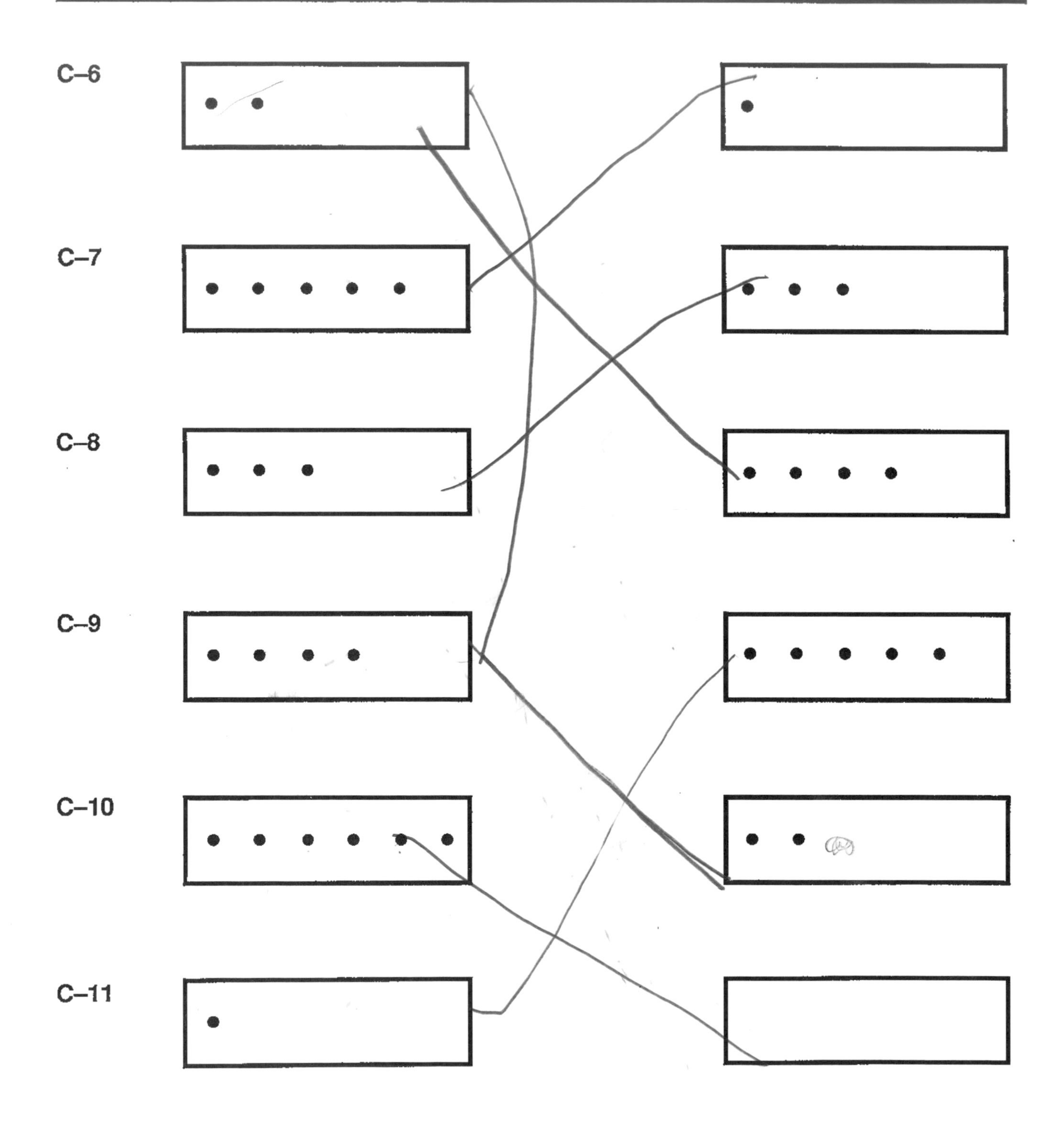

SETS OF NINE

Match the sets that make a total of nine dots.

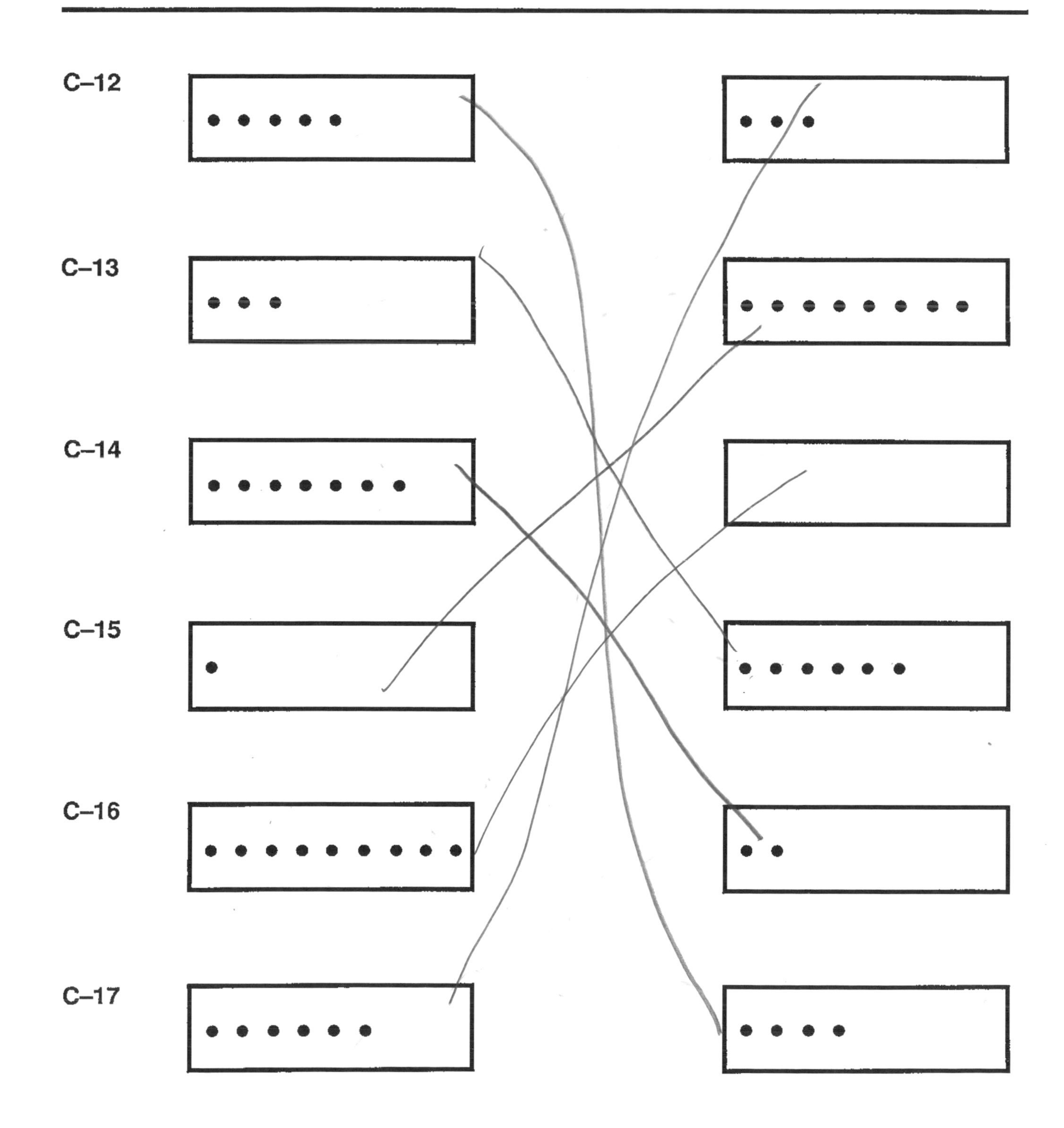

SETS OF TEN

Match the sets that make a total of ten dots.

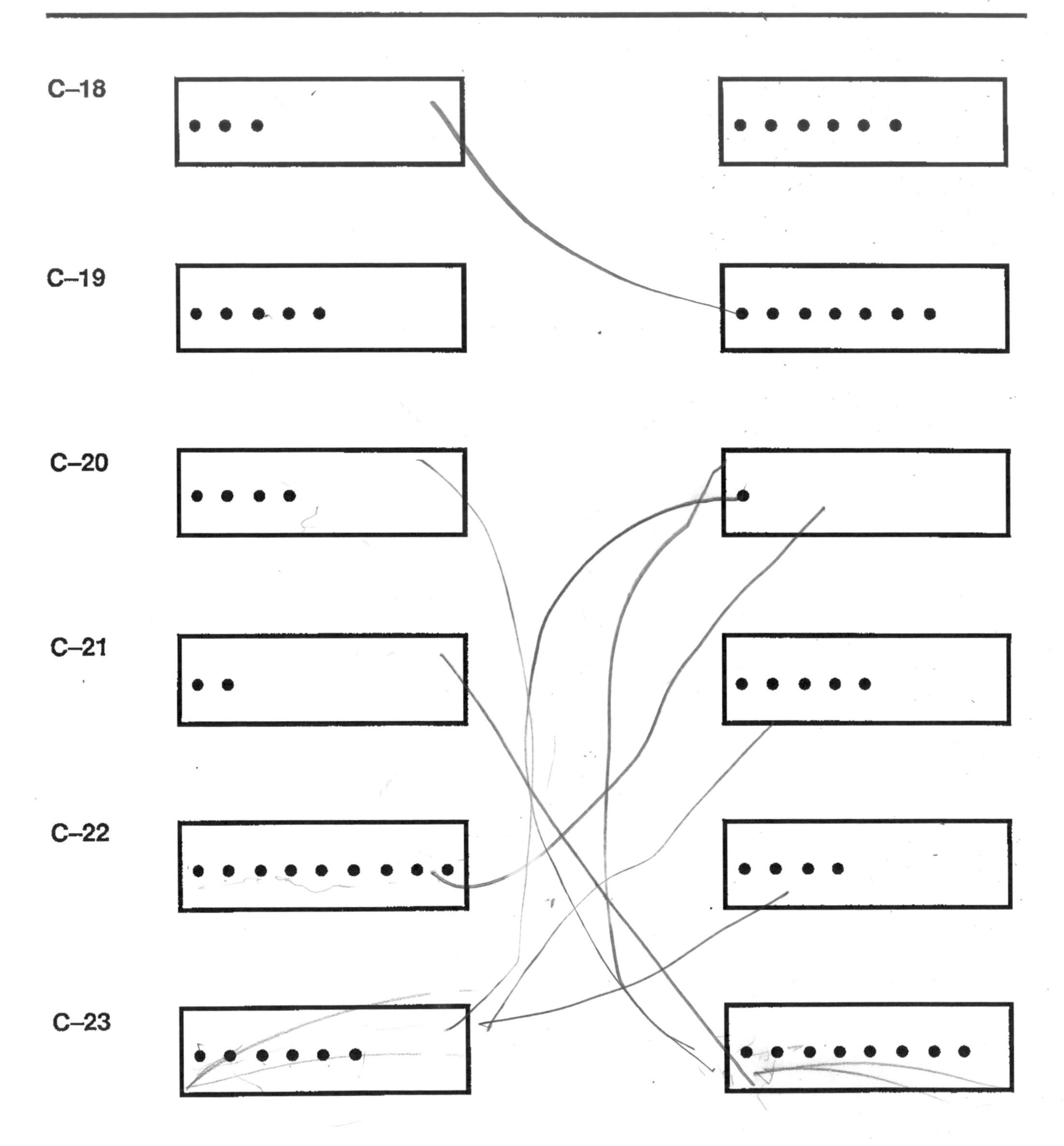

NUMBER PATTERNS

Count the number of white squares in each row. Write the number in the chart.
Count the number of shaded squares in each row. Write the number in the chart.
Write the total number of squares in each row in the chart.

C–24

SQUARES

	White	Shaded	Total
Example:	2	0	2
	___	___	___
	___	___	___

C–25

SQUARES

White	Shaded	Total
___	___	___
___	___	___
___	___	___
___	___	___

C–26

SQUARES

White	Shaded	Total
___	___	___
___	___	___
___	___	___
___	___	___
___	___	___

NUMBER PATTERNS

Count the number of white squares in each row. Write the number in the chart.
Count the number of shaded squares in each row. Write the number in the chart.
Write the total number of squares in each row in the chart.

C–27

SQUARES

White	Shaded	Total

C–28

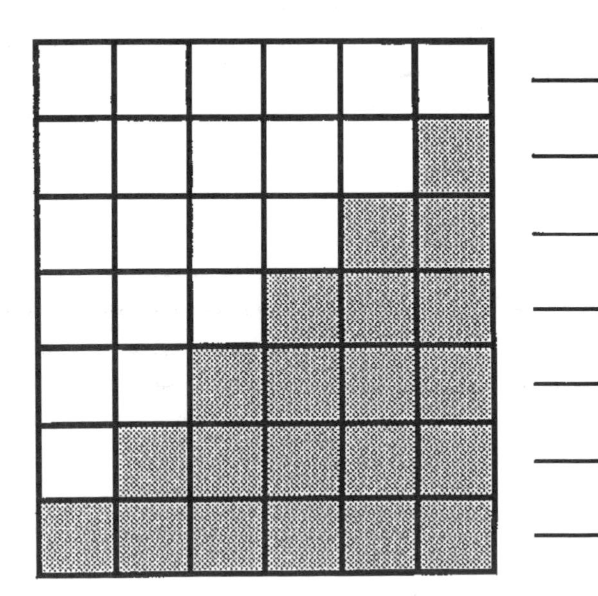

SQUARES

White	Shaded	Total

MAKING CHANGE

Which sets of coins are equal to one dime?
Circle the numbers of the sets.

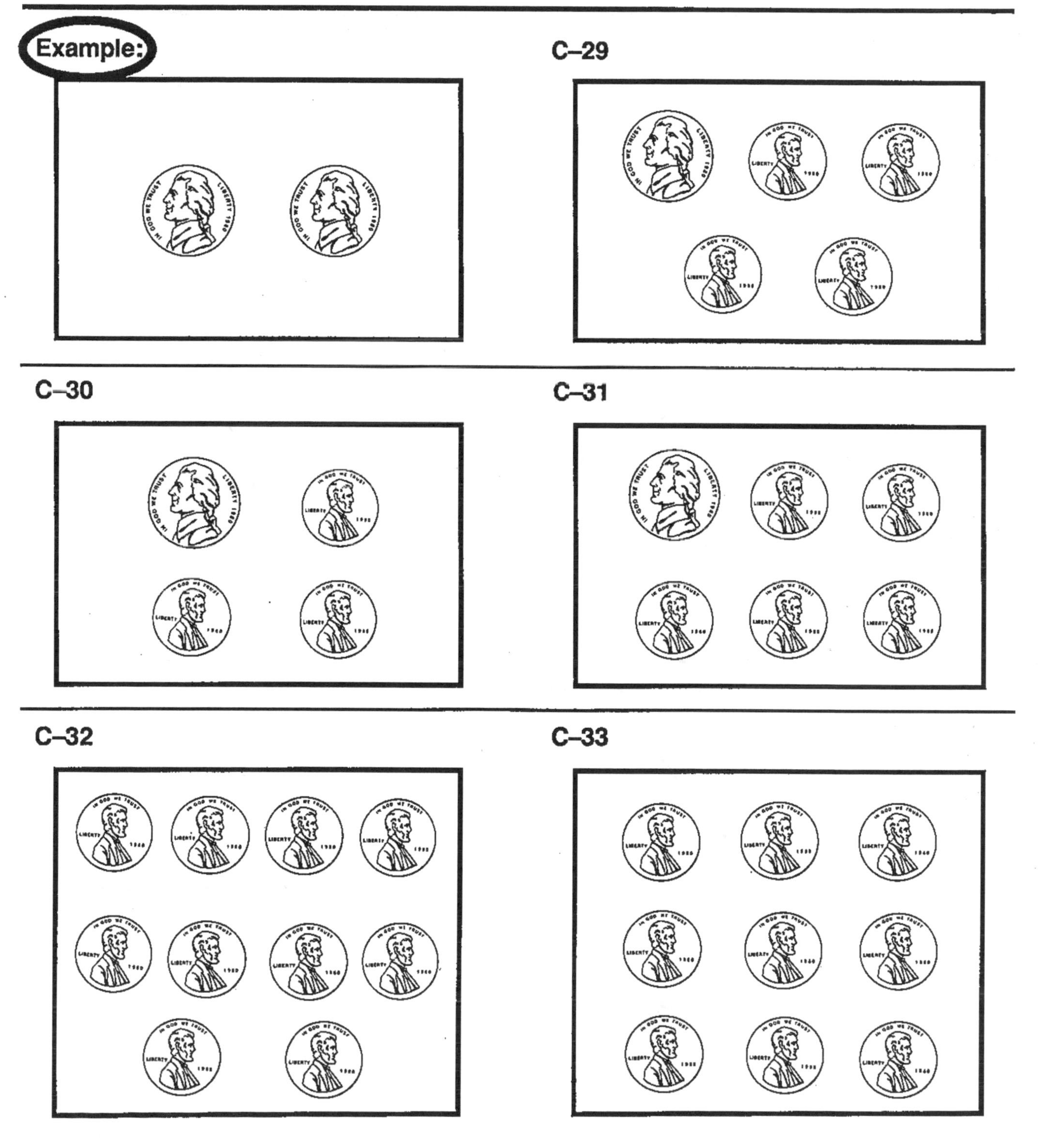

MAKING CHANGE

Which sets of coins are equal to one quarter?
Circle the numbers of the sets.

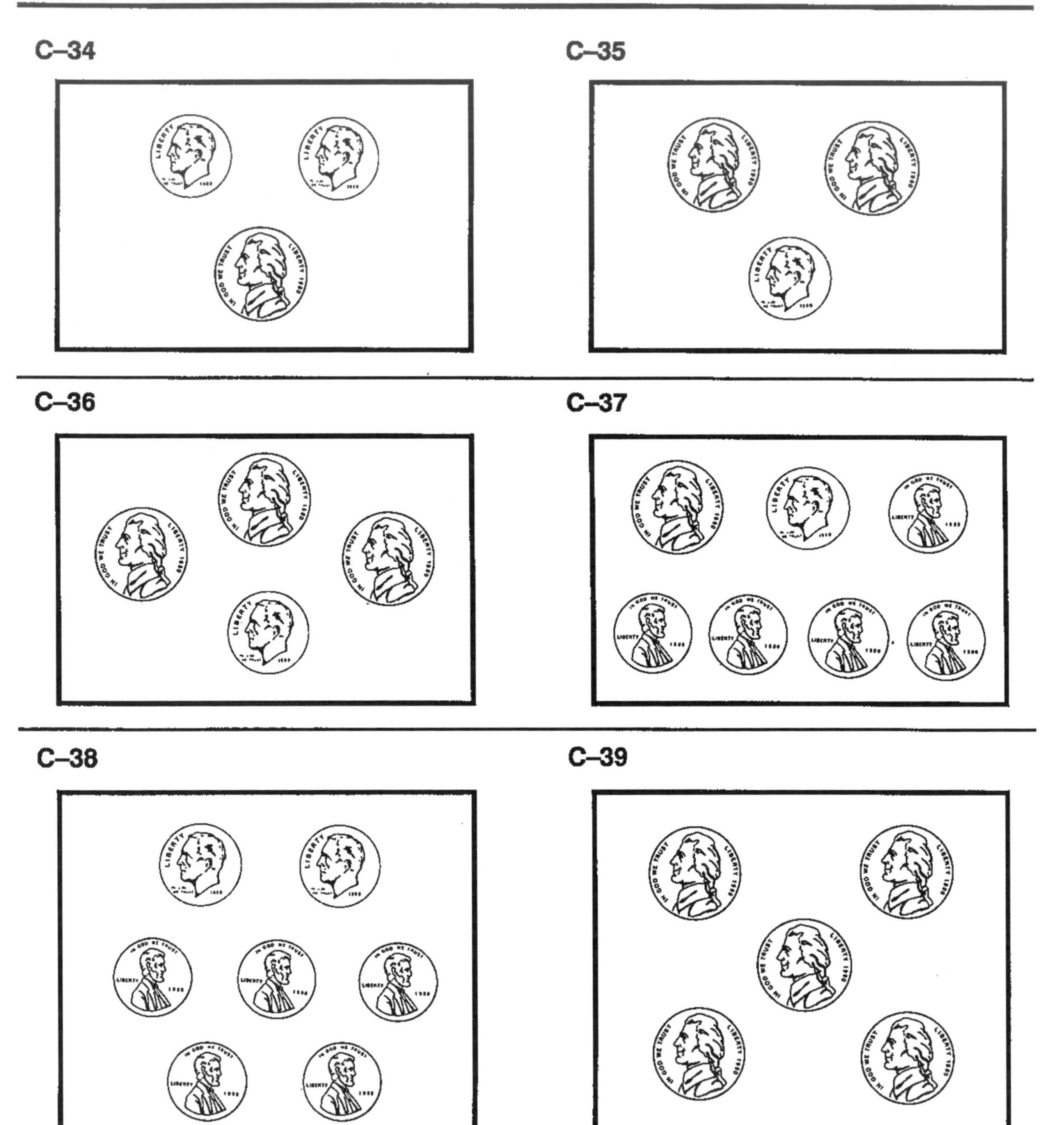

MAKING SETS OF COINS

Put an X on the coins that are needed to make the number in the circle.

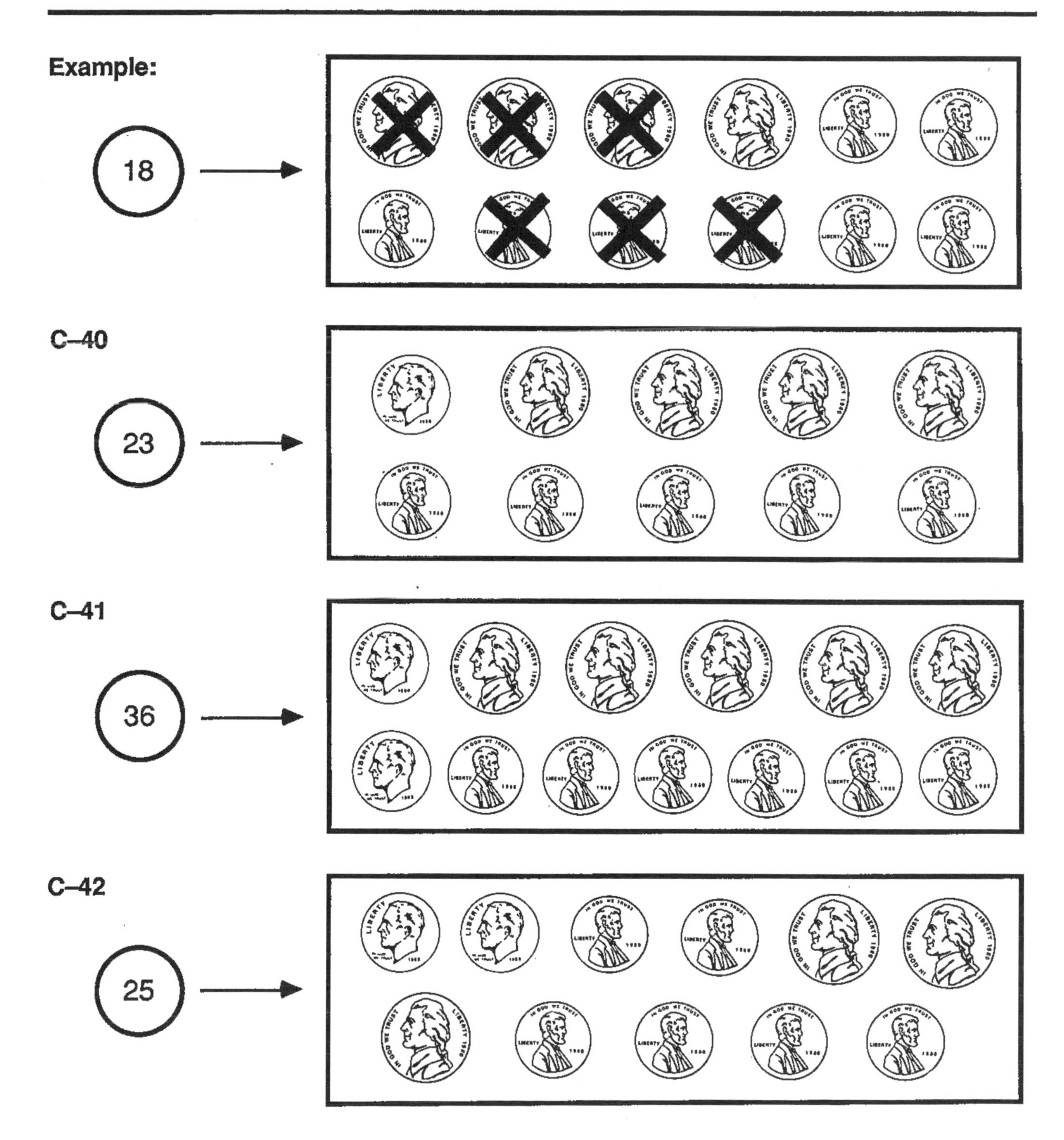

MAKING SETS OF COINS

Put an X on the coins that are needed to make the number in the circle.

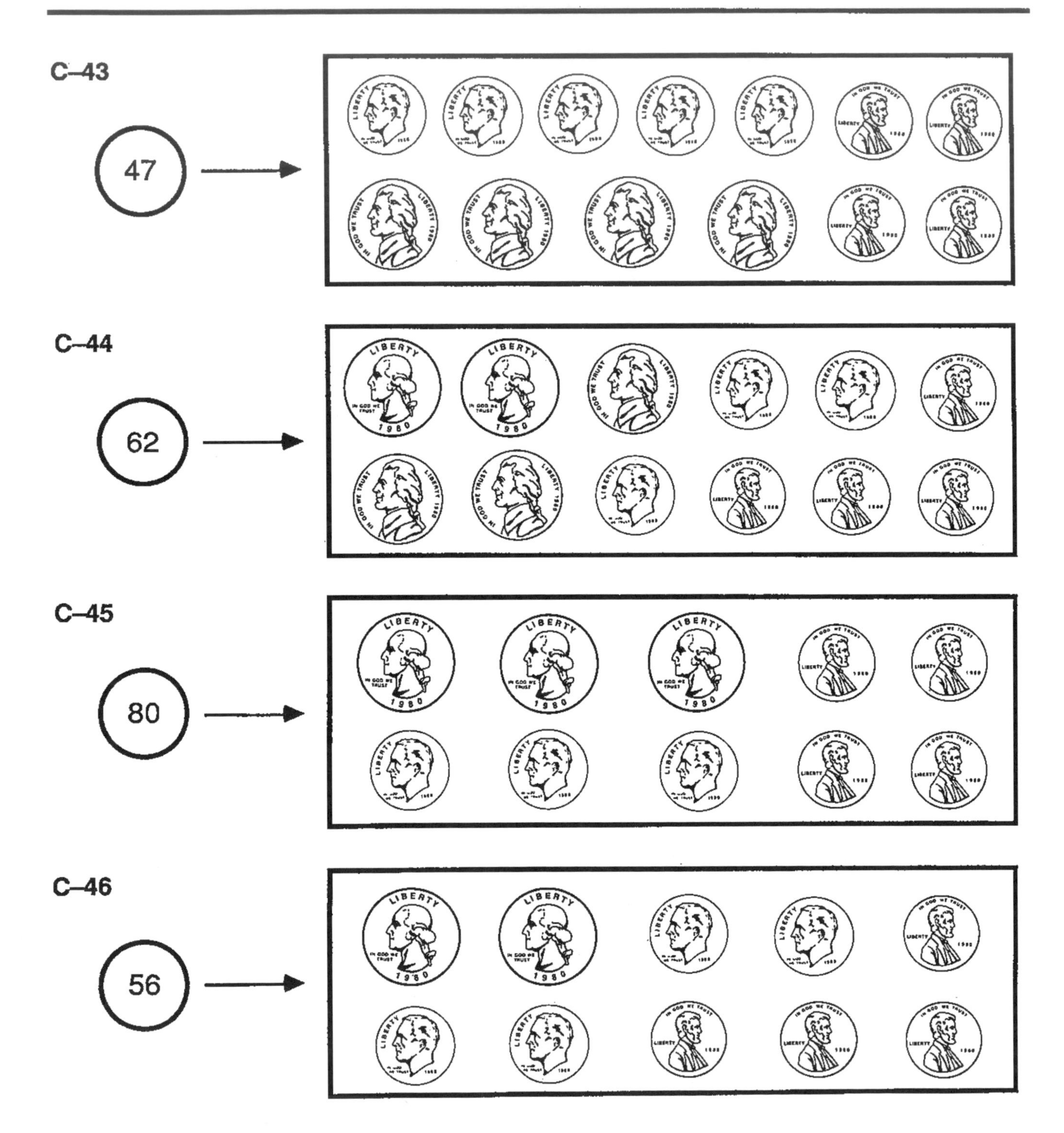

SUMS OF FIVE

Write the number of white circles in the first box.
Write the number of black circles in the second box.
Write the sum of the two numbers in the third box.

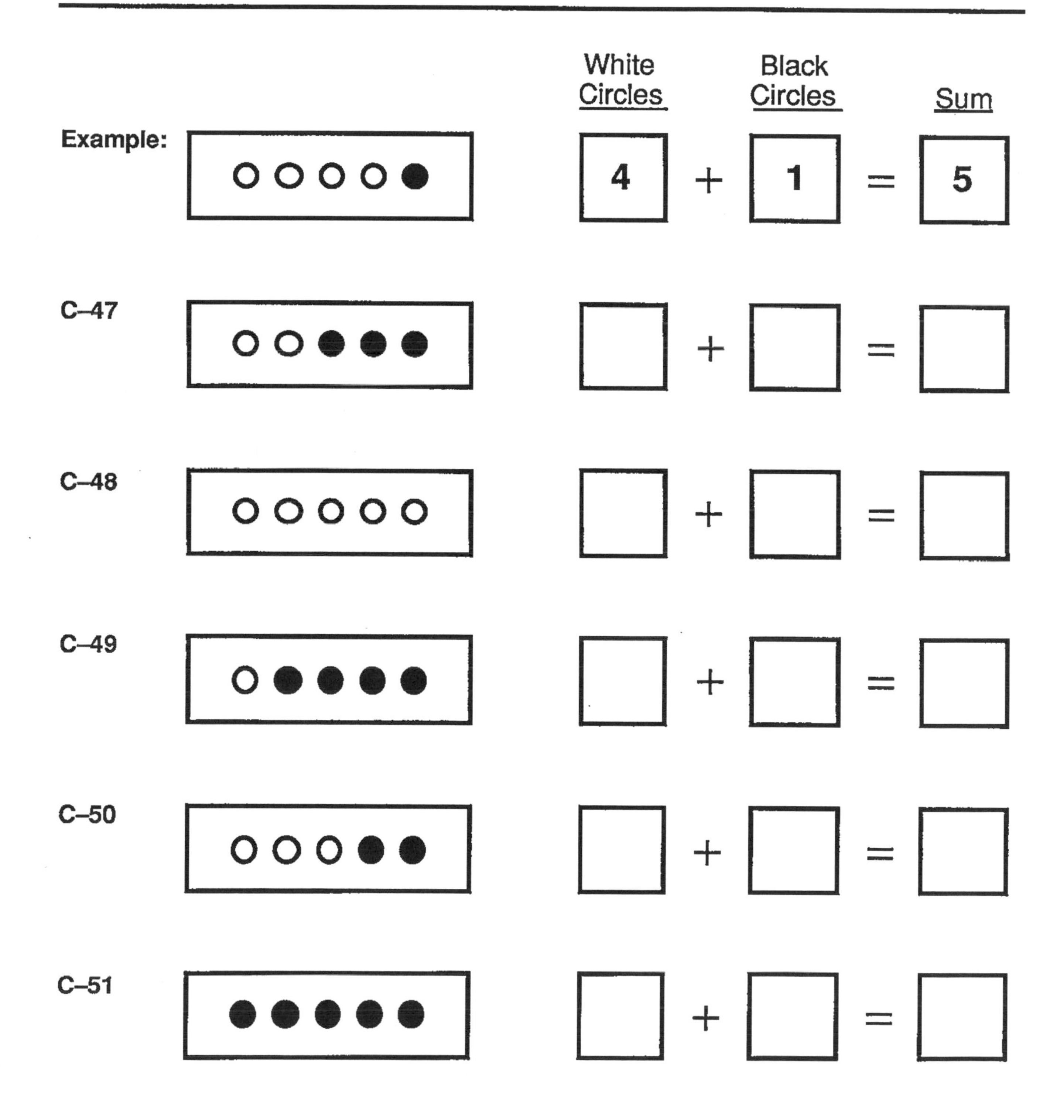

SUMS OF SIX

Write the number of white circles in the first box.
Write the number of black circles in the second box.
Write the sum of the two numbers in the third box.

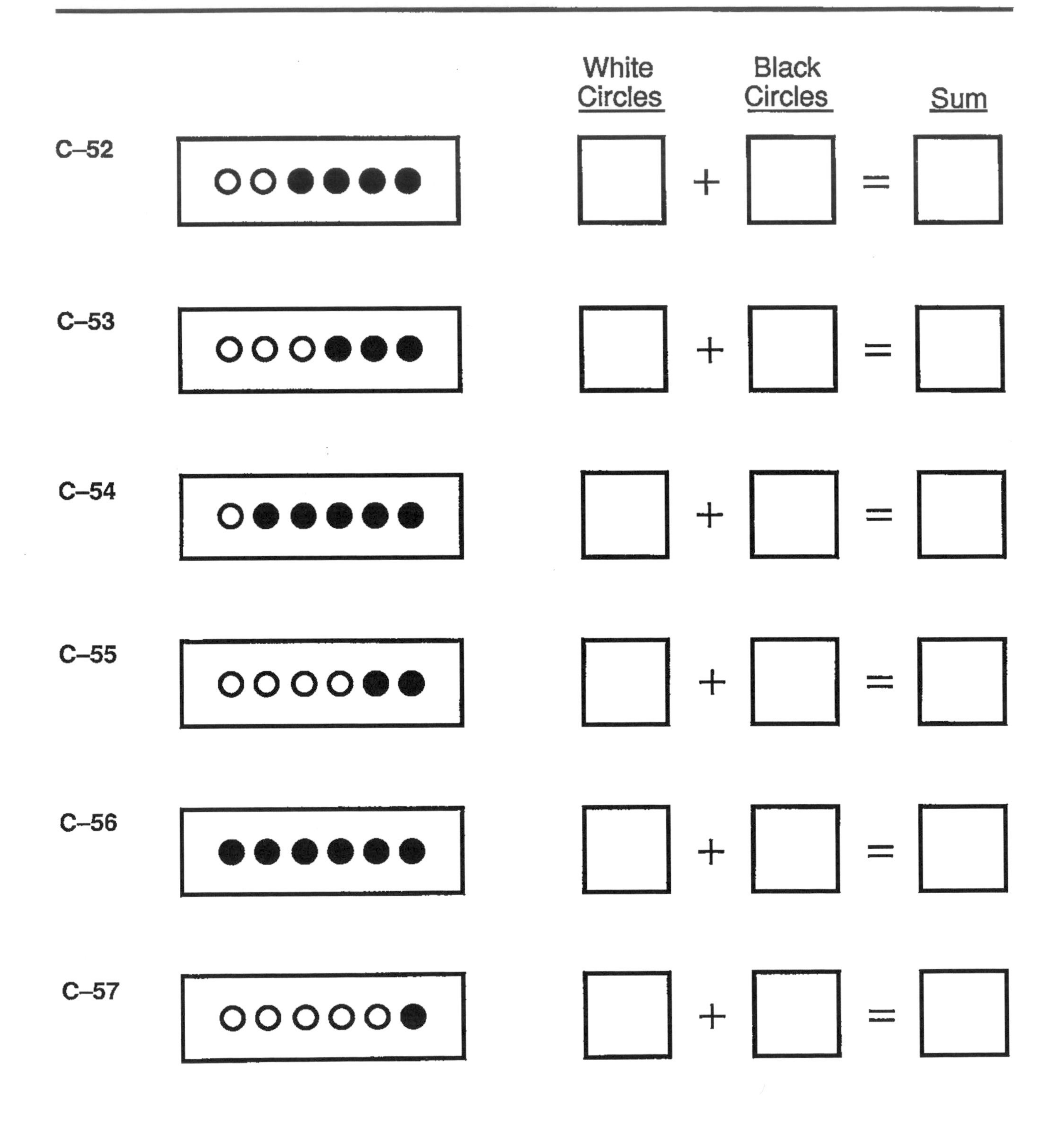

SUMS OF SIX AND SEVEN

Look at the number sentence.
Complete the sum.
Darken the correct number of circles for each sentence.

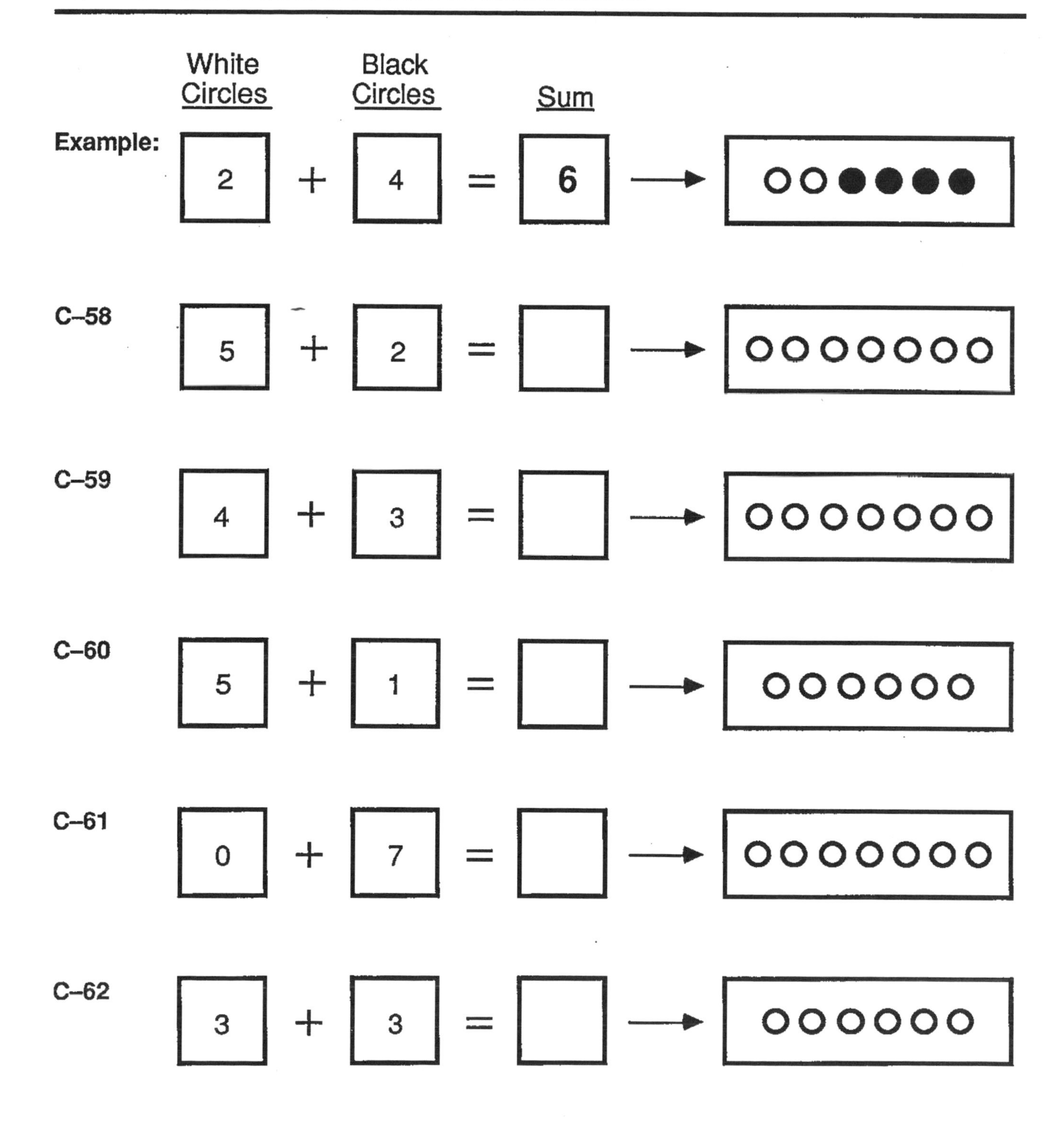

SUMS OF NINE AND TEN

Look at the number sentence.
Complete the sum.
Darken the correct number of circles for each sentence.

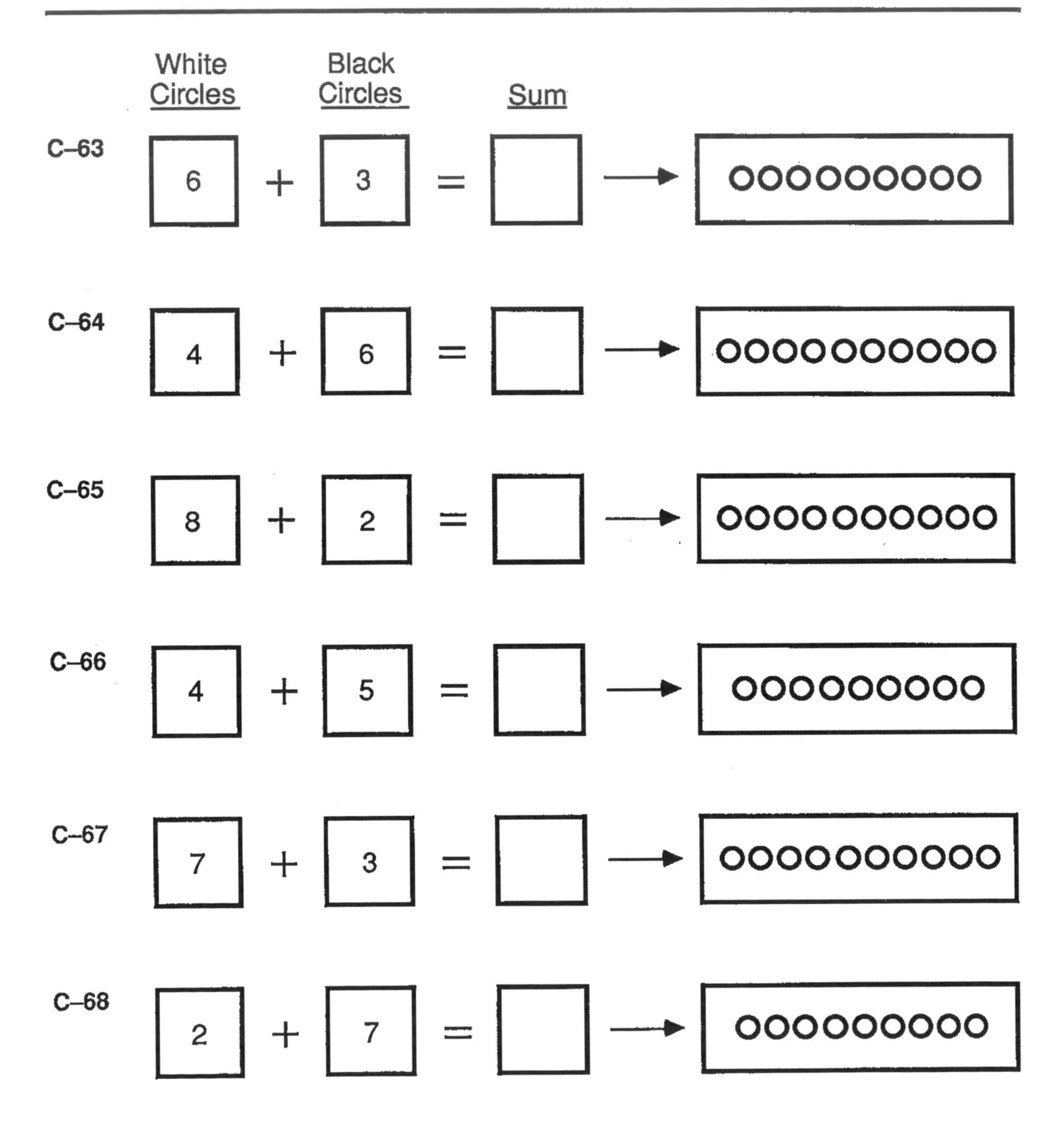

GROUPING BY TENS

Make groups of ten by filling in ten circles.
Write the number of tens and ones in the boxes

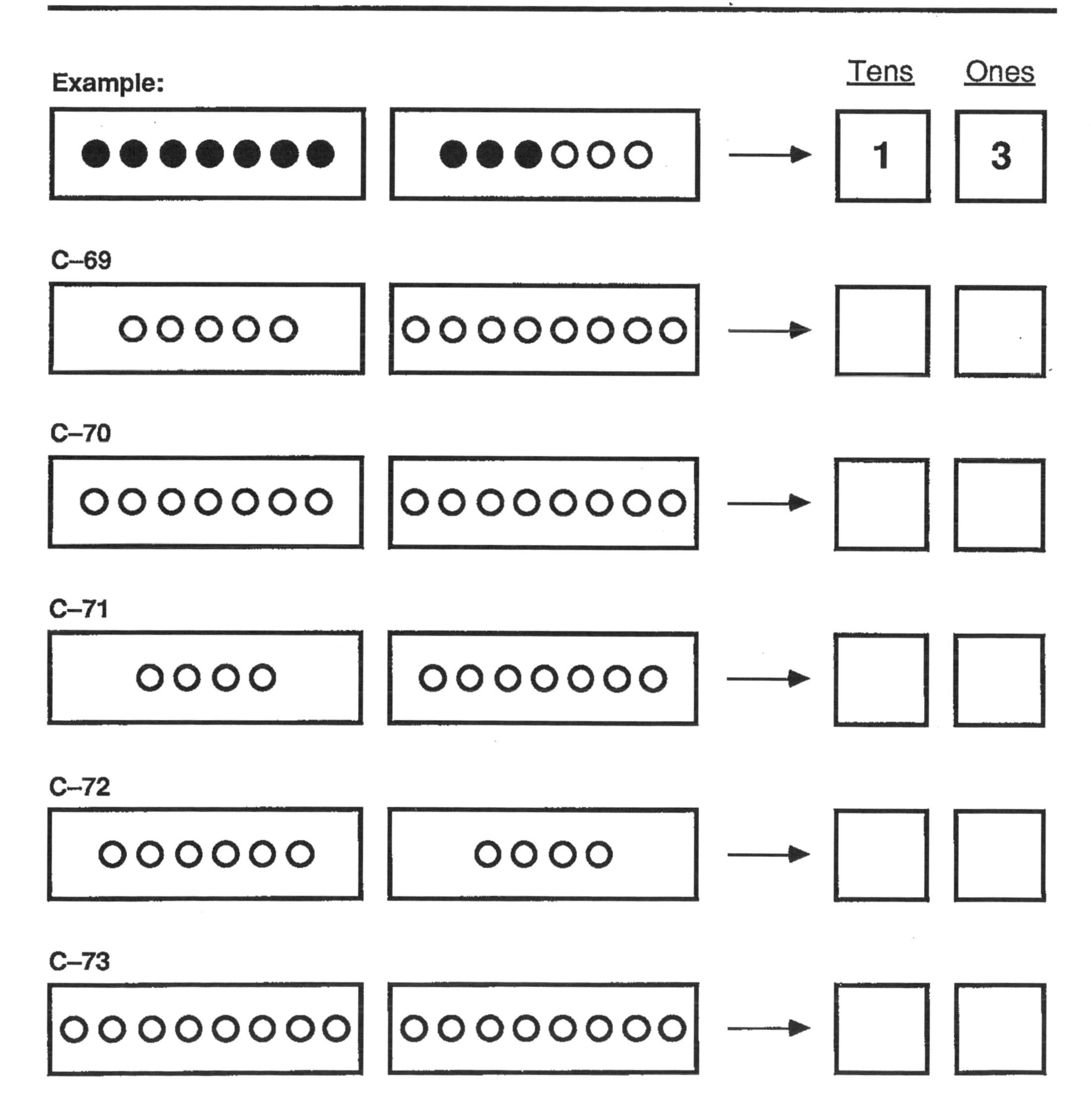

GROUPING BY TENS

Draw a line around groups of ten circles.
Write the number of tens and ones in the boxes.

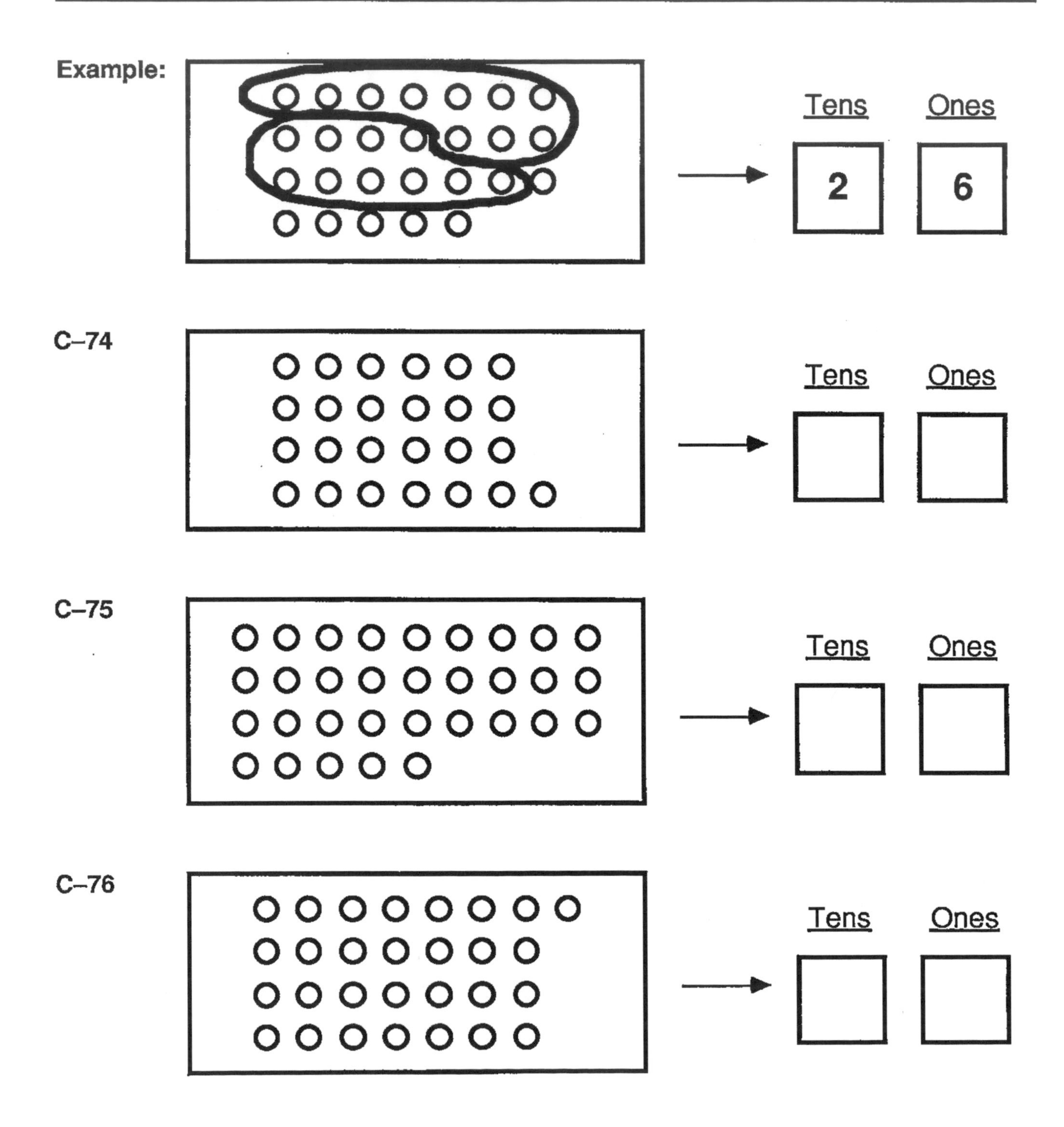

SUMS THAT ARE EQUAL

Circle all the problems in each row whose sums are equal to the first number in that row. There may be more than one correct answer.

Example:	14	6 + 7	(8 + 6)	4 + 9	(6 + 8)
C–77	9	5 + 5	3 + 6	6 + 4	4 + 4
C–78	16	8 + 8	9 + 8	6 + 9	7 + 9
C–79	11	1 + 9	9 + 2	5 + 6	8 + 4
C–80	12	9 + 2	8 + 4	3 + 8	4 + 9
C–81	8	7 + 2	6 + 1	2 + 6	7 + 1
C–82	18	6 + 9	9 + 9	8 + 9	7 + 9
C–83	15	9 + 6	9 + 7	6 + 9	8 + 8

COMPARING SUMS

Find the sum of each addition problem below.
Write all the problems whose sums are less than 15 in the box on the left.
Write all the problems whose sums are more than 15 in the box on the right.

3 + 5   9 + 9   4 + 5   10 + 9

10 + 10   7 + 5   9 + 8   9 + 5

8 + 9   3 + 2   7 + 9   10 + 7

8 + 5   8 + 10   6 + 7   4 + 5

C–84 Less than 15 (<)

Example:
3 + 5

C–85 Greater than 15 (>)

C–86 Circle the problem with the largest sum in each box.

C–87 Place an X on the problem with the smallest sum in each box.

C–88 Which problem has the largest sum that is less than 15? ____________

C–89 Which problem has the smallest sum that is more than 15? ____________

COMPLETING SUMS OF TEN

Write a number in the box to make a sum of ten.

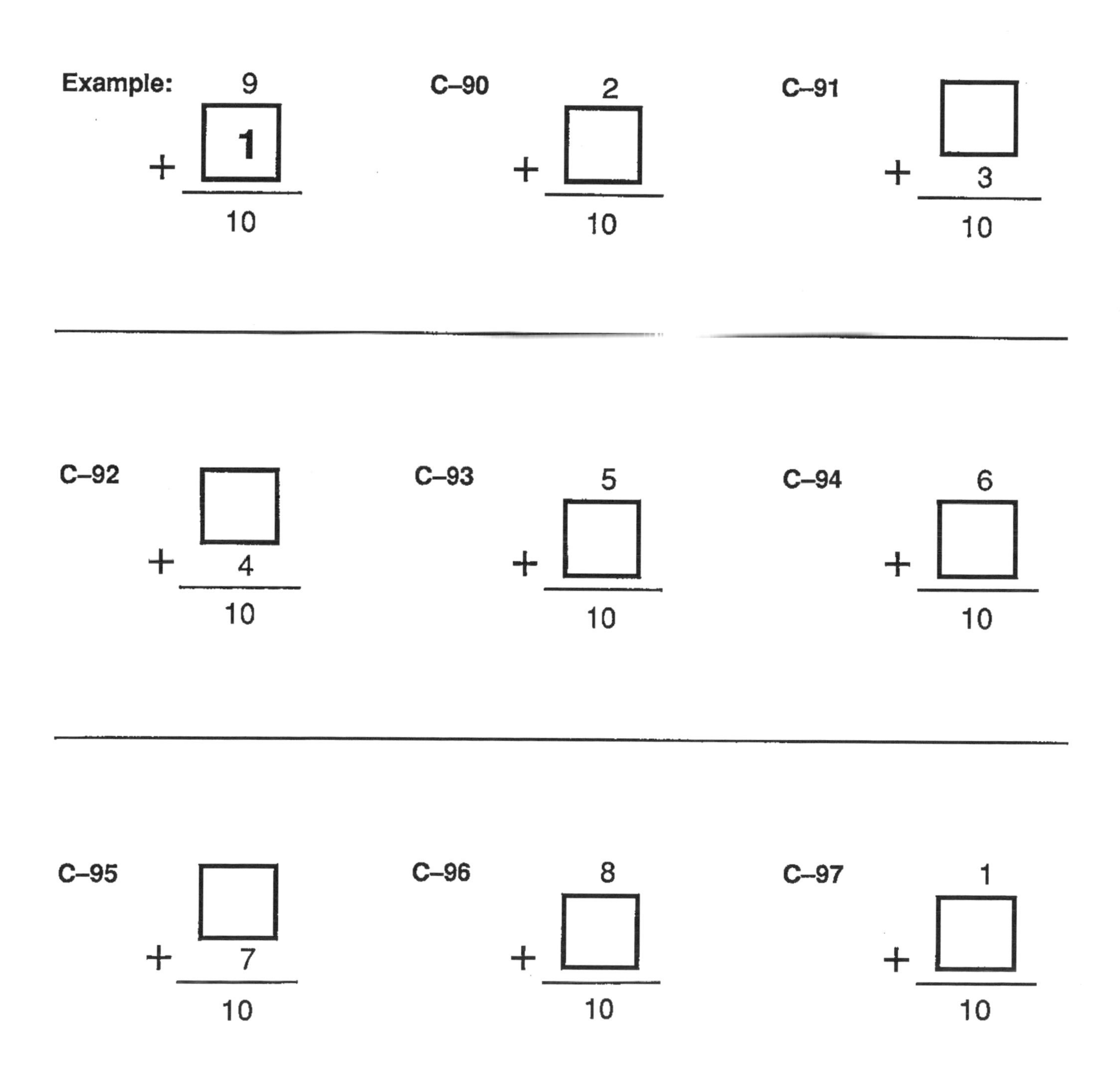

COMPLETING SUMS OF TEN

Write a number in the box to make a sum of ten.

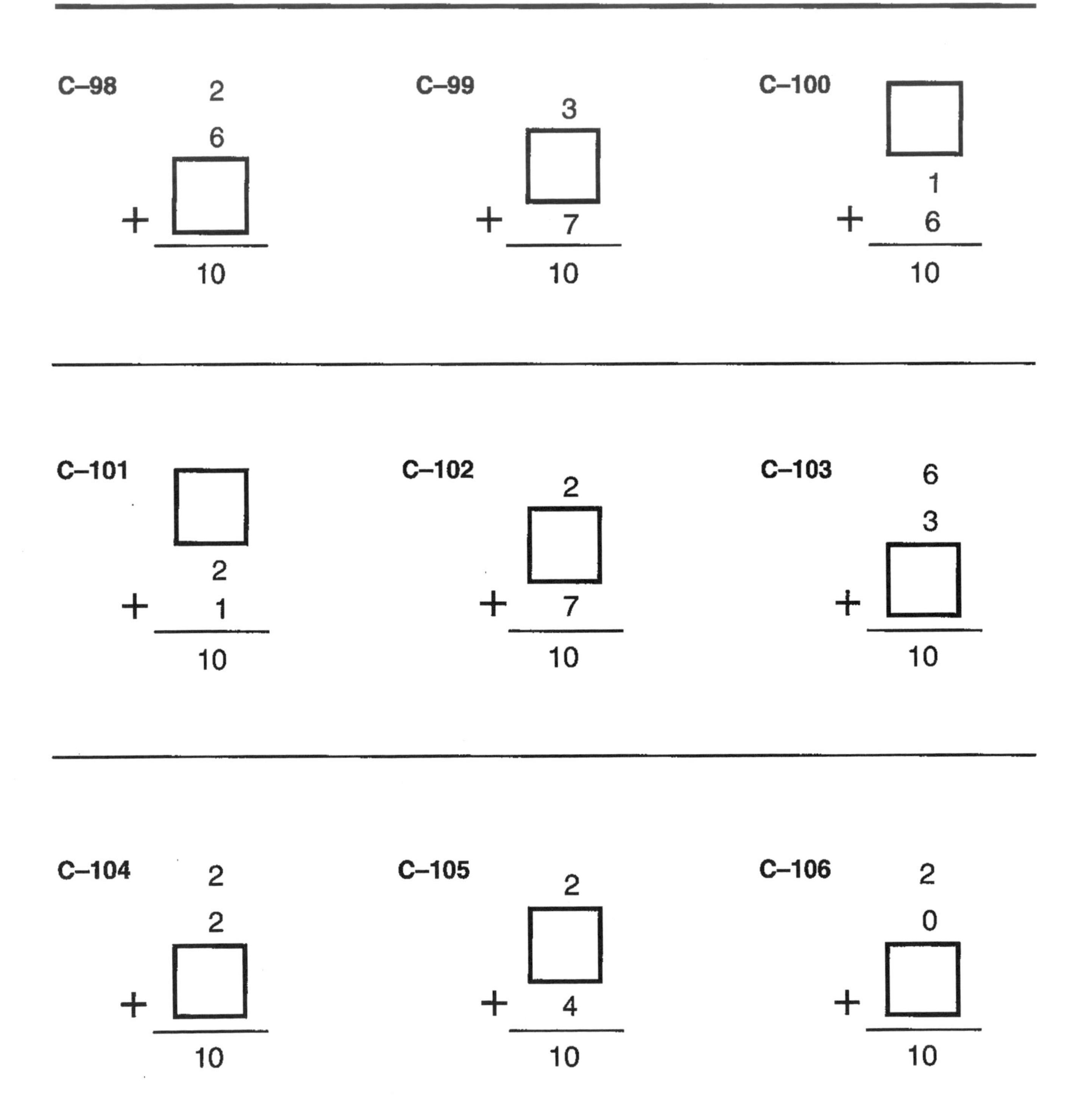

FINDING SUMS OF TEN

Circle two numbers that make a sum of ten.

Example:	5	(8)	6	3	(2)	1
C–107	4	5	7	8	9	5
C–108	3	4	5	7	8	3
C–109	1	8	9	3	4	5
C–110	9	5	3	4	2	6
C–111	7	2	6	3	5	9
C–112	4	2	5	7	1	8
C–113	8	5	4	3	6	1

FINDING SUMS OF TEN

The first number is circled in each row.
Circle two more numbers so that the three numbers make a sum of ten.

Example:	(6)	5	(3)	6	(1)	8
C–114	(4)	8	5	1	7	4
C–115	(7)	4	2	5	1	8
C–116	(3)	4	6	3	5	9
C–117	(5)	6	4	1	5	7
C–118	(2)	3	2	4	6	5
C–119	(6)	4	2	3	2	5
C–120	(8)	1	3	2	4	1

MAKING LENGTHS EQUAL

Compare the lengths of A and B.
Draw a line around the number of squares that are needed to make A equal to B.

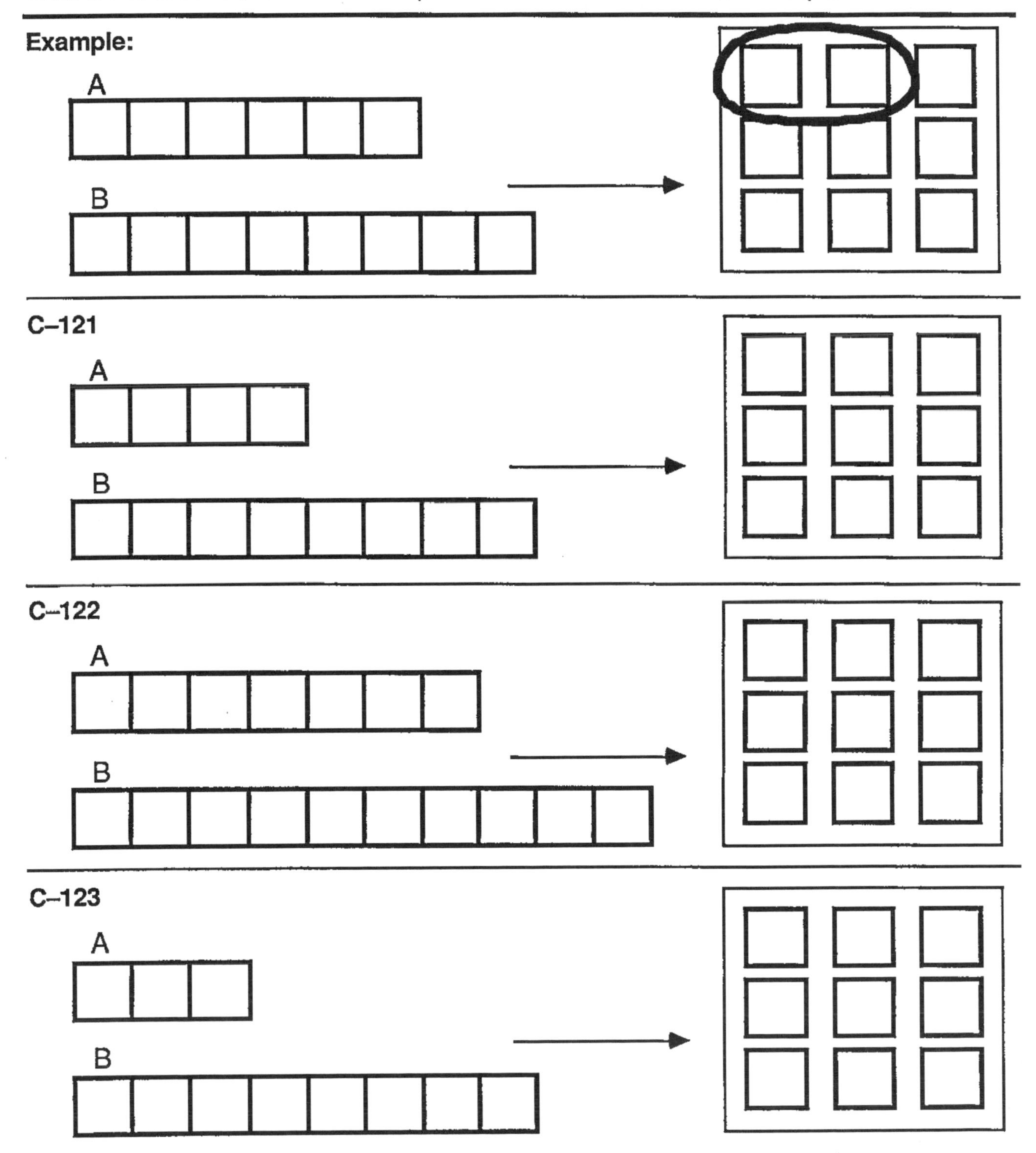

MAKING LENGTHS EQUAL

Compare the lengths of A and B.
Draw a line around the number of squares that are needed to make A equal to B.

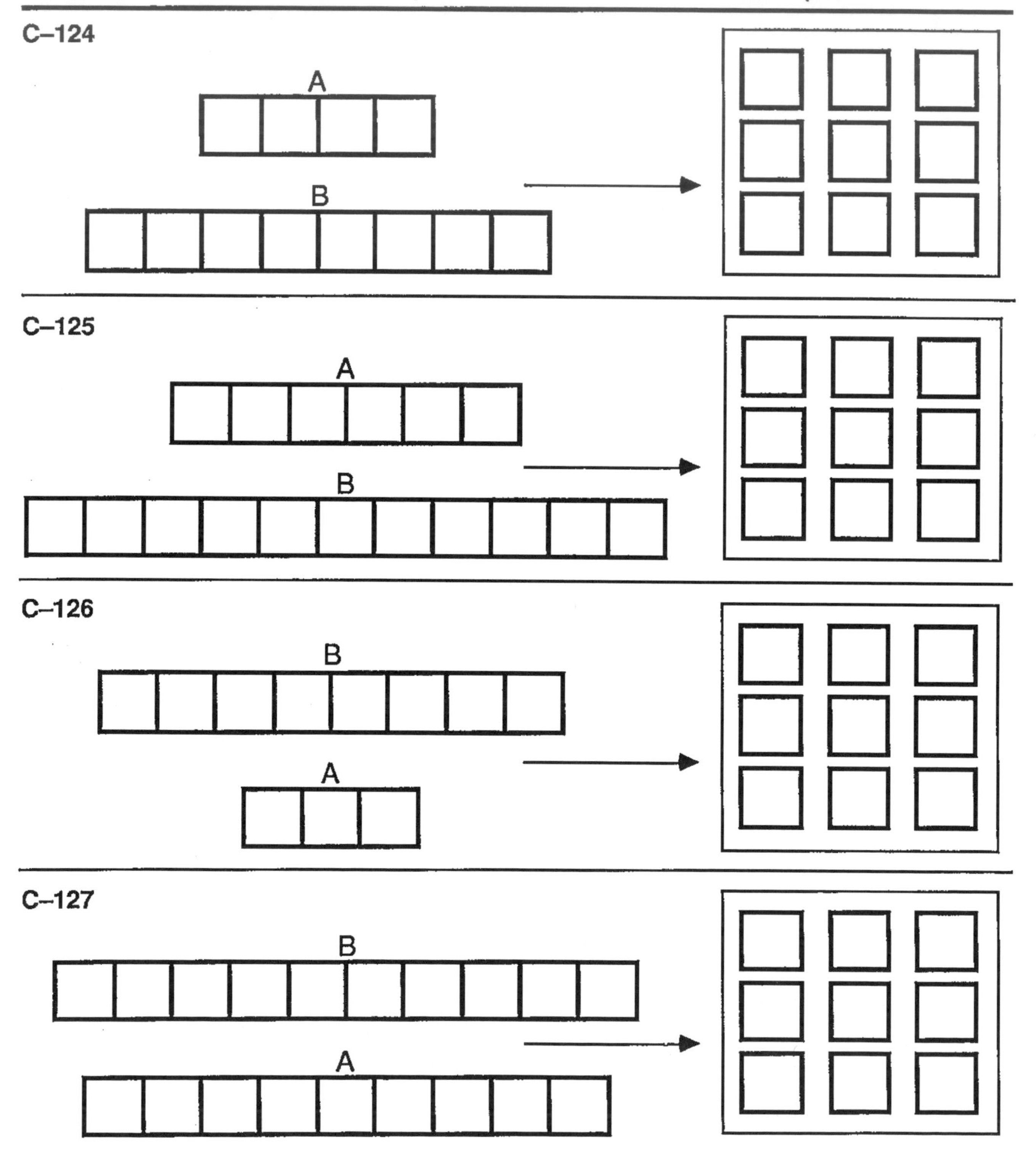

MAKING LENGTHS EQUAL

Compare the lengths of A and B.
Write the number of squares in B in the first box.
Write the number of squares in A in the second box.
Write the number of squares that are needed to make A equal to B in the third box.

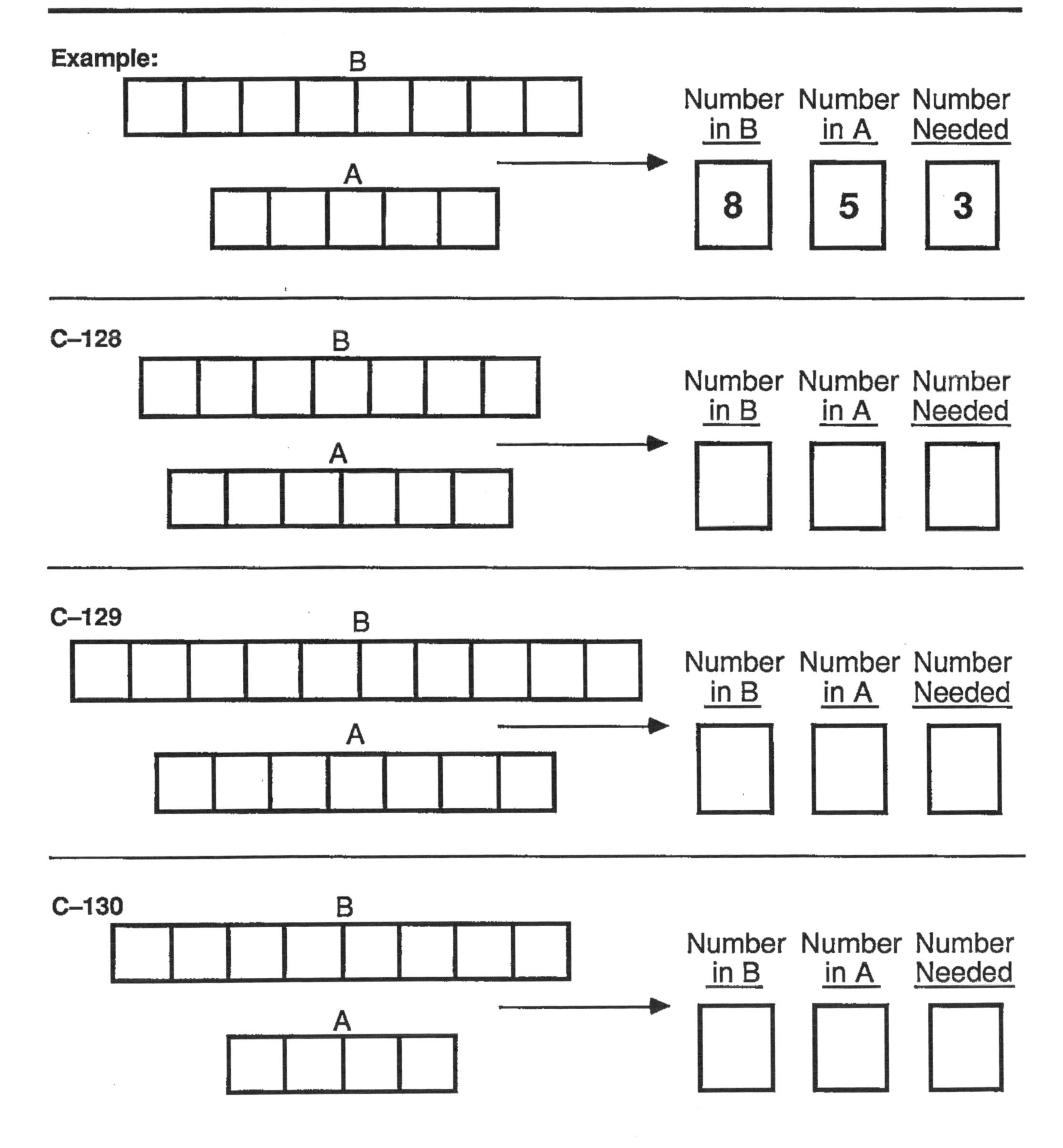

MAKING FIGURES EQUAL

Compare figures A and B.
Write the number of squares in figure B in the first box.
Write the number of squares in figure A in the second box.
Write the number of squares that are needed to make A equal to B in the third box.

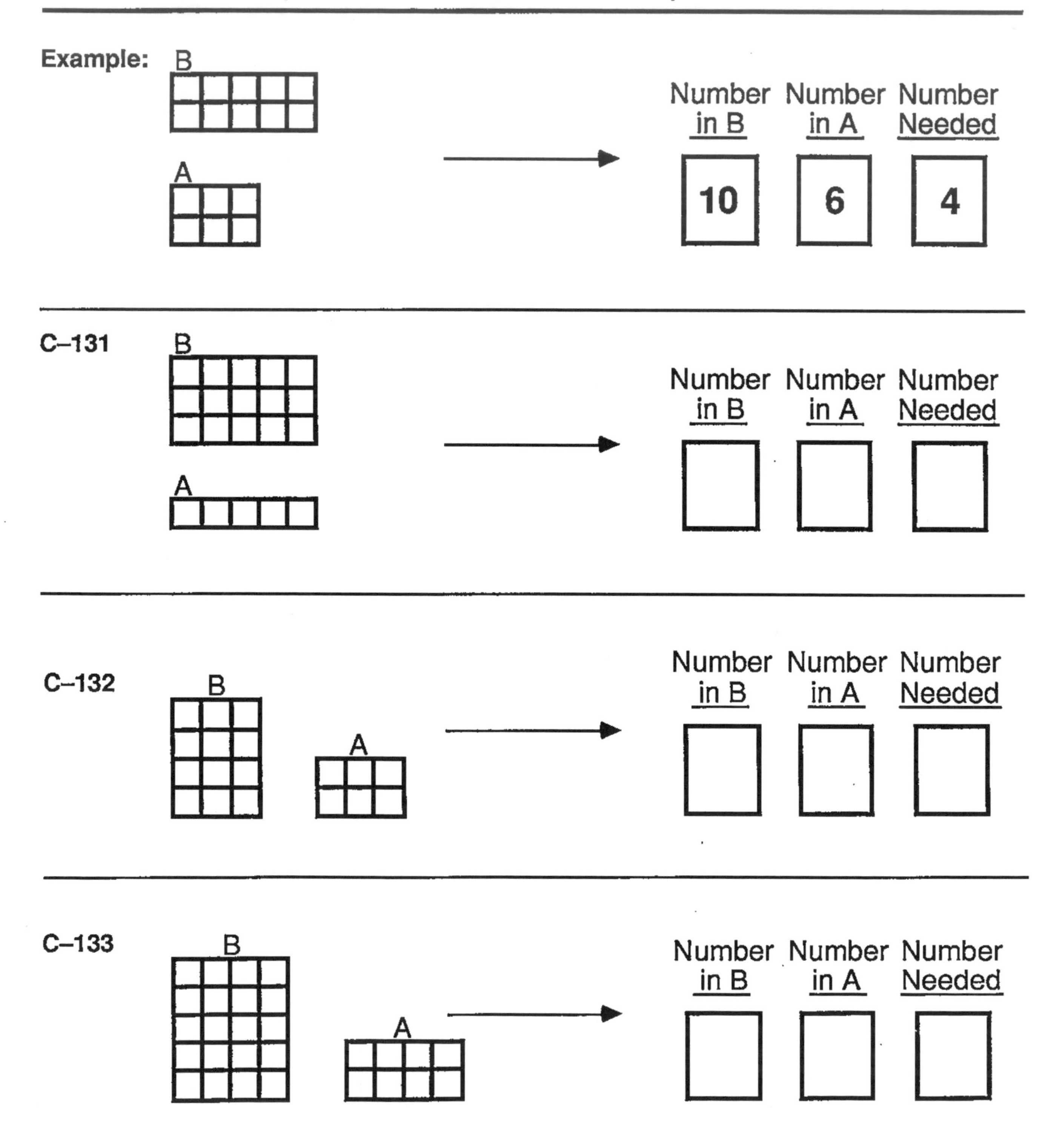

MISSING ADDENDS

Pick numbers from the set below to complete the sums.
You may need to use some numbers more than once.

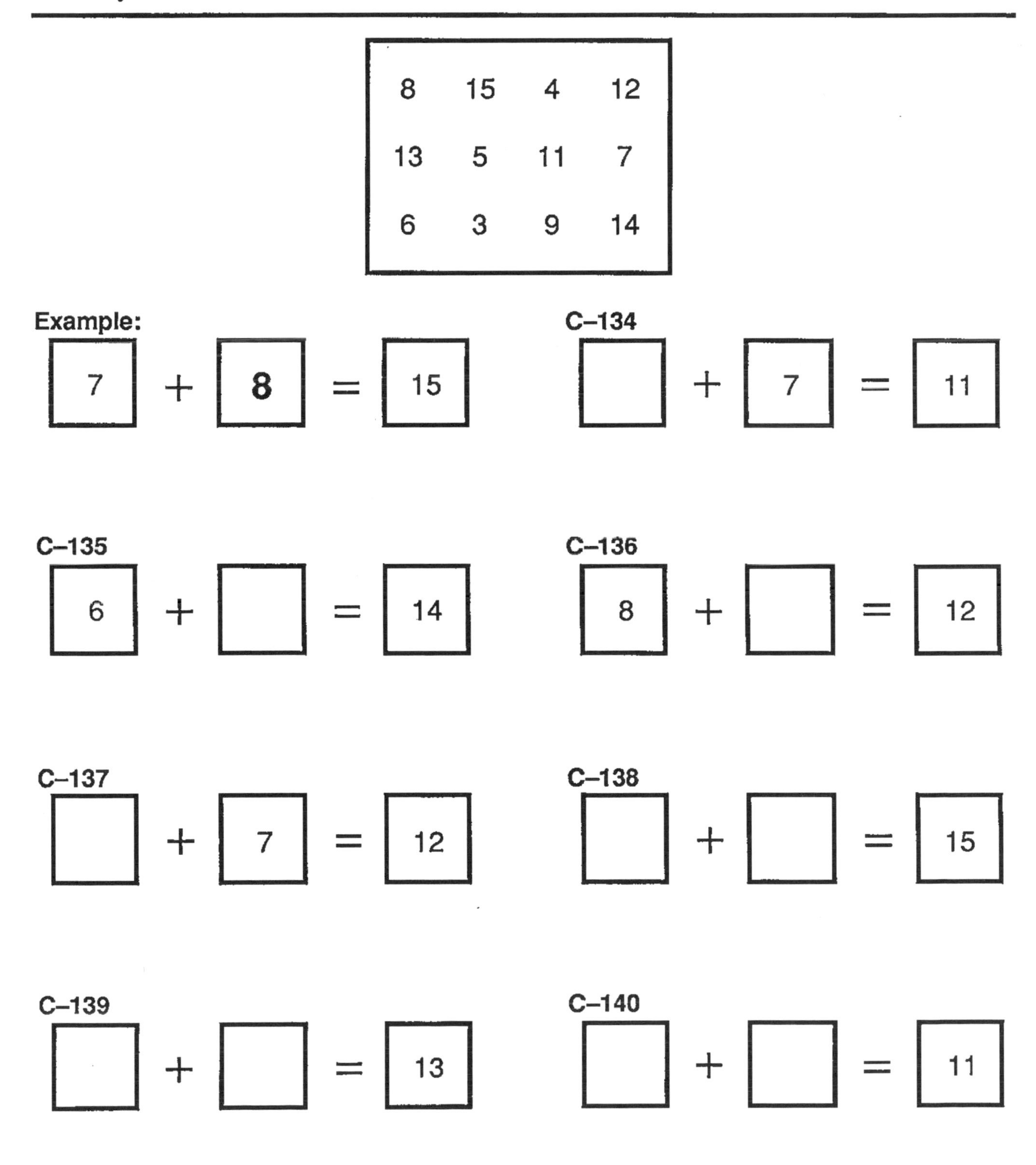

MISSING ADDENDS

Write the correct number in the box.

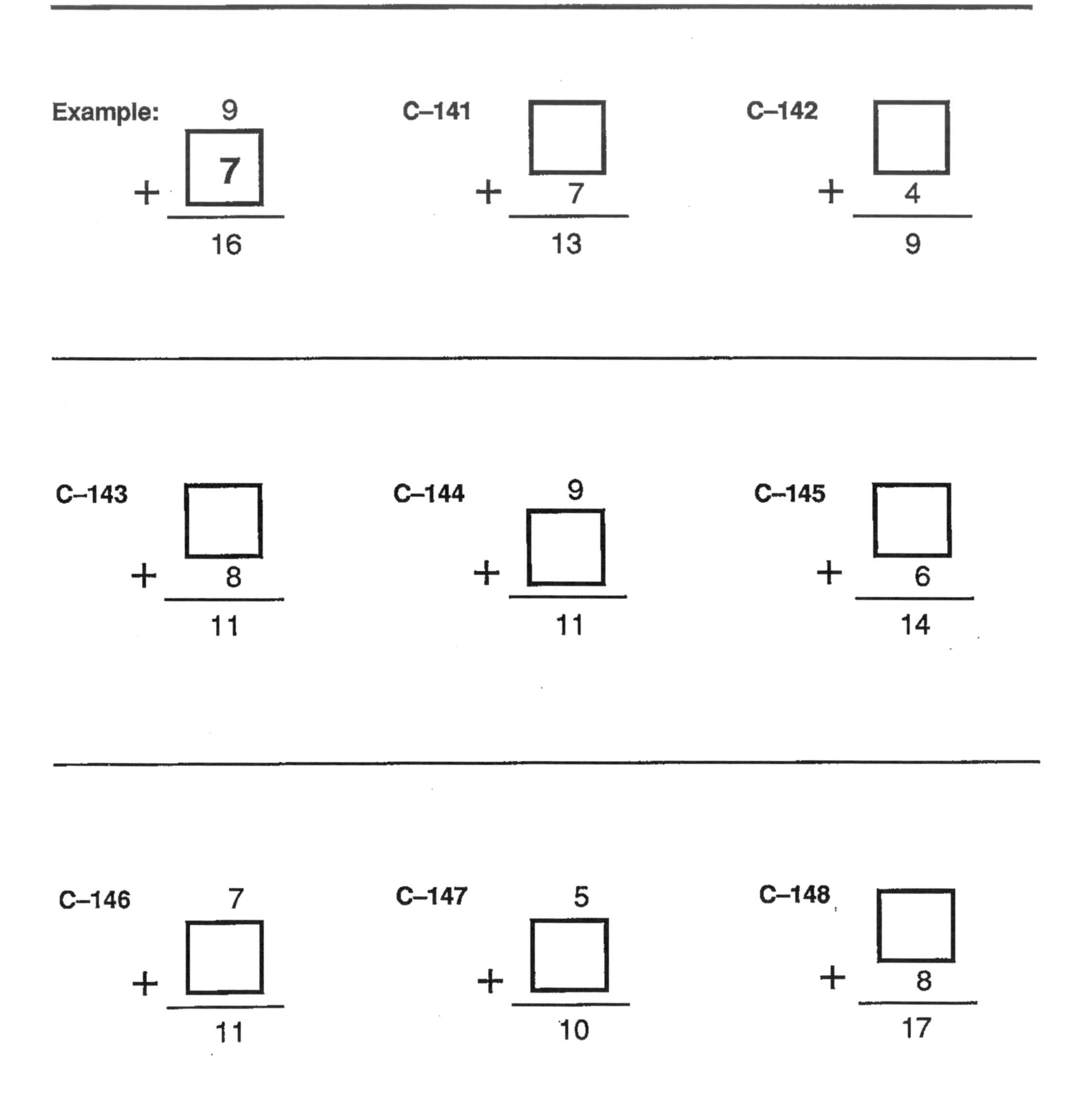

COMPLETING DIFFERENCES

Pick numbers from the set below to complete the differences.
You may need to use some numbers more than once.

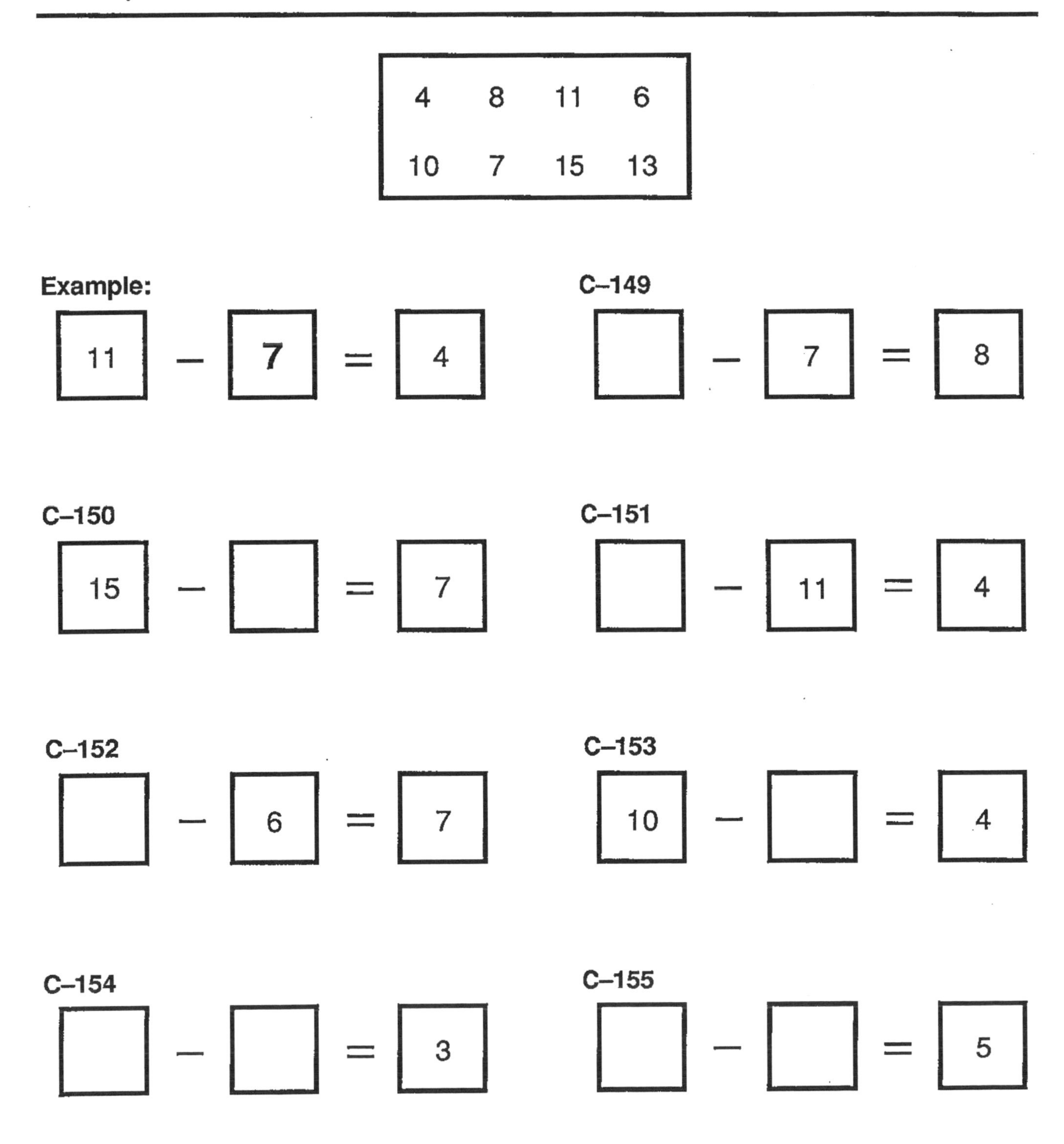

COMPLETING DIFFERENCES

Write the correct number in the box.

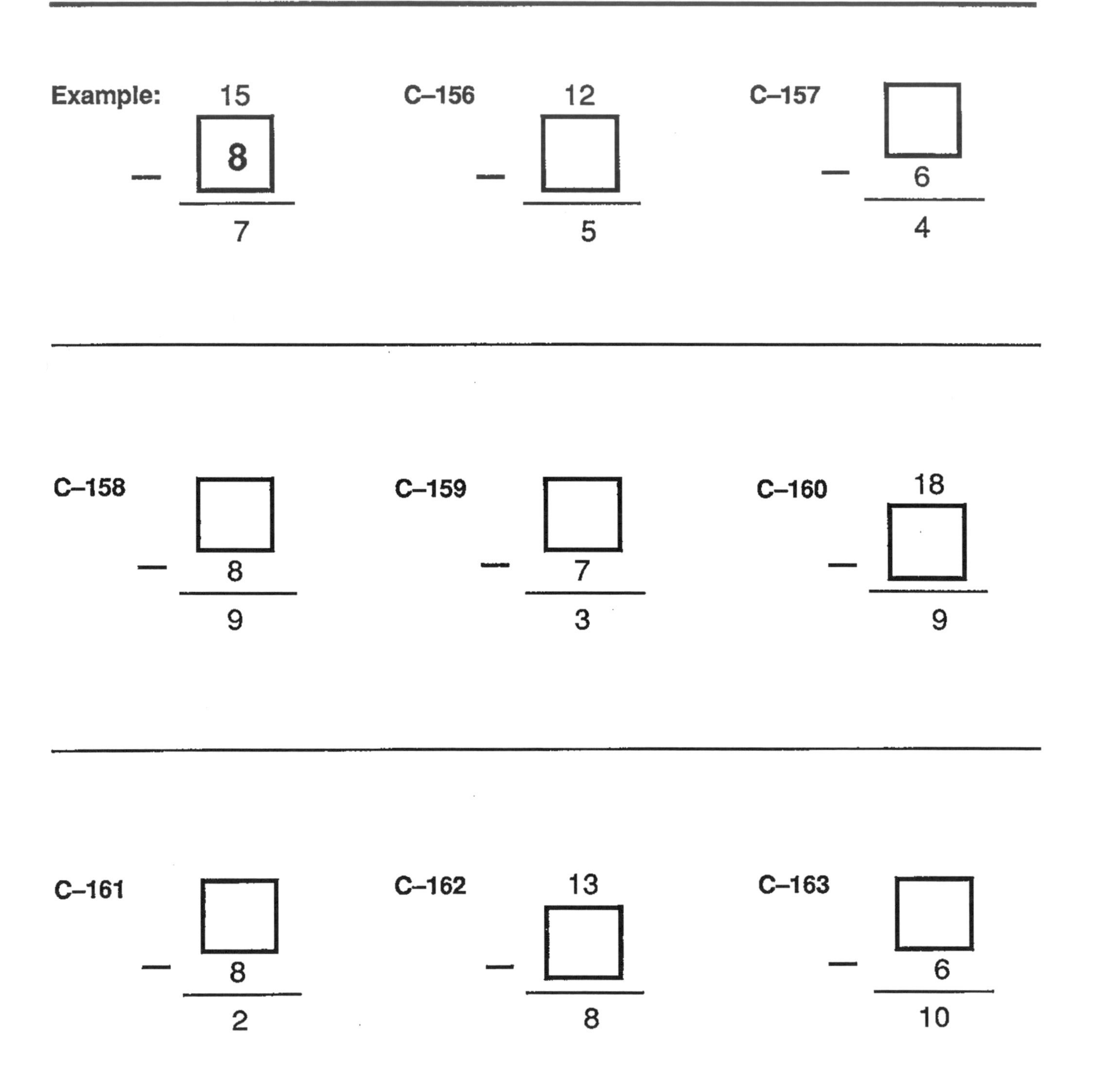

DIFFERENCES THAT ARE EQUAL

Circle all the problems in each row whose differences equal the first number in that row. There may be more than one correct answer.

Example:	6	(12 – 6)	13 – 8	(11 – 5)	14 – 7
C–164	5	13 – 6	12 – 7	13 – 7	15 – 8
C–165	8	15 – 8	12 – 4	16 – 8	11 – 4
C–166	3	12 – 9	8 – 4	9 – 5	7 – 4
C–167	7	9 – 7	12 – 6	15 – 8	16 – 8
C–168	5	14 – 9	15 – 7	9 – 3	13 – 9
C–169	6	15 – 9	9 – 4	13 – 6	12 – 6
C–170	4	12 – 9	13 – 9	7 – 2	13 – 8

COMPARING DIFFERENCES

Find the difference of each subtraction problem below.
Write all the problems whose differences are less than 10 in the box on the left.
Write all the problems whose differences are more than 10 in the box on the right.

15 – 7	18 – 6	13 – 7	16 – 9
16 – 3	17 – 6	14 – 9	15 – 3
18 – 9	16 – 2	18 – 4	14 – 7
17 – 3	13 – 5	17 – 2	12 – 5

C–171 Less than 10 (<)

Example:
15 – 7

C–172 Greater than 10 (>)

C–173 Circle the problem with the largest difference in each box.

C–174 Place an X on the problem with the smallest difference in each box.

C–175 Which problem has the largest difference that is less than 10? ____________

C–176 Which problem has the smallest difference that is more than 10? ____________

EQUAL SETS

Match the sets that have the same amount of money.

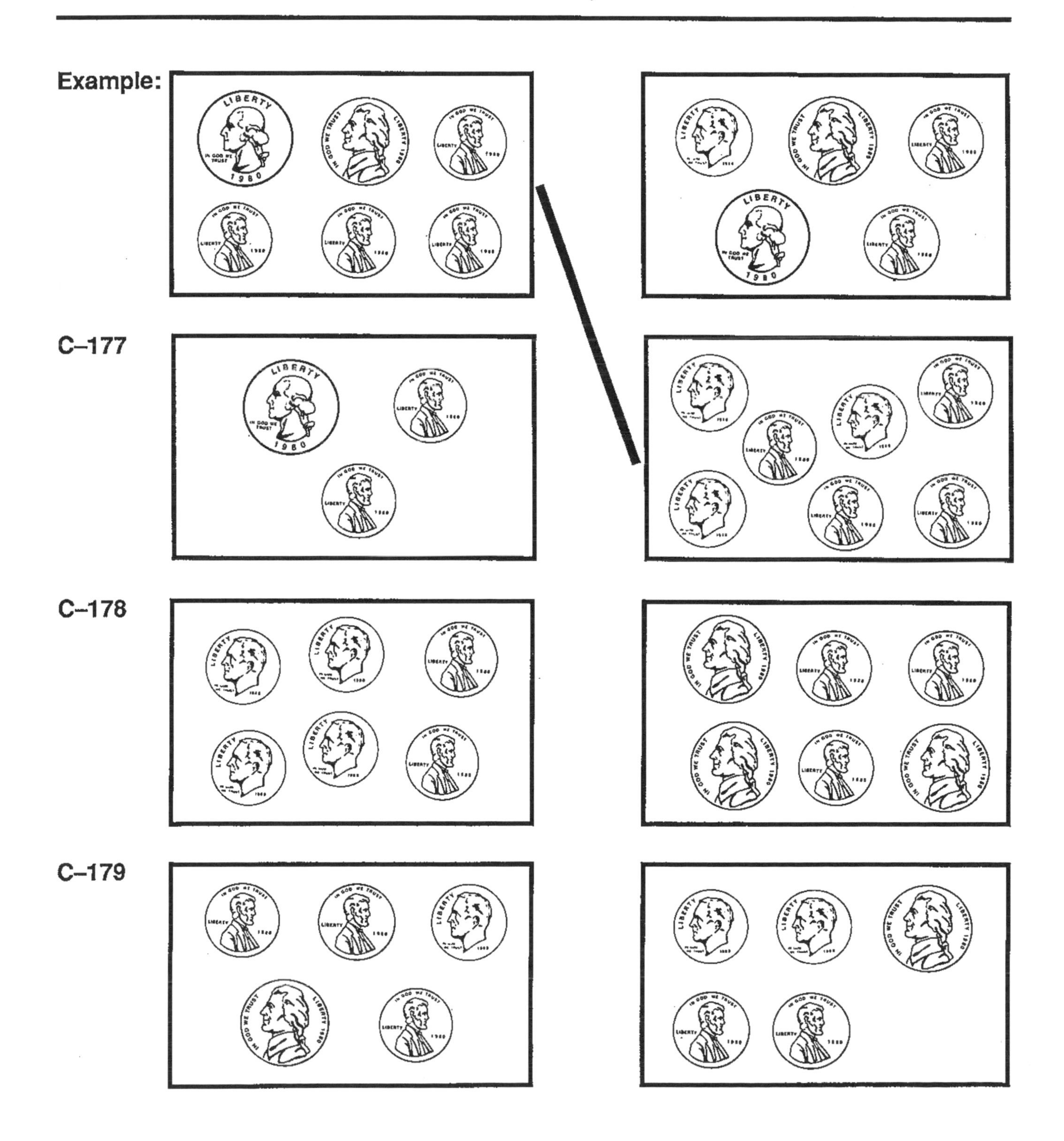

EQUAL SETS

Match the sets that have the same amount of money.

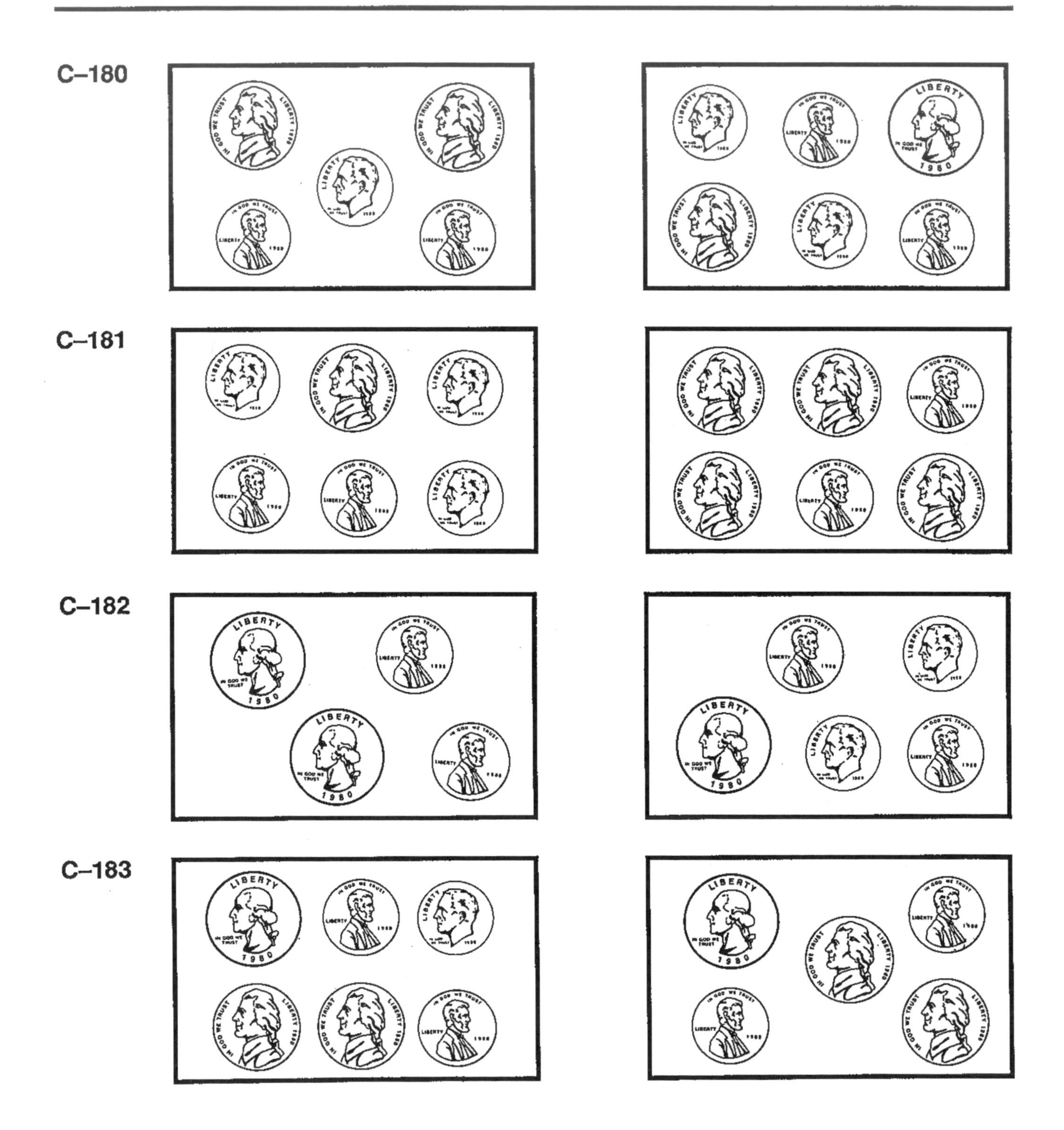

EQUAL SETS

Circle the number that shows the amount of money in the set.

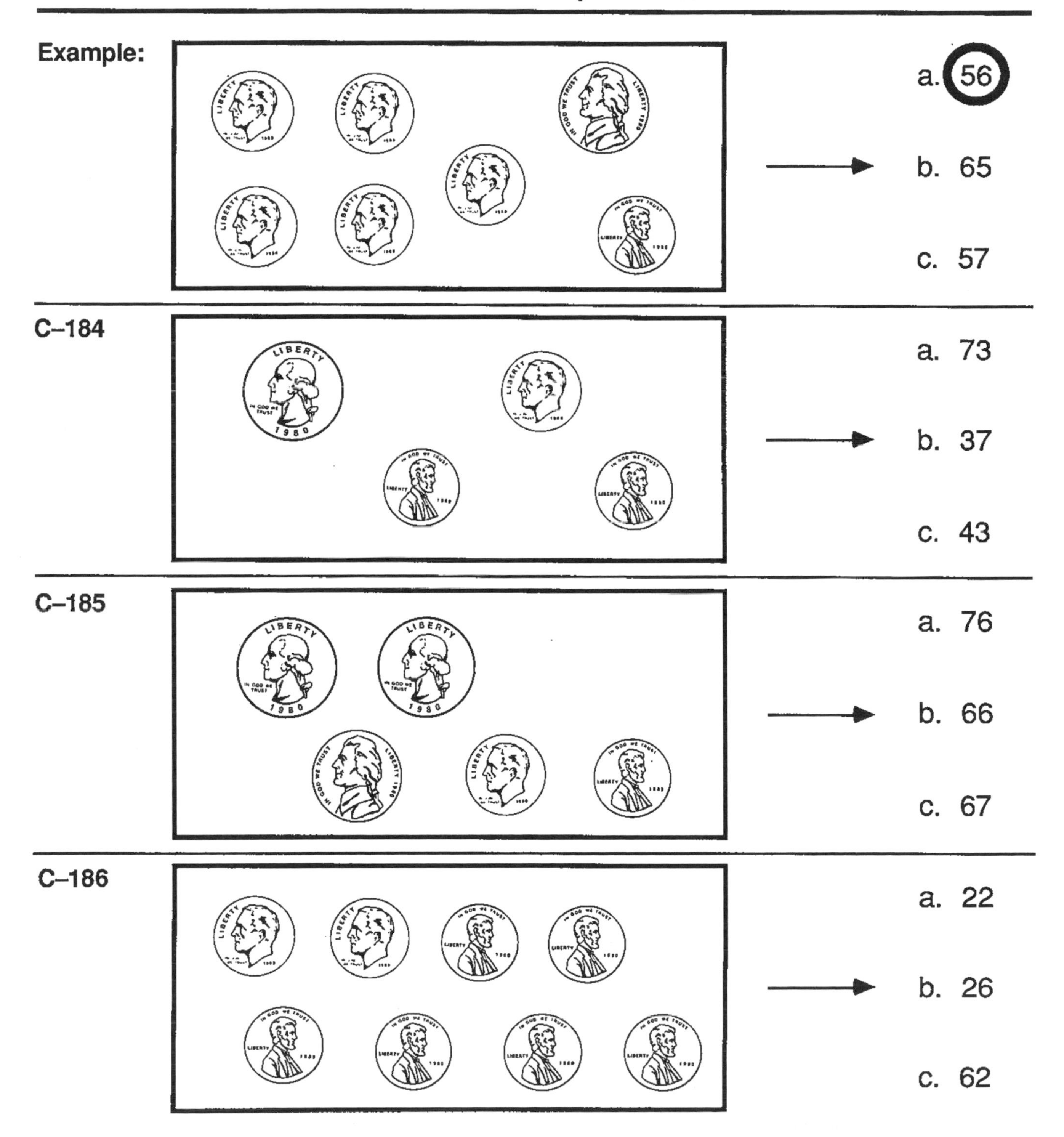

Example: a. 56 (circled) b. 65 c. 57

C–184 a. 73 b. 37 c. 43

C–185 a. 76 b. 66 c. 67

C–186 a. 22 b. 26 c. 62

EQUAL SETS

Circle the number that shows the amount of money in the set.

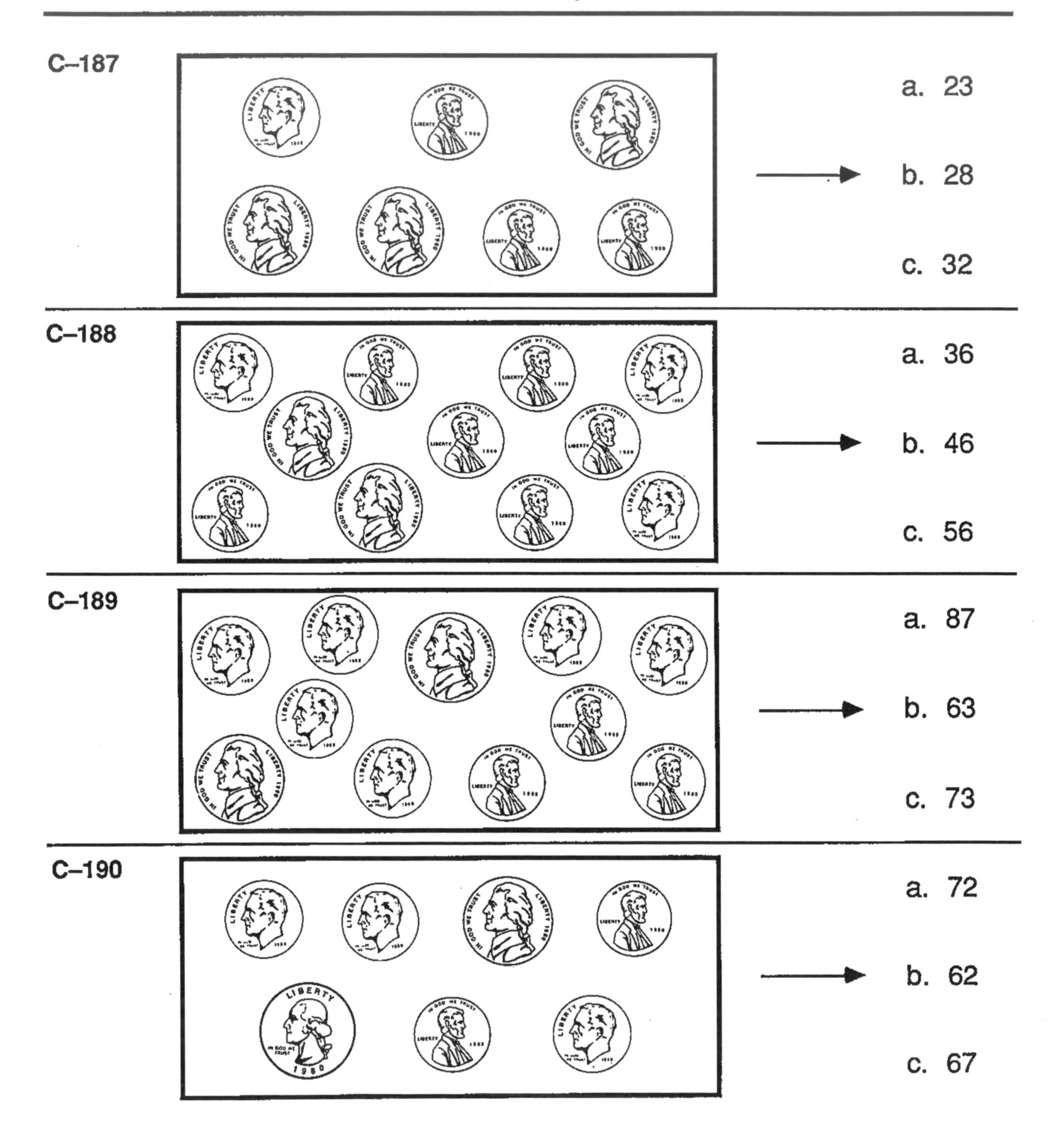

COUNTING ARRAYS

Write the number of cubes in each row.
Write the total number of cubes in the circle.

Example: □ □ □ □ → 4
□ □ □ □ → 4
(8)

C–191 □ □ □ □ → ____
□ □ □ □ → ____
□ □ □ □ → ____
□ □ □ □ → ____
◯

C–192 □ □ □ □ → ____
□ □ □ □ → ____
□ □ □ □ → ____
□ □ □ □ → ____
□ □ □ □ → ____
◯

C–193 □ □ □ □ → ____
□ □ □ □ → ____
□ □ □ □ → ____
◯

COUNTING ARRAYS

Write the number of cubes in each row.
Write the total number of cubes in the circle.

C–194

□□□□□□ → ____

□□□□□□ → ____

◯

C–195

□□□□□□ → ____

□□□□□□ → ____

□□□□□□ → ____

□□□□□□ → ____

◯

C–196

□□□□□□ → ____

□□□□□□ → ____

□□□□□□ → ____

□□□□□□ → ____

□□□□□□ → ____

◯

C–197

□□□□□□ → ____

□□□□□□ → ____

□□□□□□ → ____

◯

COUNTING ARRAYS

For each set write the number of rows in the first box.
Write the number of cubes in each row in the second box.
Write the total number of cubes in the third box.

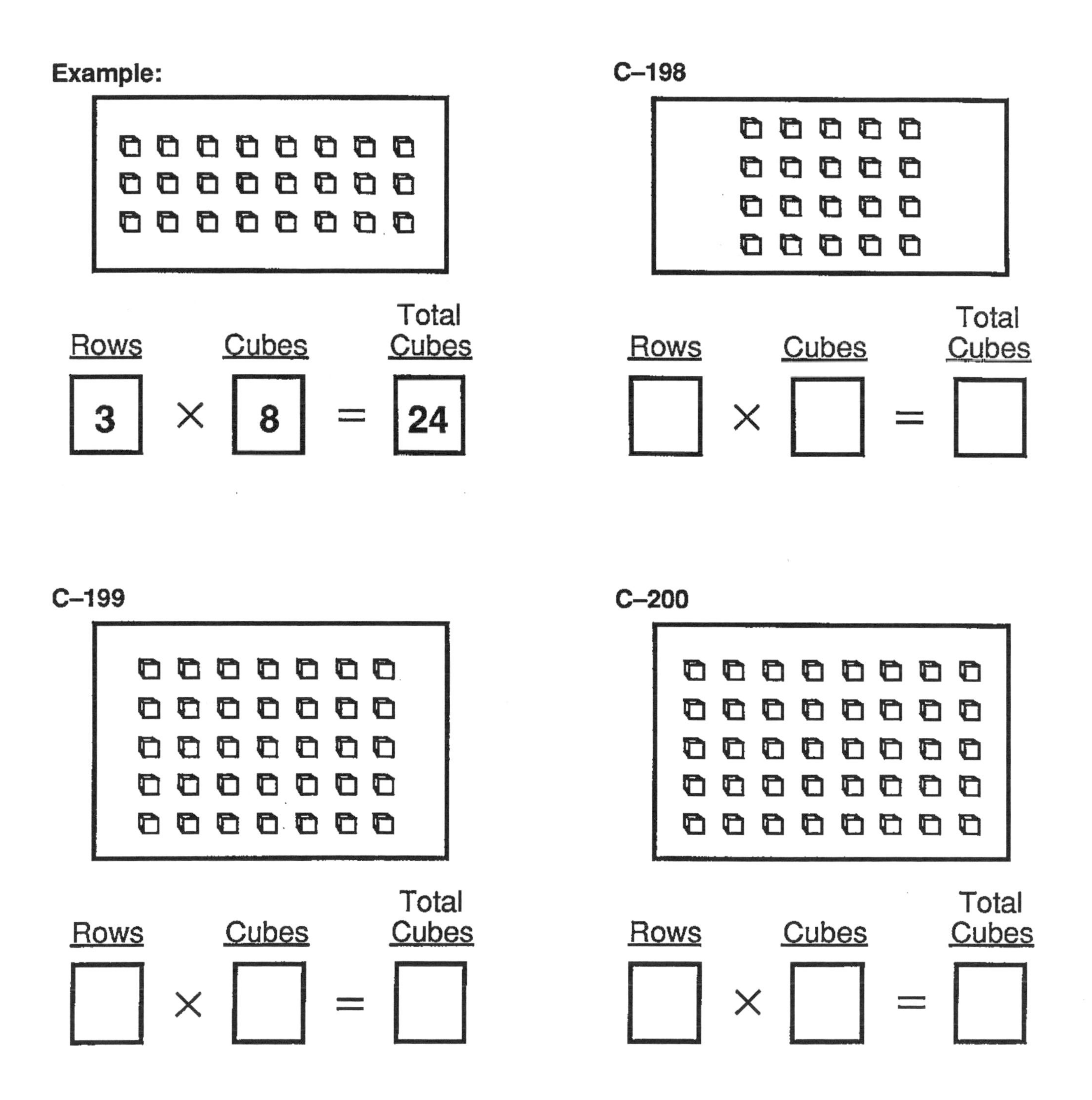

COUNTING ARRAYS

In each set write the number of rows in the first box.
Write the number of cubes in each row in the second box.
Write the total number of cubes in the third box.

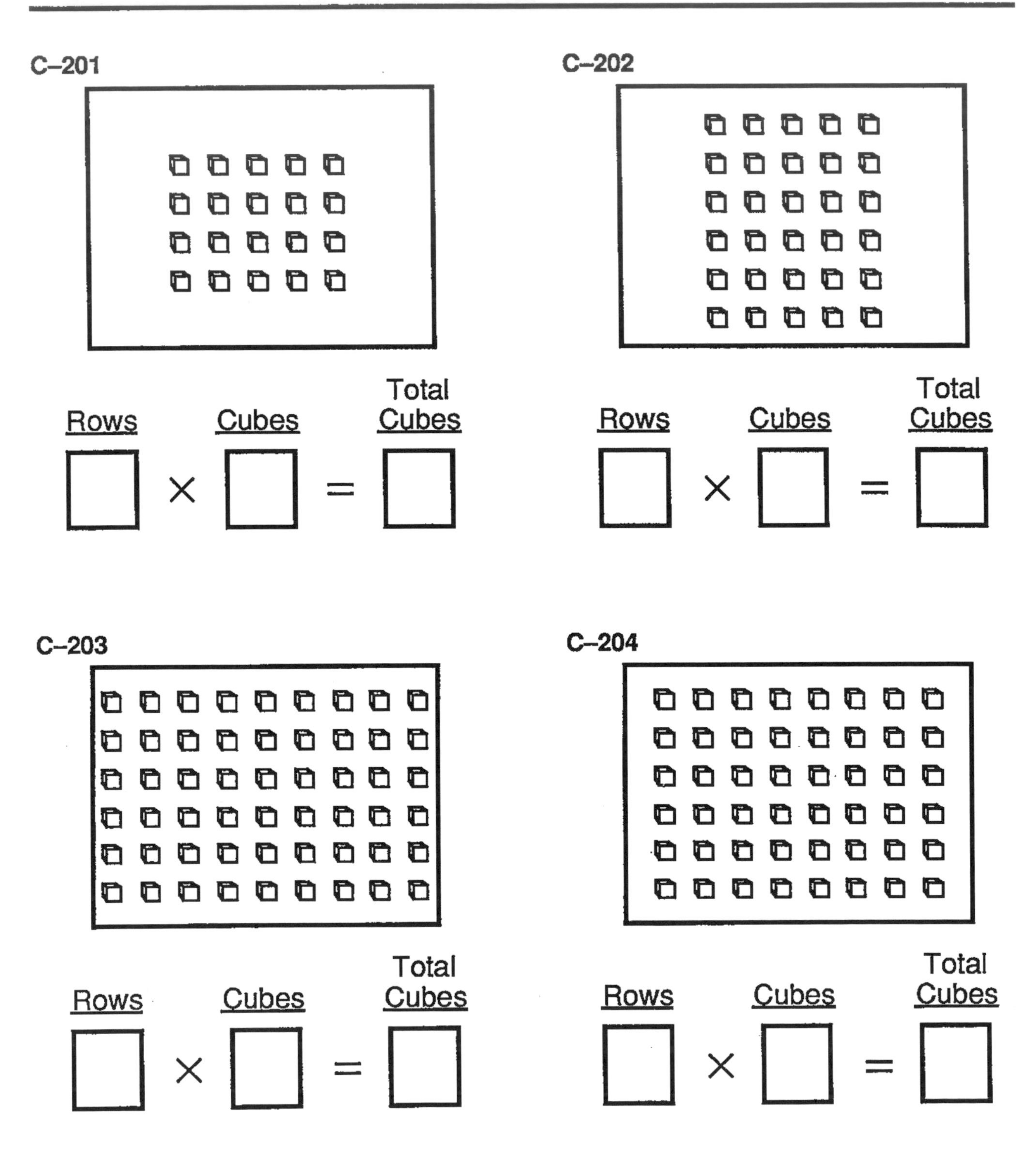

PRODUCTS THAT ARE EQUAL

Circle all the problems in each row whose products equal the first number in that row. There may be more than one correct answer.

Example:	48	7×7	(6×8)	8×7	5×8
C–205	12	4×3	2×5	4×4	2×6
C–206	45	8×5	7×7	5×9	6×8
C–207	36	4×8	9×4	5×6	6×6
C–208	16	8×2	3×4	4×4	5×3
C–209	30	4×8	7×4	5×6	6×6
C–210	18	6×3	2×9	4×4	3×7
C–211	24	4×5	6×4	3×8	5×5

COMPARING PRODUCTS

Find the product of each multiplication problem below.
Write all the problems whose products are less than 40 in the box on the left.
Write all the problems whose products are more than 40 in the box on the right.

2×8	6×3	7×7	9×3
7×8	8×9	4×8	6×7
3×5	8×8	9×9	5×5
7×9	4×4	4×9	6×9

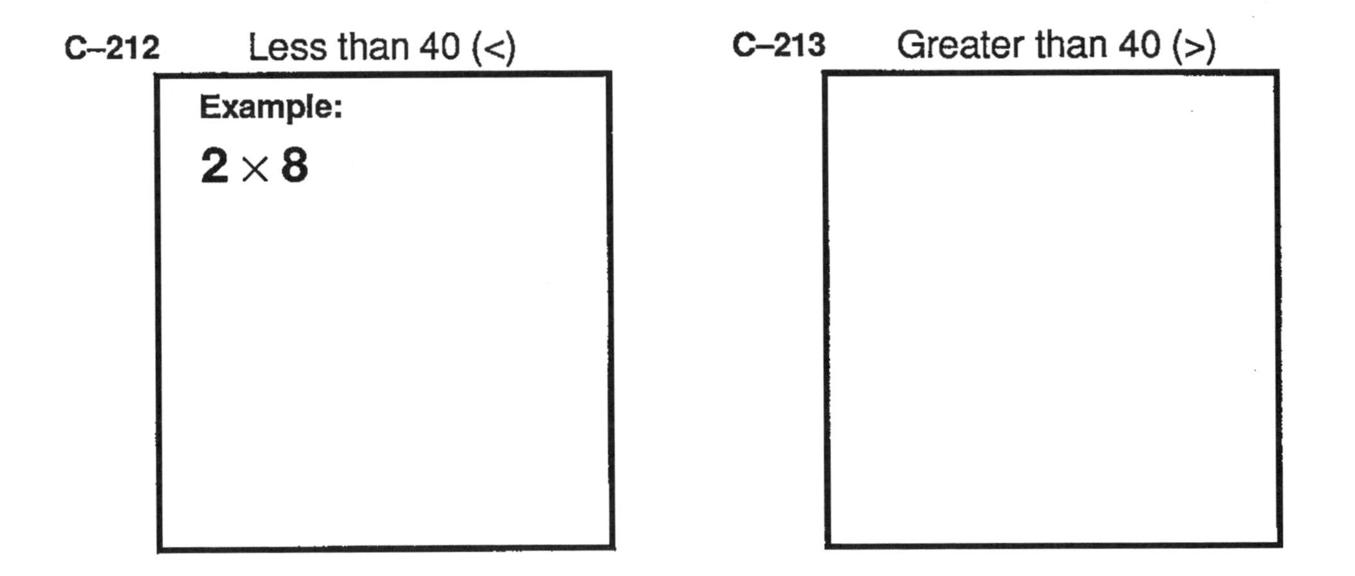

C–214 Circle the problem with the largest product in each box.

C–215 Place an X on the problem with the smallest product in each box.

C–216 Which problem has the largest product that is less than 40? ________

C–217 Which problem has the smallest product that is more than 40? ________

MISSING FACTORS

Write the correct number in the box.

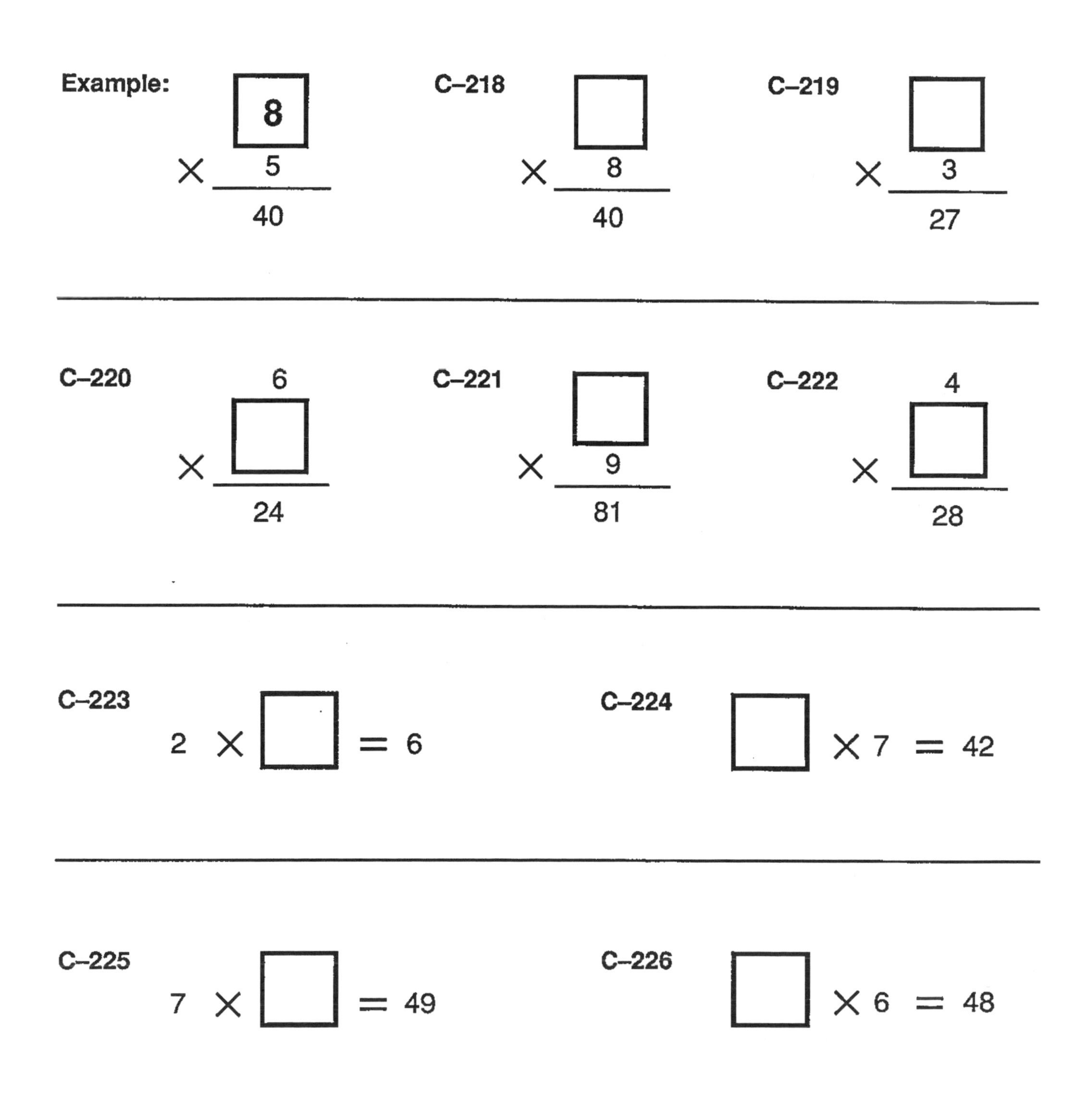

MISSING FACTORS

Write the correct numbers in the boxes.

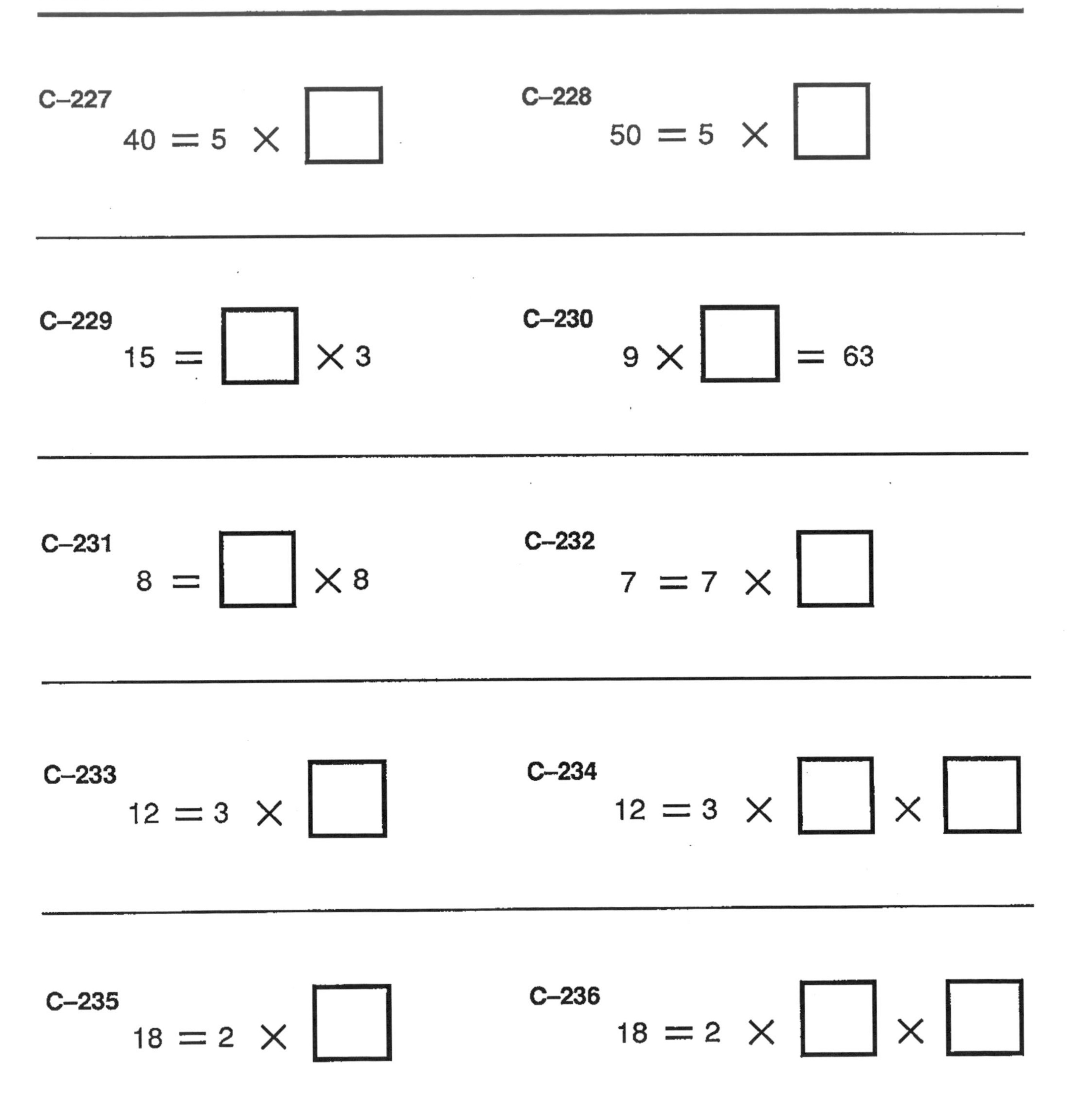

USING OPERATIONS

Choose two different numbers from the set below that will give you…

2	6	7	5
8	3	9	4

Example: the largest sum.

C–237 the smallest sum.

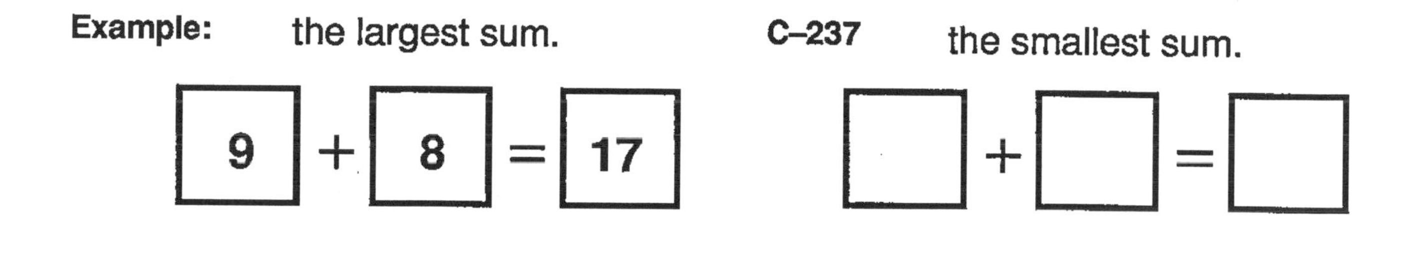

C–238 the largest difference.

C–239 the smallest difference.

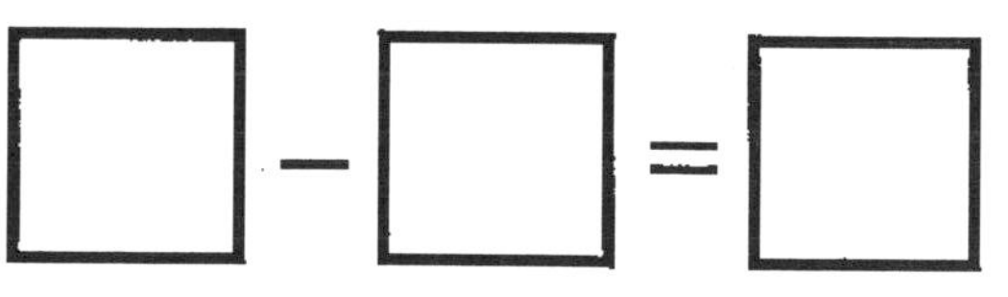

C–240 the largest product.

C–241 the smallest product.

USING OPERATIONS

Choose two different numbers from the set below that will give you…

2	4	7	5
6	8	10	3

C–242 the largest sum.

C–243 the smallest sum.

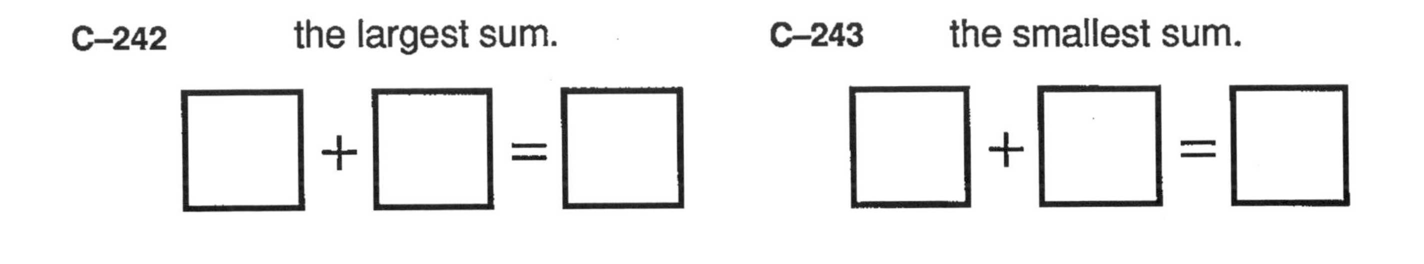

C–244 the largest difference.

C–245 the smallest difference.

C–246 the largest product.

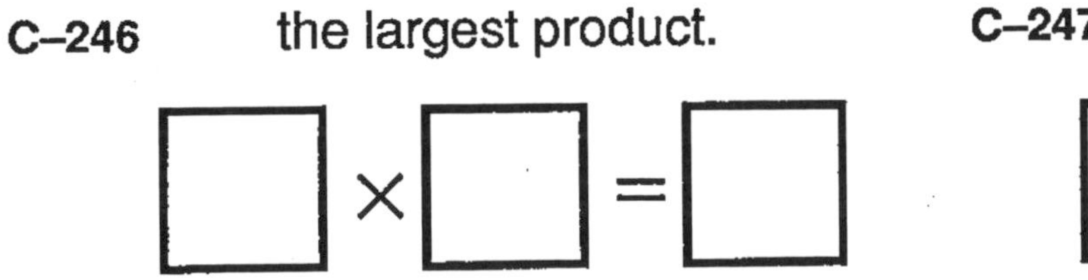

C–247 the smallest product.

WHICH OPERATION DO YOU USE?

Circle the calculation that solves each problem.

Example:

The coach has 9 cans of tennis balls.
Each can holds 3 tennis balls.
How many tennis balls does the coach have?

$9 + 3$	$9 - 3$
9×3 (circled)	$9 \div 3$

C–248

There are 18 people in class but only 9 chairs.
The teacher sends for enough chairs so that everyone can be seated.
How many chairs do they need?

$18 + 9$	$18 - 9$
18×9	$18 \div 9$

C–249

There are 12 eggs in a carton.
You use 4 to make scrambled eggs.
How many are left in the carton?

$12 + 4$	$12 - 4$
12×4	$12 \div 4$

C–250

Four quarters equals one dollar.
John has 20 quarters.
How many dollars does John have?

$20 + 4$	$20 - 4$
20×4	$20 \div 4$

C–251

Eric has 6 dollars.
He earns 3 more dollars.
How many dollars does he have?

$6 + 3$	$6 - 3$
6×3	$6 \div 3$

WHICH OPERATION DO YOU USE?

Circle the calculation that solves each problem.

C–252 A family drove 2 miles to town.
On the way back they took a longer
route which was 4 miles.
How many miles more was the longer route?

$4 + 2$	$4 - 2$
4×2	$4 \div 2$

C–253 Our team played in two play-off games.
We scored 12 points in the first game and
6 points in the second game.
What was the total number of points we scored?

$12 + 6$	$12 - 6$
12×6	$12 \div 6$

C–254 A penny roll holds 50 pennies.
Tim has 3 penny rolls.
How many pennies does Tim have?

$50 + 3$	$50 - 3$
50×3	$50 \div 3$

C–255 A large pizza is cut into 12 pieces.
Ann wants to divide it evenly among
herself and 3 friends.
How many pieces should each person get?

$12 + 3$	$12 - 3$
$12 + 4$	$12 - 4$
12×3	$12 \div 3$
12×4	$12 \div 4$

C–256 Amy and 4 of her friends sold raffle tickets.
Each sold 10 tickets.
How many did they sell all together?

$4 + 10$	$10 - 4$
$5 + 10$	$10 - 5$
4×10	$10 \div 4$
5×10	$10 \div 5$

ROUNDING TO 10

Circle the number nearest in size to the number in the box.

	Box					
Example:	8	→	(10)	40	30	20
C–257	12	→	30	20	40	10
C–258	18	→	20	30	10	0
C–259	24	→	10	20	40	30
C–260	48	→	30	40	50	60
C–261	76	→	70	60	80	50
C–262	14	→	10	30	20	40
C–263	34	→	40	20	30	50

ROUNDING TO 10 AND 100

Round each number in the top set to the nearest 10.
Round each number in the bottom set to the nearest 100.

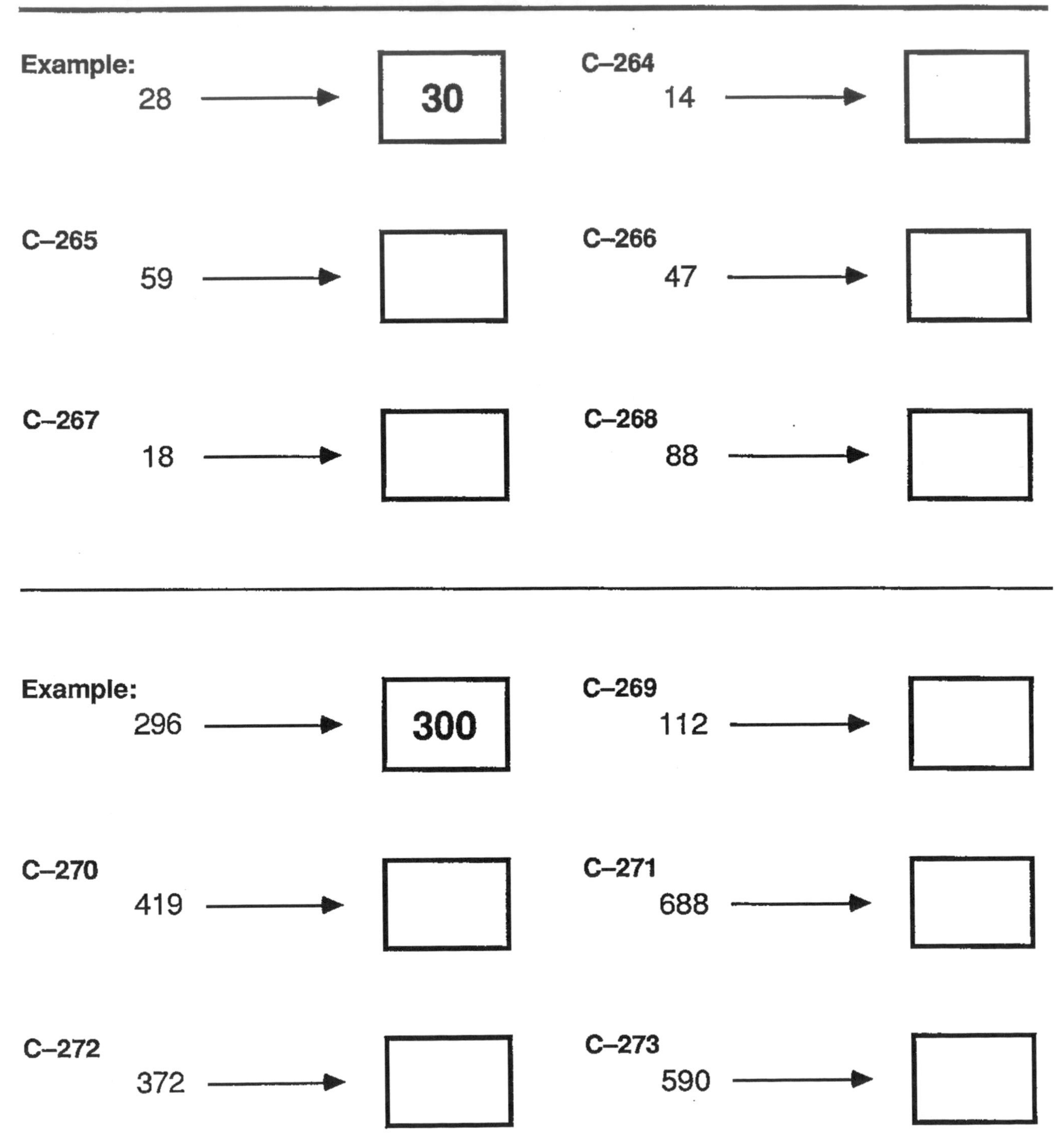

ROUNDING

Look at the numbers in the box.
Put all the numbers closer to 40 than 50 in the box on the left.
Put all the numbers closer to 50 than 40 in the box on the right.

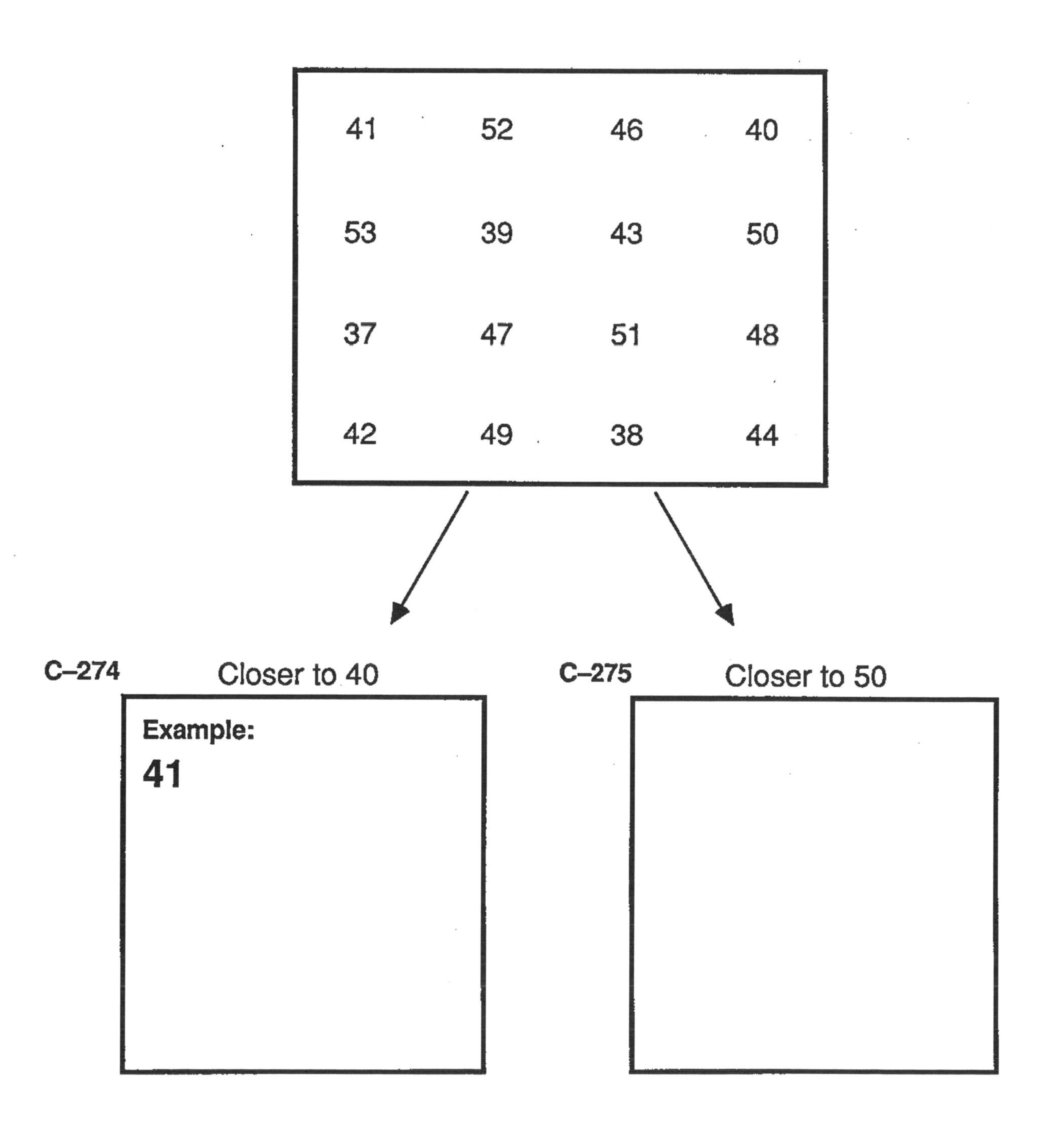

ROUNDING

Look at the addition problems in the box.
Put all the problems whose sums are closer to 10 than 20 in the box on the left.
Put all the problems whose sums are closer to 20 than 10 in the box on the right.

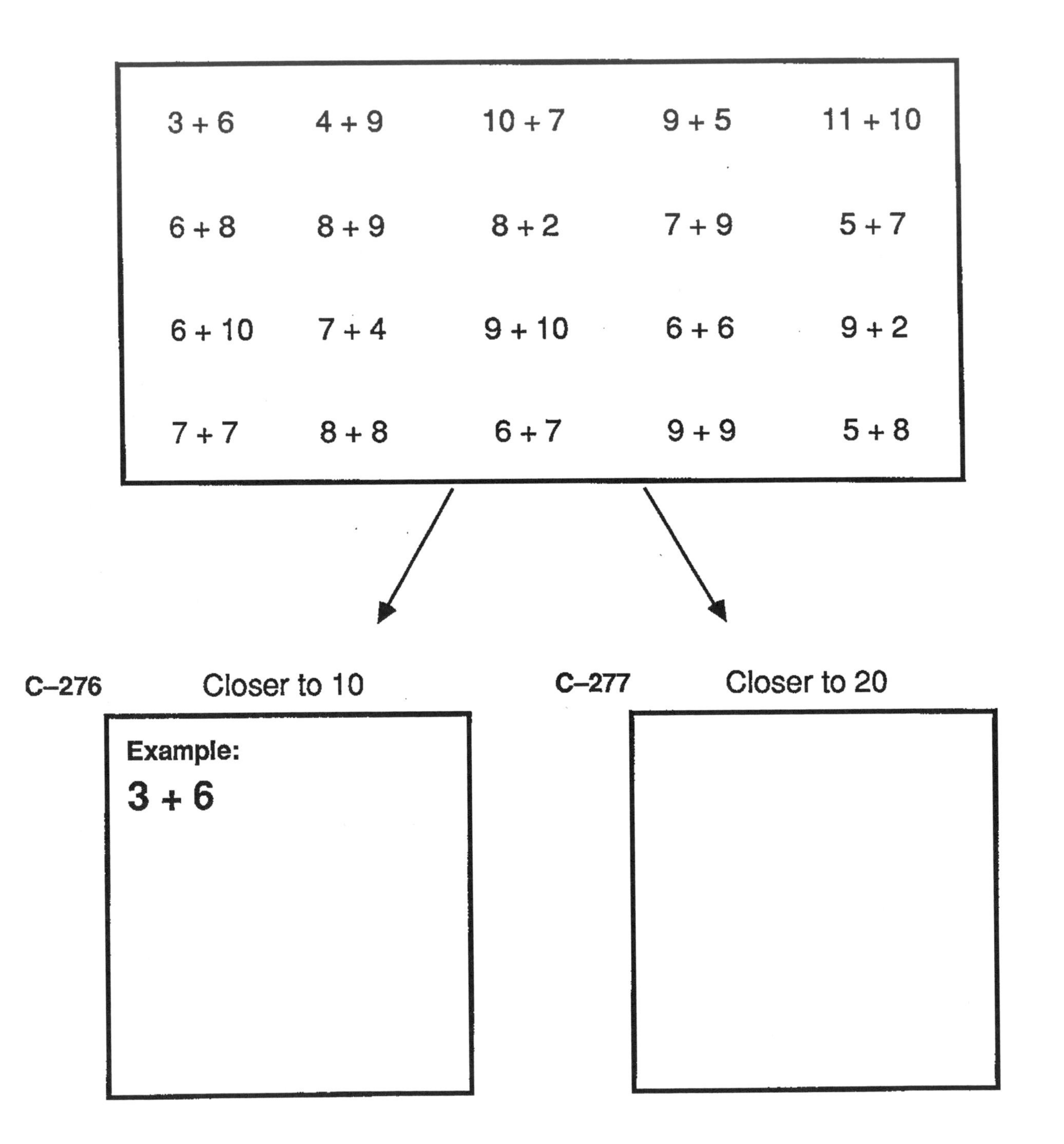

MULTIPLYING BY 10 AND 100

Write the answers in the boxes.

Example:

$5 \times 3 =$ **15**

$5 \times 30 =$ **150**

C–278

$2 \times 8 =$ ☐

$20 \times 8 =$ ☐

C–279

$9 \times 4 =$ ☐

$9 \times 40 =$ ☐

C–280

$6 \times 5 =$ ☐

$6 \times 50 =$ ☐

C–281

$4 \times 2 =$ ☐

$4 \times 200 =$ ☐

C–282

$4 \times 7 =$ ☐

$400 \times 7 =$ ☐

C–283

$3 \times 300 =$ ☐

C–284

$8 \times 90 =$ ☐

C–285

$700 \times 5 =$ ☐

C–286

$6 \times 800 =$ ☐

ESTIMATING PRODUCTS

Round the underlined number to the nearest 10.
Write the answer in the circle.
Multiply the rounded answer by the number in the dotted box.
Write the product in the box.

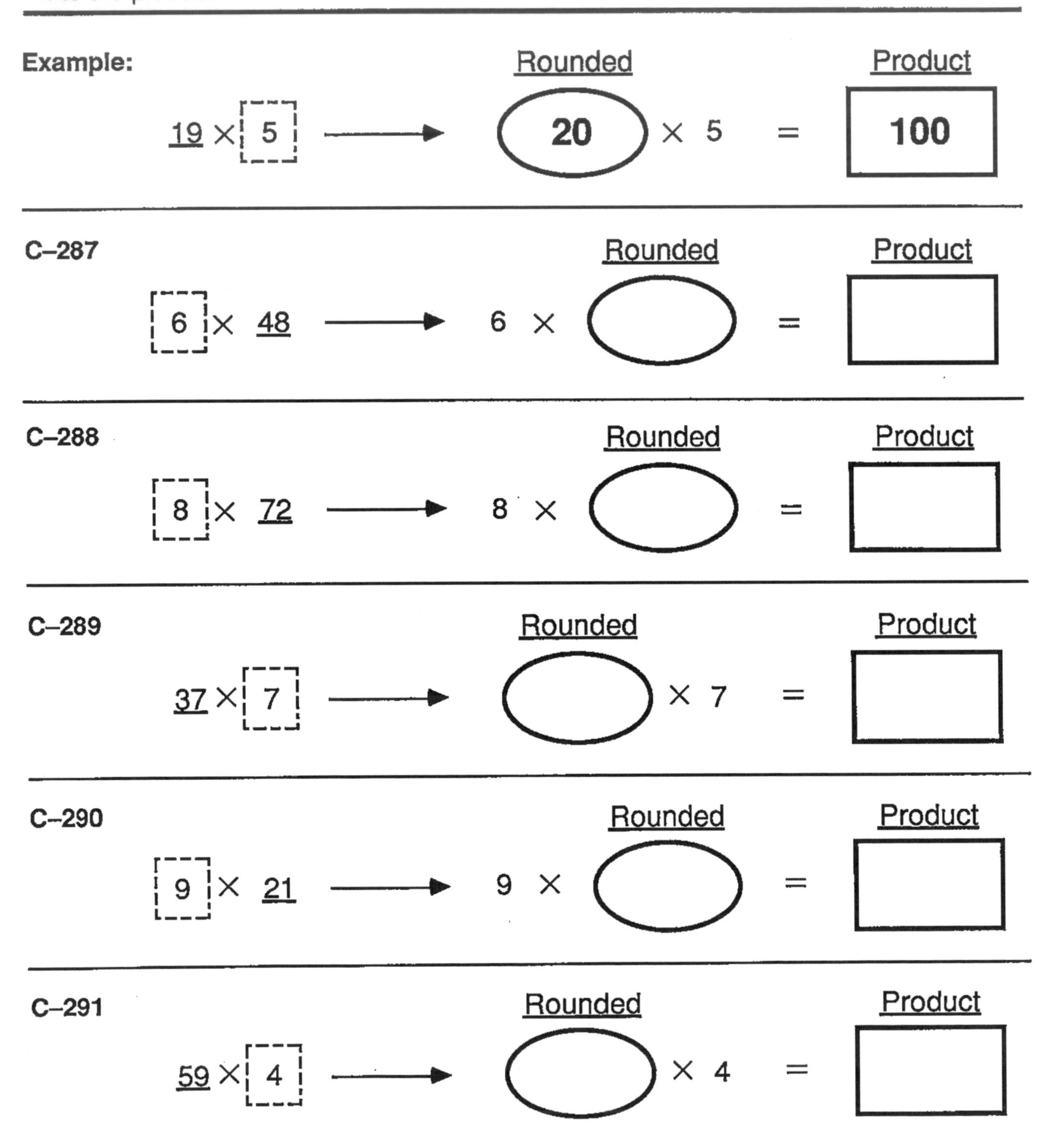

COMPARING LENGTHS

Squares are joined together to make two rods.
Circle the number that tells how many squares must be added to make the two equal.

Example:

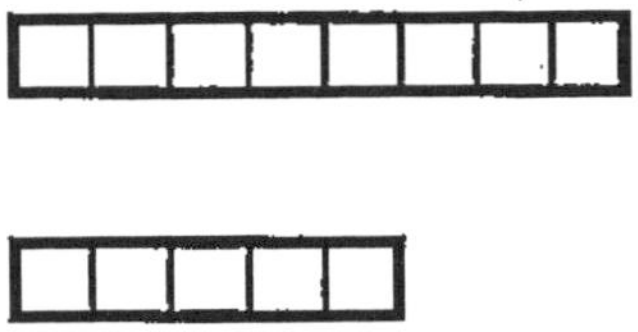

a. 6
b. 3
c. 5

D–1

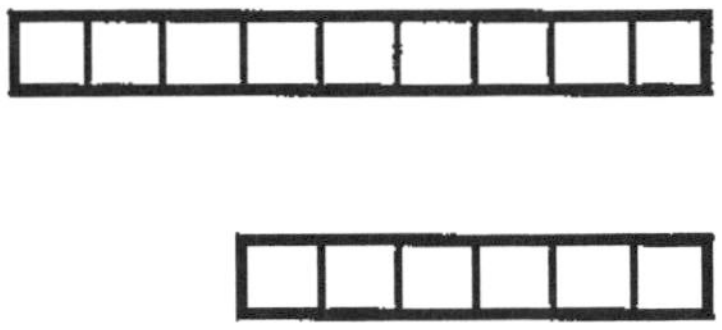

a. 4
b. 3
c. 6

D–2

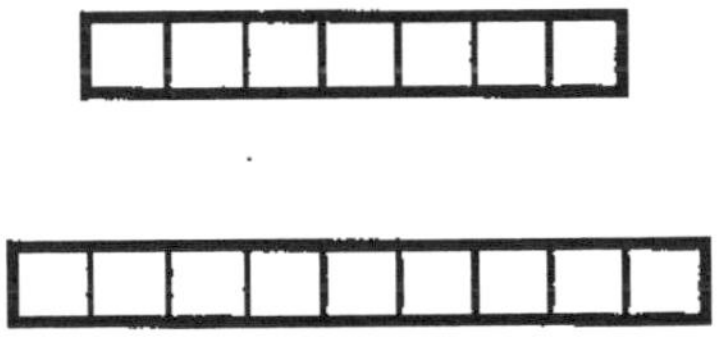

a. 6
b. 3
c. 2

D–3

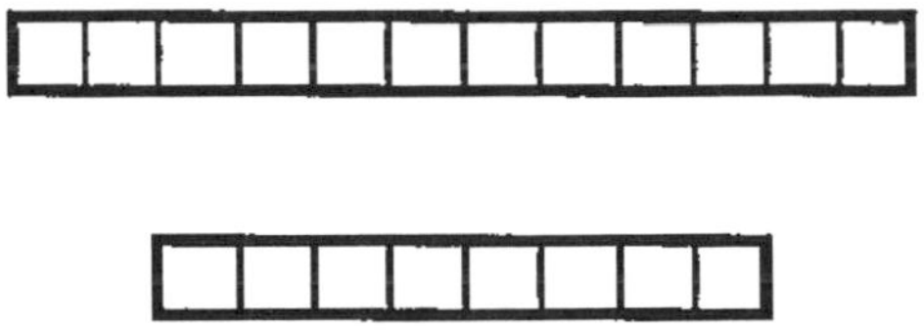

a. 4
b. 3
c. 5

D–4

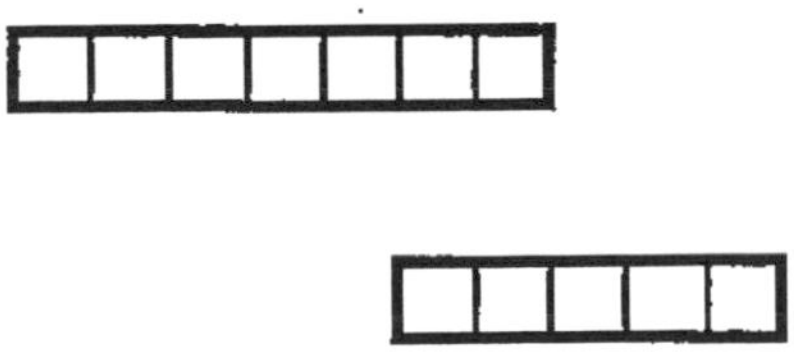

a. 2
b. 5
c. 7

D–5

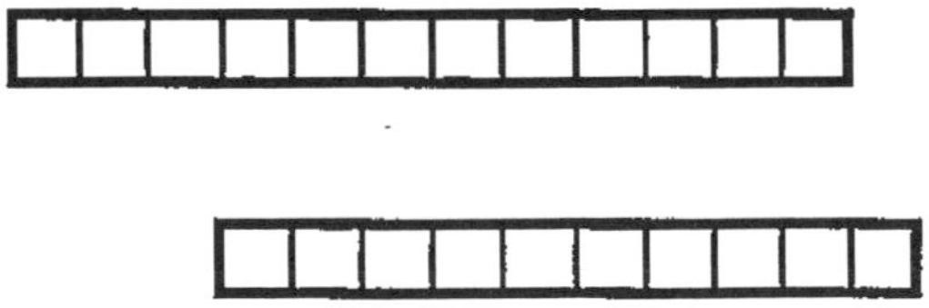

a. 4
b. 2
c. 3

D–6

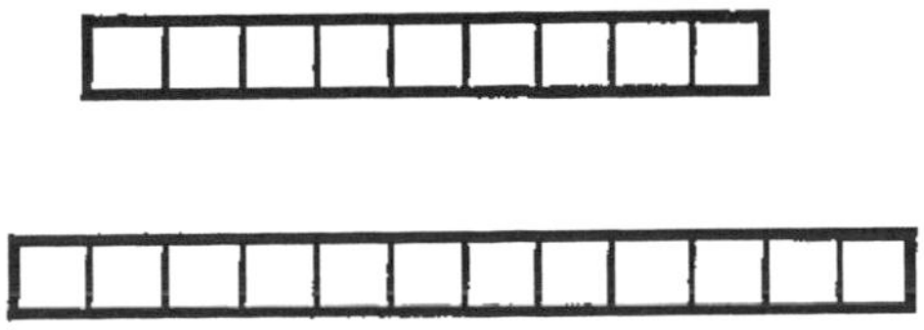

a. 3
b. 9
c. 4

D–7

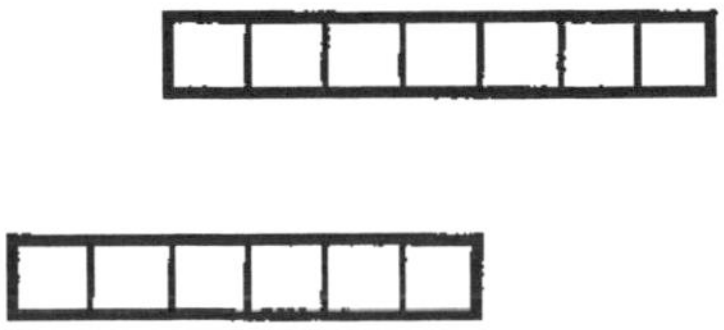

a. 2
b. 3
c. 1

COMPARING LENGTHS

Squares are joined together to make a rod.
Circle the number that tells how many squares must be added to make a length of 10.

Example:

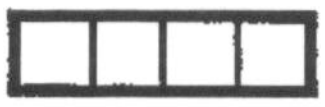

a. 8
b. 4
c. 6

D–8

a. 7
b. 6
c. 3

D–9

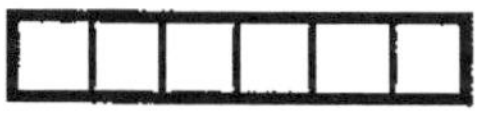

a. 6
b. 8
c. 4

D–10

a. 4
b. 8
c. 2

D–11

a. 2
b. 0
c. 1

D–12

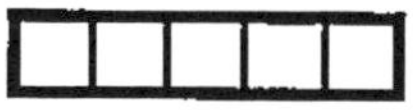

a. 5
b. 4
c. 6

D–13

a. 1
b. 2
c. 4

D–14

a. 1
b. 3
c. 0

FINDING LENGTHS OF PATHS

Squares are joined together to make a path.
Count the squares to find the length of the path from A to B.
Write the answer in the box.

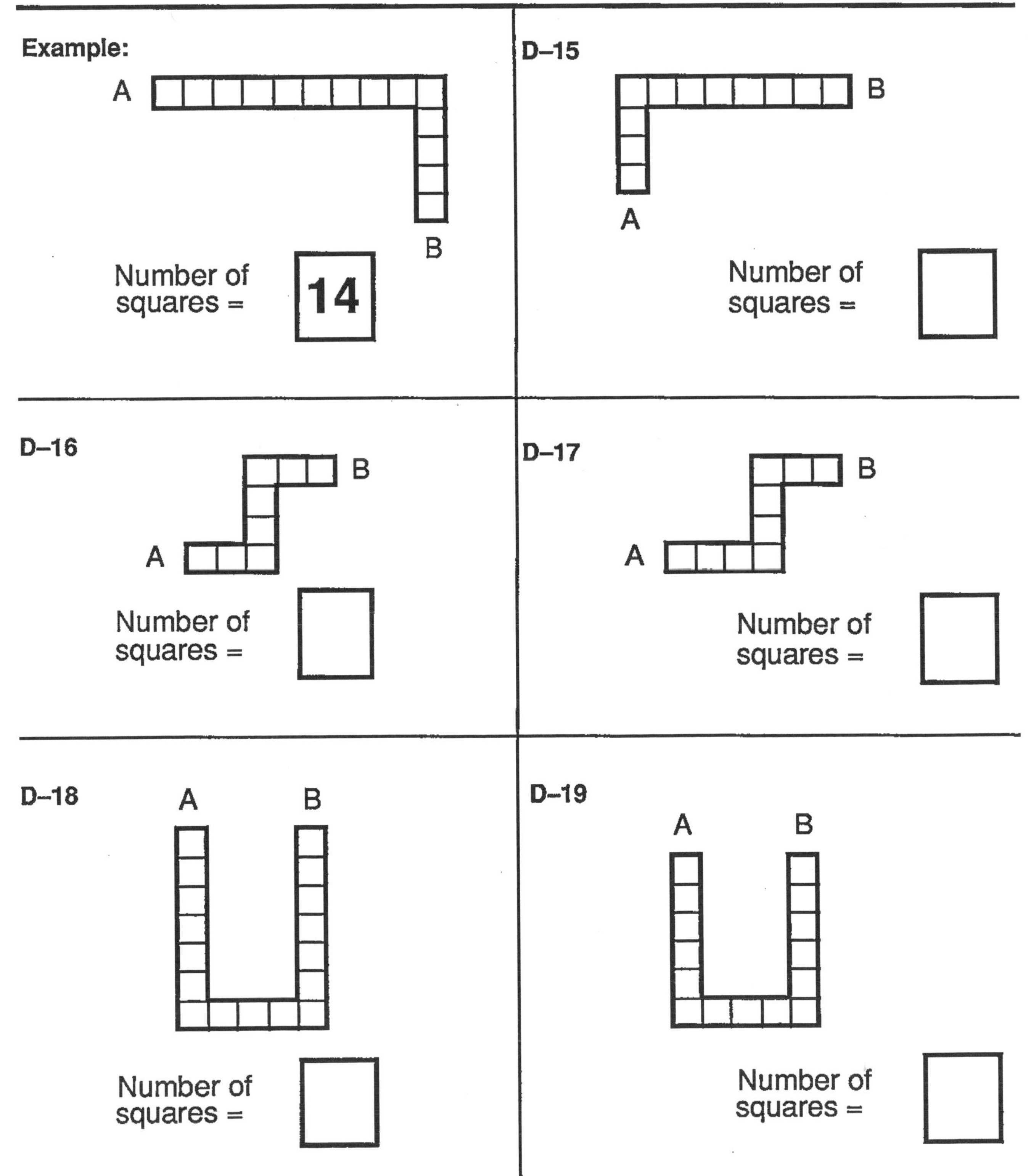

FINDING LENGTHS OF PATHS

Squares are joined together to make a path.
Count the squares to find the length of the path from A to B.
Write the answer in the box.

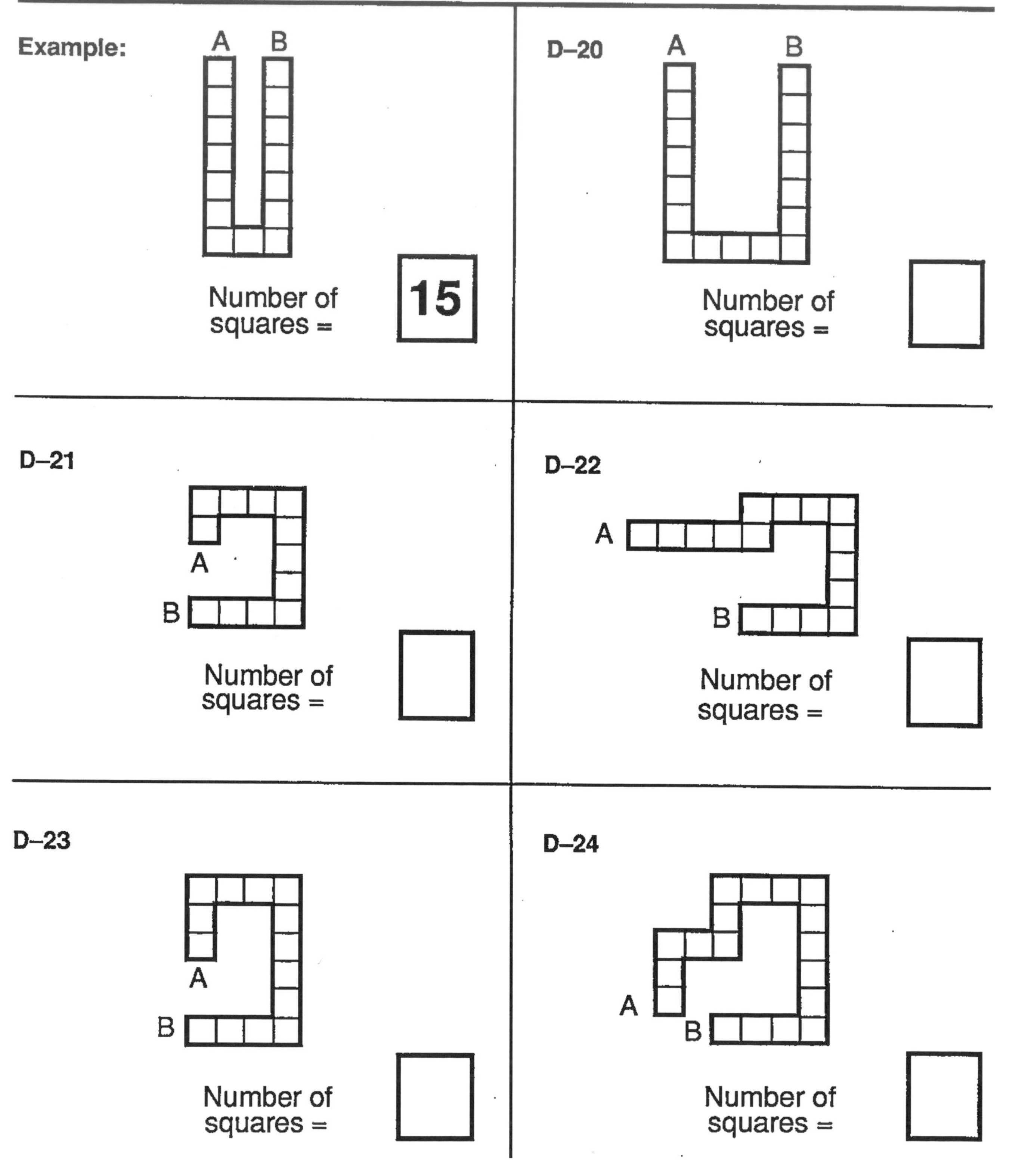

FINDING LENGTHS OF PATHS

Find the length of the path from A to B.
Write the answer in the box.
Put an X on all the paths that are the same length as the path in the example.

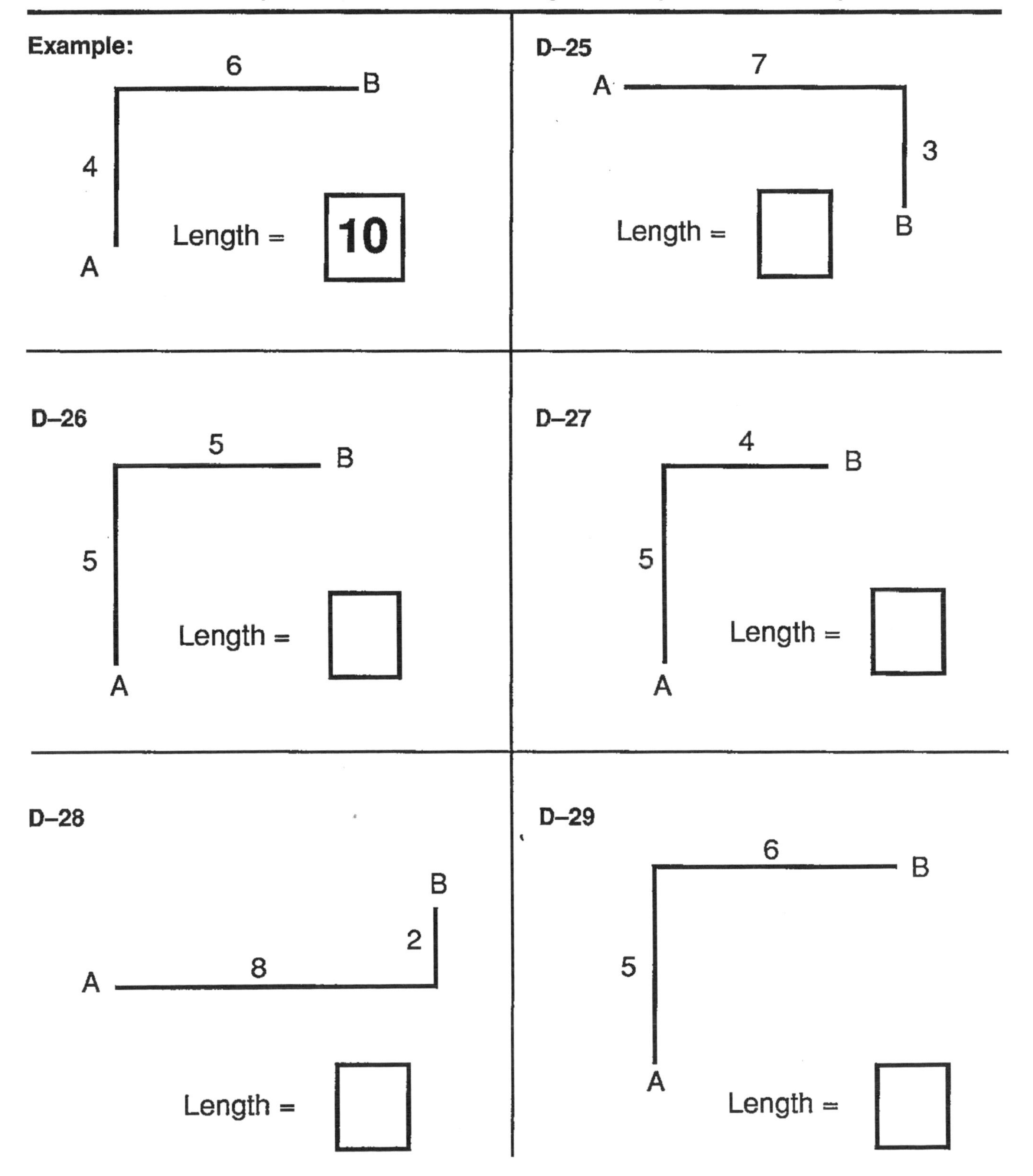

FINDING LENGTHS OF PATHS

Find the length of the path from A to B.
Write the answer in the box.
Put an X on all the paths that are the same length as the path in the example.

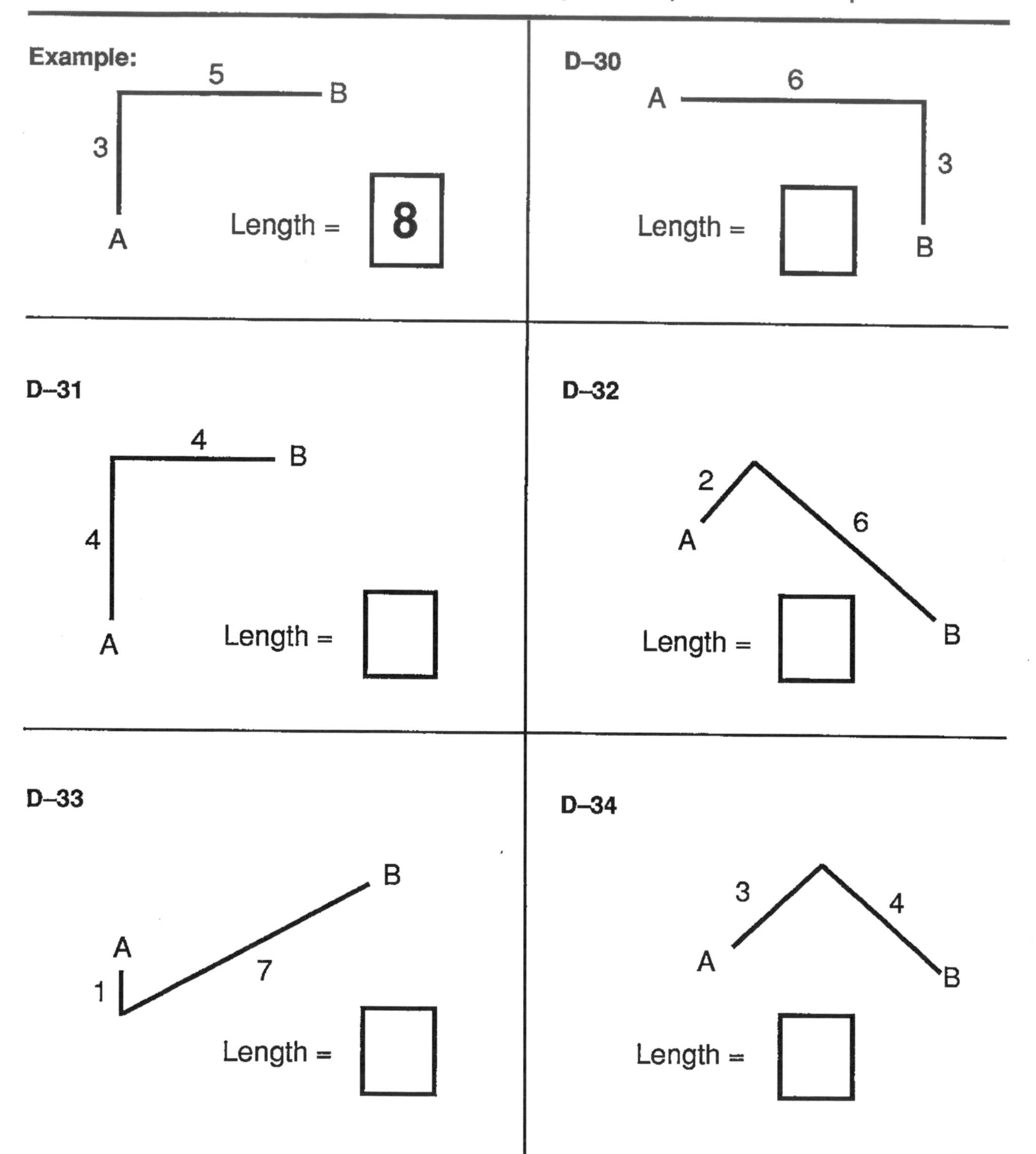

FINDING LENGTHS OF PATHS

Find the length of each path. Write the answer in the box.
Draw a line between boxes that contain paths that are the same length.

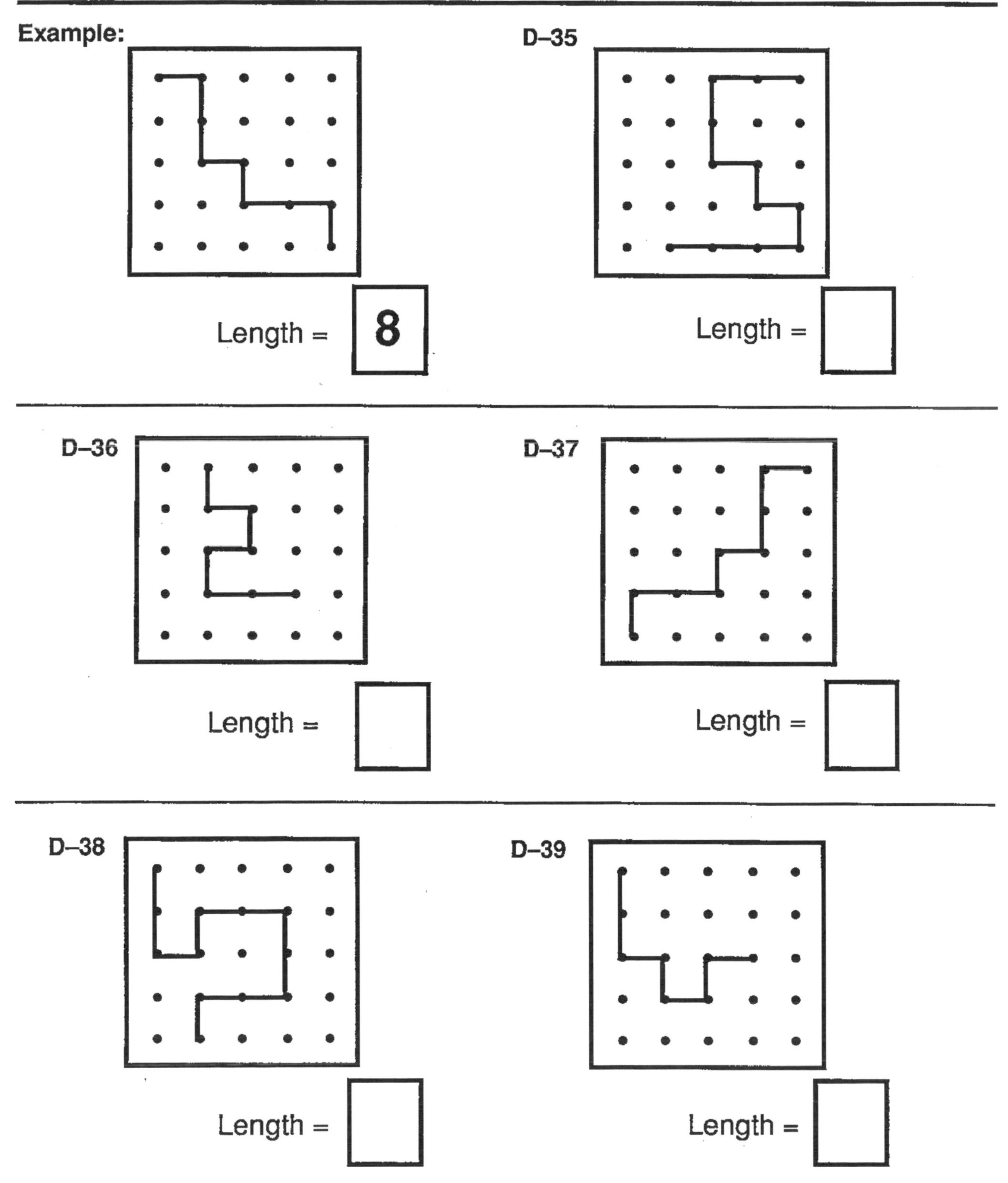

FINDING LENGTHS OF PATHS

Find the length of each path. Write the answer in the box.
Draw a line between boxes that contain paths that are the same length.

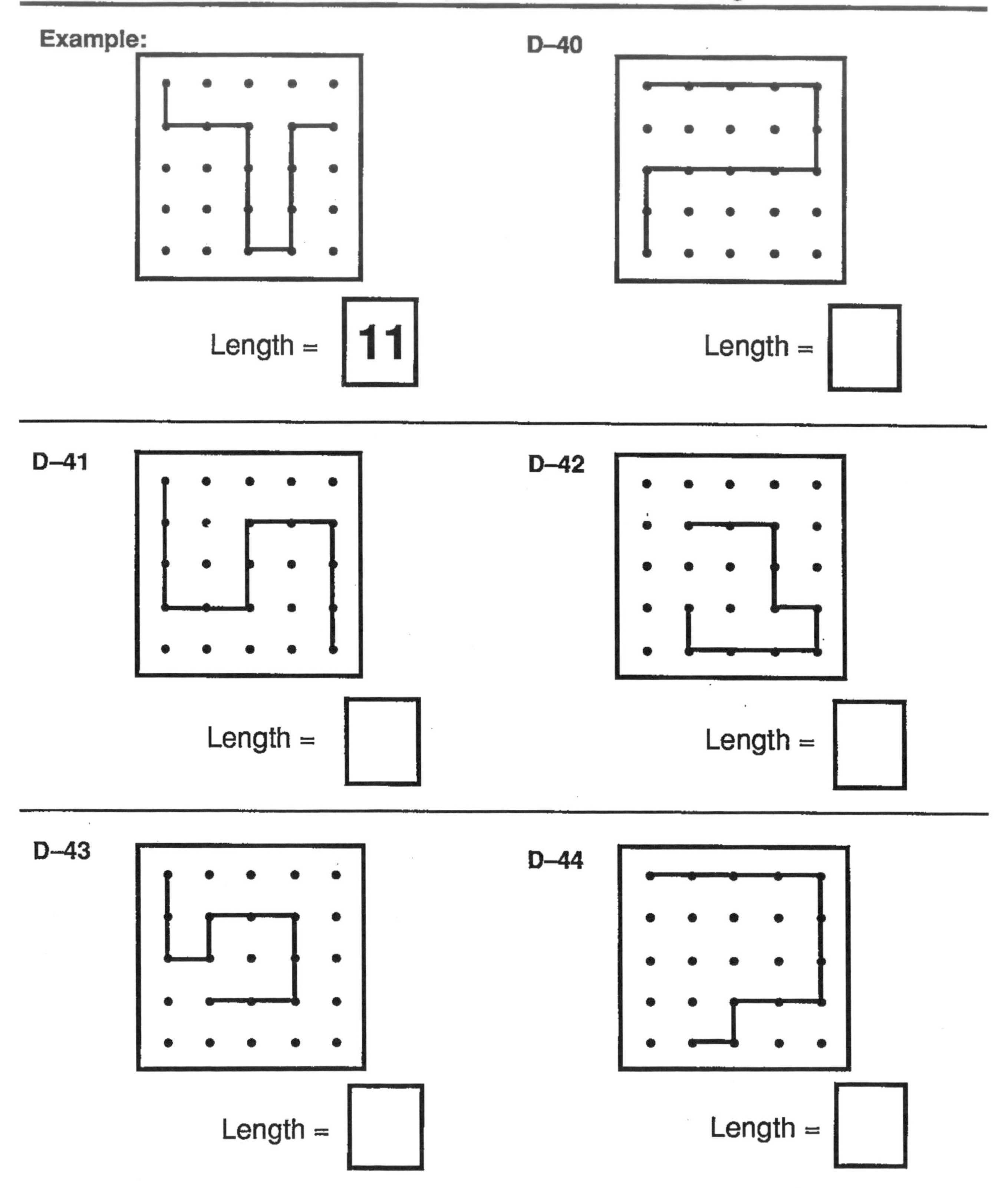

DRAWING PATHS

The length of a path is written in the box.
Draw a path from A to B equal to that length.
Use only horizontal and vertical lines.

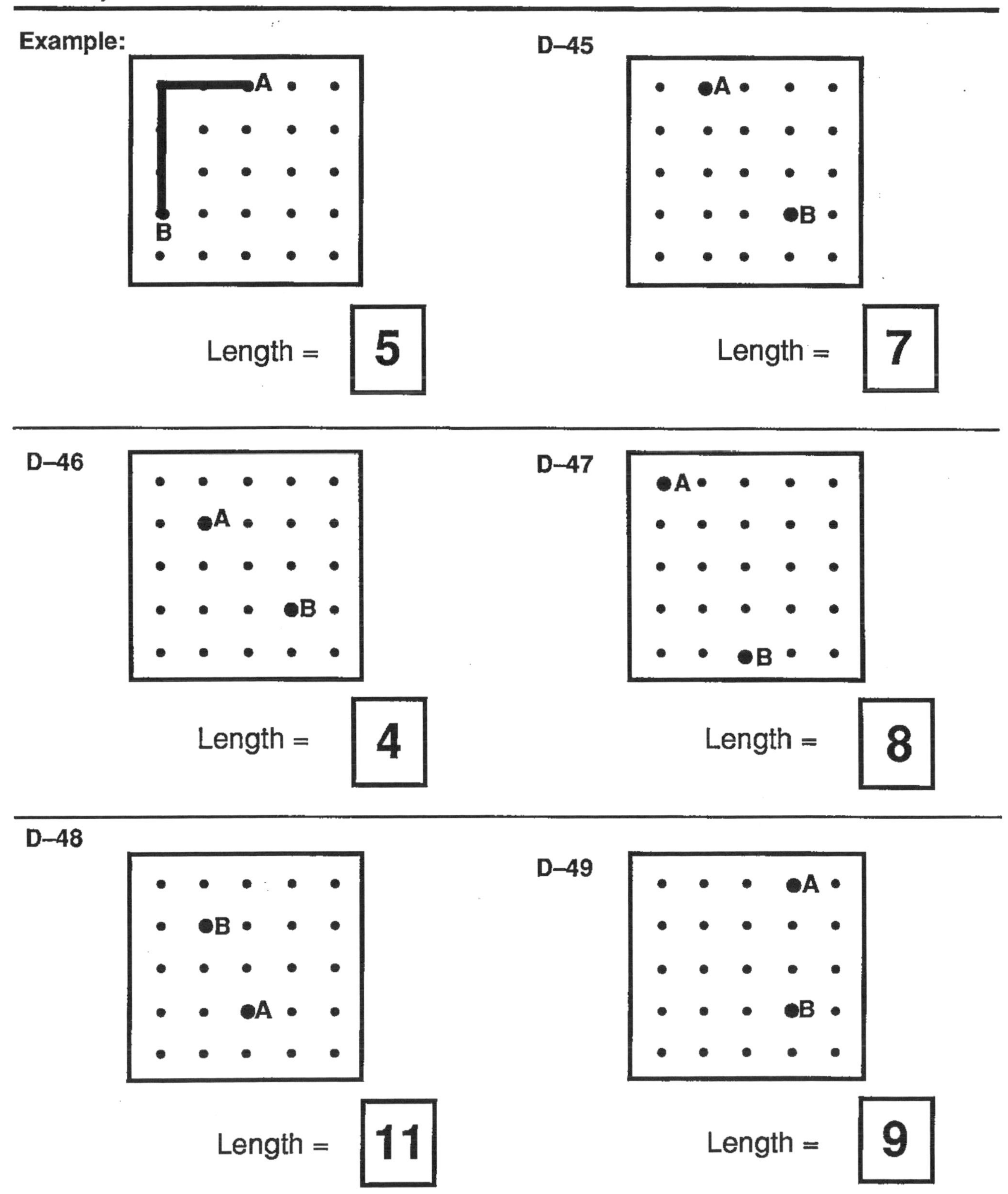

DRAWING PATHS

Find the length of the path from A to B. Write the answer in the box.
Draw a path from X to B that is the same length.
Use only horizontal and vertical lines.

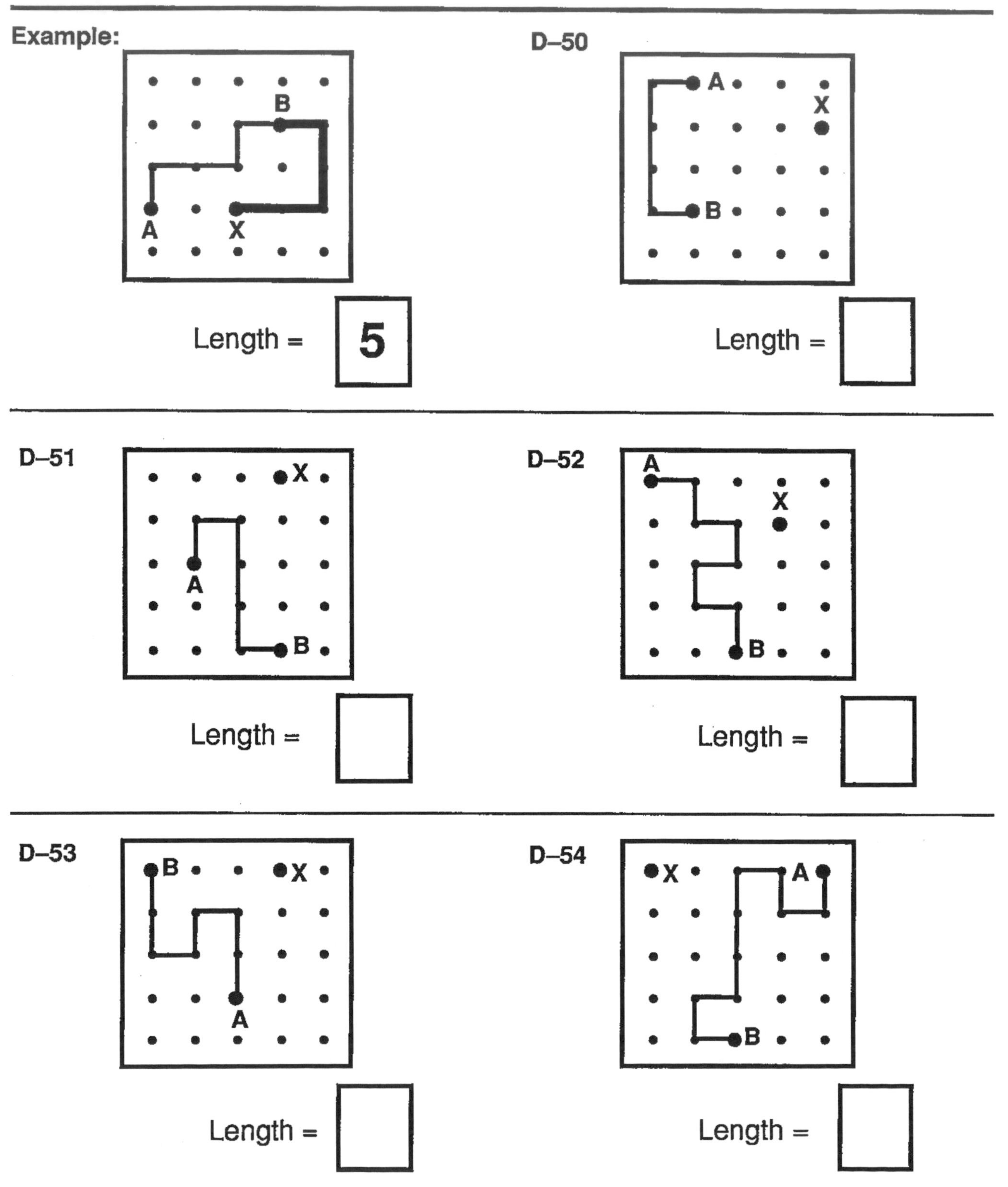

DRAWING LONGER PATHS

Find the length of the path from A to B. Write the answer in the box.
Draw a path from X to B that is one unit longer than the path from A to B.
Use only horizontal and vertical lines.

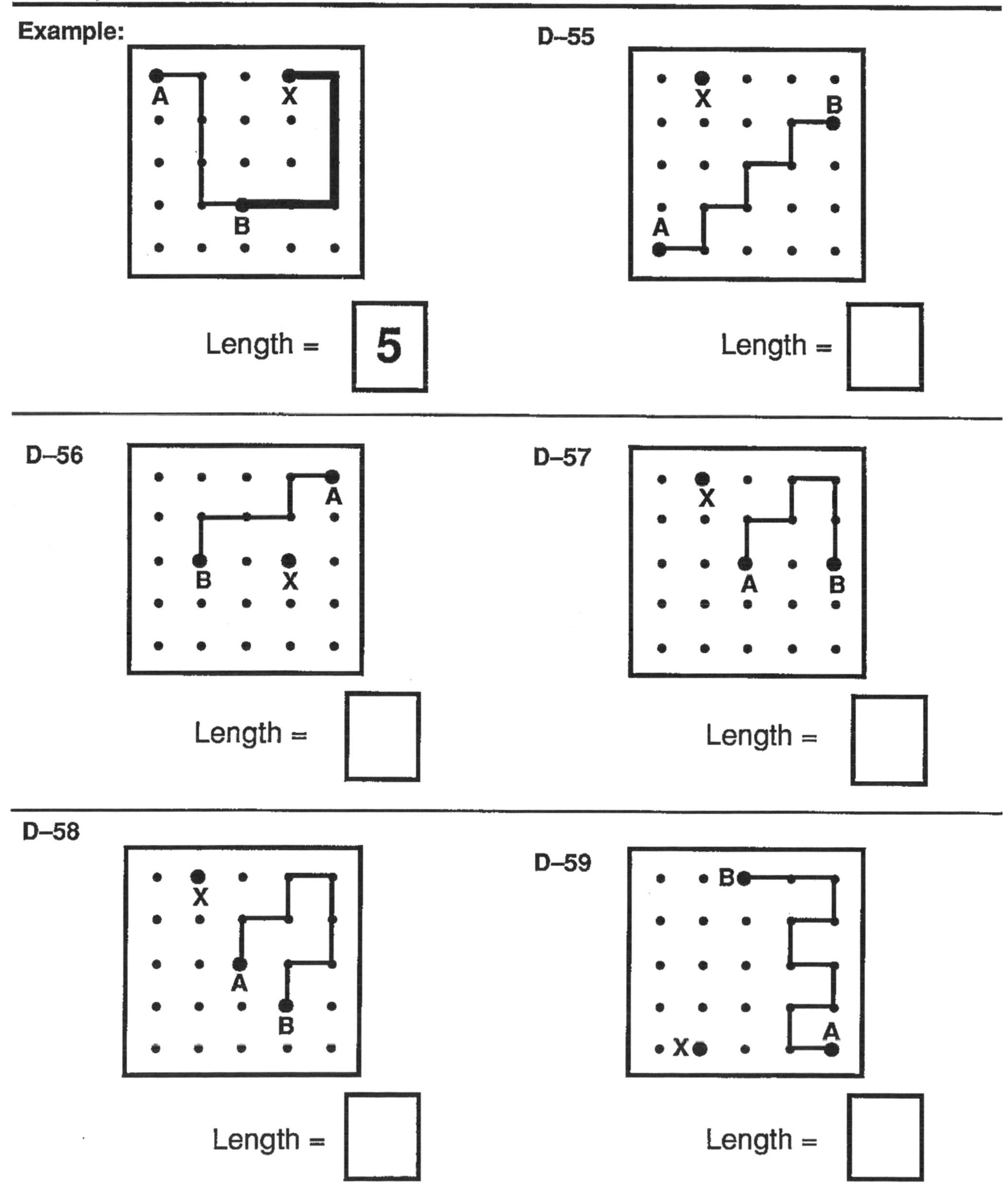

DRAWING SHORTER PATHS

Find the length of the path from A to B. Write the answer in the box.
Draw a path from X to B that is two units shorter than the path from A to B.
Use only horizontal and vertical lines.

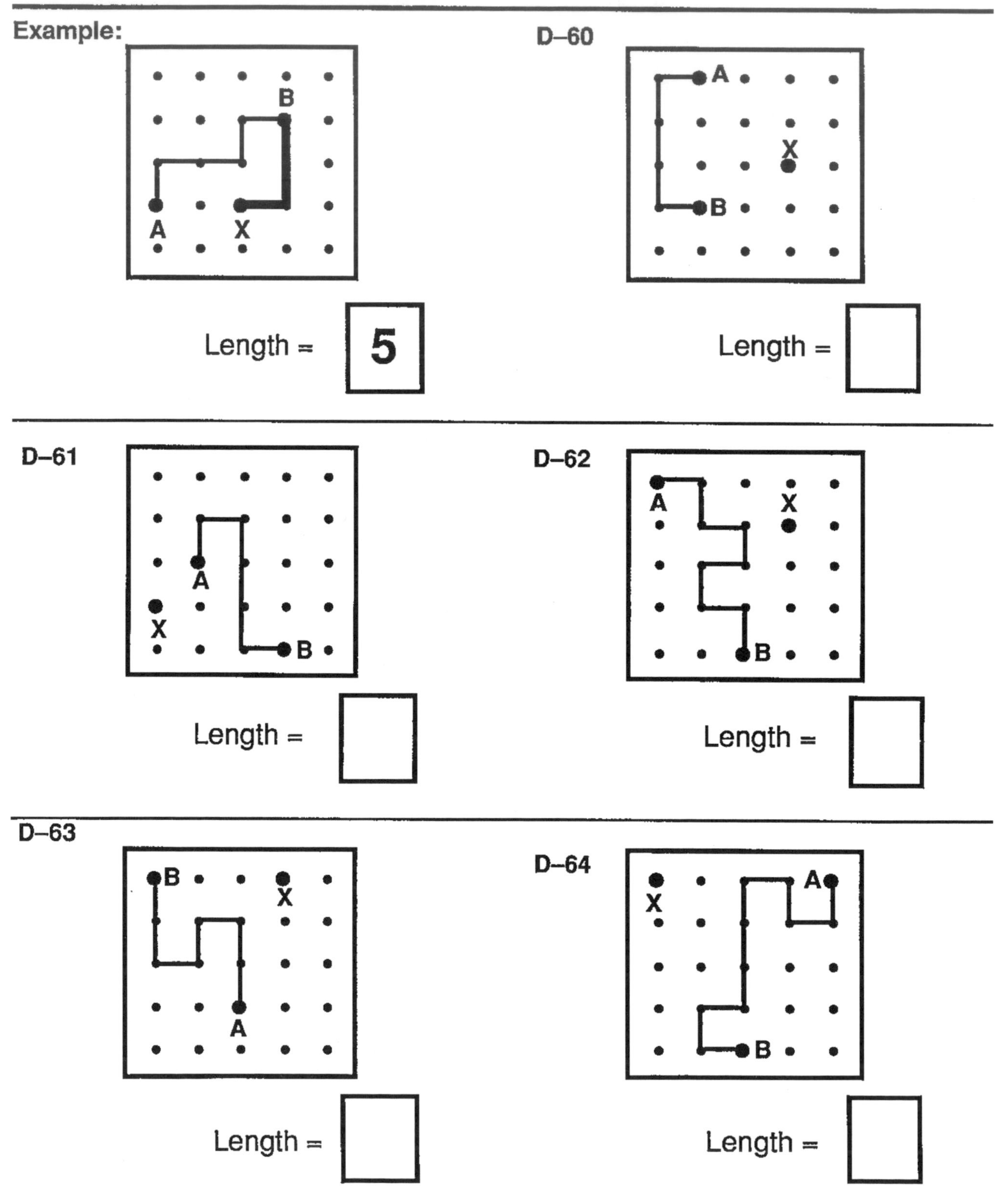

DRAWING PATHS

Find the length of the path from A to B to C. Write the answer in the box.
Draw a path from A to X to C that is the same length.
Use only horizontal and vertical lines.

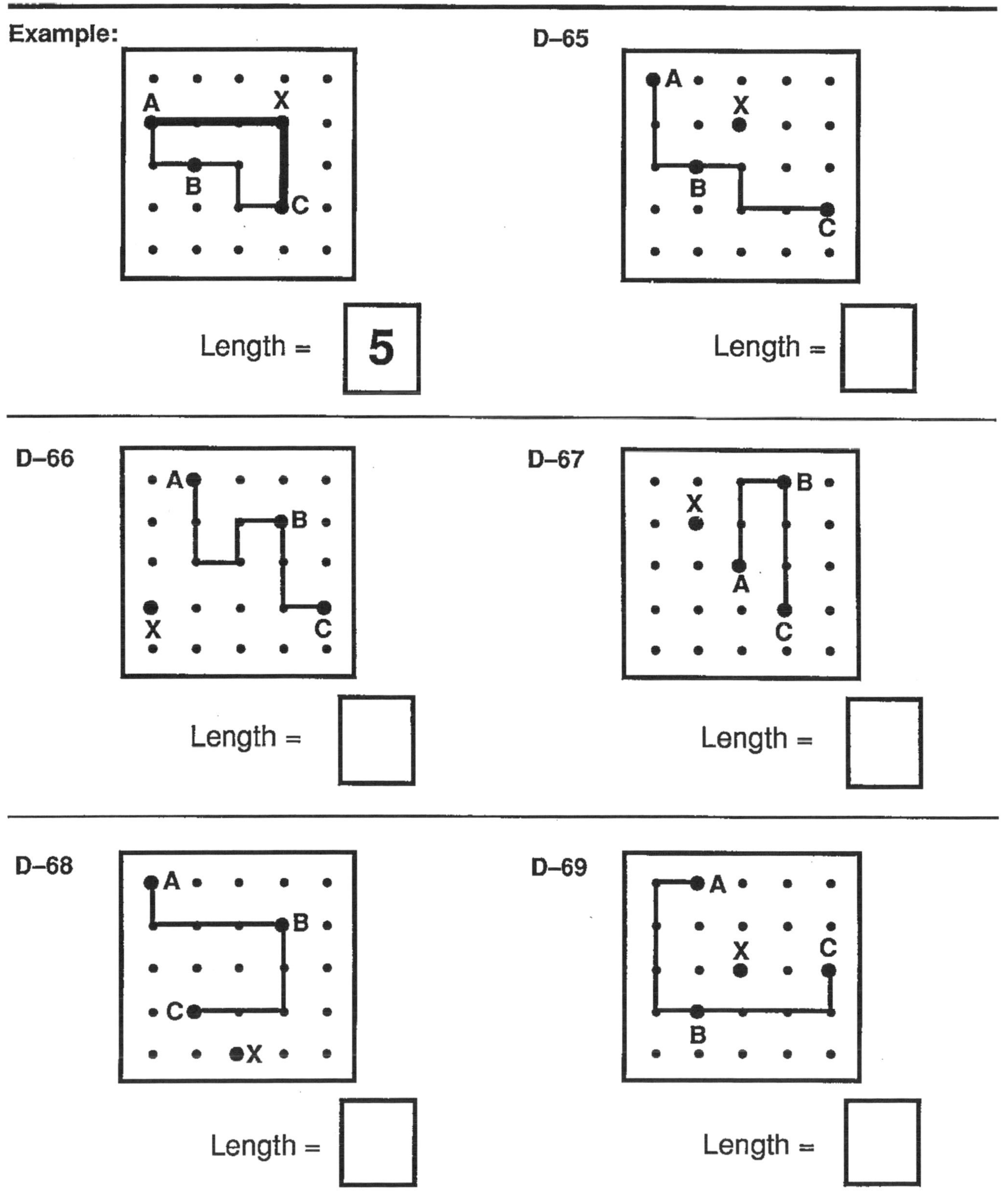

DRAWING SHORTER PATHS

Find the length of the path from A to B. Write the answer in the box.
Draw a path from A to X to B that is two units shorter.
Use only horizontal and vertical lines.

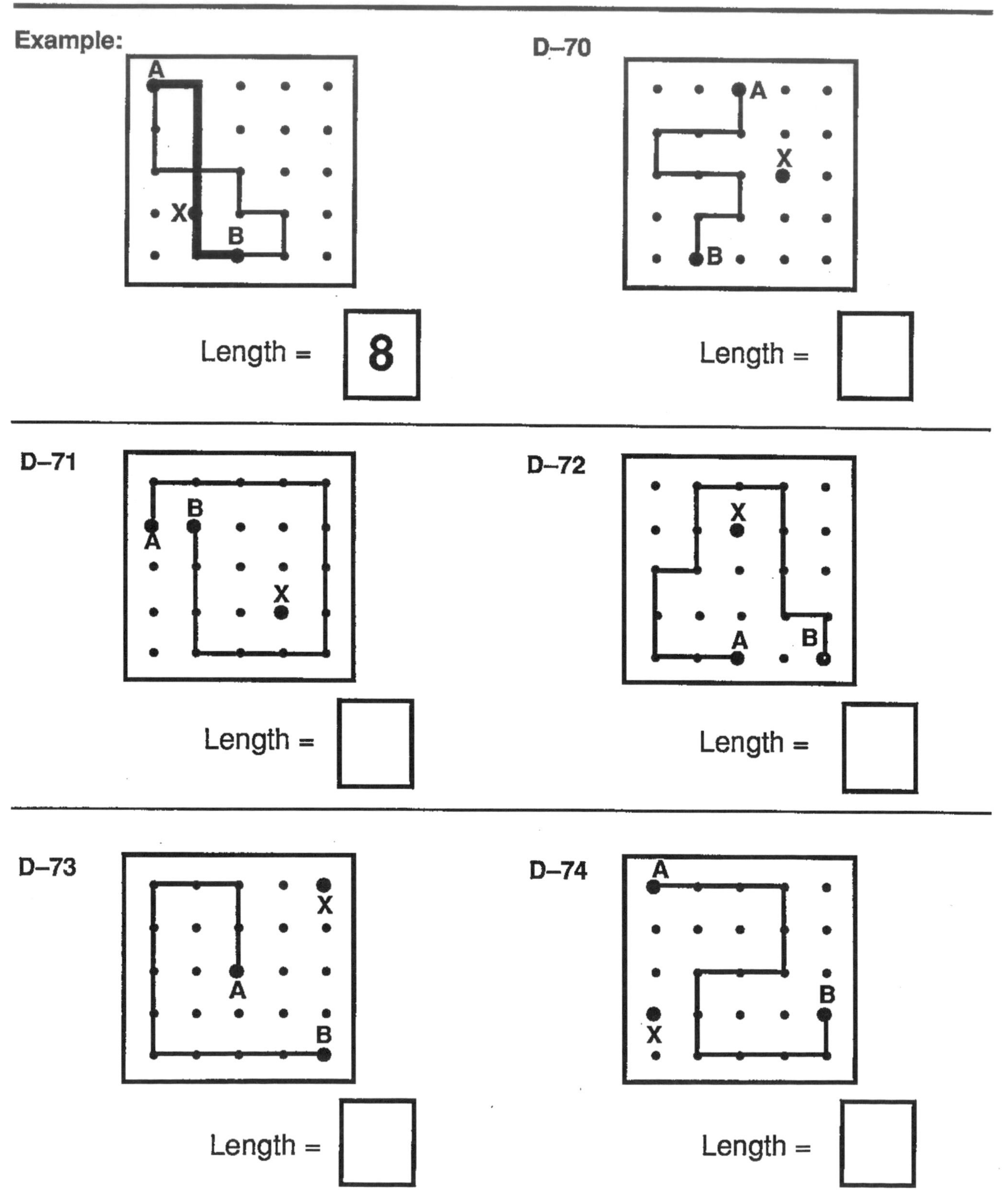

FINDING LONGER PATHS

One person walks along the dotted path.
Another person walks along the solid path.
Circle the name of the person who walks the longer distance.

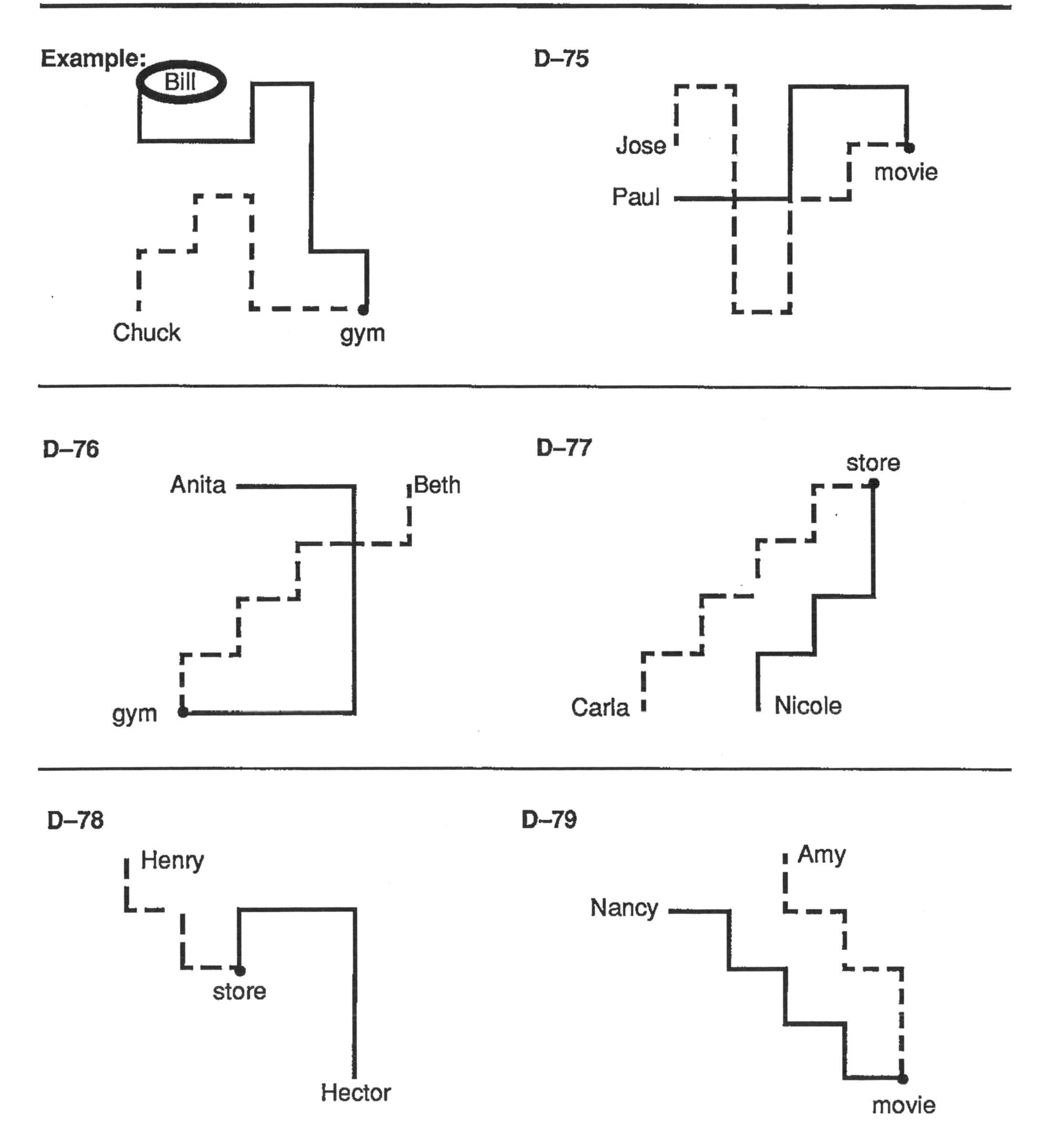

FINDING SHORTER PATHS

One person walks along the dotted path.
Another person walks along the solid path.
Circle the name of the person who walks the longer distance.

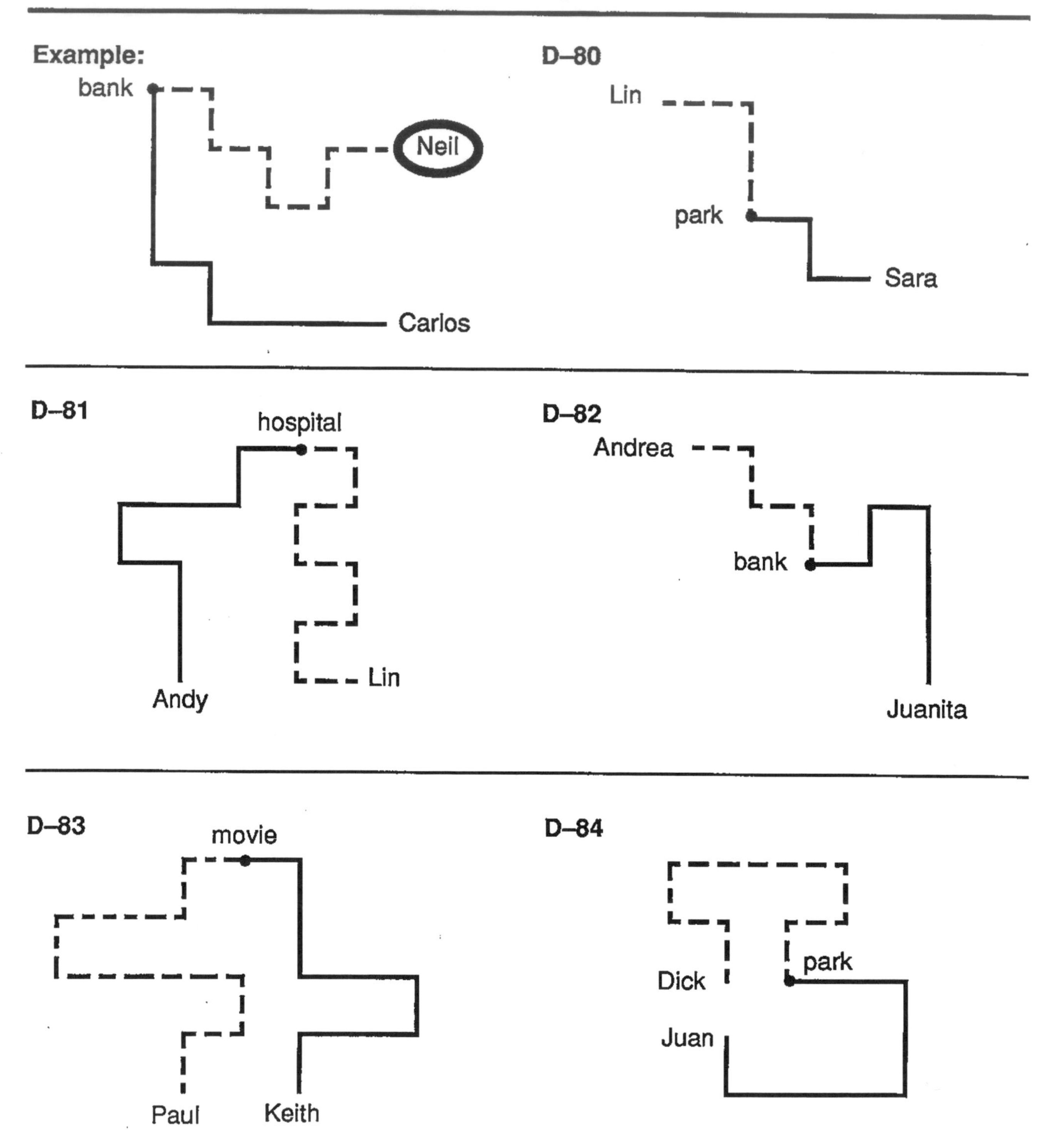

COMPARING PATHS

One person walks along the dotted path.
Another person walks along the solid path.
Circle the name of the person who walks the longer distance.

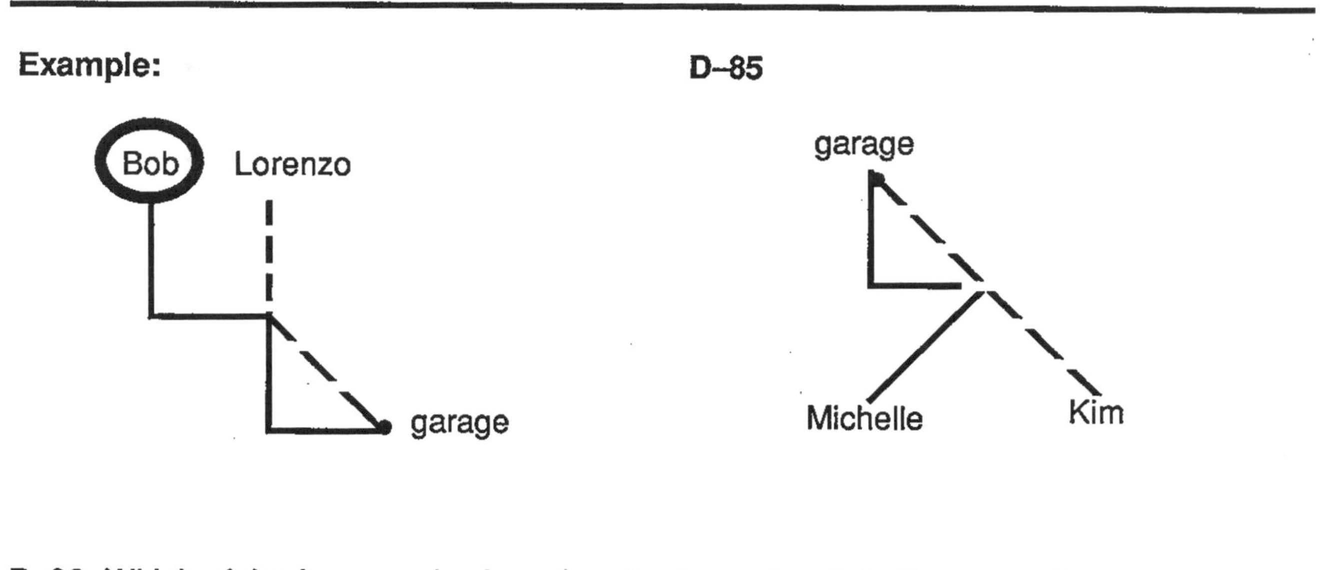

D–86 Which of the four people above has the longest walk to the garage? ________

D–87 Which of the four people above has the shortest walk to the garage? ________

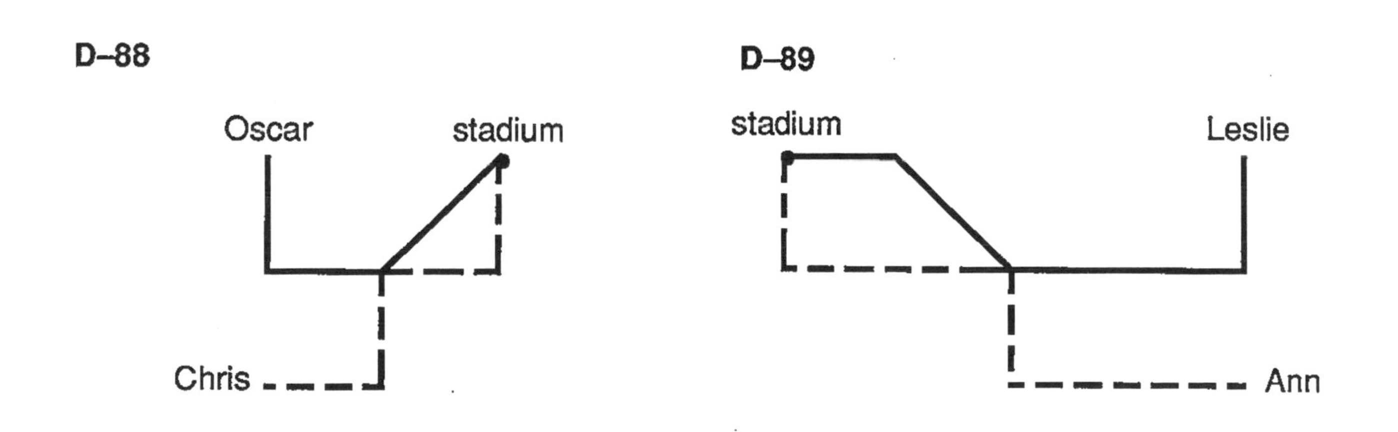

D–90 Which of the four people above has the longest walk to the stadium? ________

D–91 Which of the four people above has the shortest walk to the stadium? ________

COMPARING PATHS

One person walks along the dotted path.
Another person walks along the solid path.
Circle the name of the person who walks the longer distance.

Example: **D–92**

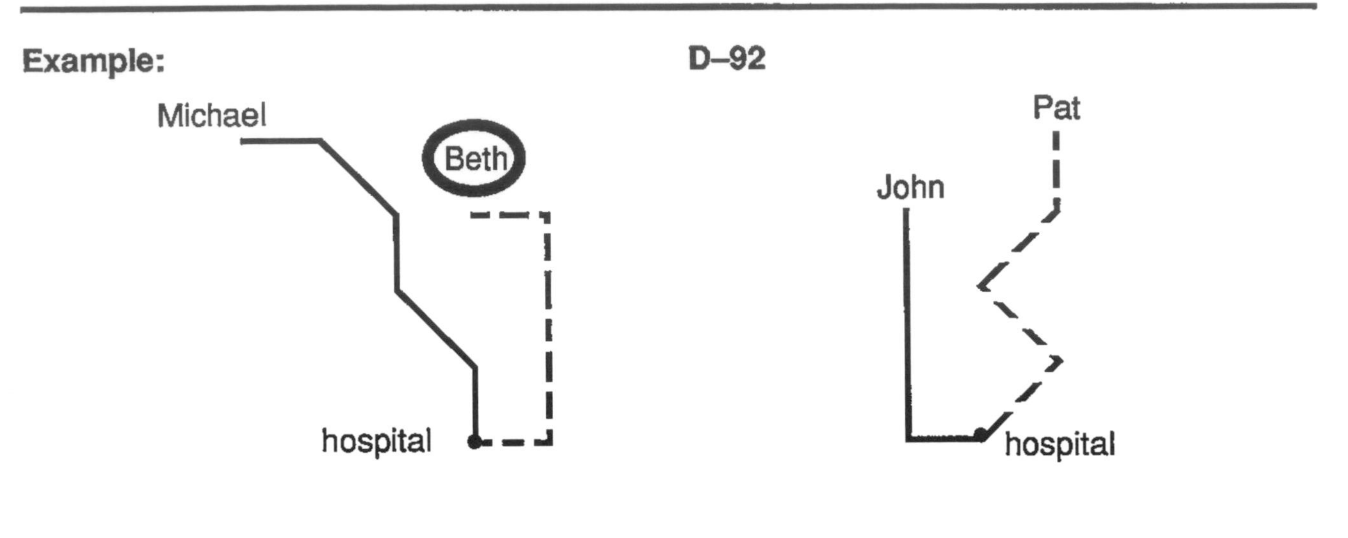

D–93 Which of the four people above has the longest walk to the hospital? ________

D–94 Which of the four people above has the shortest walk to the hospital? ________

D–95 **D–96**

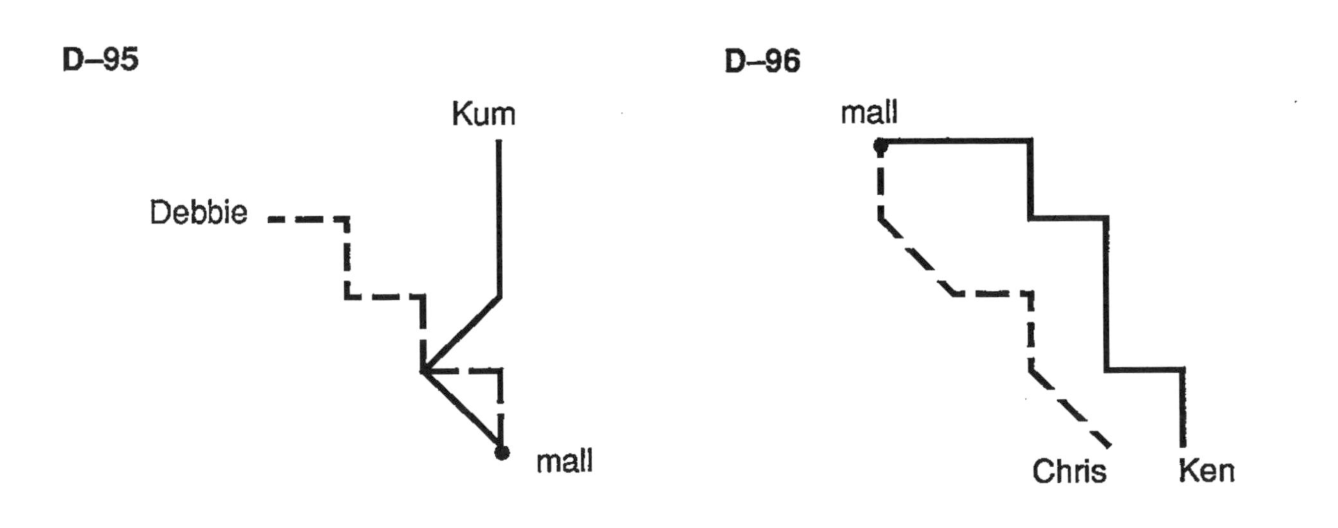

D–97 Which of the four people above has the longest walk to the mall? ________

D–98 Which of the four people above has the shortest walk to the mall? ________

DISTANCE AROUND FIGURES

Find the distance around each figure.
Write the answer in the box.

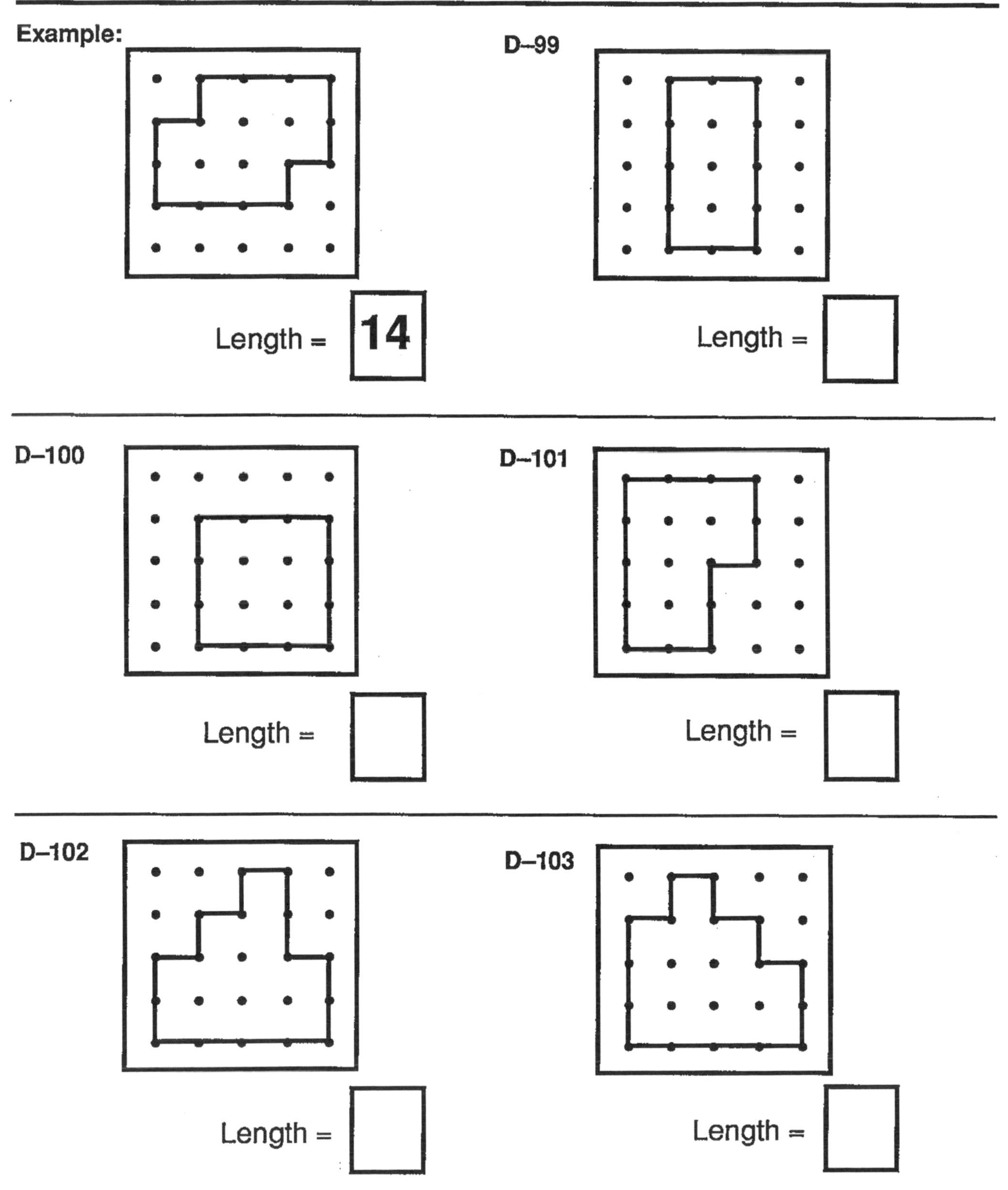

DISTANCE AROUND FIGURES

Find the distance around each figure.
Write the answer in the box.

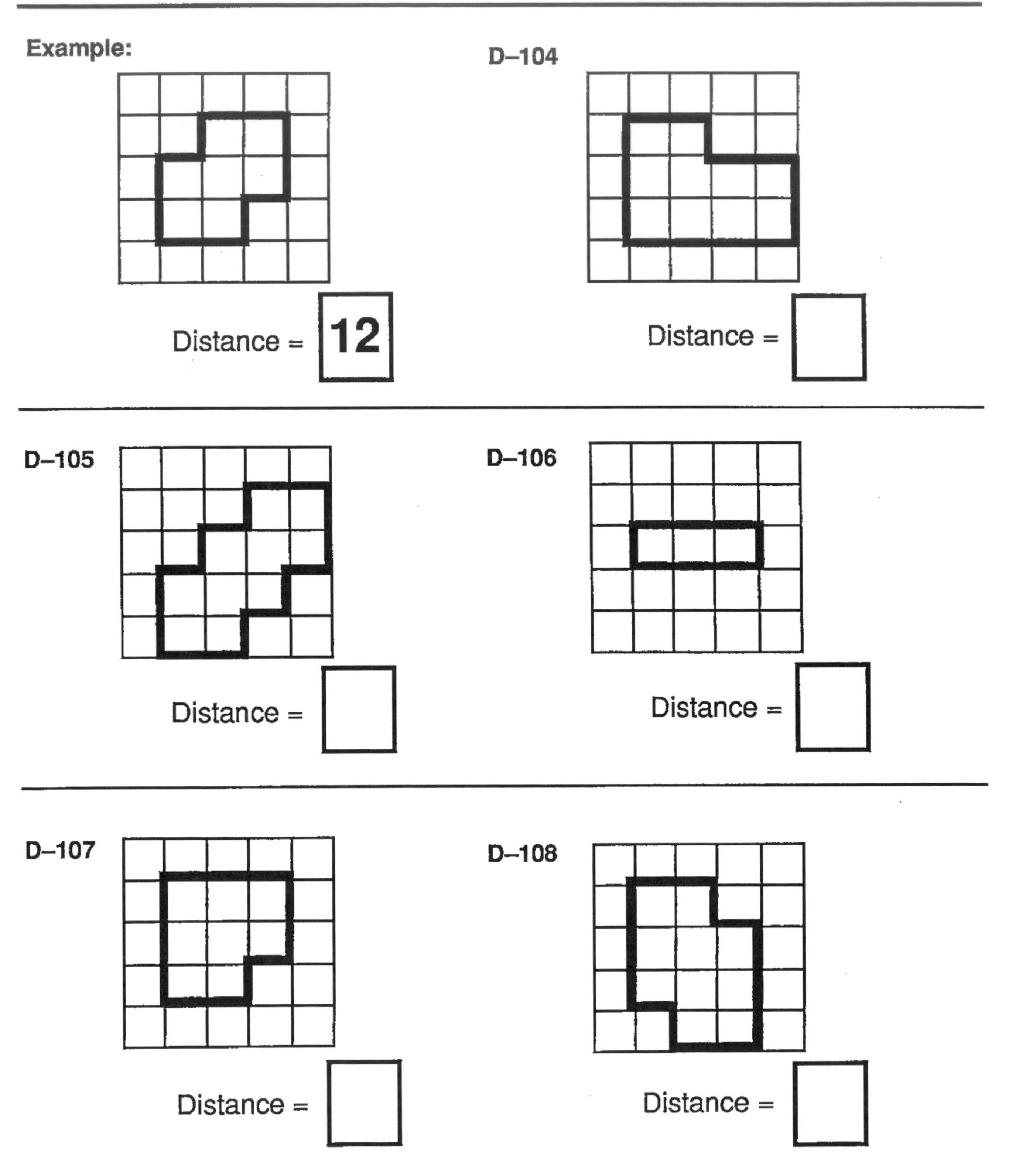

DISTANCE AROUND FIGURES

The numbers give the length of each side of the figure.
Match the figure with the distance around the figure.

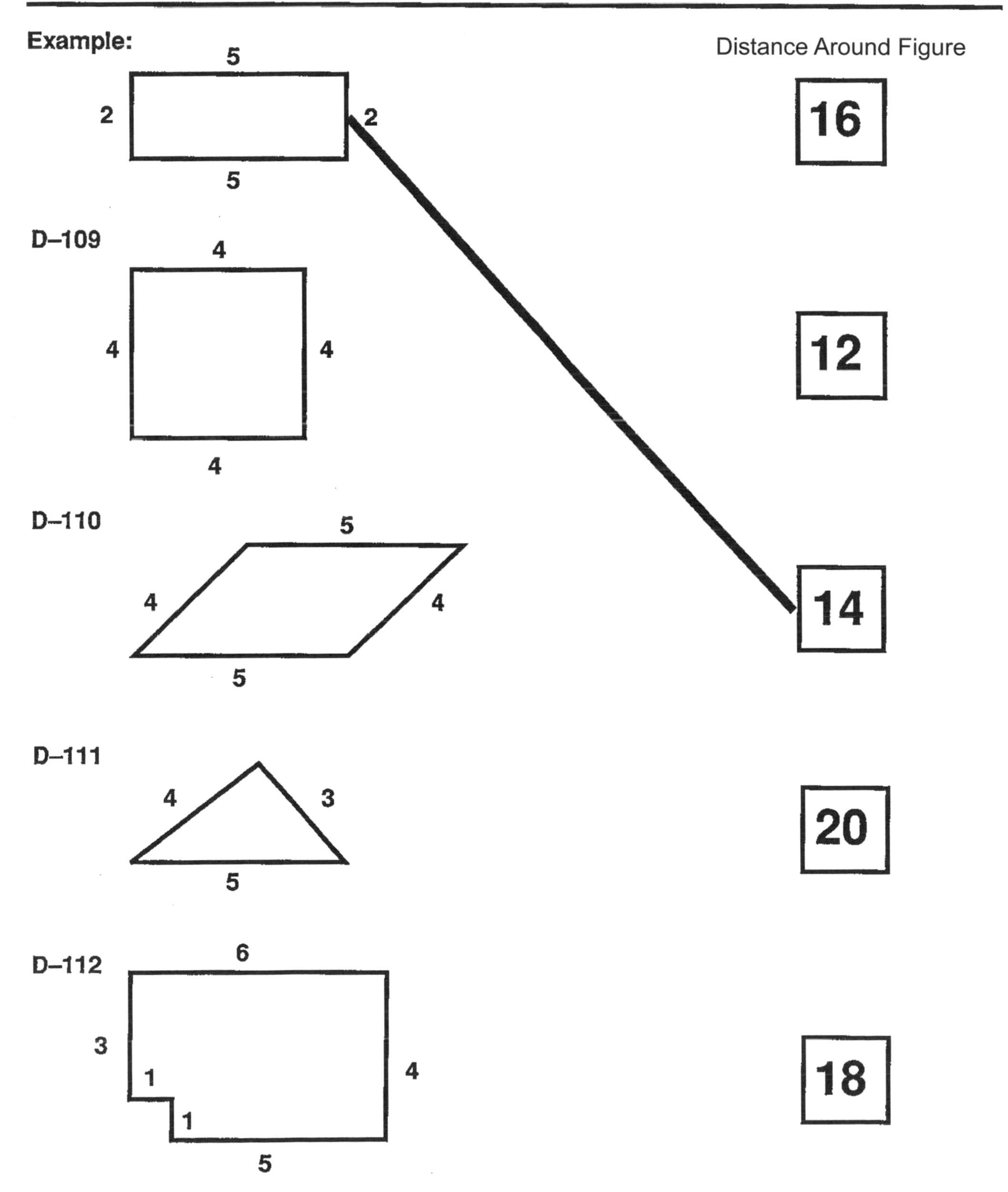

DISTANCE AROUND FIGURES

Find the distance around each figure.
Match the figures with the same distance.
Write the matching distance in the circle.

Example:

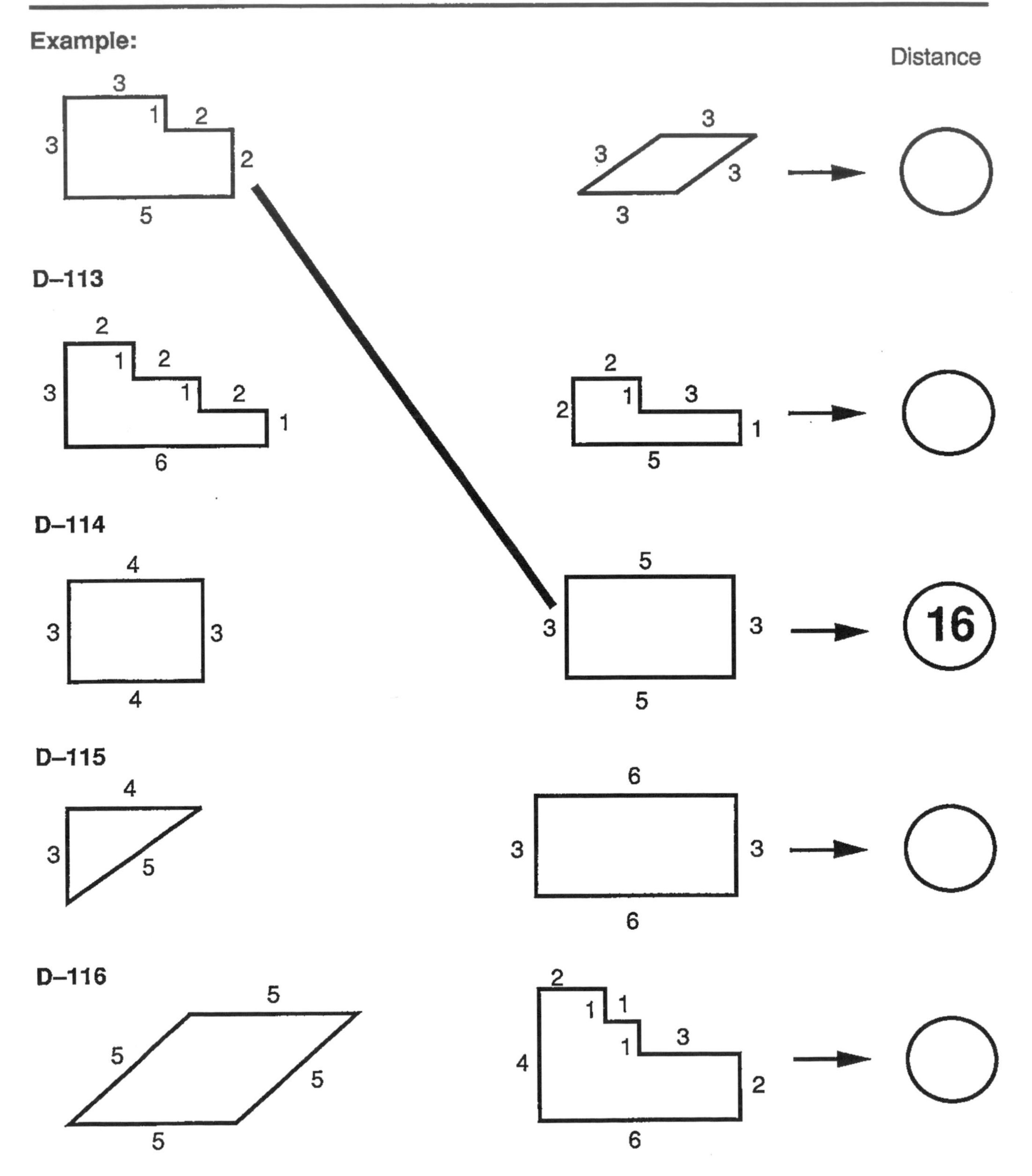

DISTANCES AROUND FIGURES

The figures below are made from one square and one rectangle.
Find the distance around the edges of the new figure.
Do not count the dotted line where the square and rectangle join together.

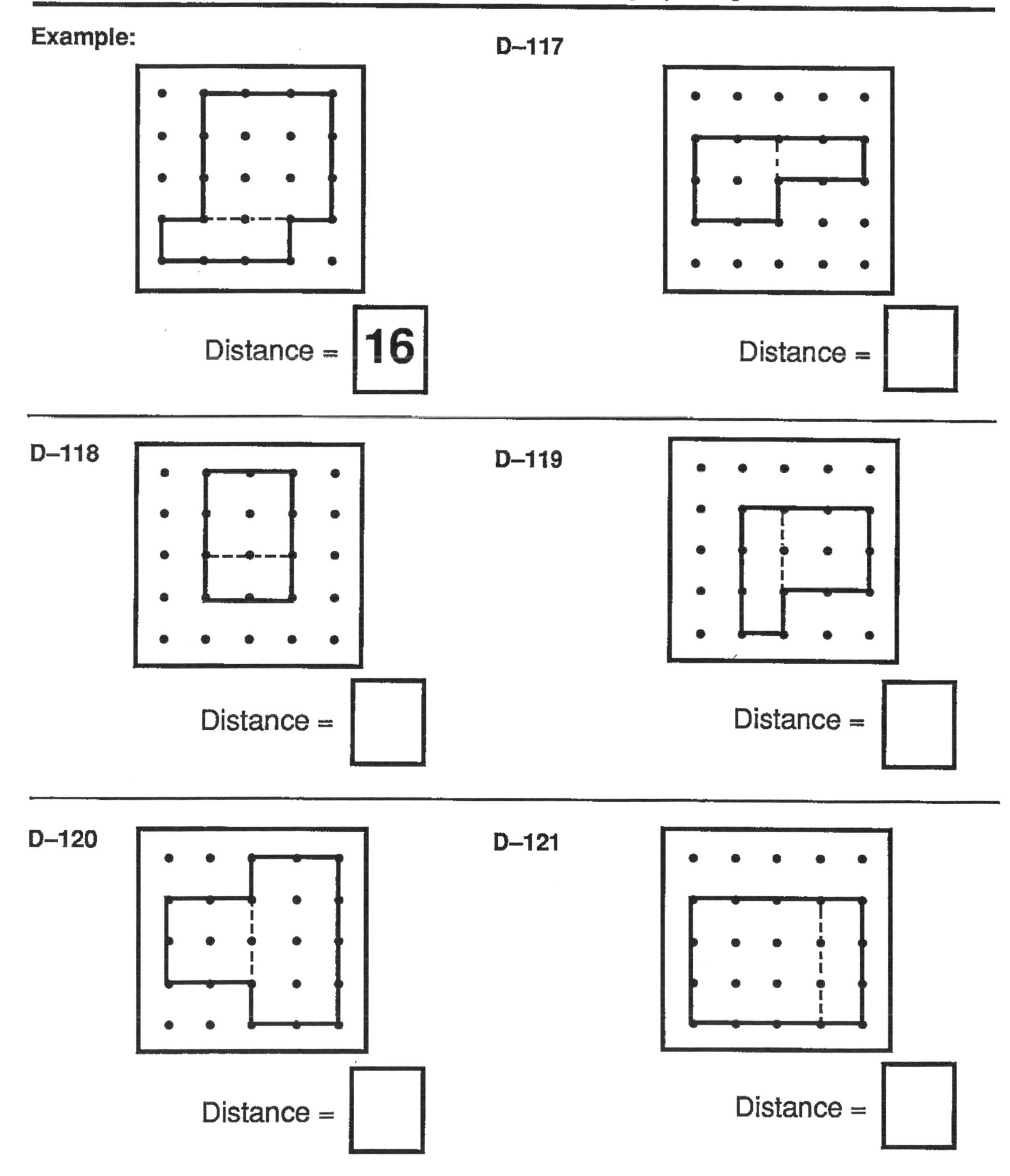

DISTANCES AROUND FIGURES

The figures below are made from three rectangles.
Find the distance around the edges of the new figure.
Do not count the dotted lines where the rectangles join together.

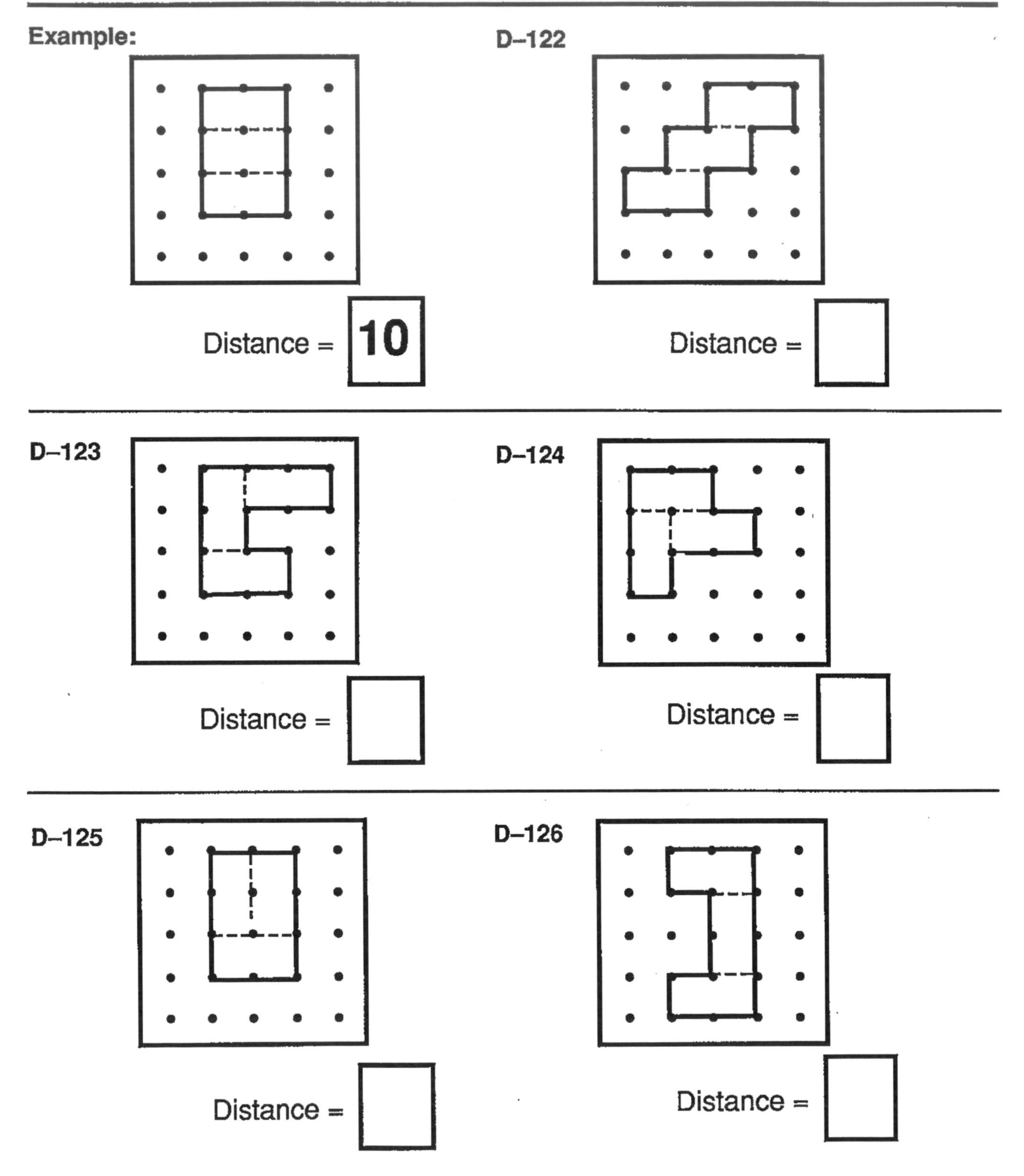

DISTANCES AROUND FIGURES

Three rhombuses, like the shaded one, are joined together to make a new figure.
The length of each side is 2.
Find the distance around the edges of each new figure.

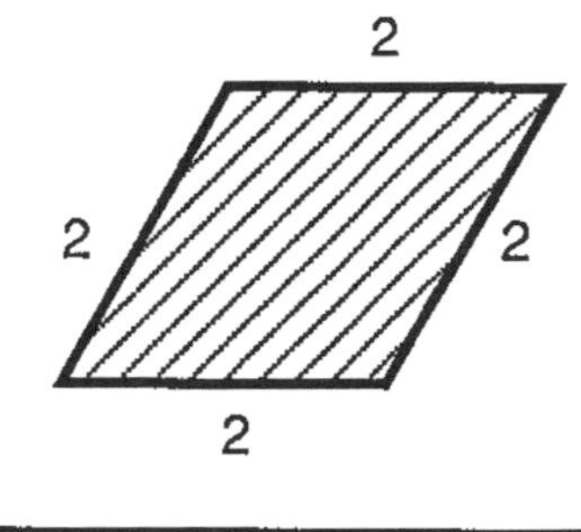

Example:

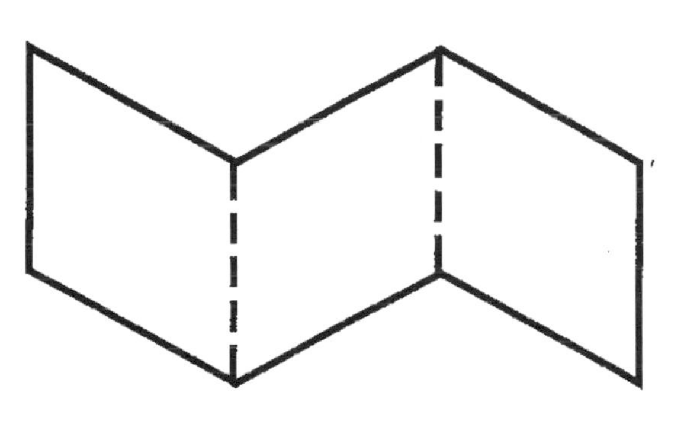

Distance = **16**

D–127

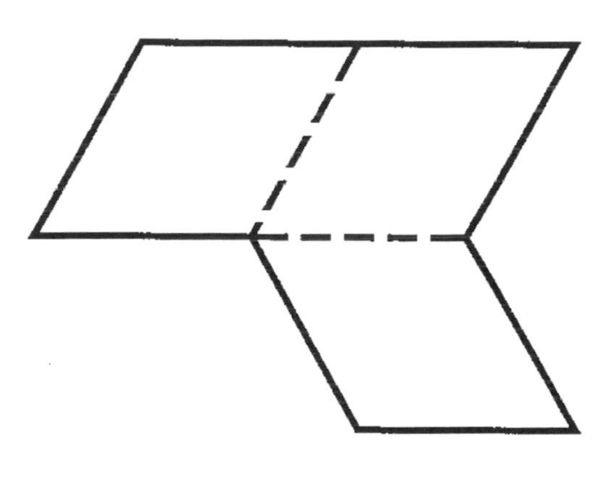

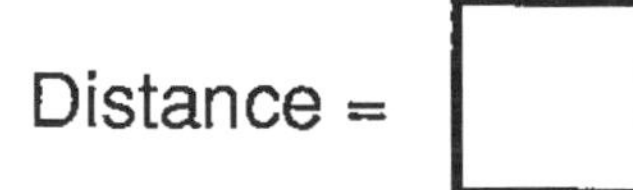

D–128

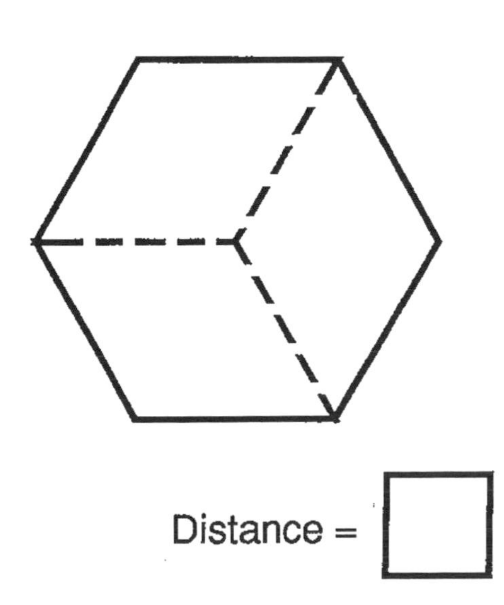

Distance =

D–129

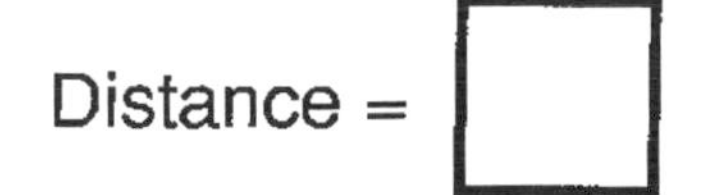

DISTANCES AROUND FIGURES

The three shaded shapes below are joined together to make new figures.
The numbers give the length of the sides.
Find the distance around the edges of each new figure.

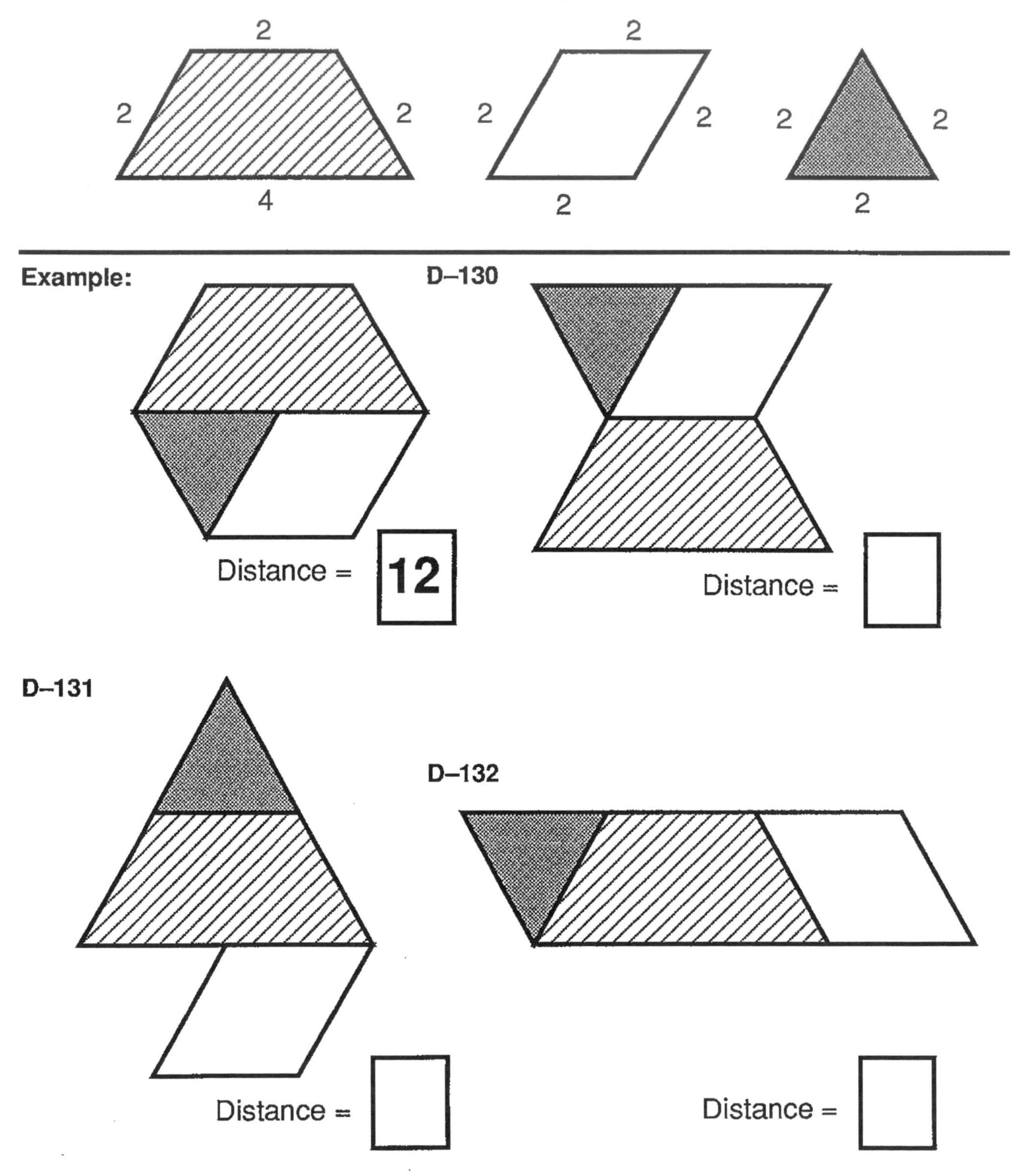

DRAWING FIGURES

The distance around each figure is written in the box.
Complete each figure to match that distance.
Use only horizontal and vertical lines.

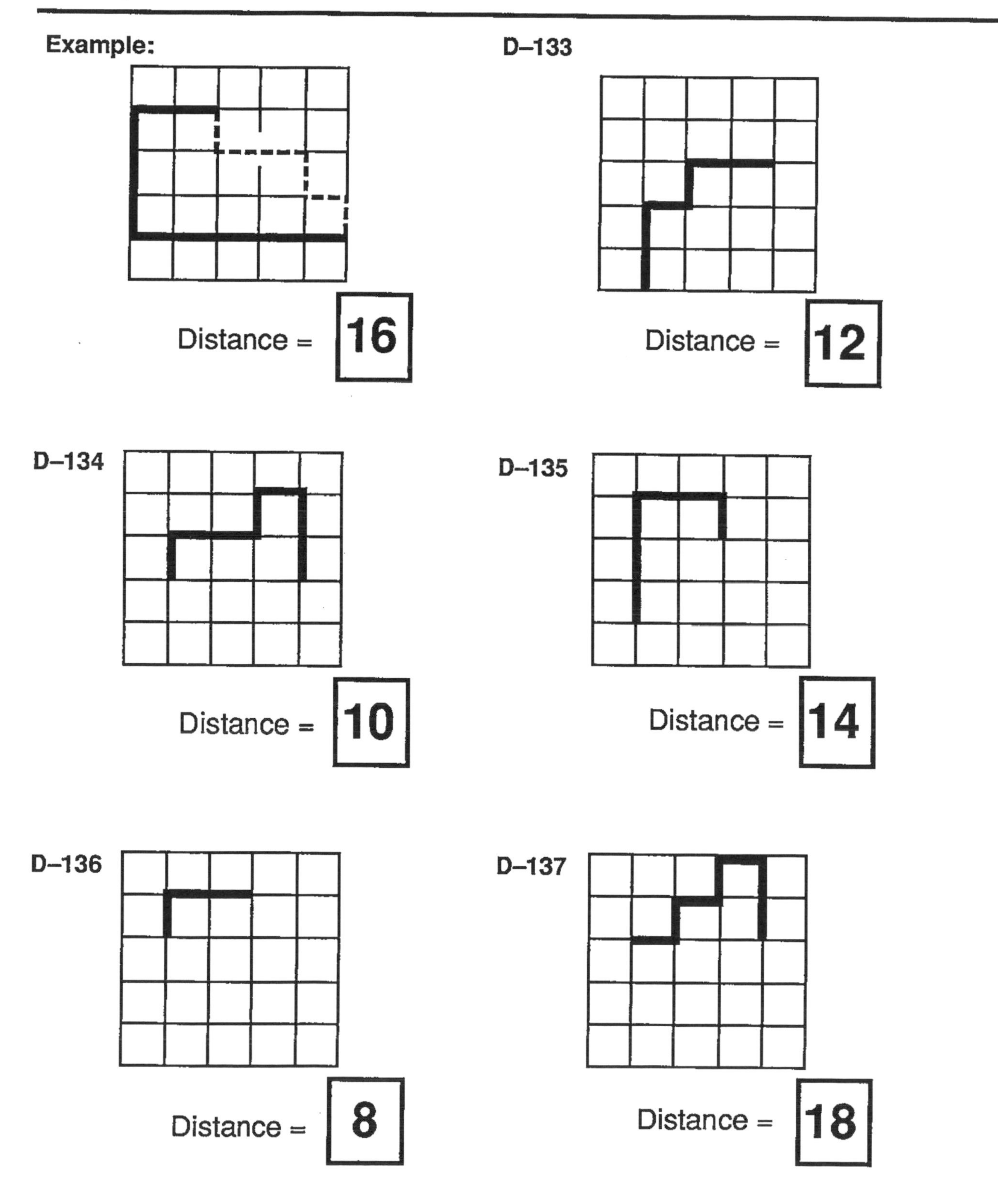

DRAWING FIGURES

The distance around a figure is written in the box.
Draw a figure with the distance indicated in each box.
Use only horizontal and vertical lines.

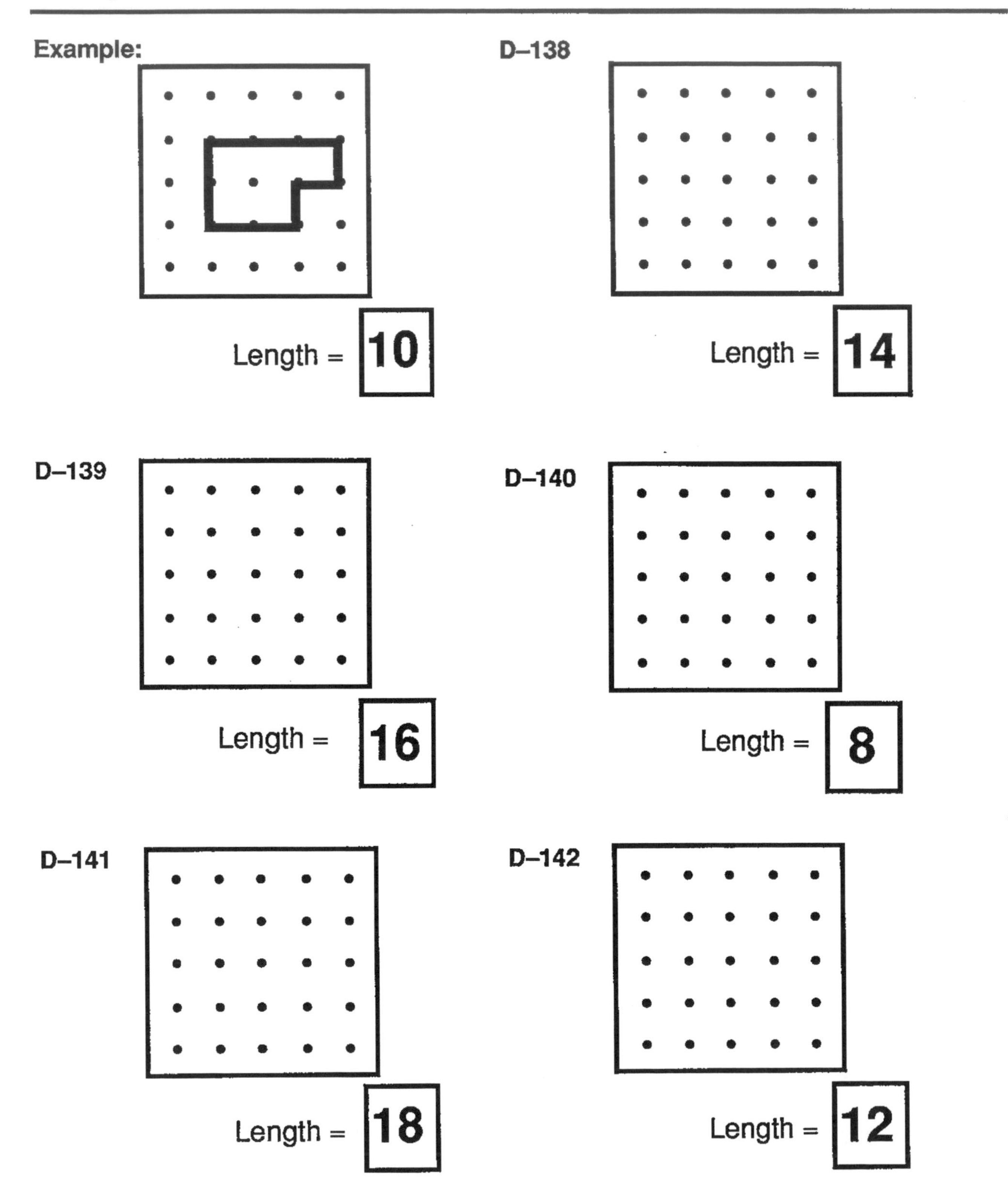

FINDING MISSING LENGTHS

The numbers give the length of some sides of the figure.
Write the missing lengths in the circles.

Example:

D–143

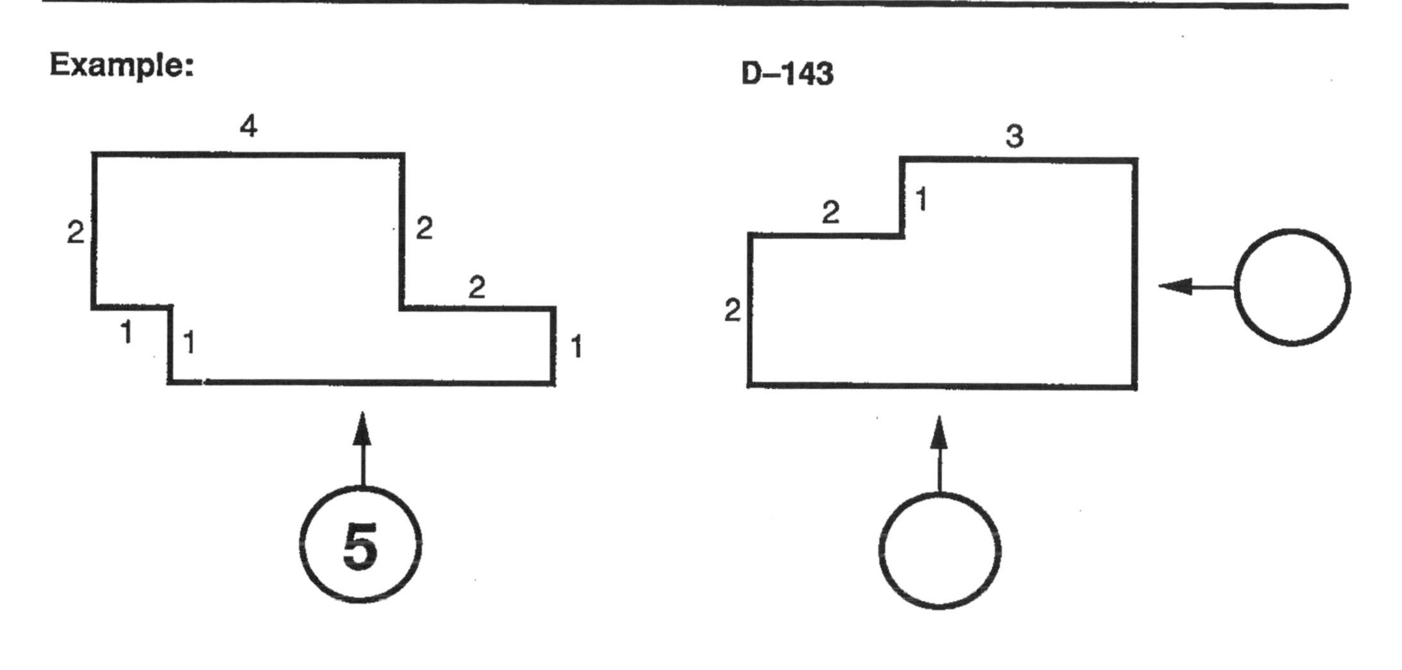

D–144

D–145

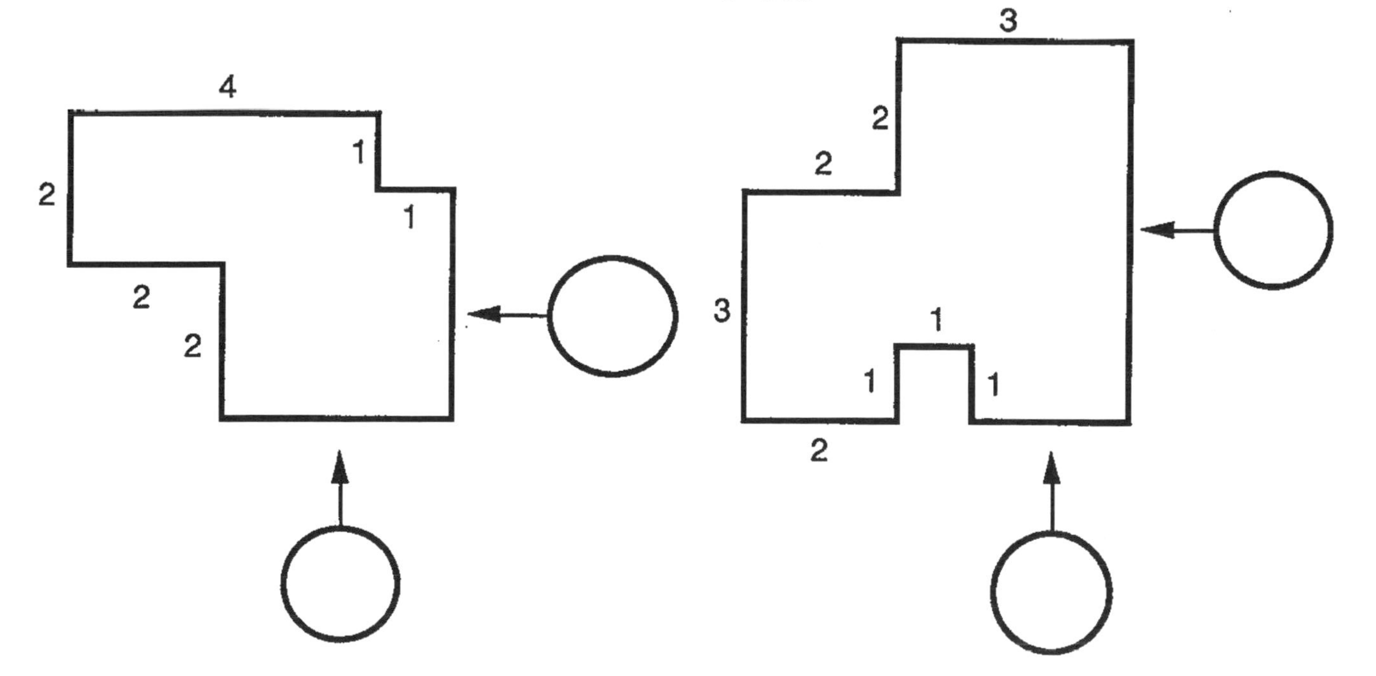

FINDING MISSING LENGTHS

Write the missing lengths in the circles.
Find the distance around the figure.
Write the distance in the box.

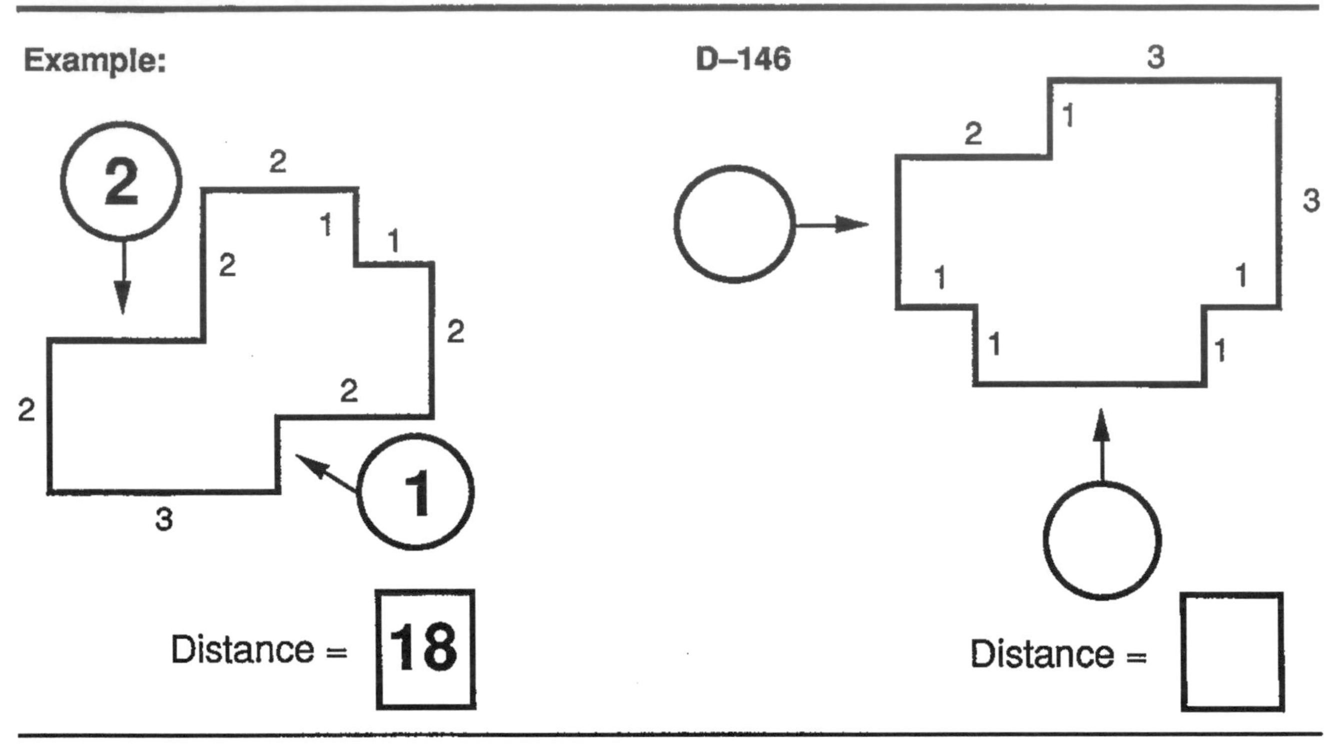

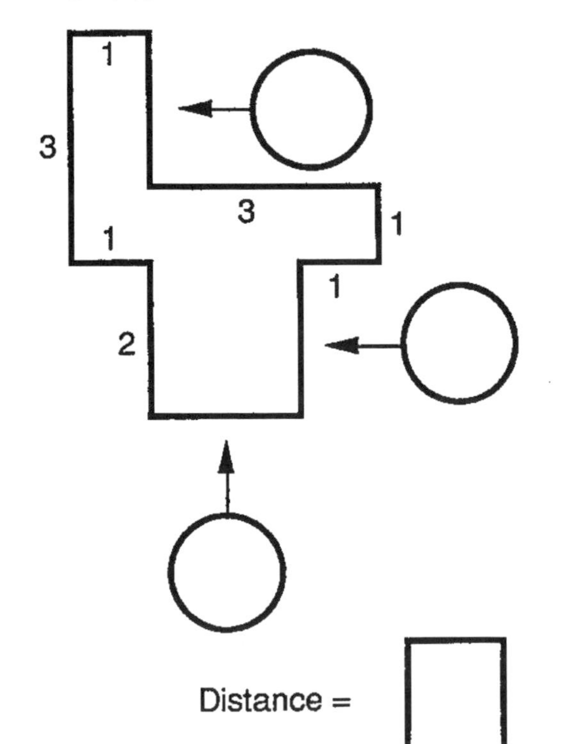

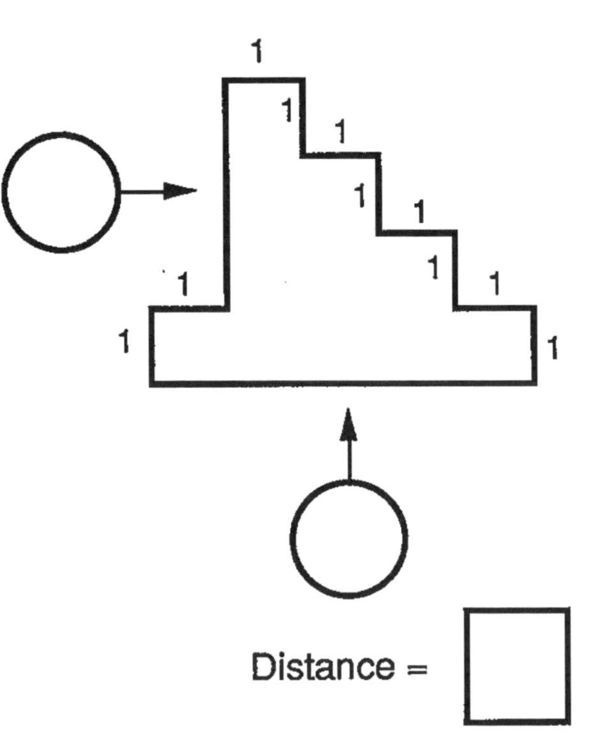

FINDING AREA BY COUNTING

Count the number of squares in each figure.
Place the answer in the area box.

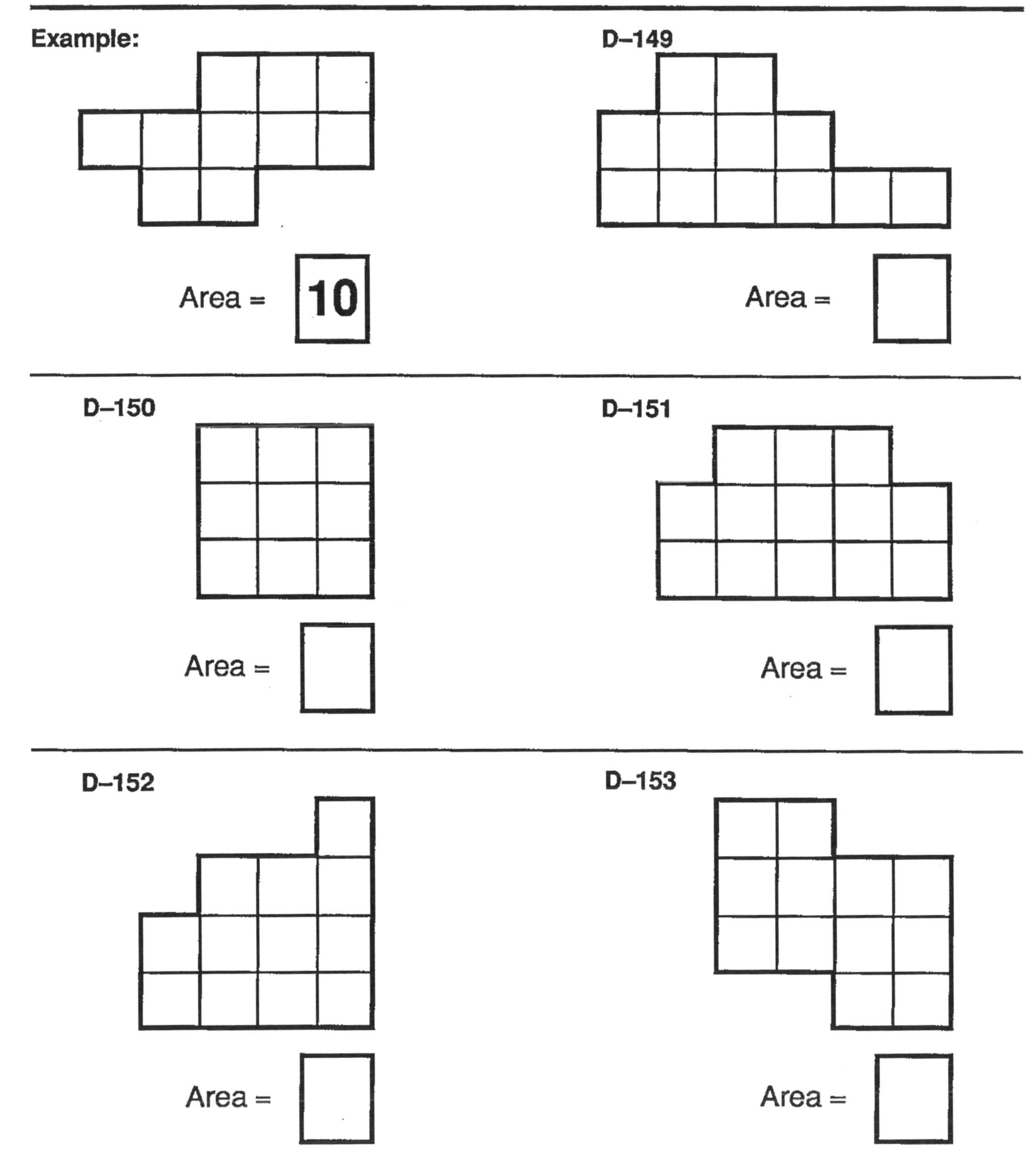

FINDING AREA BY COUNTING

Count the number of squares in each figure.
Place the answer in the area box.

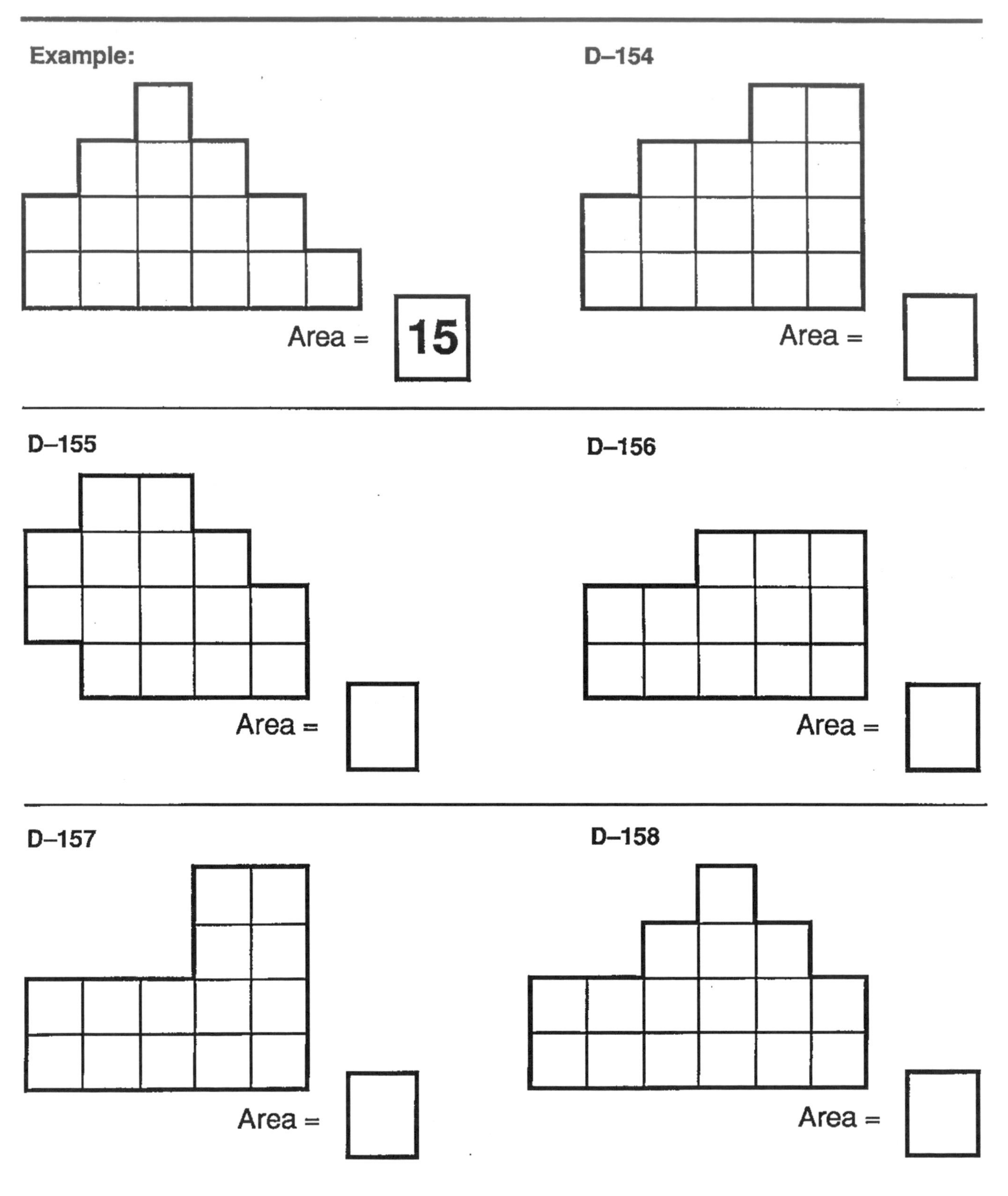

PATTERN COUNTING

Count the number of squares in each row or column.
Write the answer on the blank indicated by the arrow.
Write the total number of squares in the circle.

Example:

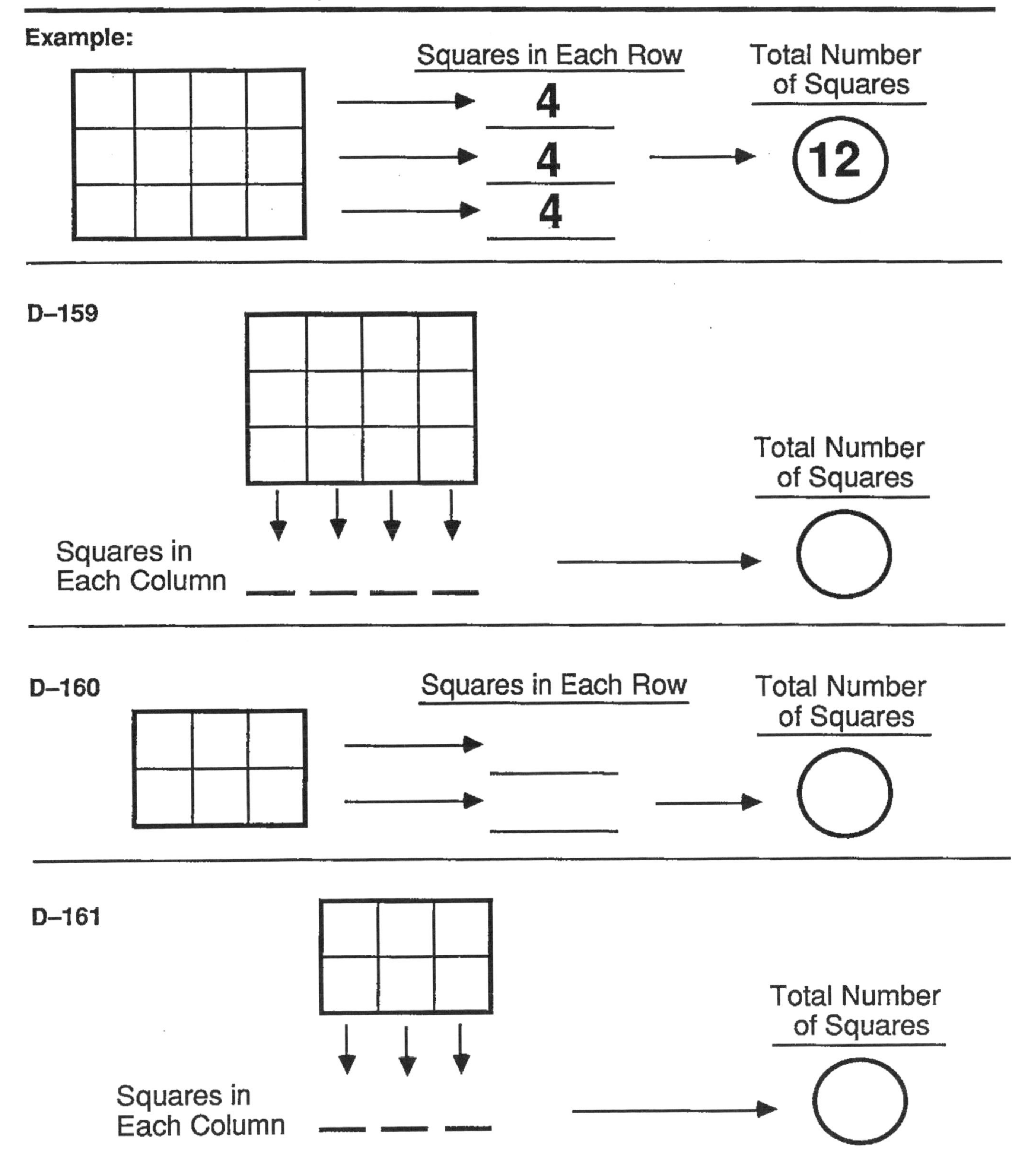

PATTERN COUNTING

Count the number of squares in each row or column.
Write the answer on the blank indicated by the arrow.
Write the total number of squares in the circle.

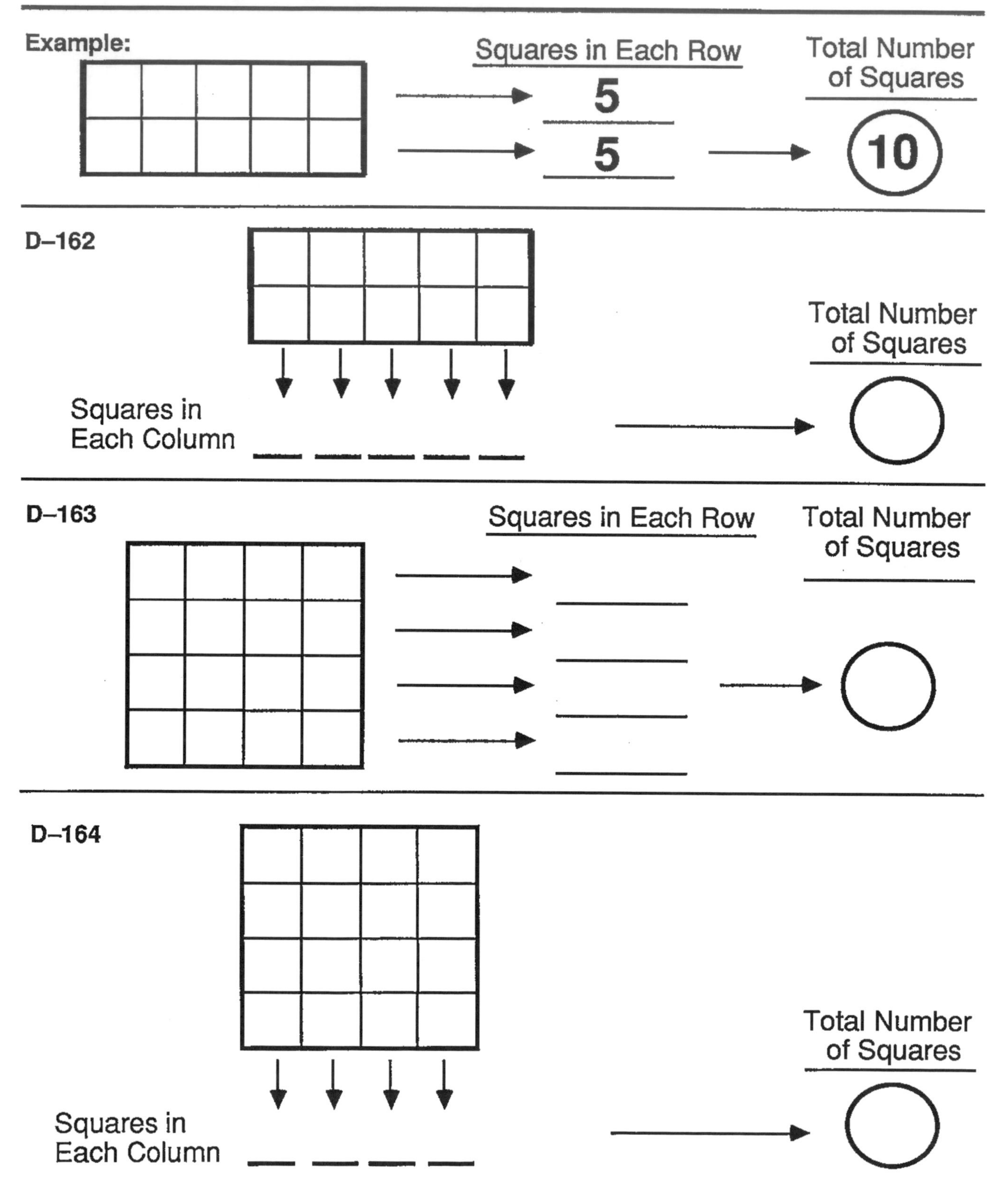

FINDING AREA BY COUNTING

Count the number of squares in each figure.

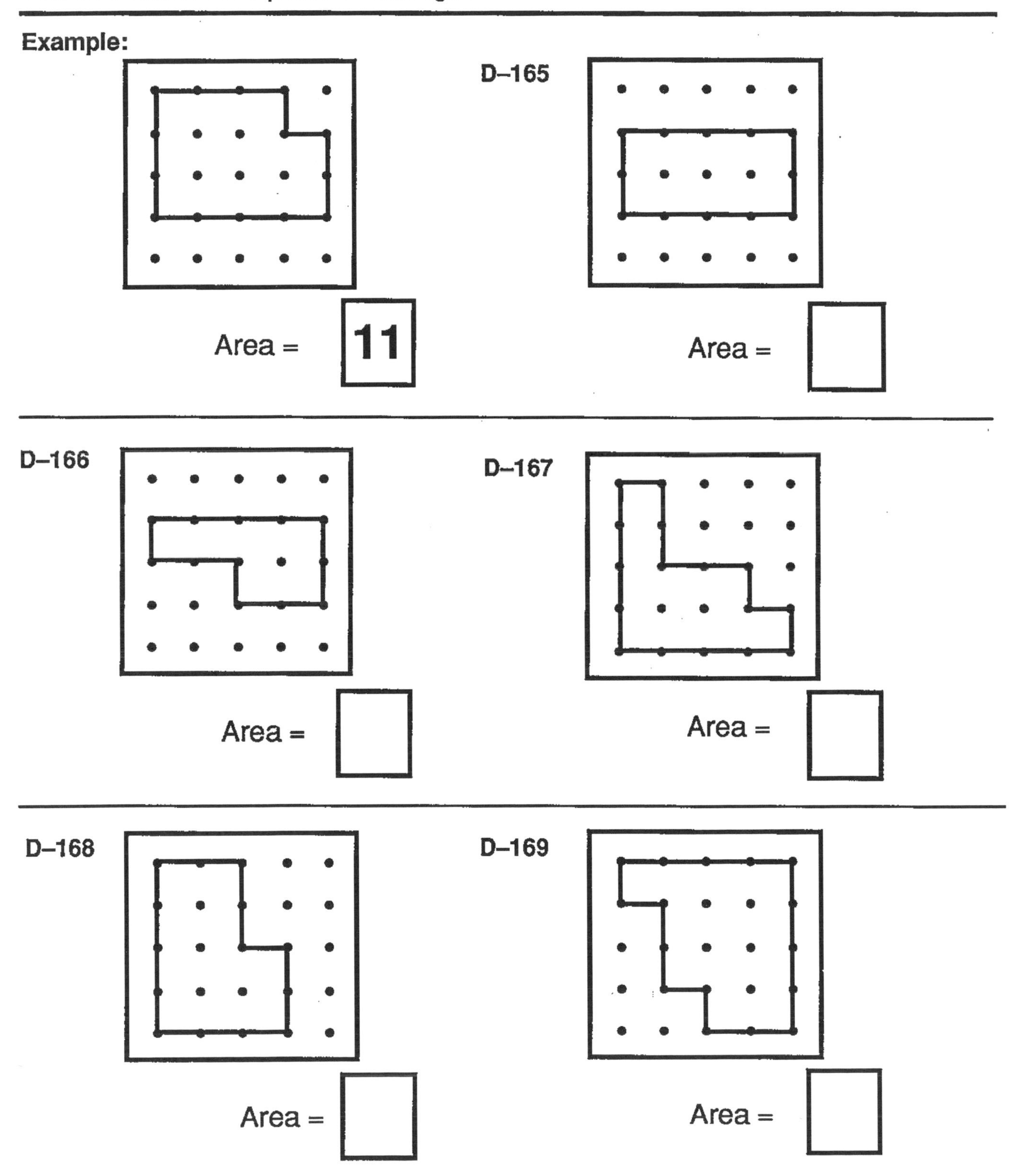

FINDING AREA BY COUNTING

Count the number of squares in each figure.

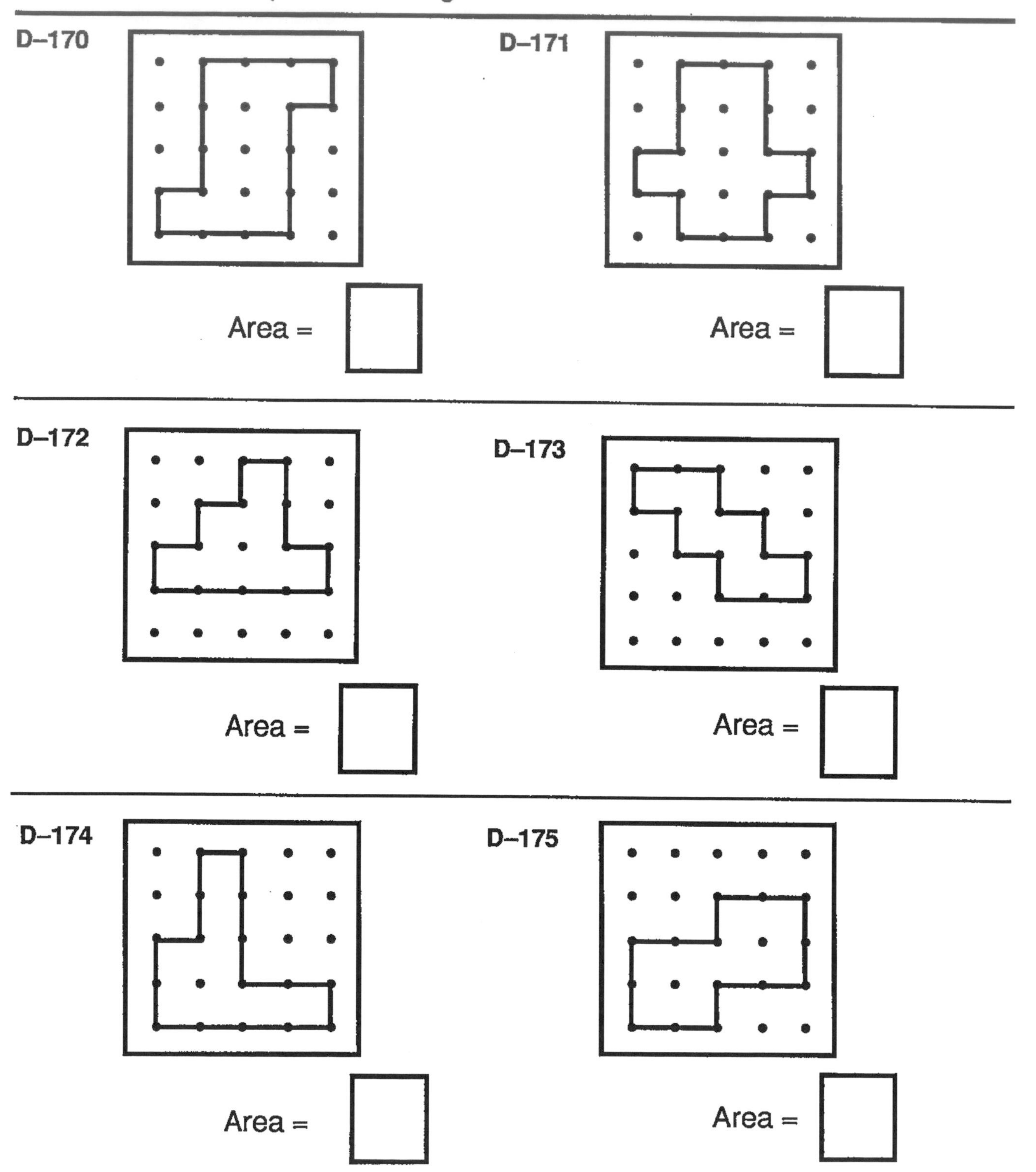

COMPLETING THE RECTANGLE

Add lines to each figure to make it into one rectangle. Remember—a square is a rectangle. Find the number of squares needed to complete the rectangle.

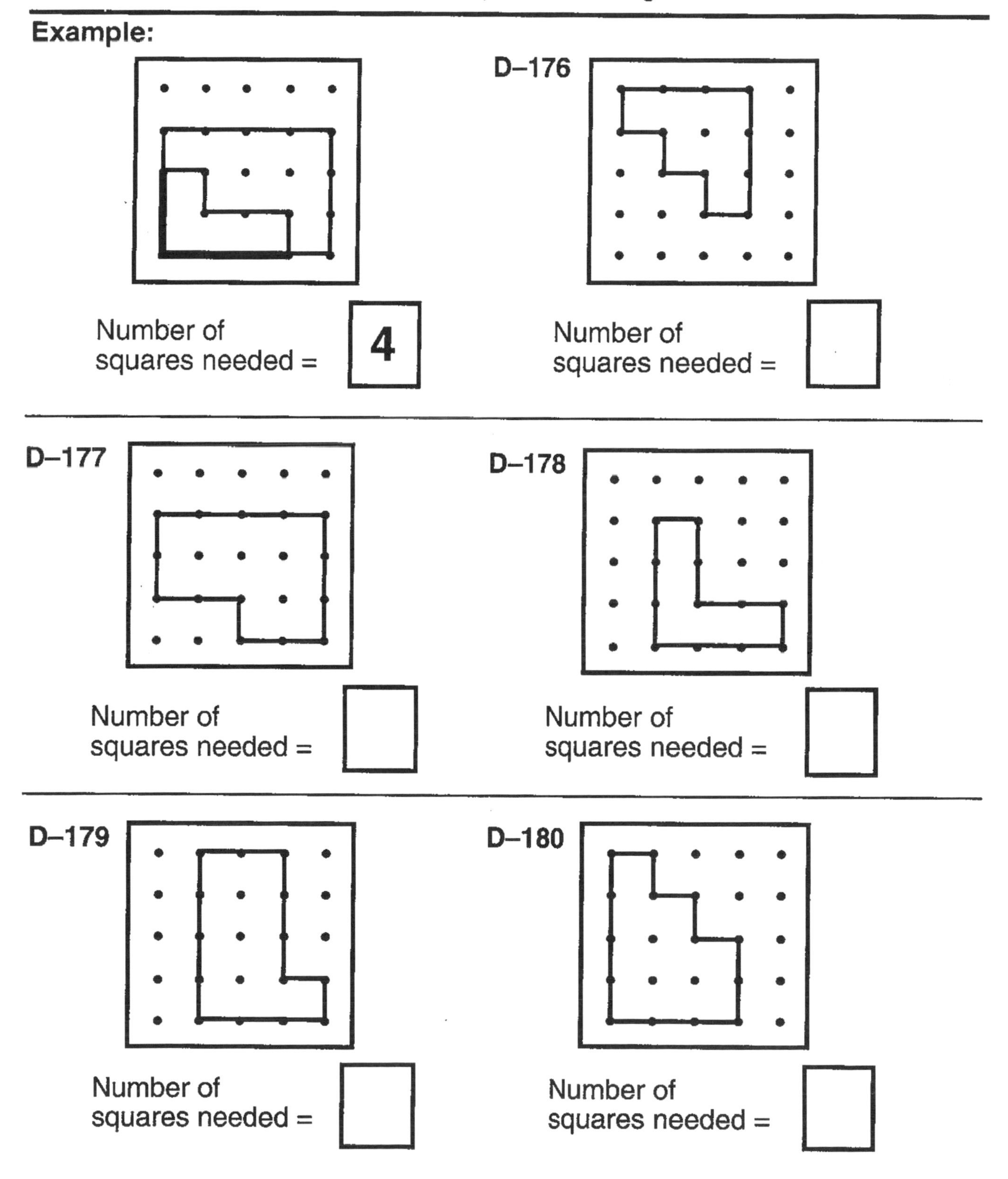

COMPLETING THE RECTANGLE

The numbers give the lengths of the edges.
The dotted lines complete the rectangle.
Find the number of squares needed to complete the rectangle.

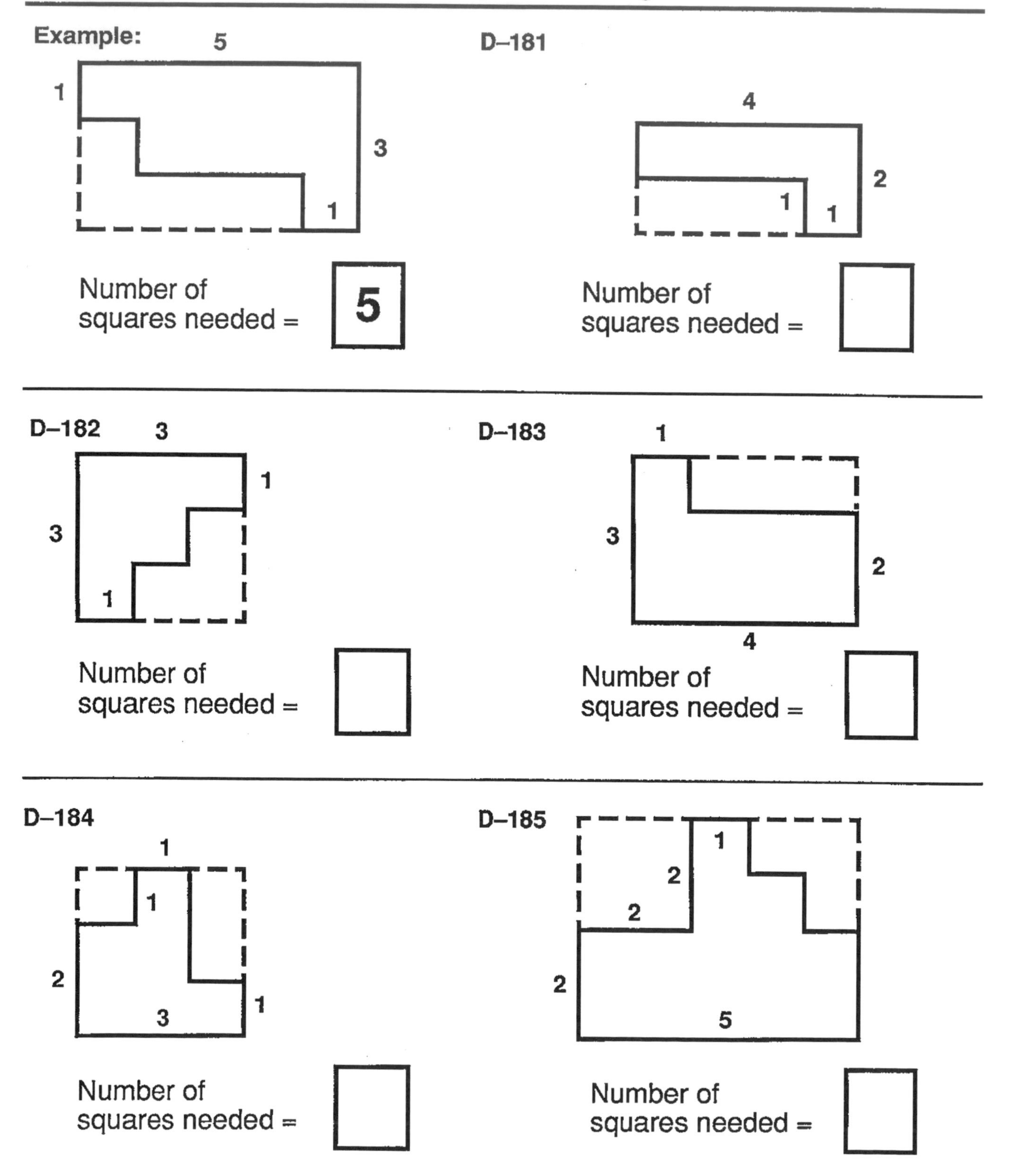

FINDING AREA BY COUNTING

Units are marked on the edges of the figures.
Connect the marks to divide the figures into squares.
Count the number of squares in each figure.

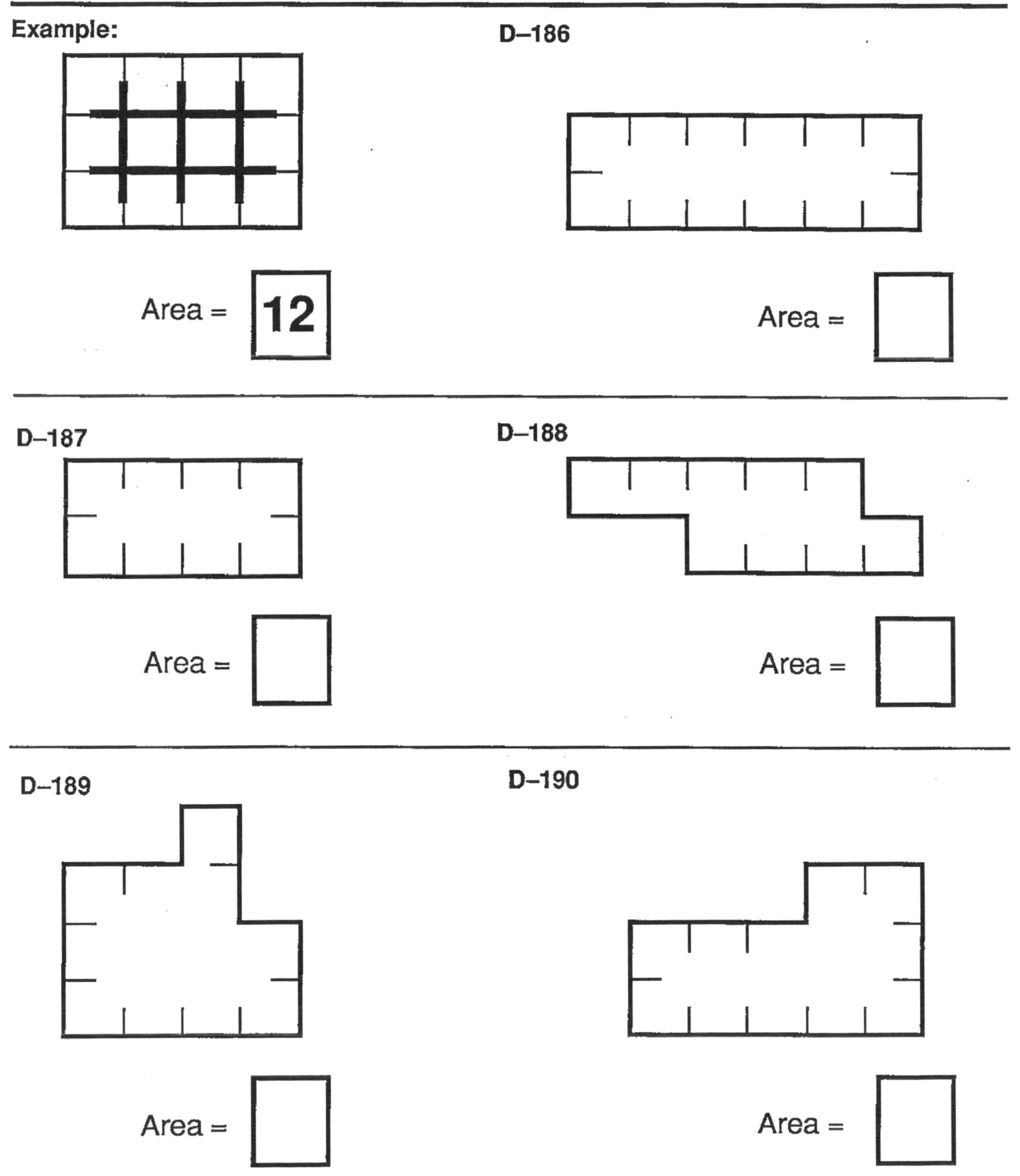

FINDING AREA BY COUNTING

Units are marked on the edges of the figures.
Connect the marks to divide the figures into squares.
Count the number of squares in each figure.

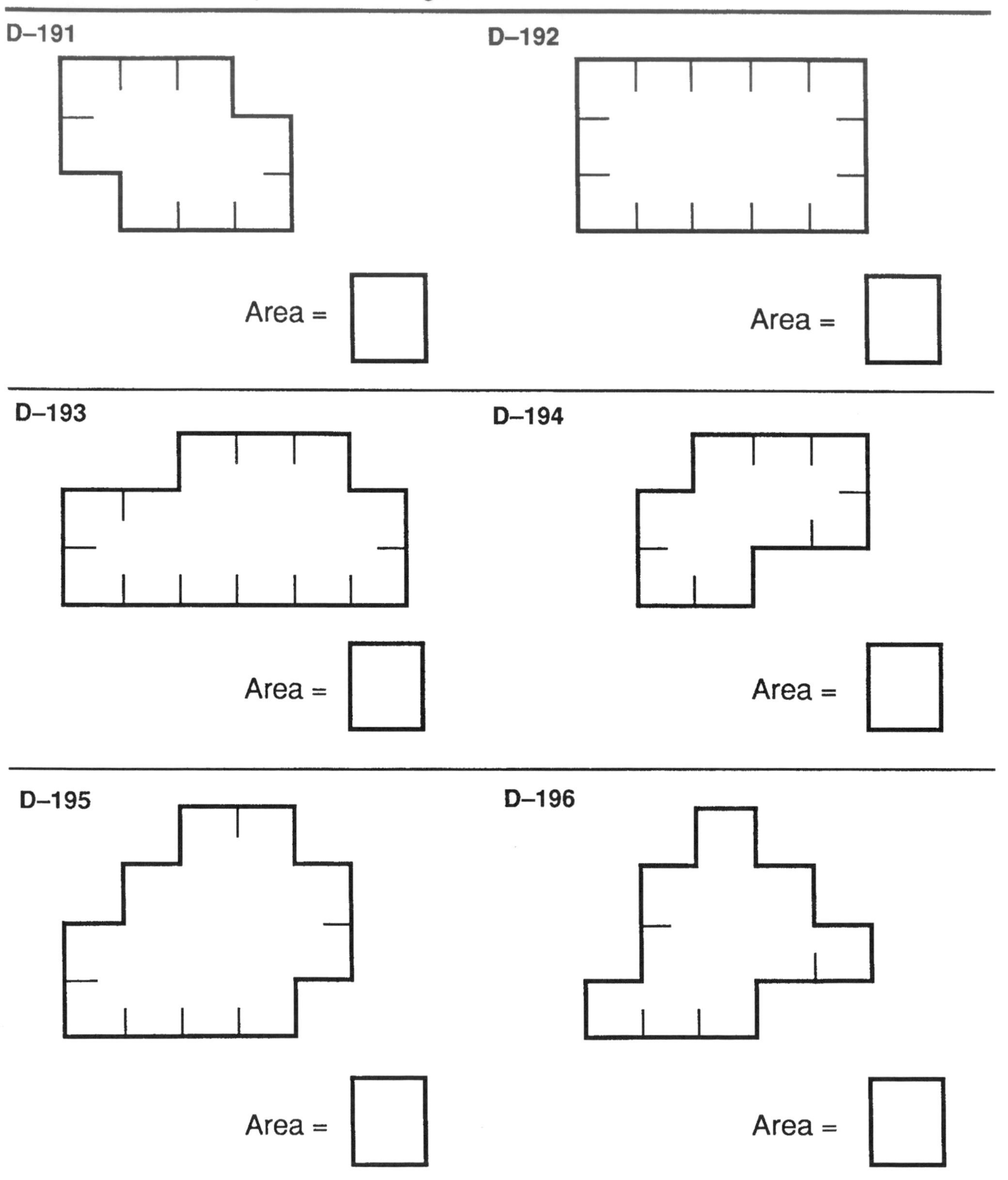

COMPUTING AREA

The square is divided into four regions.

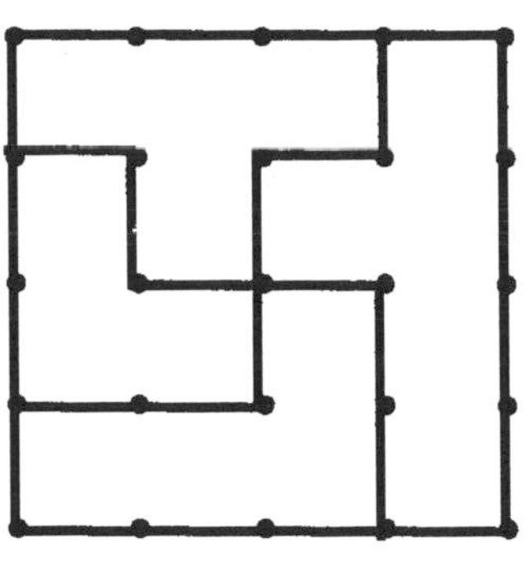

Find each figure in the square.
Write the area of the figure in the box.

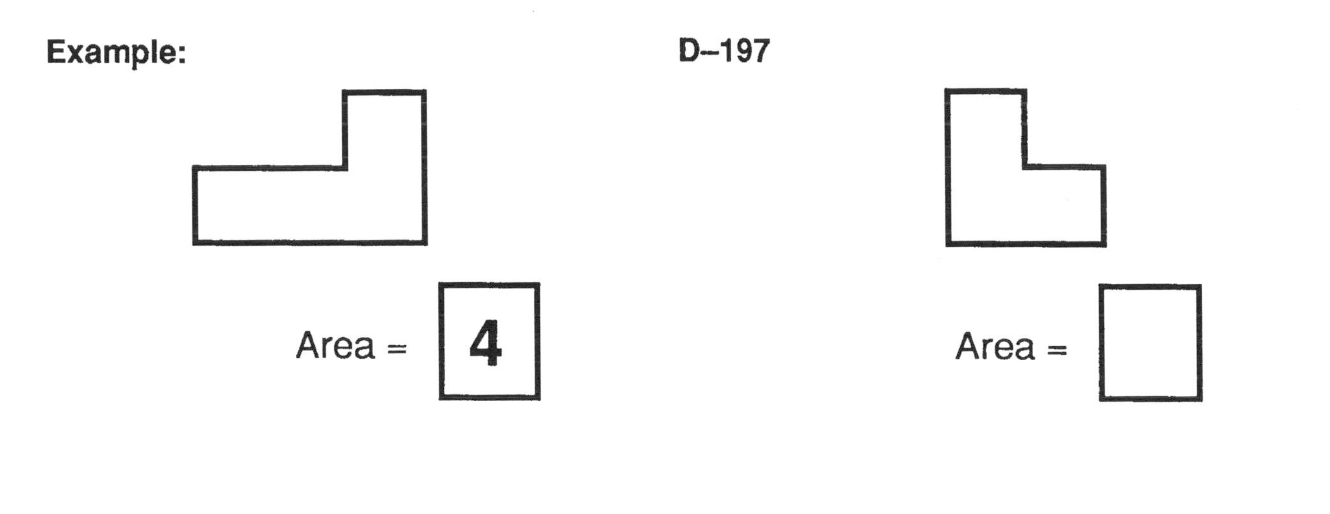

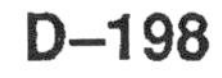

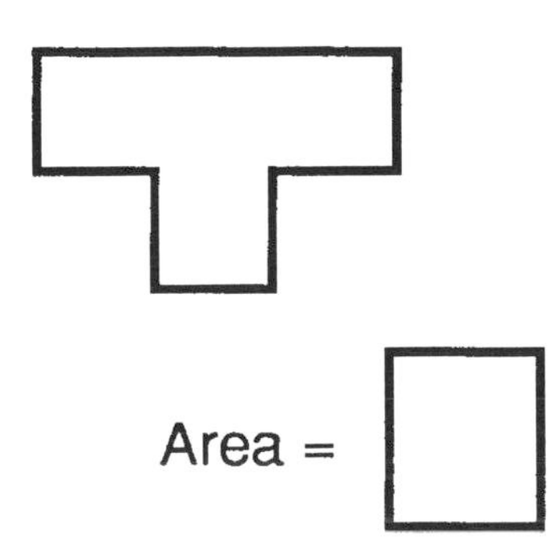

Area =

D–199

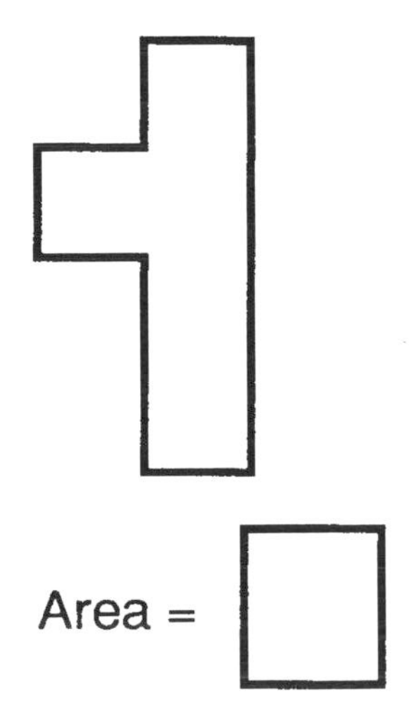

Area =

COMPUTING AREA

The rectangle is divided into six regions.

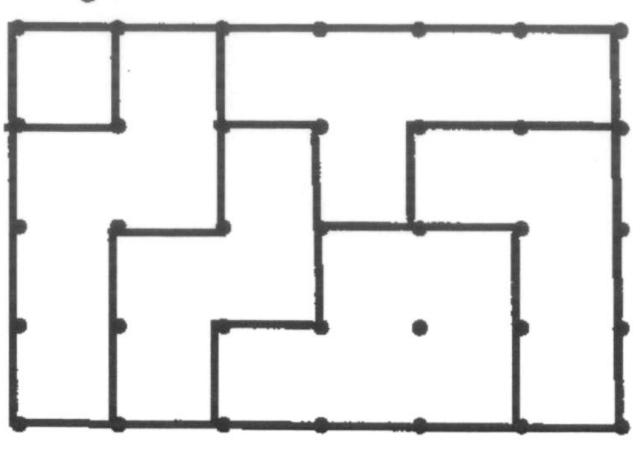

Find each figure in the rectangle.
Write the area of the figure in the box.

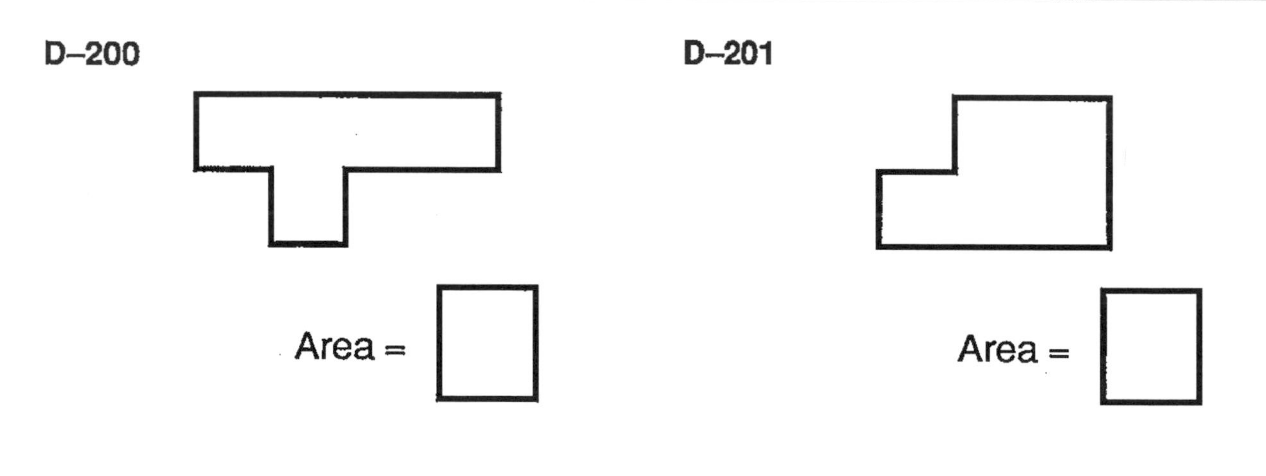

D–200

Area =

D–201

Area =

D–202

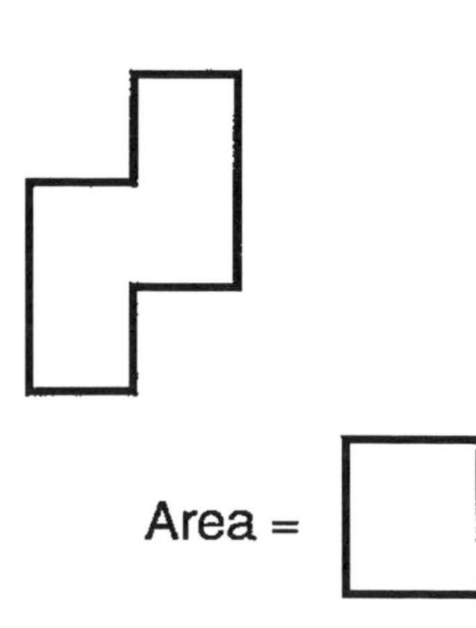

Area =

D–203

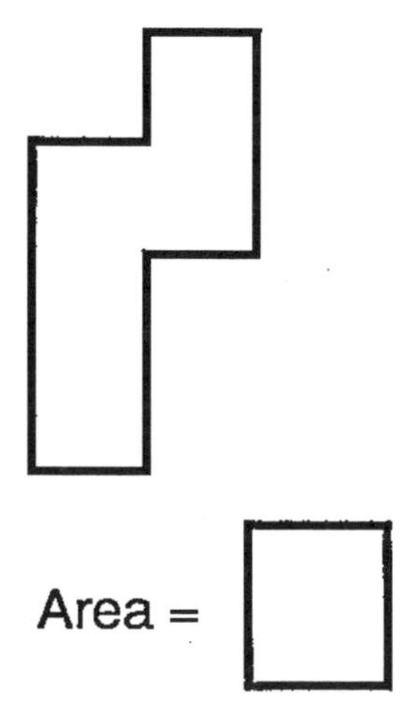

Area =

COMPUTING AREA

The square is divided into five regions.
The numbers give the area of each region.

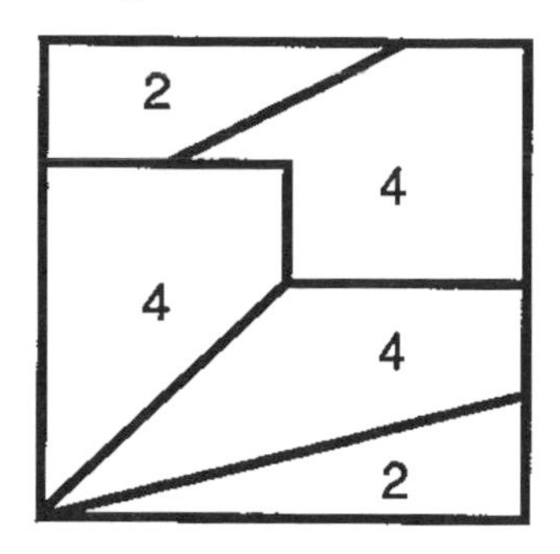

Each figure below can be found in the square.
Find the area of each figure.
Write the area of the figure in the box.

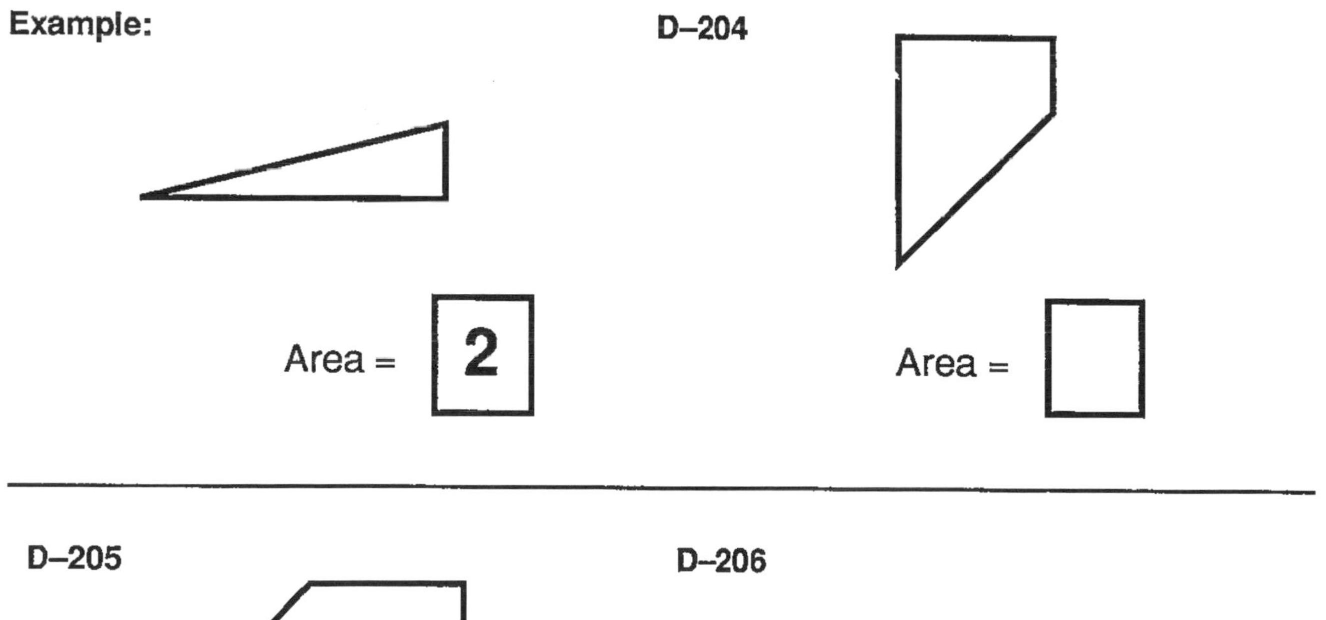

D–205

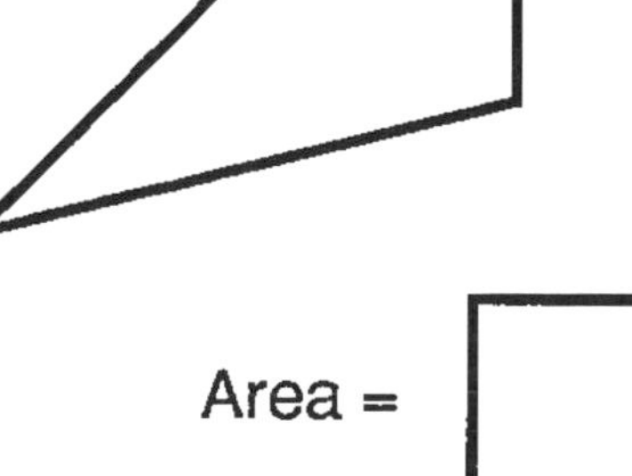

Area =

D–206

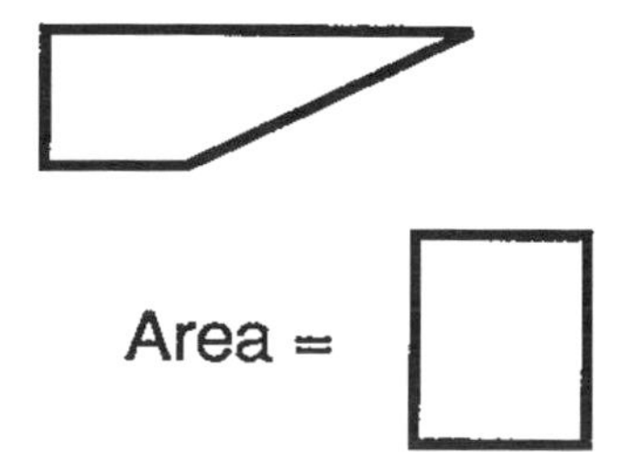

Area =

COMPUTING AREA

The square is divided into five regions.
The numbers give the area of each region.

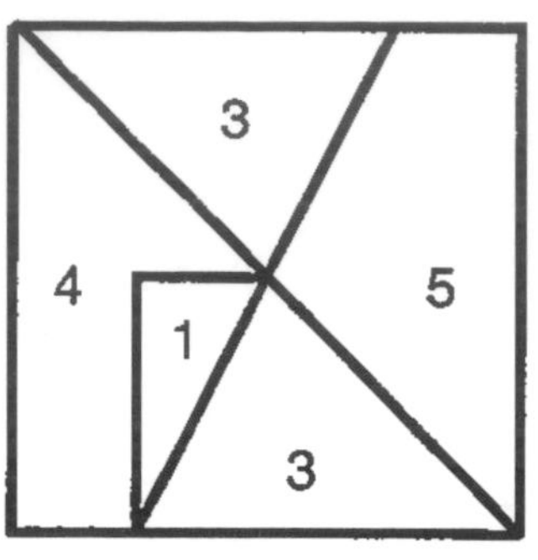

Each figure below can be found in the square.
Find the area of each figure.
Write the area in the box.

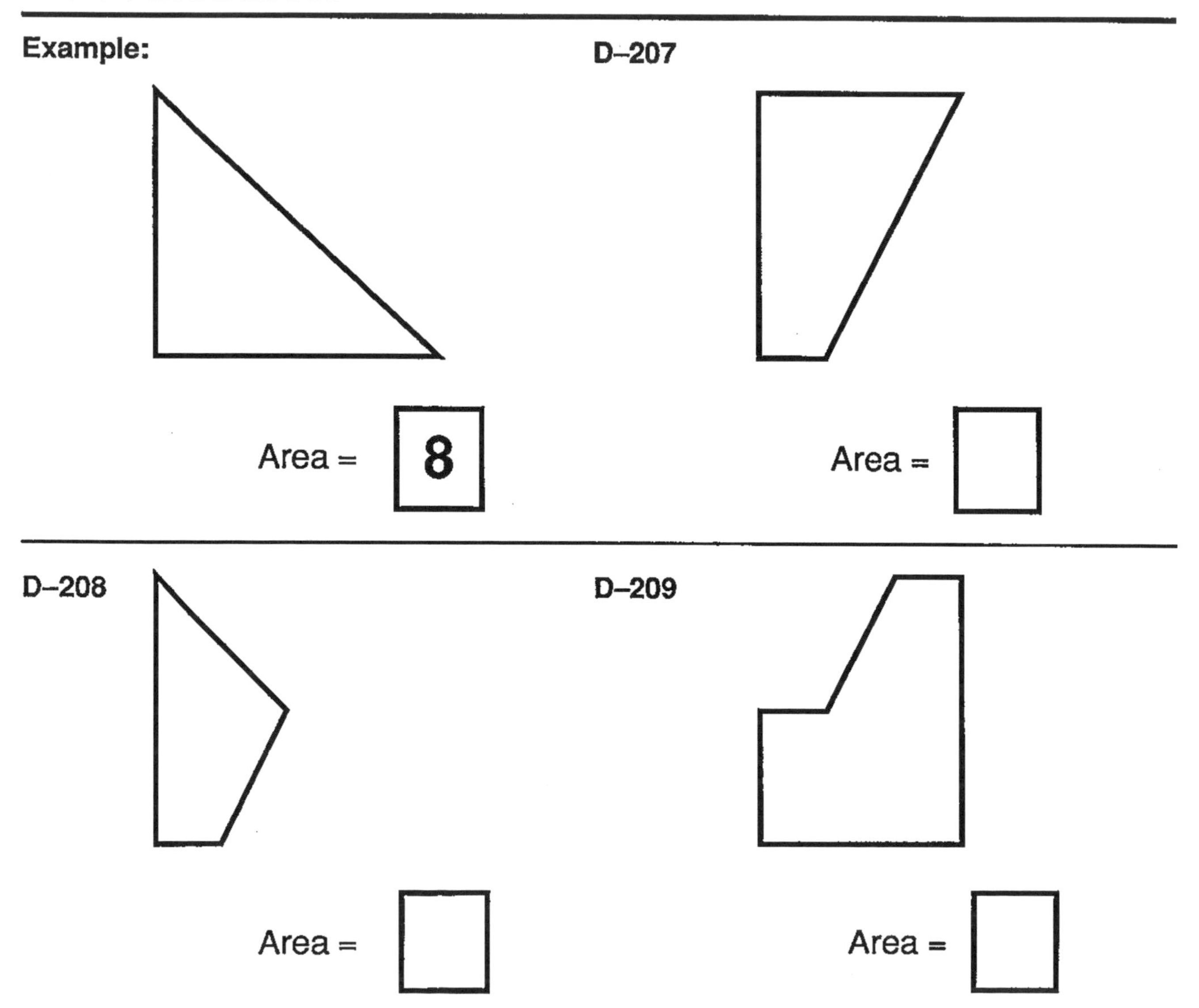

AREA USING 1/2 UNITS

The area of the square is 1.

This square is divided into two triangles.
The area of one triangle is 1/2.

Divide each figure below into squares and half-squares.
Write the answers in the boxes.

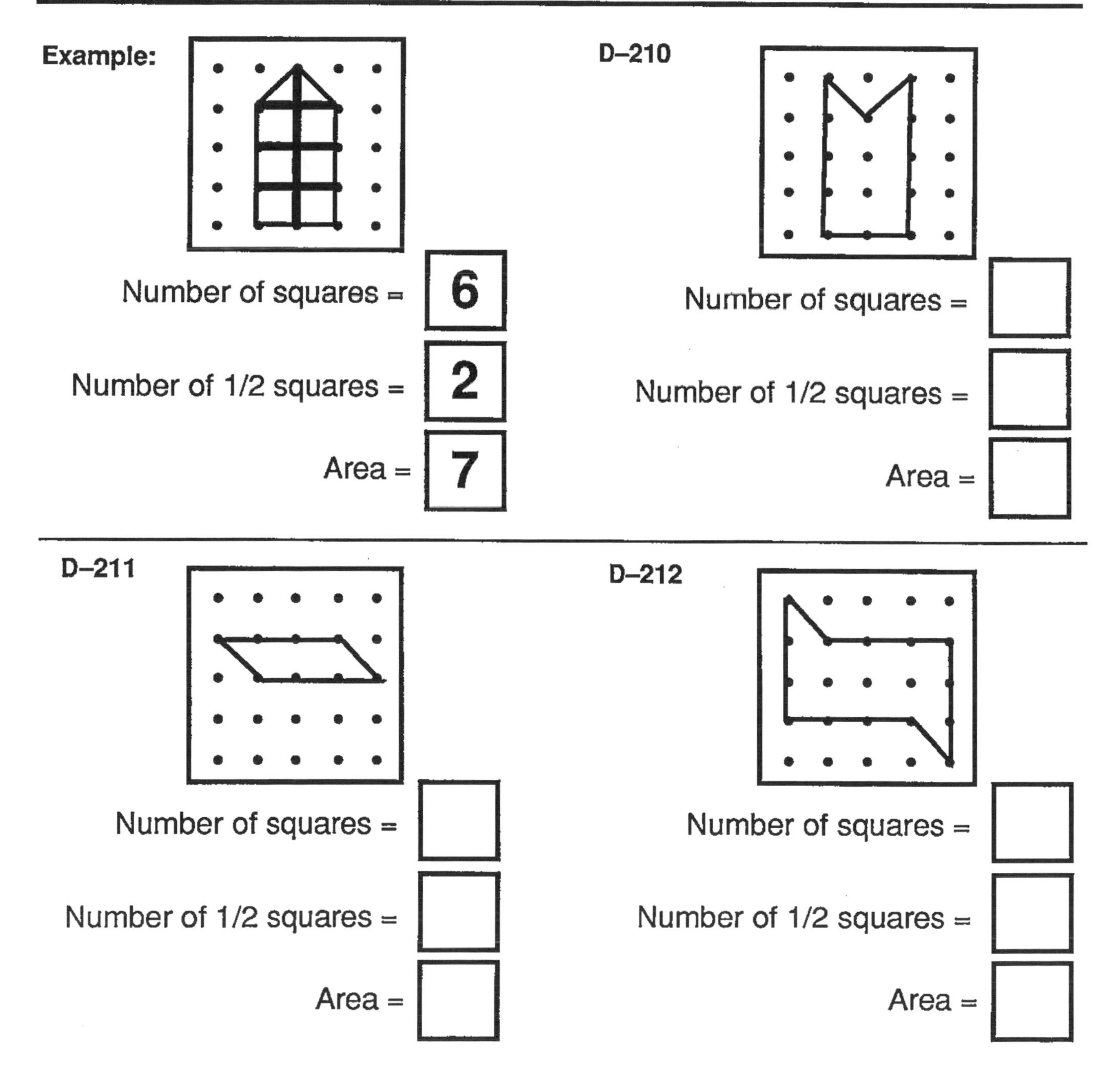

AREA USING 1/2 UNITS

Divide each figure into squares and half-squares.
Write the answers in the boxes.

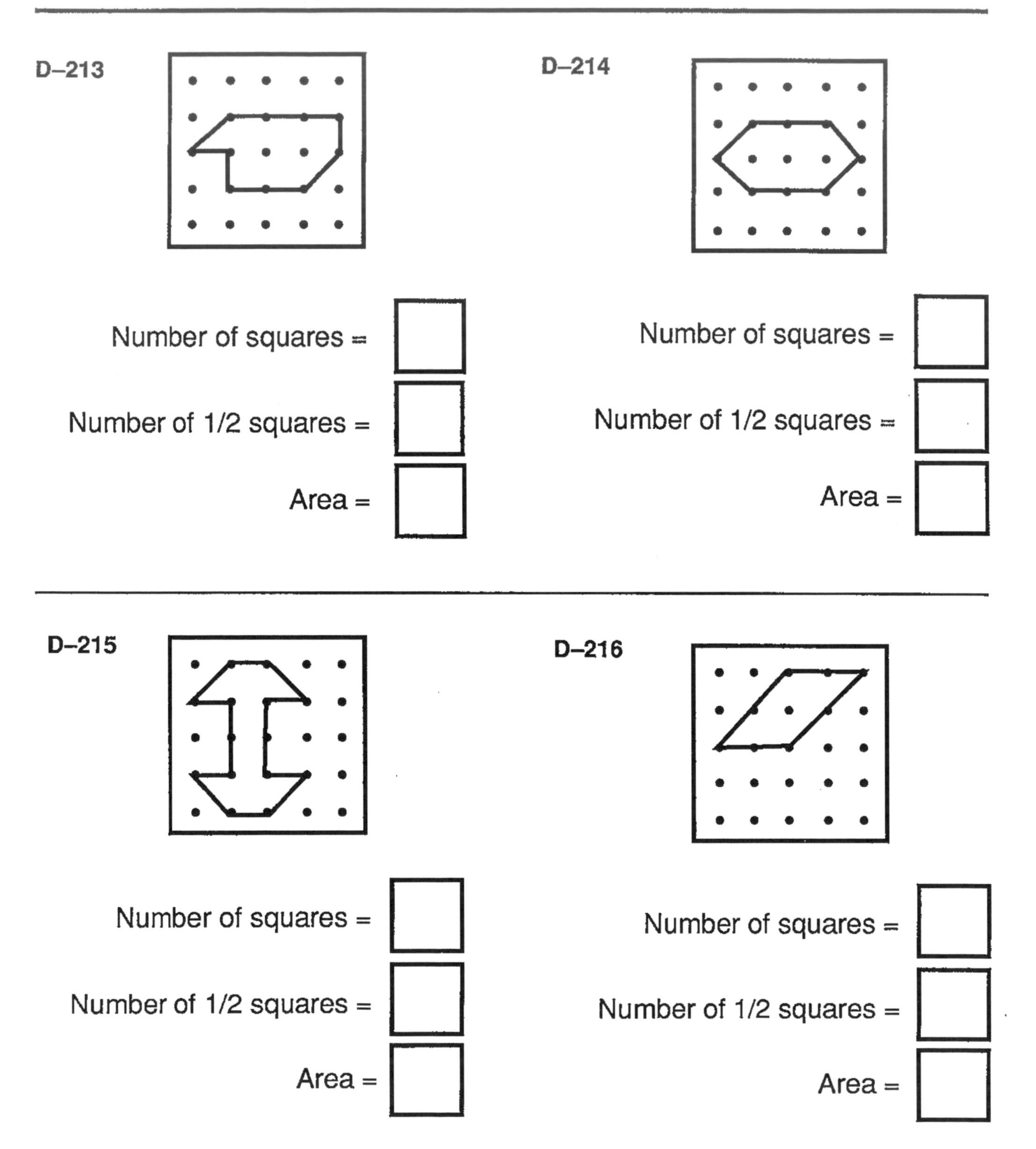

DRAWING FIGURES

The area is written in the box.
Draw a figure with that area.

Example:

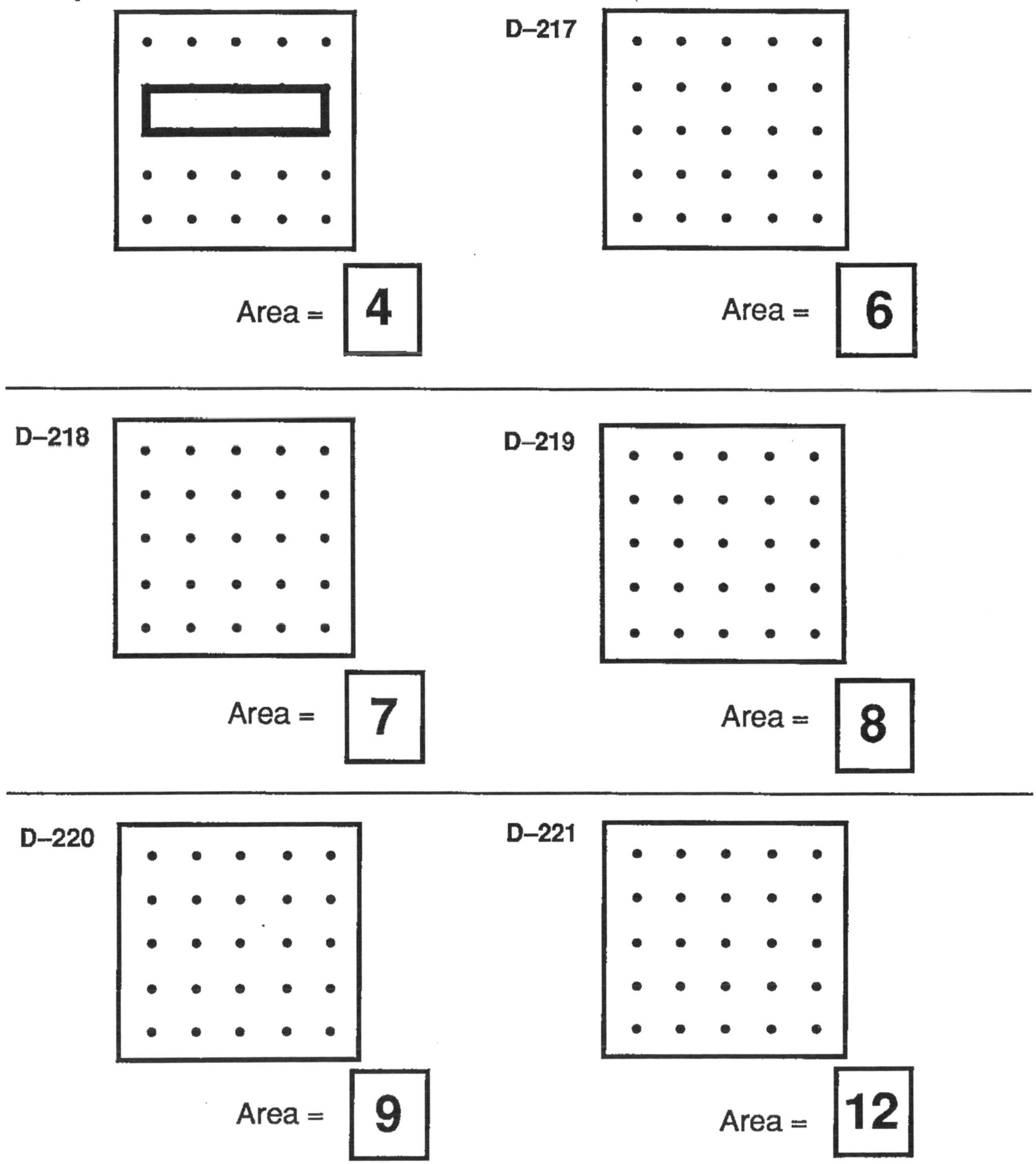

DRAWING FIGURES

The area is written in the box.
Part of a figure has been drawn.
Complete the figure with that area.

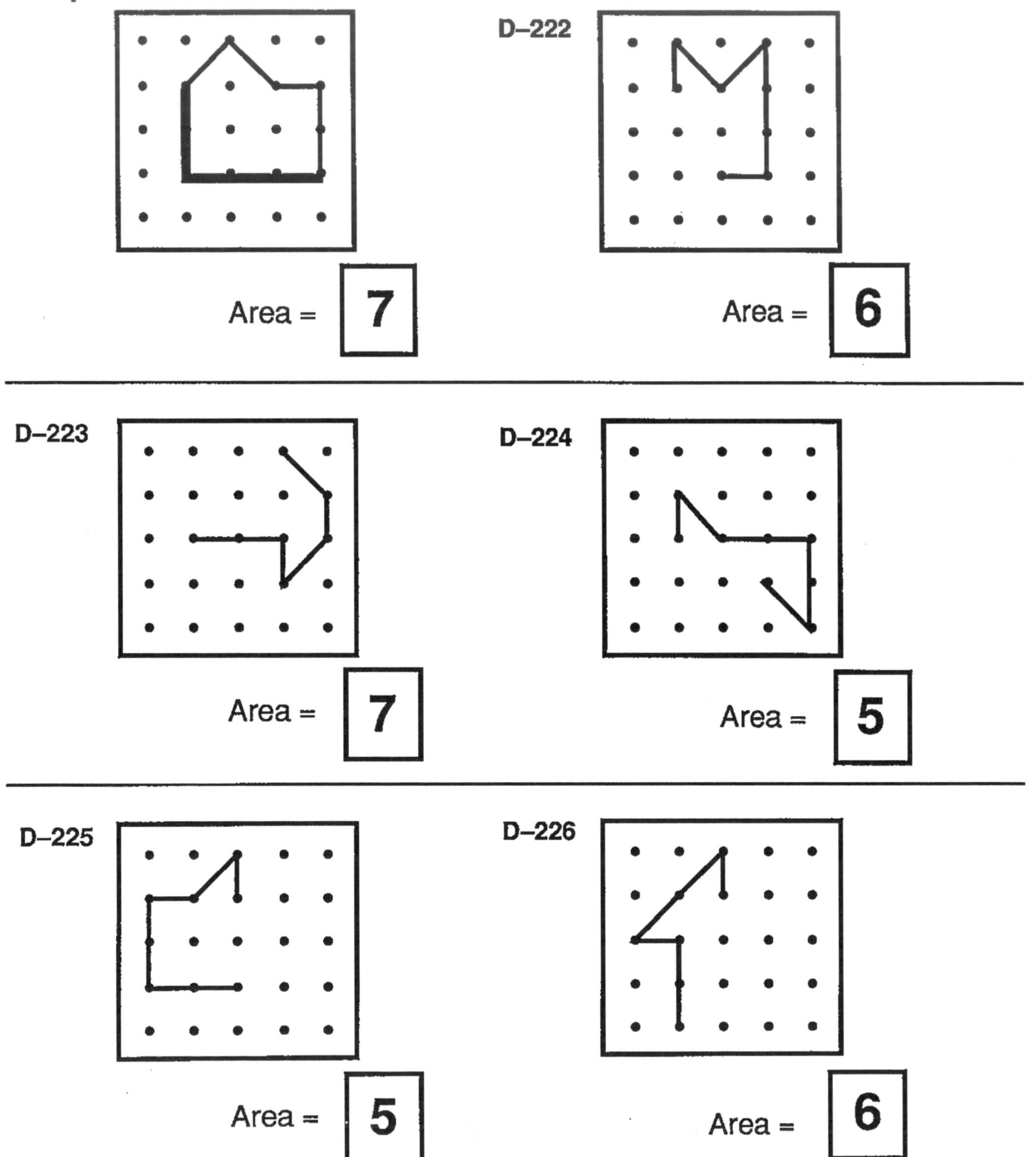

ESTIMATING AREA

Circle the number you think is closest to the area of the figure.

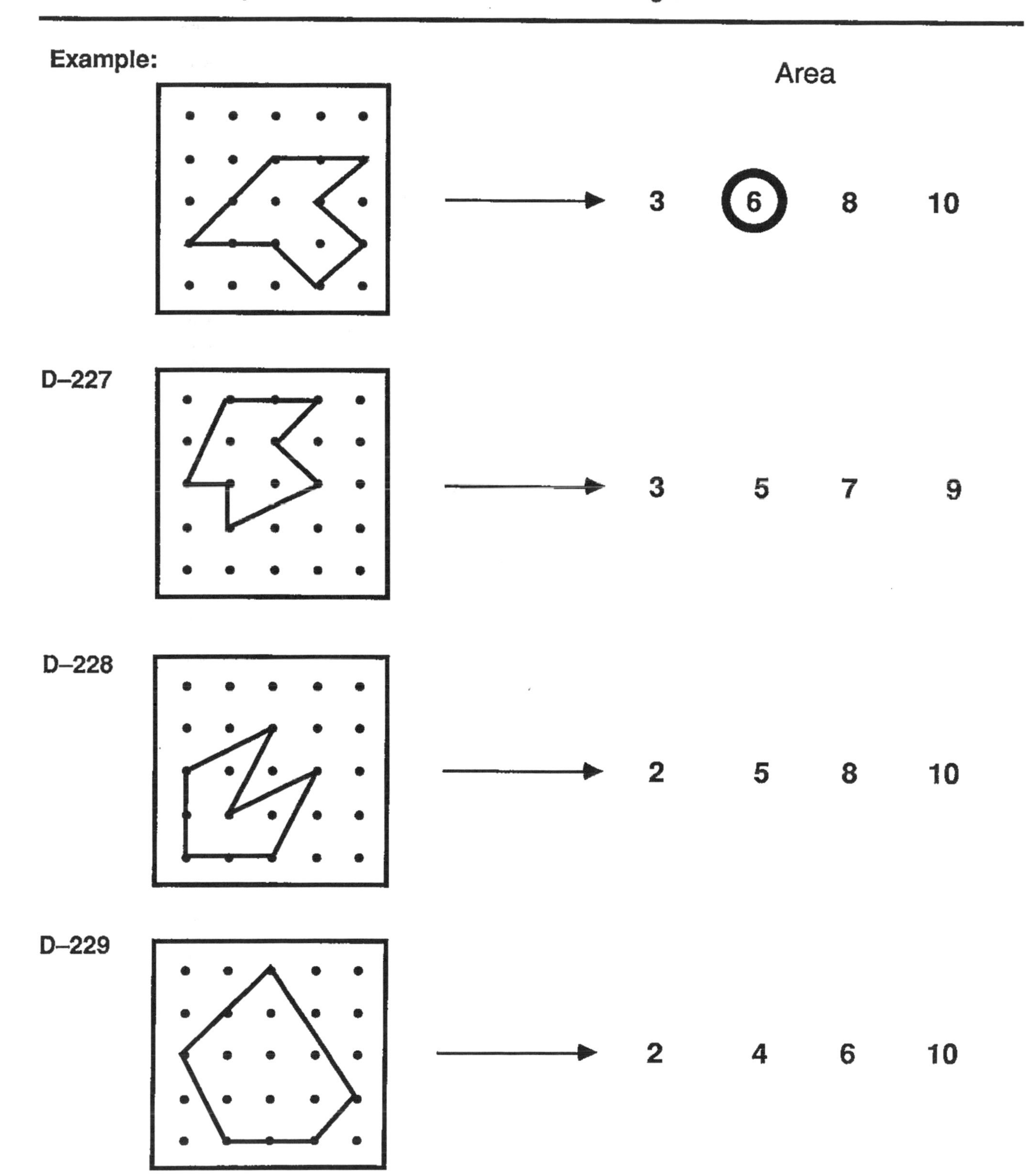

ESTIMATING AREA

Put an X on the figure in each exercise with the larger area.

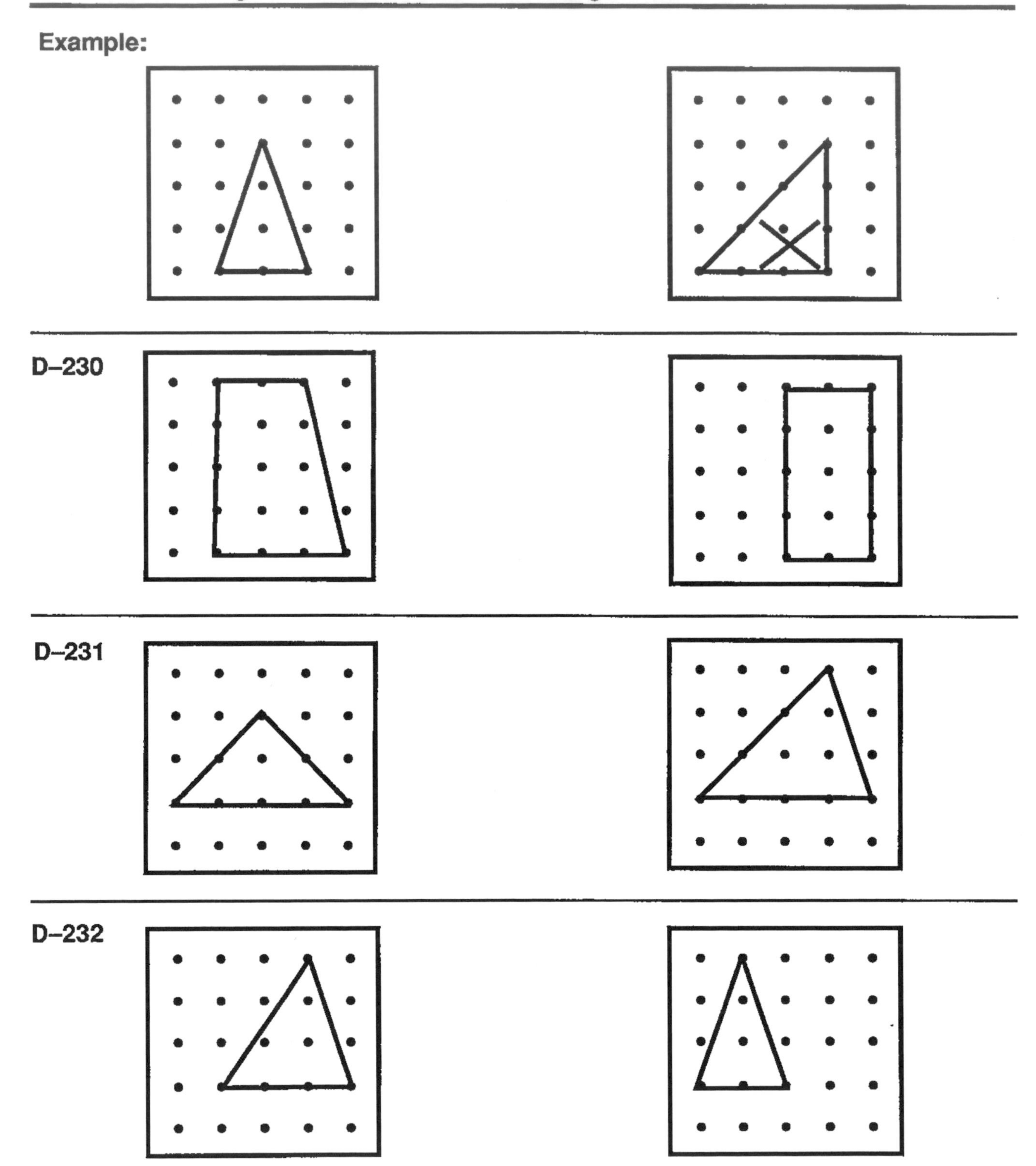

WHAT COMPUTATION DO YOU USE?

Circle the computation that solves the problem.

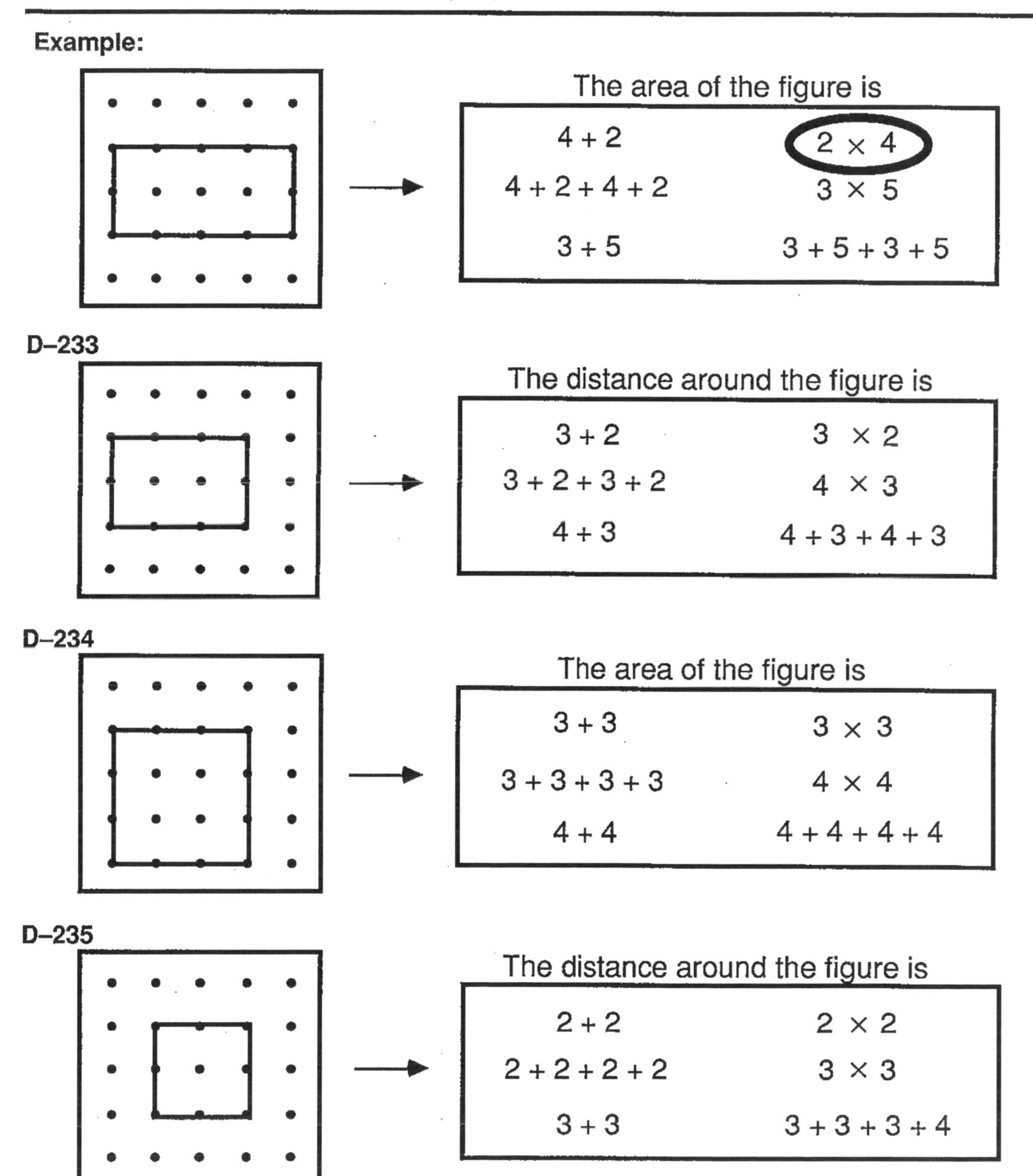

WHAT COMPUTATION DO YOU USE?

Circle the computation that solves the problem.

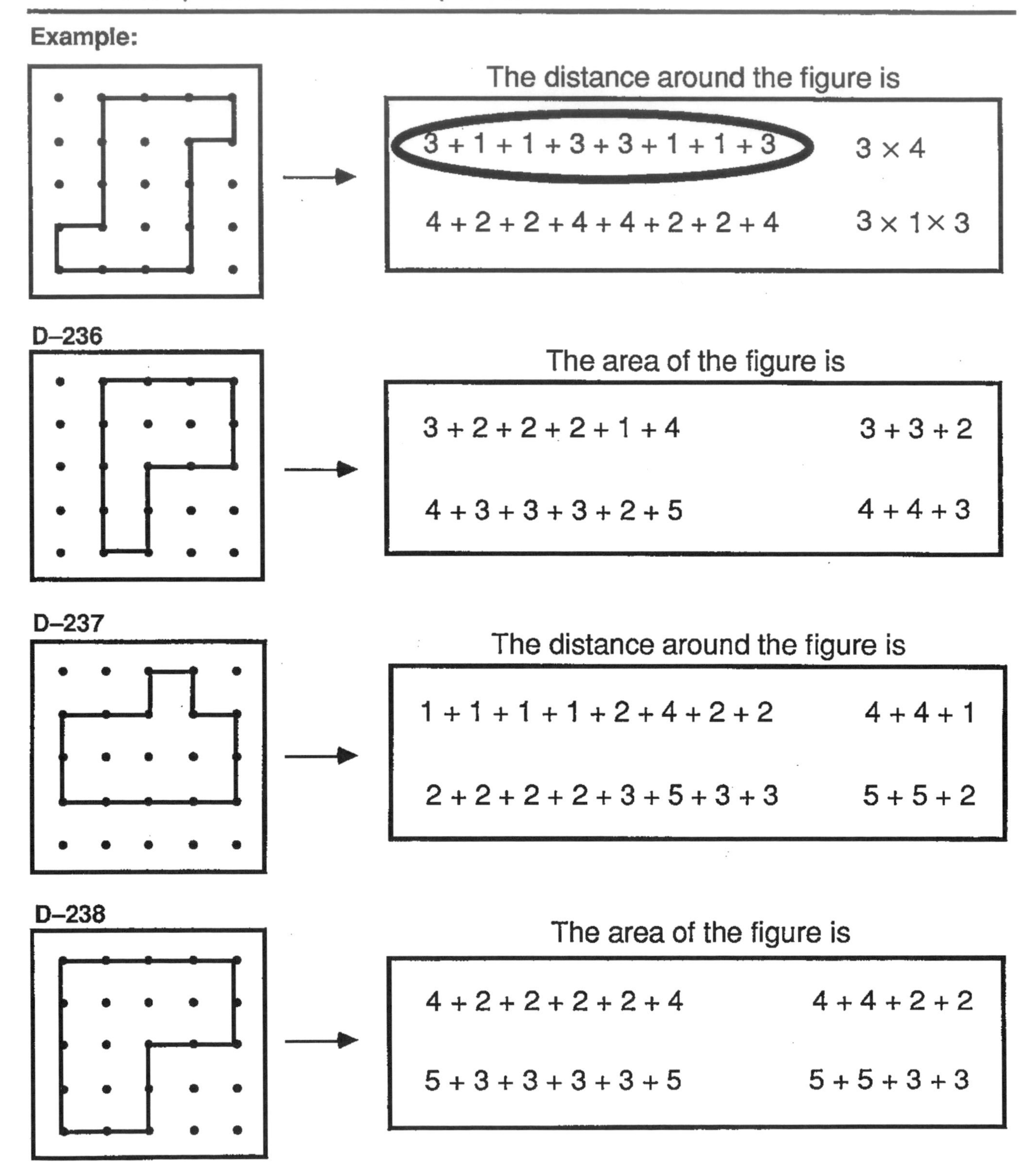

COMPARING NUMBERS

Circle the largest number in each set.
Draw a line under the smallest number.

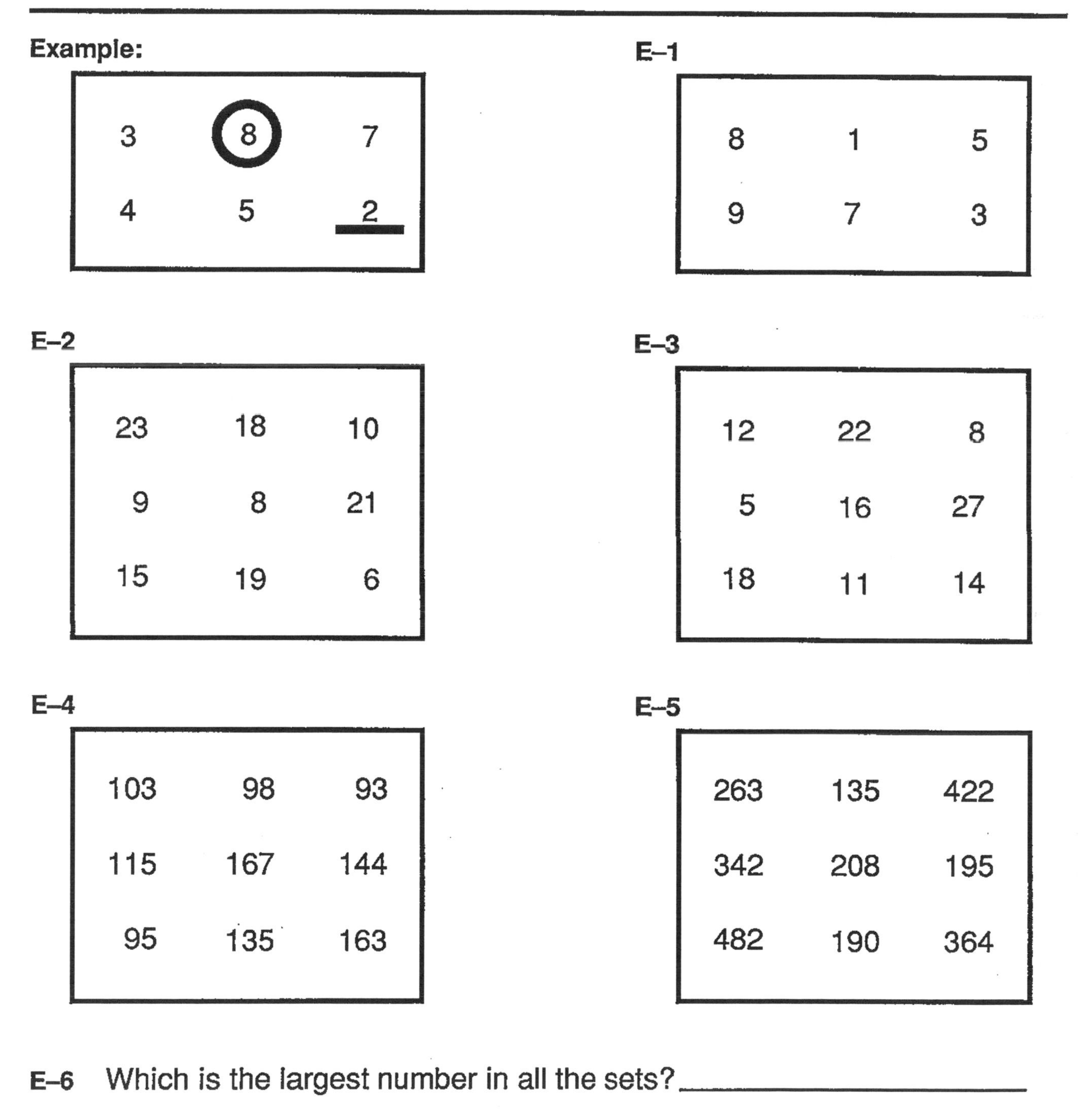

E–6 Which is the largest number in all the sets? ______________

E–7 Which is the smallest number in all the sets? ______________

COMPARING NUMBERS

Circle the largest value in each set.
Draw a line under the smallest value.

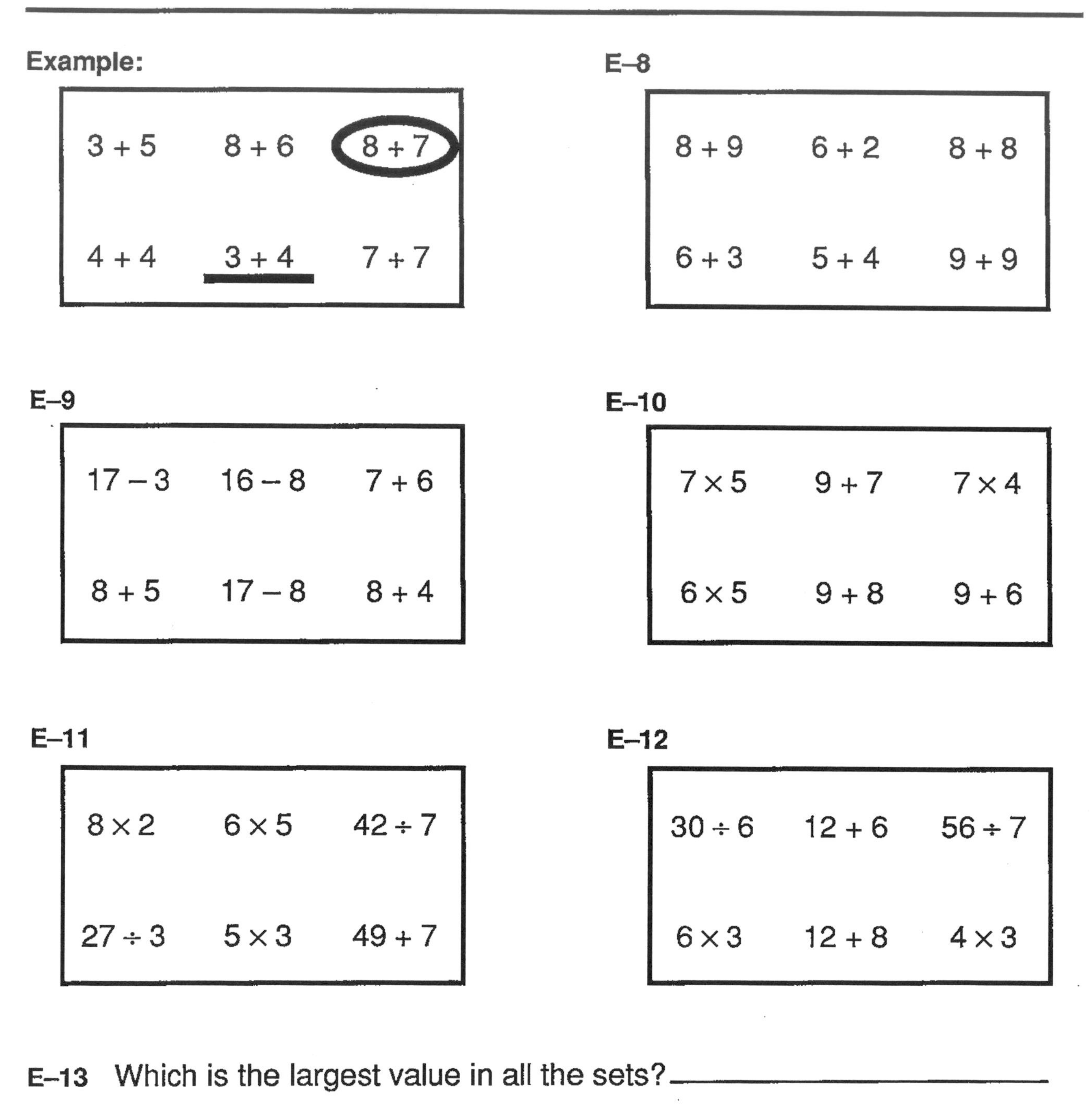

Example:

$3 + 5$	$8 + 6$	$8 + 7$ (circled)
$4 + 4$	$3 + 4$ (underlined)	$7 + 7$

E–8

$8 + 9$	$6 + 2$	$8 + 8$
$6 + 3$	$5 + 4$	$9 + 9$

E–9

$17 - 3$	$16 - 8$	$7 + 6$
$8 + 5$	$17 - 8$	$8 + 4$

E–10

7×5	$9 + 7$	7×4
6×5	$9 + 8$	$9 + 6$

E–11

8×2	6×5	$42 \div 7$
$27 \div 3$	5×3	$49 + 7$

E–12

$30 \div 6$	$12 + 6$	$56 \div 7$
6×3	$12 + 8$	4×3

E–13 Which is the largest value in all the sets? ____________________

E–14 Which is the smallest value in all the sets? ____________________

ORDERING NUMBERS

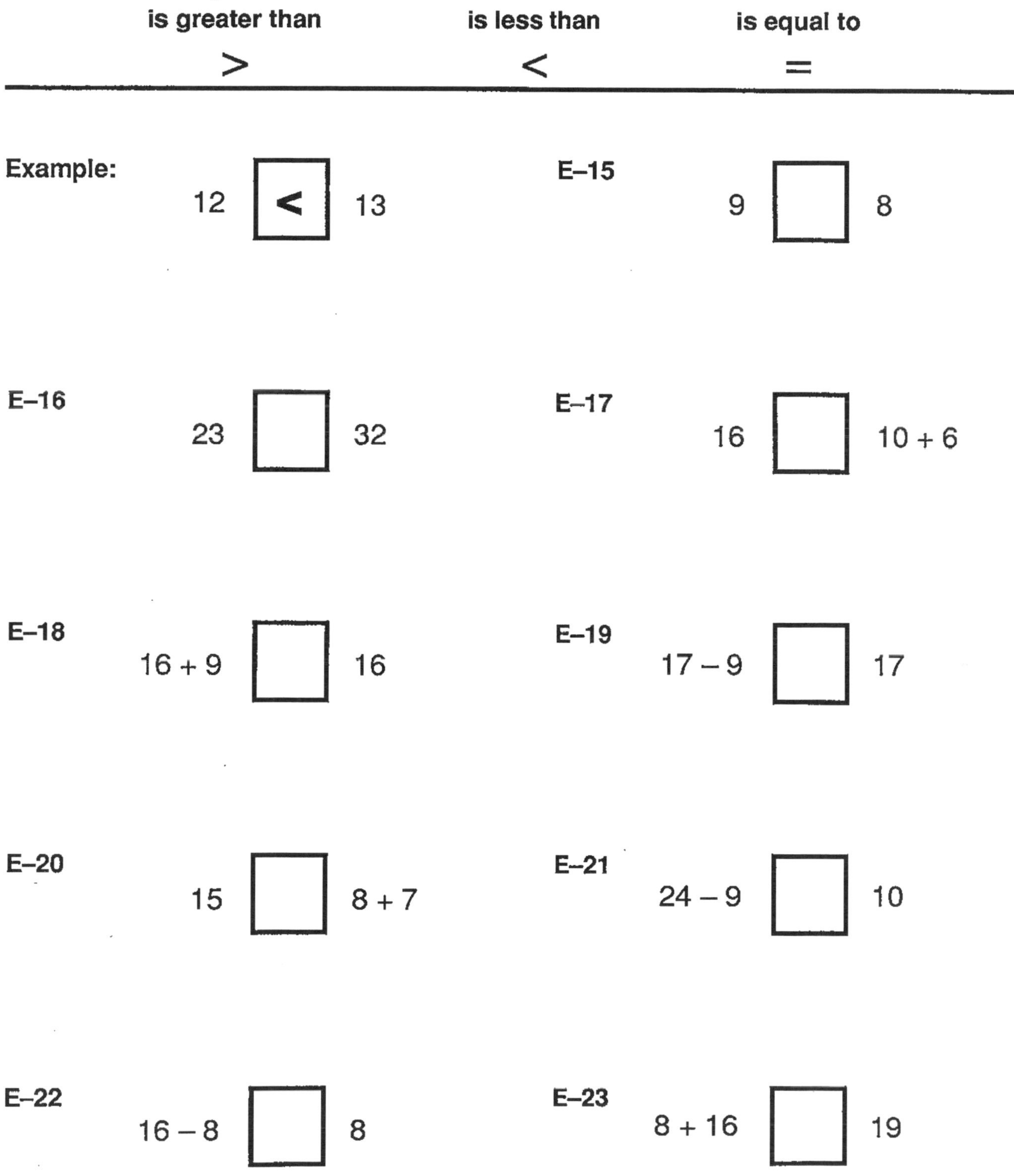

The symbols below are used to compare numbers.
Write the correct symbol in the box.

is greater than	is less than	is equal to
$>$	$<$	$=$

Example: $12 \; \boxed{<} \; 13$

E–15 $9 \; \square \; 8$

E–16 $23 \; \square \; 32$

E–17 $16 \; \square \; 10 + 6$

E–18 $16 + 9 \; \square \; 16$

E–19 $17 - 9 \; \square \; 17$

E–20 $15 \; \square \; 8 + 7$

E–21 $24 - 9 \; \square \; 10$

E–22 $16 - 8 \; \square \; 8$

E–23 $8 + 16 \; \square \; 19$

ORDERING NUMBERS

The symbols below are used to compare numbers.

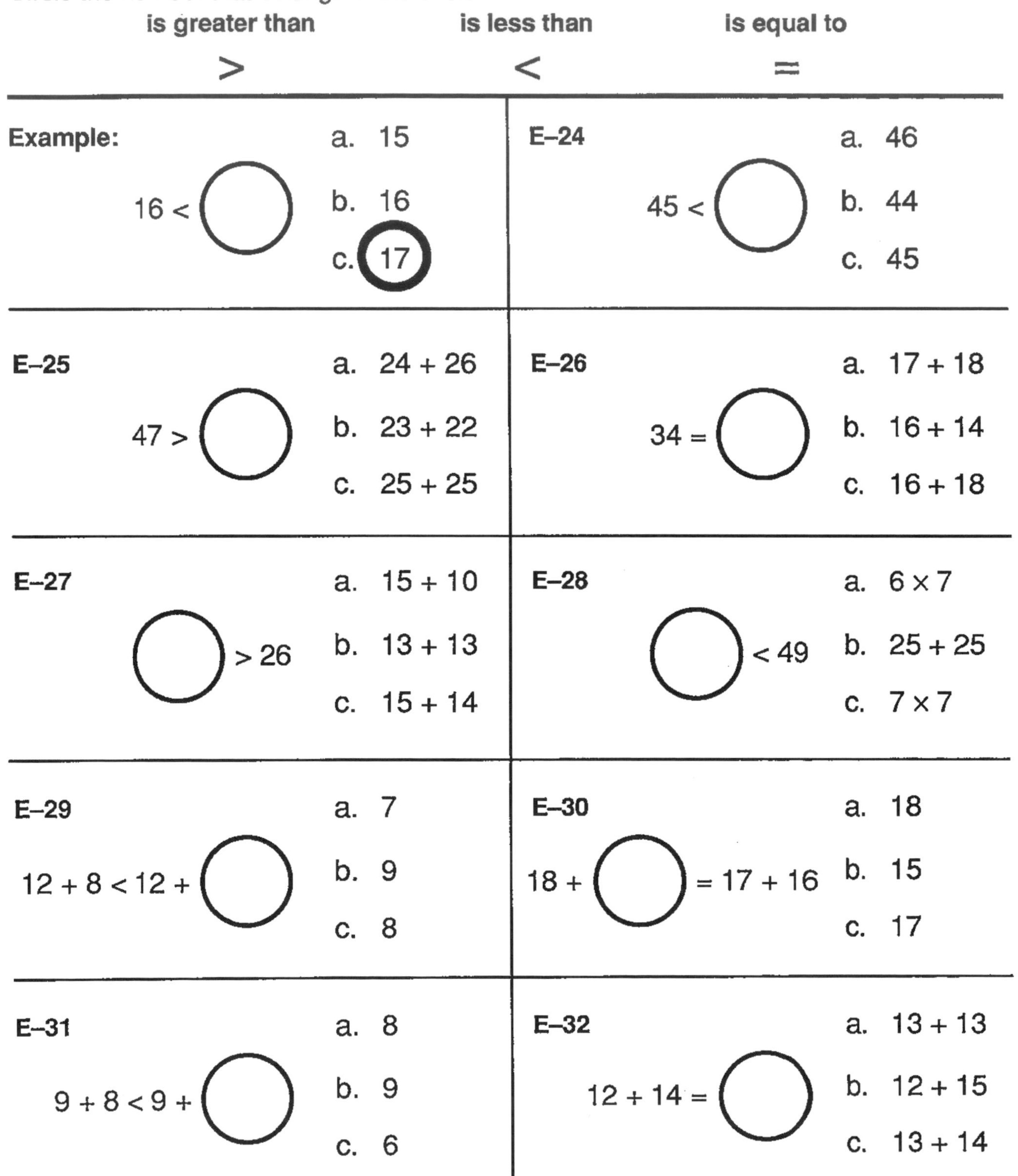

Circle the number that belongs in the circle.

is greater than	is less than	is equal to
$>$	$<$	$=$

Example: $16 < \bigcirc$
a. 15
b. 16
c. 17 (circled)

E–24 $45 < \bigcirc$
a. 46
b. 44
c. 45

E–25 $47 > \bigcirc$
a. $24 + 26$
b. $23 + 22$
c. $25 + 25$

E–26 $34 = \bigcirc$
a. $17 + 18$
b. $16 + 14$
c. $16 + 18$

E–27 $\bigcirc > 26$
a. $15 + 10$
b. $13 + 13$
c. $15 + 14$

E–28 $\bigcirc < 49$
a. 6×7
b. $25 + 25$
c. 7×7

E–29 $12 + 8 < 12 + \bigcirc$
a. 7
b. 9
c. 8

E–30 $18 + \bigcirc = 17 + 16$
a. 18
b. 15
c. 17

E–31 $9 + 8 < 9 + \bigcirc$
a. 8
b. 9
c. 6

E–32 $12 + 14 = \bigcirc$
a. $13 + 13$
b. $12 + 15$
c. $13 + 14$

ORDERING NUMBERS

The symbols below are used to compare numbers.
Circle the numbers that belong in the circle.

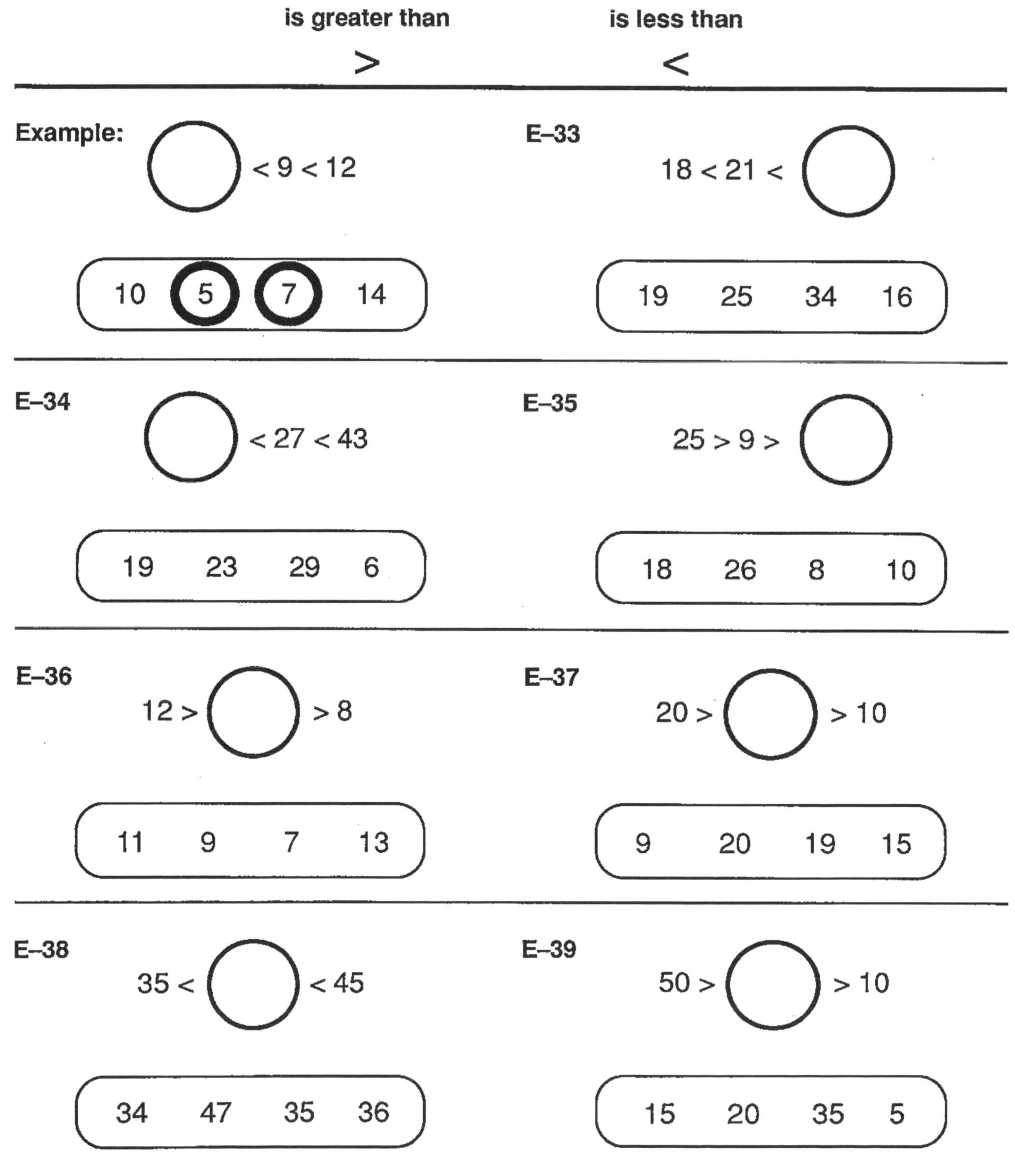

ORDERING NUMBERS

Fill in the shapes with the three numbers to make a true sentence.

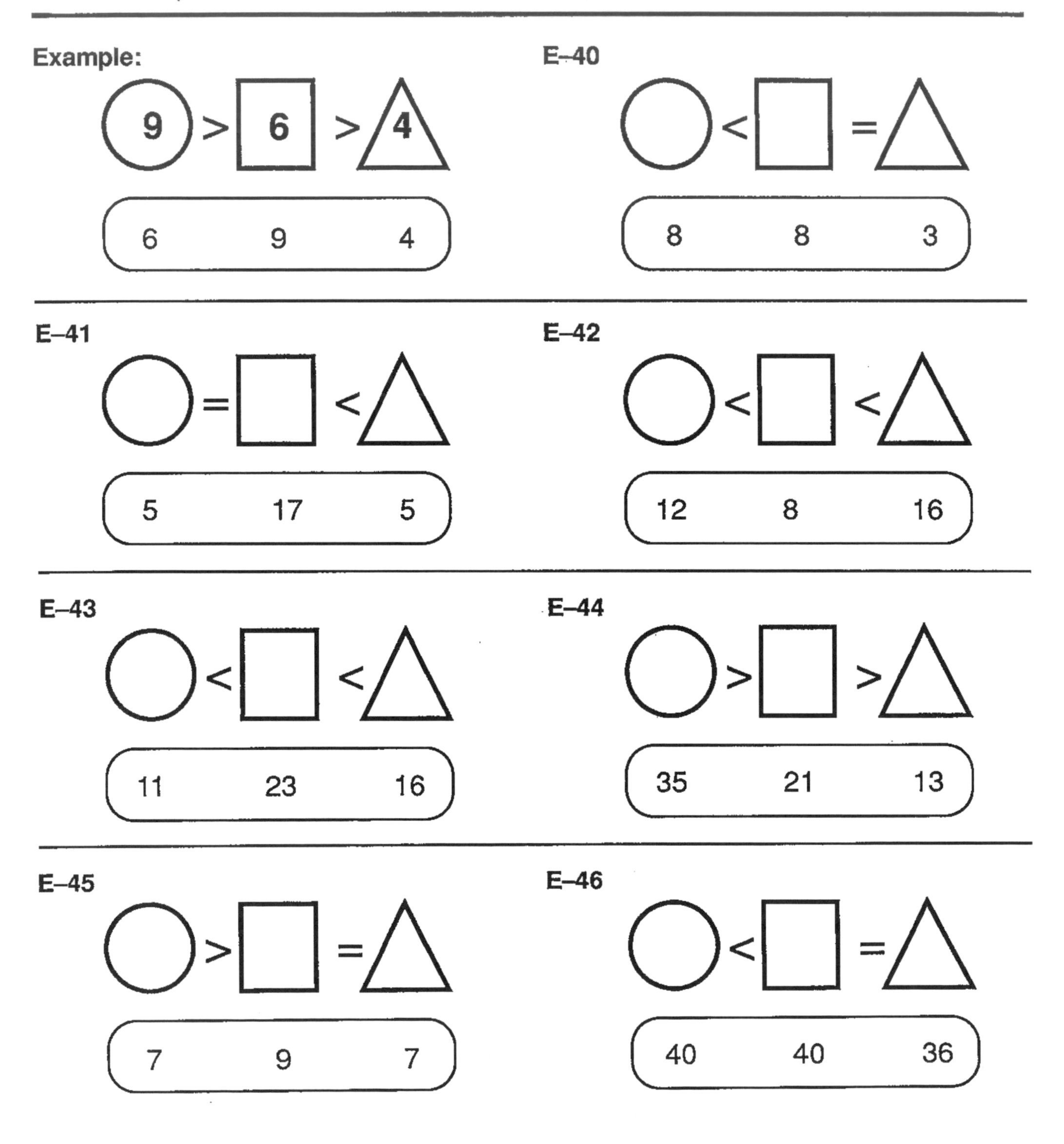

USING THE ORDER RELATIONS

Draw a line around the true sentence.

Example:

$4 \times 5 < 20$

$4 \times 5 = 20$ (circled)

$4 \times 5 > 20$

E–47

$6 \times 5 = 25$

$6 \times 5 < 25$

$6 \times 5 > 25$

E–48

$9 + 8 < 15$

$9 + 8 > 15$

$9 + 8 = 15$

E–49

$18 - 7 < 18$

$18 - 7 > 18$

$18 \times 7 = 18$

E–50

$15 + 12 = 28$

$16 + 12 = 28$

$16 + 13 < 28$

E–51

$14 < 13 + 3$

$14 > 13 + 3$

$14 < 13 - 3$

E–52

$6 + 4 > 10$

$7 \times 5 < 12$

$17 - 7 > 7$

E–53

$100 < 16 + 32$

$50 > 50 - 32$

$40 > 40 \times 3$

USING THE ORDER RELATIONS

Write the correct symbol in the box.

is greater than	is less than	is equal to
$>$	$<$	$=$

Example:

$3 + 4 \; \boxed{<} \; 12$

$3 + 4 \; \boxed{>} \; 5$

$3 + 4 \; \boxed{=} \; 7$

E–54

$5 + 6 \; \square \; 11$

$5 + 7 \; \square \; 11$

$5 \times 7 \; \square \; 11$

E–55

$9 \times 9 \; \square \; 18$

$9 + 9 \; \square \; 18$

$9 - 9 \; \square \; 18$

E–56

$4 \; \square \; 12 - 6$

$7 \; \square \; 12 - 6$

$5 \; \square \; 12 - 6$

E–57

$20 \; \square \; 13 + 7$

$20 \; \square \; 7 + 13$

$20 \; \square \; 13 - 7$

E–58

$19 + 7 \; \square \; 27$

$8 + 19 \; \square \; 27$

$18 + 19 \; \square \; 27$

E–59

$23 + 23 \; \square \; 60$

$37 + 15 \; \square \; 60$

$15 \times 4 \; \square \; 60$

E–60

$90 \; \square \; 43 + 43$

$90 \; \square \; 43 \times 2$

$90 \; \square \; 43 - 43$

USING ORDER RELATIONS

A number is missing from each sentence.
Circle all the numbers that will make a true sentence.

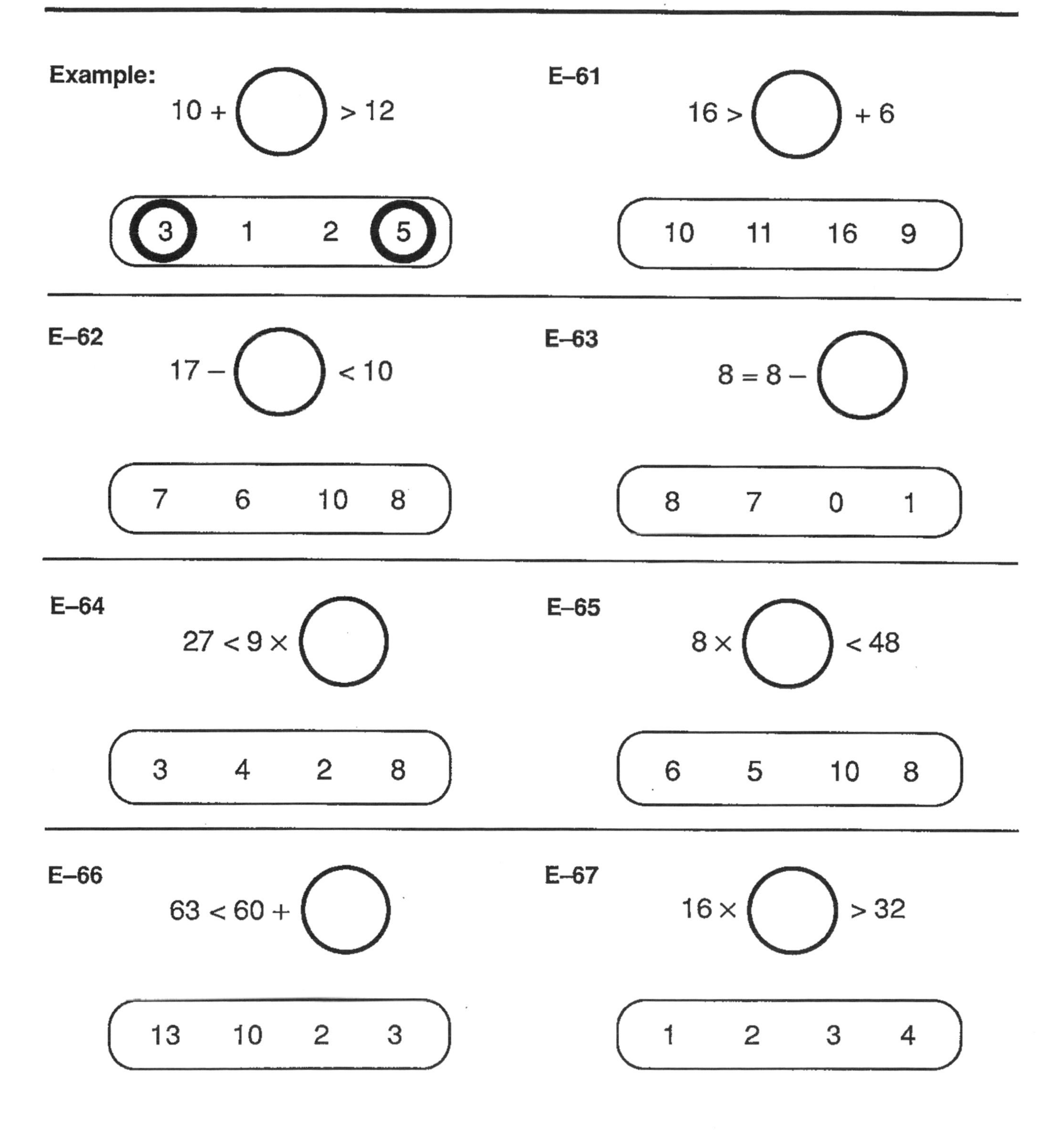

USING ORDER RELATIONS

A number is missing from each sentence.
Circle all the numbers that will make a true sentence.

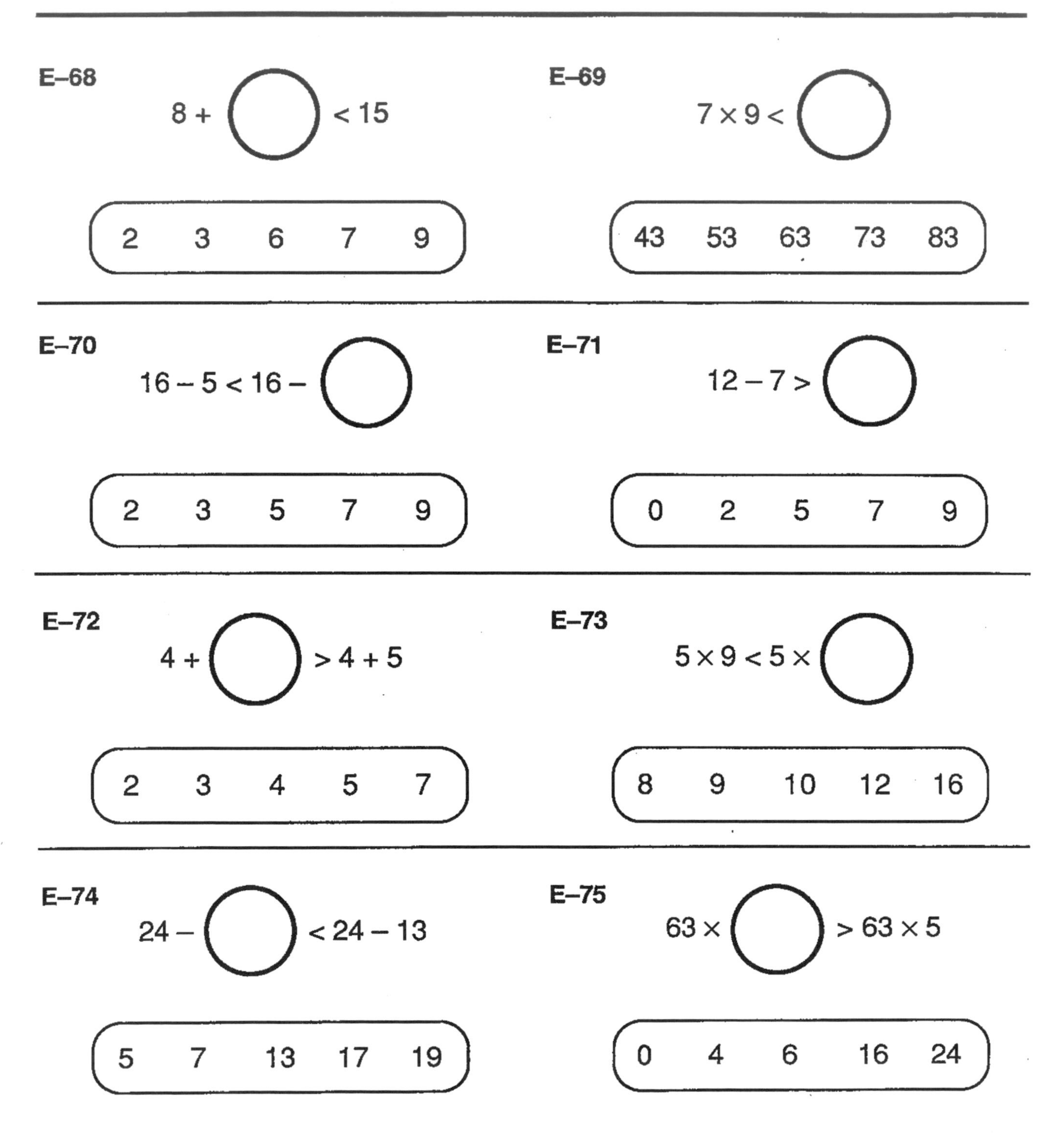

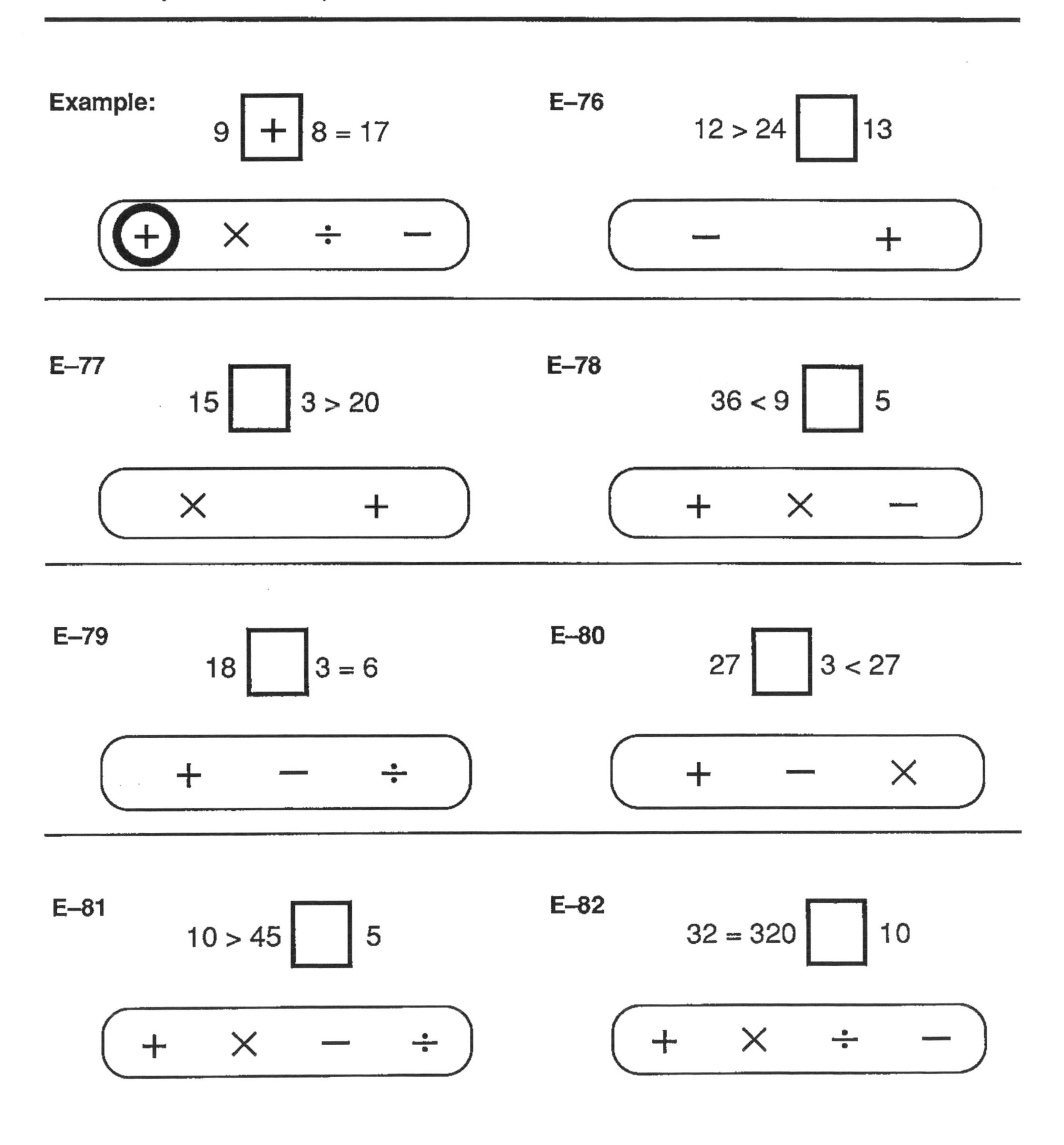

USING ARITHMETIC OPERATIONS

Circle the operation that makes the sentence true.
Write the symbol of that operation in the box.

Example: $9 \boxed{+} 8 = 17$

(+) × ÷ −

E–76 $12 > 24 \square 13$

− +

E–77 $15 \square 3 > 20$

× +

E–78 $36 < 9 \square 5$

+ × −

E–79 $18 \square 3 = 6$

+ − ÷

E–80 $27 \square 3 < 27$

+ − ×

E–81 $10 > 45 \square 5$

+ × − ÷

E–82 $32 = 320 \square 10$

+ × ÷ −

USING ARITHMETIC OPERATIONS

The four arithmetic operations are listed below.
Write one operation in the box that makes the sentence true.

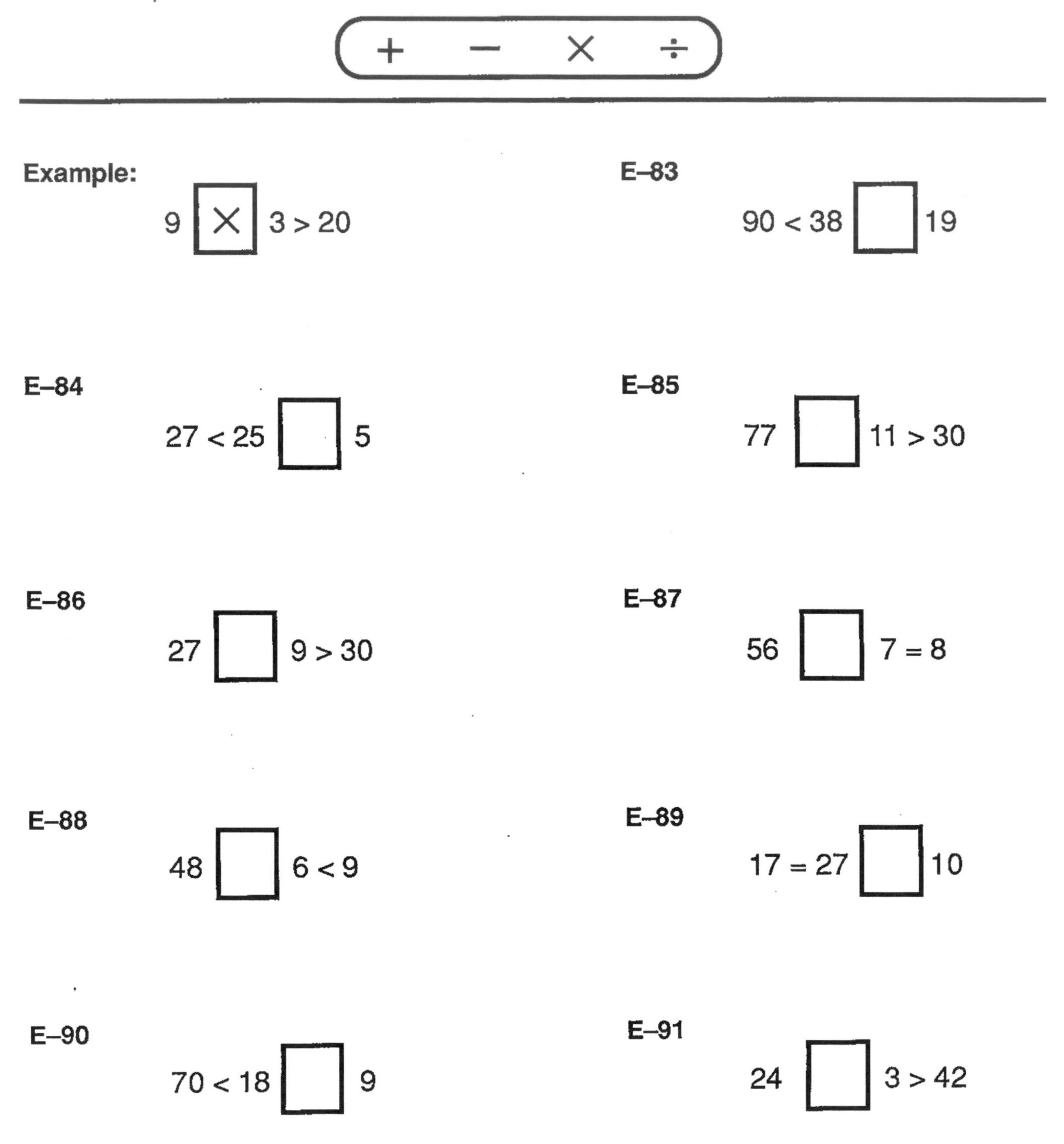

MAKING TRUE SENTENCES

The first number in each pair is a box number.
The second number is a circle number.
Circle all the pairs that will make the sentence true.

Example: $\square + \bigcirc = 12$

a. (7, 5) circled	b. (4, 8) circled
c. 6, 7	d. 5, 8

E–92 $\square + \bigcirc > 16$

a. 7, 9	b. 8, 9
c. 9, 9	d. 8, 8

E–93 $46 > \bigcirc \times \square$

a. 6, 7	b. 6, 6
c. 7, 7	d. 6, 8

E–94 $\square - \bigcirc = 9$

a. 13, 6	b. 13, 5
c. 18, 8	d. 17, 8

E–95 $8 < \bigcirc \div \square$

a. 48, 8	b. 63, 7
c. 48, 6	d. 64, 8

E–96 $\square \times \bigcirc < 50$

a. 7, 7	b. 7, 8
c. 8, 8	d. 6, 9

MAKING TRUE SENTENCES

The first number in each pair is a box number. The second number is a circle number.
Use the numbers from two of the pairs to make the sentences true.
Draw arrows to show which pairs go with the sentences.

Example:

a. 3, 4

b. 5, 5 → $8 + \boxed{5} > 7 + \textcircled{5}$

c. 3, 5 → $8 + \boxed{3} < 7 + \textcircled{5}$

E–97

a. 9, 2

b. 2, 9

c. 0, 3

$\boxed{} \times 9 = \bigcirc + 9$

$\boxed{} \times 9 > \bigcirc + 9$

E–98

a. 24, 3

b. 18, 3

c. 6, 6

$\boxed{} \div 3 > 18 \div \bigcirc$

$\boxed{} \div 3 < 18 \div \bigcirc$

E–99

a. 23, 23

b. 5, 12

c. 12, 5

$12 + \boxed{} > \bigcirc + 12$

$12 + \boxed{} = \bigcirc + 12$

E–100

a. 24, 48

b. 48, 24

c. 24, 24

$54 - \boxed{} > 54 - \bigcirc$

$54 - \boxed{} < 54 - \bigcirc$

SEQUENCES OF NUMBERS

The numbers on the left begin a sequence.
Circle the row on the right that continues the sequence.

Example:

1, 3, 5, 7, 9,

a. 10, 11, 12, 13

b. 9, 11, 13, 15

c. 11, 13, 15, 17

E–101

1, 4, 7, 10, 13,

a. 15, 18, 21, 24

b. 16, 19, 22, 25

c. 14, 15, 16, 17

E–102

1, 2, 1, 3, 1, 4,

a. 1, 5, 1, 6

b. 5, 1, 6, 1

c. 4, 1, 5, 1

E–103

45, 40, 35, 30,

a. 35, 40, 45, 50

b. 20, 15, 10, 5

c. 25, 20, 15, 10

E–104

2, 1, 4, 3, 6, 5, 8, 7,

a. 7, 10, 9, 12

b. 8, 9, 10, 11

c. 10, 9, 12, 11

SEQUENCES OF NUMBERS

The numbers on the right end a sequence.
Circle the row on the left that begins the sequence.

Example:
a. 18, 20, 22, 24,
b. (circled) 2, 4, 6, 8, — 10, 12, 14, 16
c. 4, 6, 8, 10,

E–105
a. 33, 37, 41, 45,
b. 3, 7, 11, 15, — 17, 21, 25, 29
c. 1, 5, 9, 13,

E–106
a. 6, 9, 12, 15,
b. 39, 36, 33, 30, — 18, 21, 24, 27
c. 3, 6, 19, 12,

E–107
a. 25, 30, 35, 40,
b. 40, 35, 30, 25, — 20, 15, 10, 5
c. 30, 35, 40, 45,

E–108
a. 26, 29, 32, 35,
b. 3, 6, 9, 12, — 14, 17, 20, 23
c. 2, 5, 8, 11,

SEQUENCES OF NUMBERS

Each sequence has missing numbers.
Fill in the blanks.

Example: 6, 9, 12, 15, 18, 21, 24

E–109 4, 9, ____, ____, 24, 29, ____

E–110 25, 23, ____, ____, ____, 15, 13

E–111 ____, ____, 45, 50, 55, ____, ____

E–112 ____, 4, ____, ____, 10, 12, 14

E–113 4, 7, ____, ____, ____, 19, 22

E–114 ____, ____, 32, 29, 26, ____, ____

E–115 ____, 12, ____, 18, ____, 24, ____

SEQUENCES OF NUMBERS

The three dots mean that the sequence continues.
Remember that three dots do not stand for one dot per number.
Circle the row that belongs to the sequence.

Example:

3, 6, 9, 12 • • •

a. 18, 20, 22, 24
b. 25, 28, 31, 34
c. 30, 33, 36, 39

E–116

15, 20, 25, 30 • • •

a. 55, 60, 65, 70
b. 80, 75, 70, 65
c. 40, 50, 60, 70

E–117

5, 7, 9, 11 • • •

a. 22, 24, 26, 28
b. 13, 17, 21, 25
c. 19, 21, 23, 25

E–118

10, 12, 14, 16 • • •

a. 28, 26, 24, 22
b. 18, 22, 26, 30
c. 30, 32, 34, 36

E–119

4, 9, 14, 19 • • •

a. 34, 39, 44, 49
b. 24, 28, 32, 36
c. 37, 42, 47, 52

NUMBER MACHINES

The numbers in the boxes are put into number machines.
The numbers coming out are circled.
Find out what the machine in each exercise does to the numbers.
Fill in the blank circle.

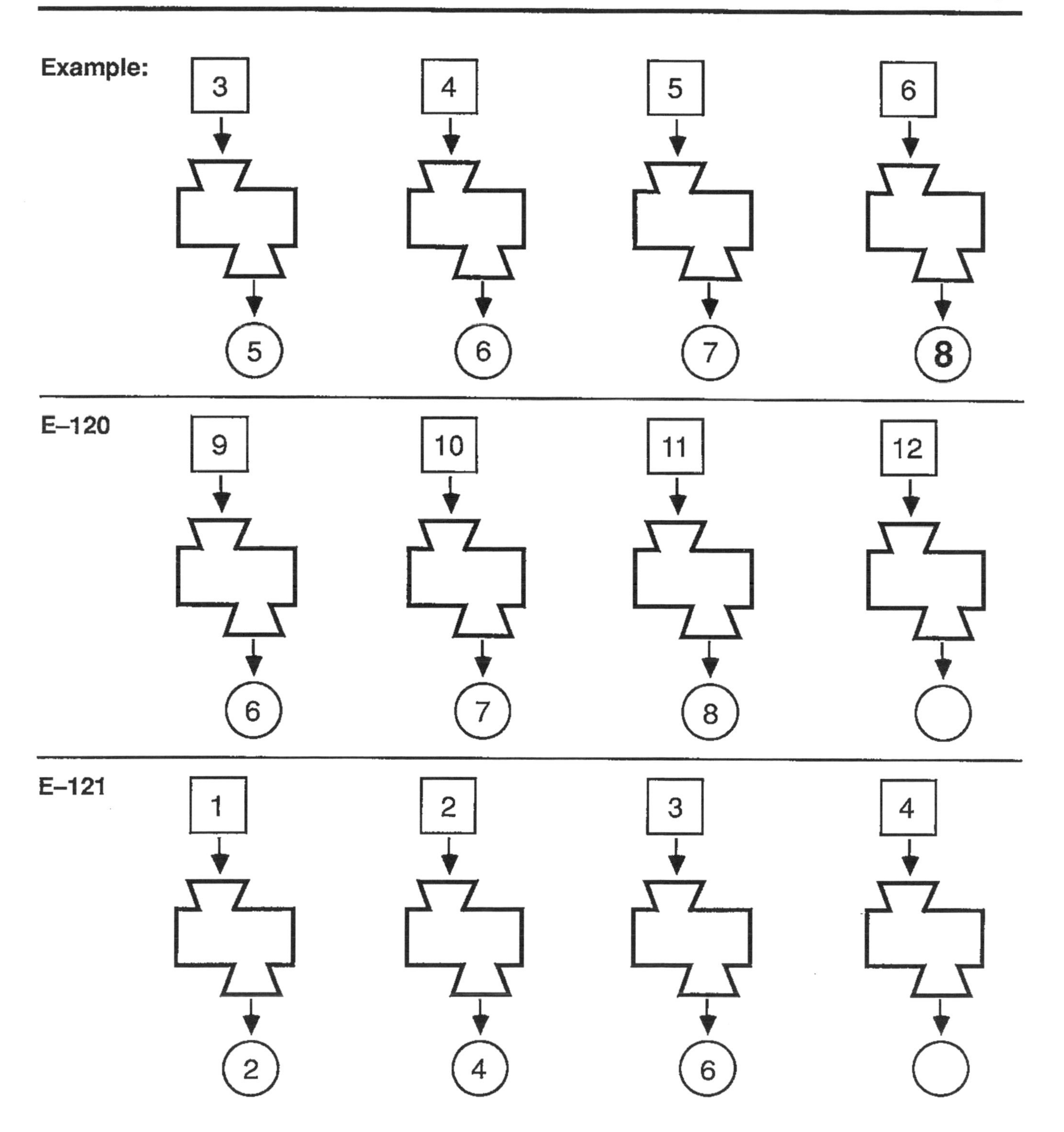

NUMBER MACHINES

The numbers in the boxes are put into number machines.
The numbers coming out are circled.
Find out what the machine in each exercise does to the numbers.
Fill in the blank circle.

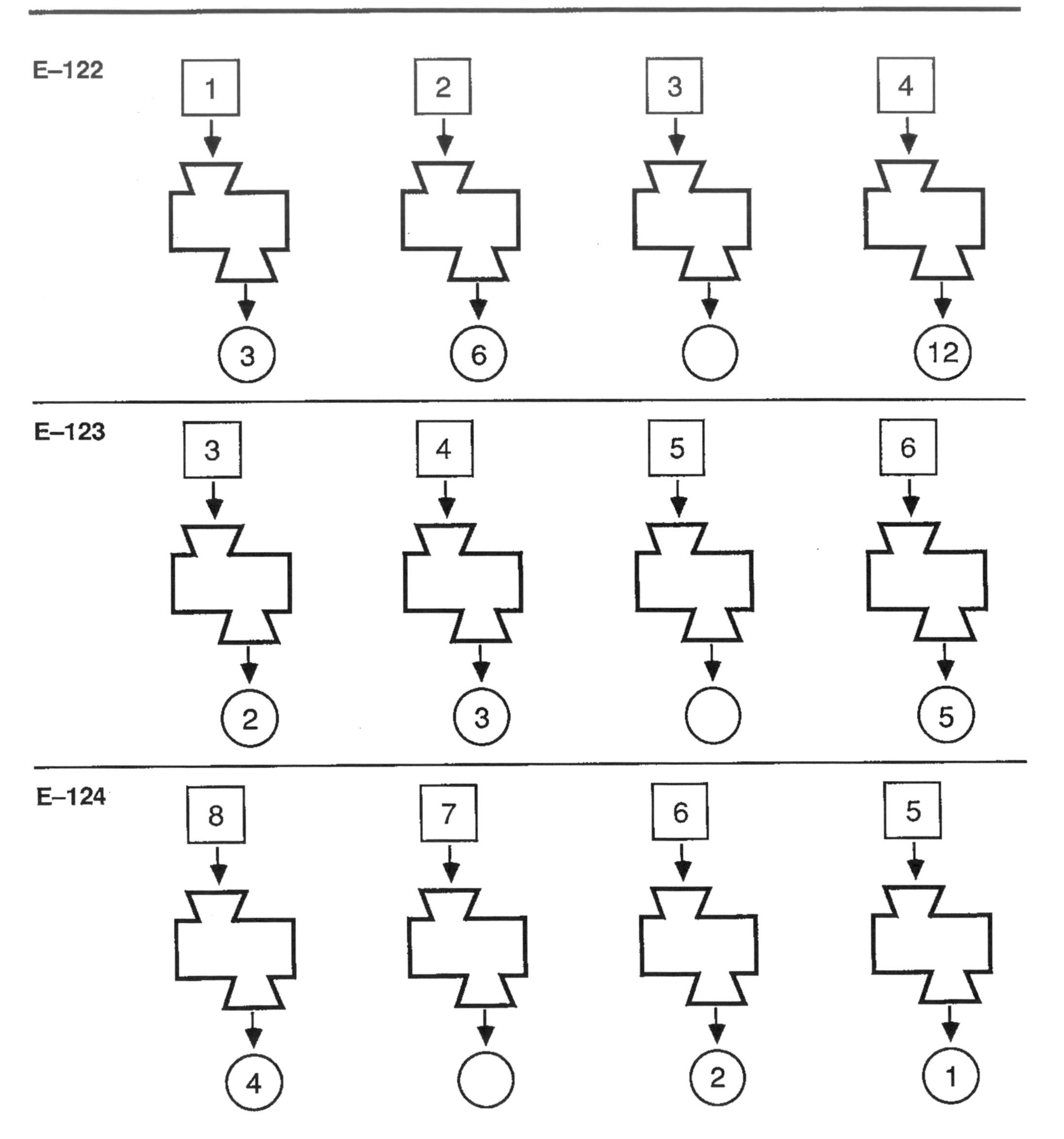

NUMBER MACHINES

The numbers in the boxes are put into number machines.
The numbers coming out are circled.
One of the circled numbers in each exercise is NOT correct.
Put an X on the wrong answer.

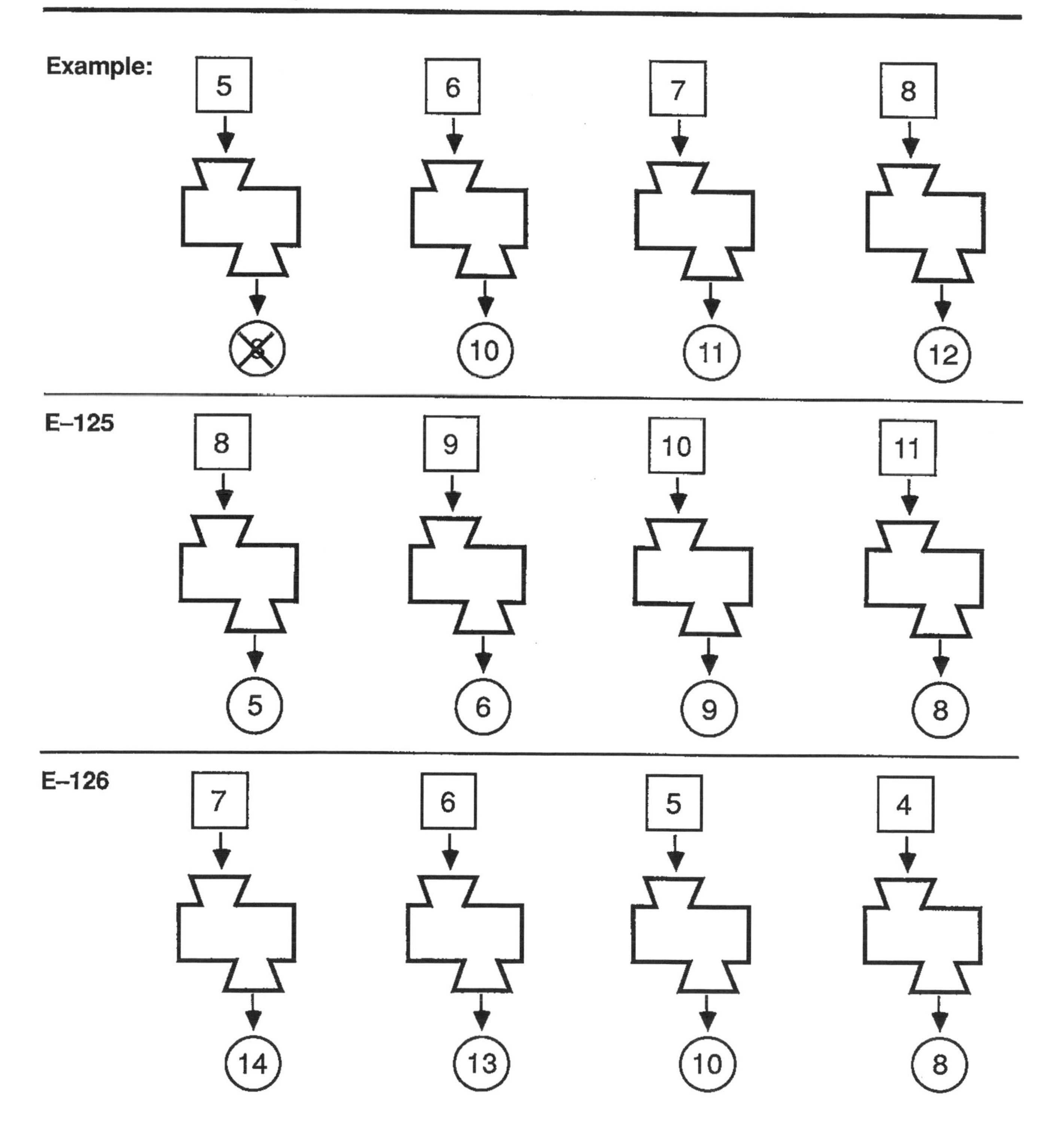

NUMBER MACHINES

The numbers in the boxes are put into number machines.
The numbers coming out are circled.
One of the circled numbers in each exercise is NOT correct.
Put an X on the wrong answer.

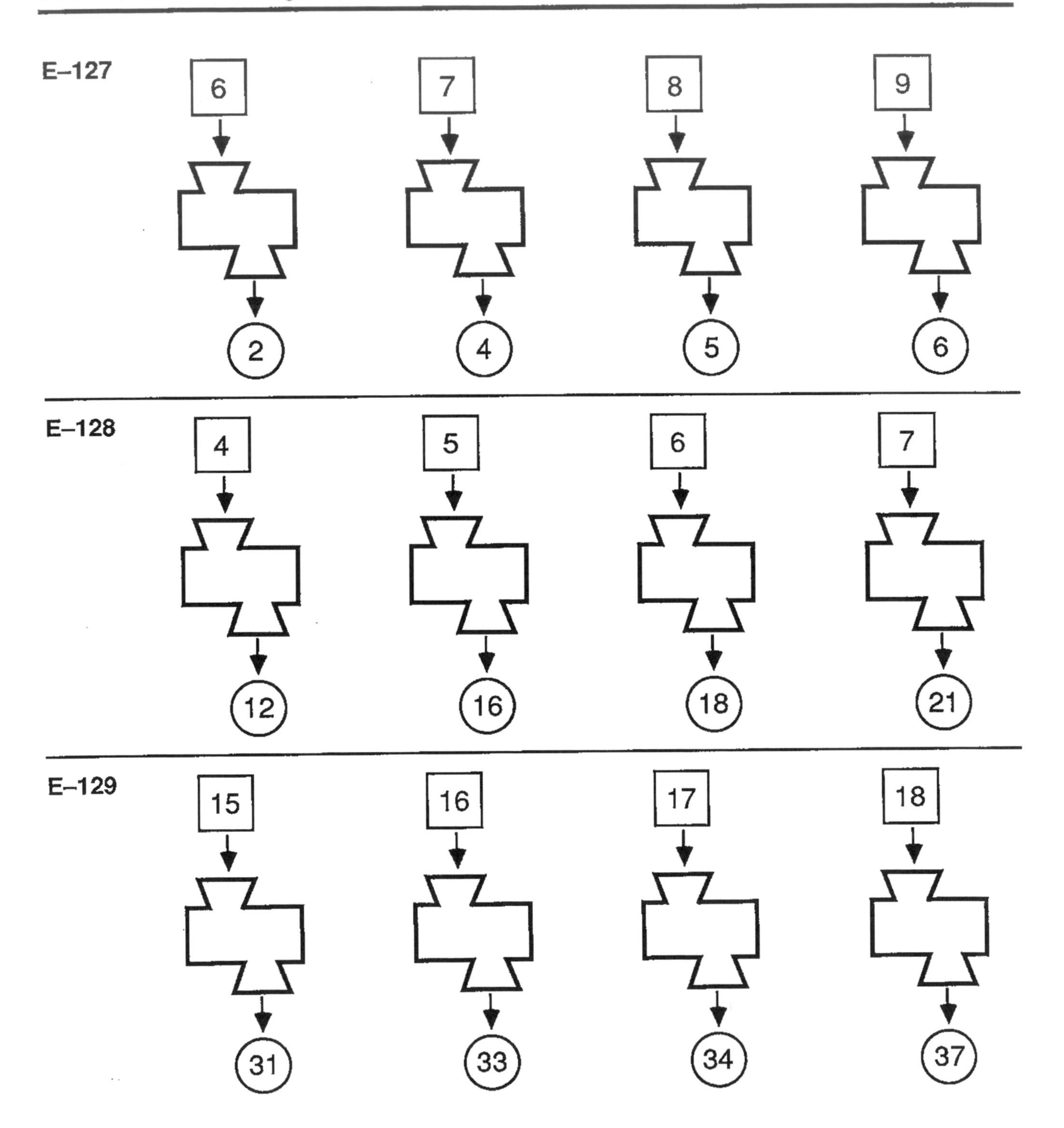

NUMBER MACHINES

The numbers in the boxes are put into number machines. The numbers coming out are circled.
Find out what the machine in each exercise does to the numbers.
Note the three dots before the last machine.
Fill in the blank circle.

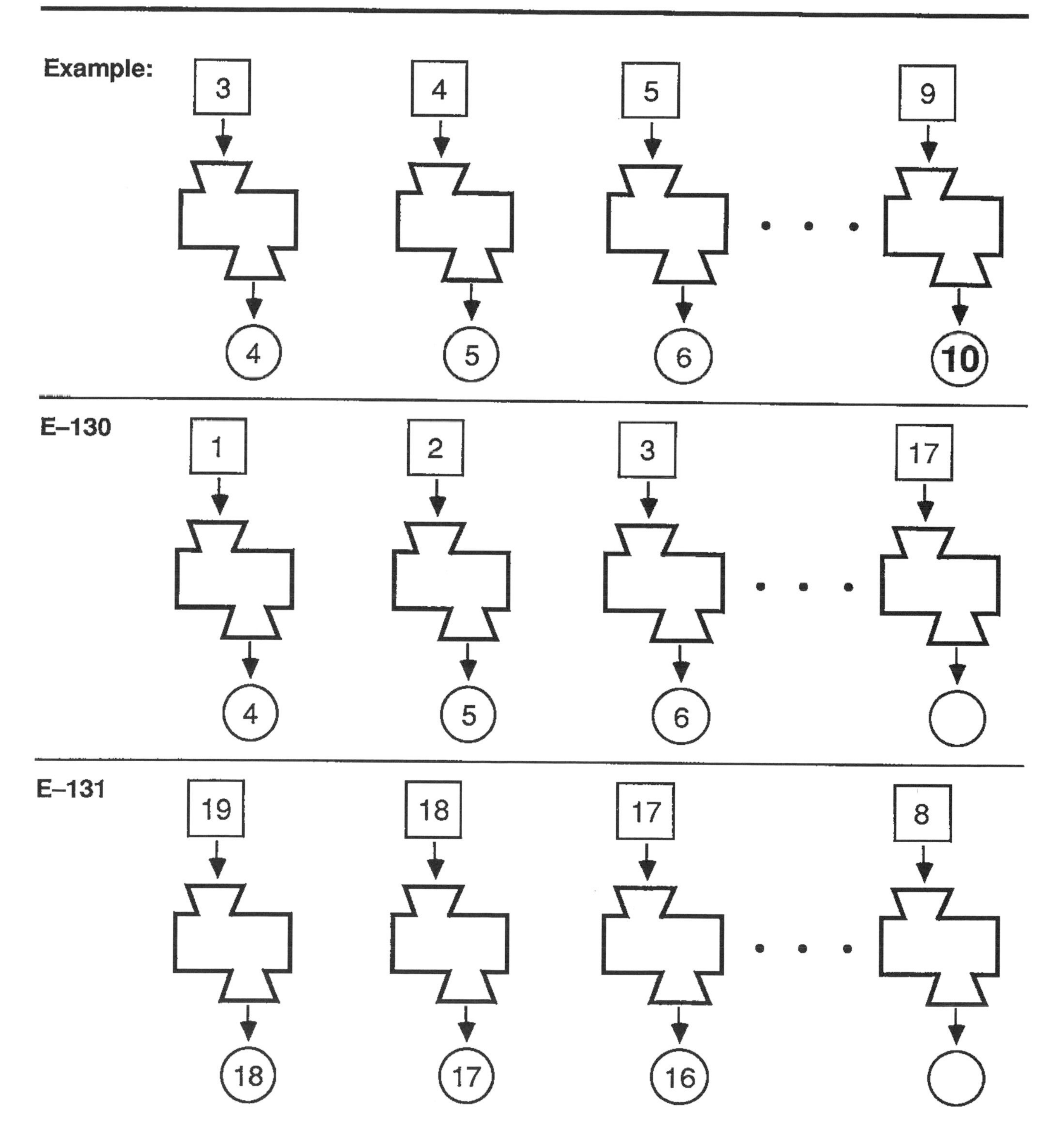

NUMBER MACHINES

The numbers in the boxes are put into number machines. The numbers coming out are circled.
Find out what the machine in each exercise does to the numbers.
Note the three dots before the last machine.
Fill in the blank circle.

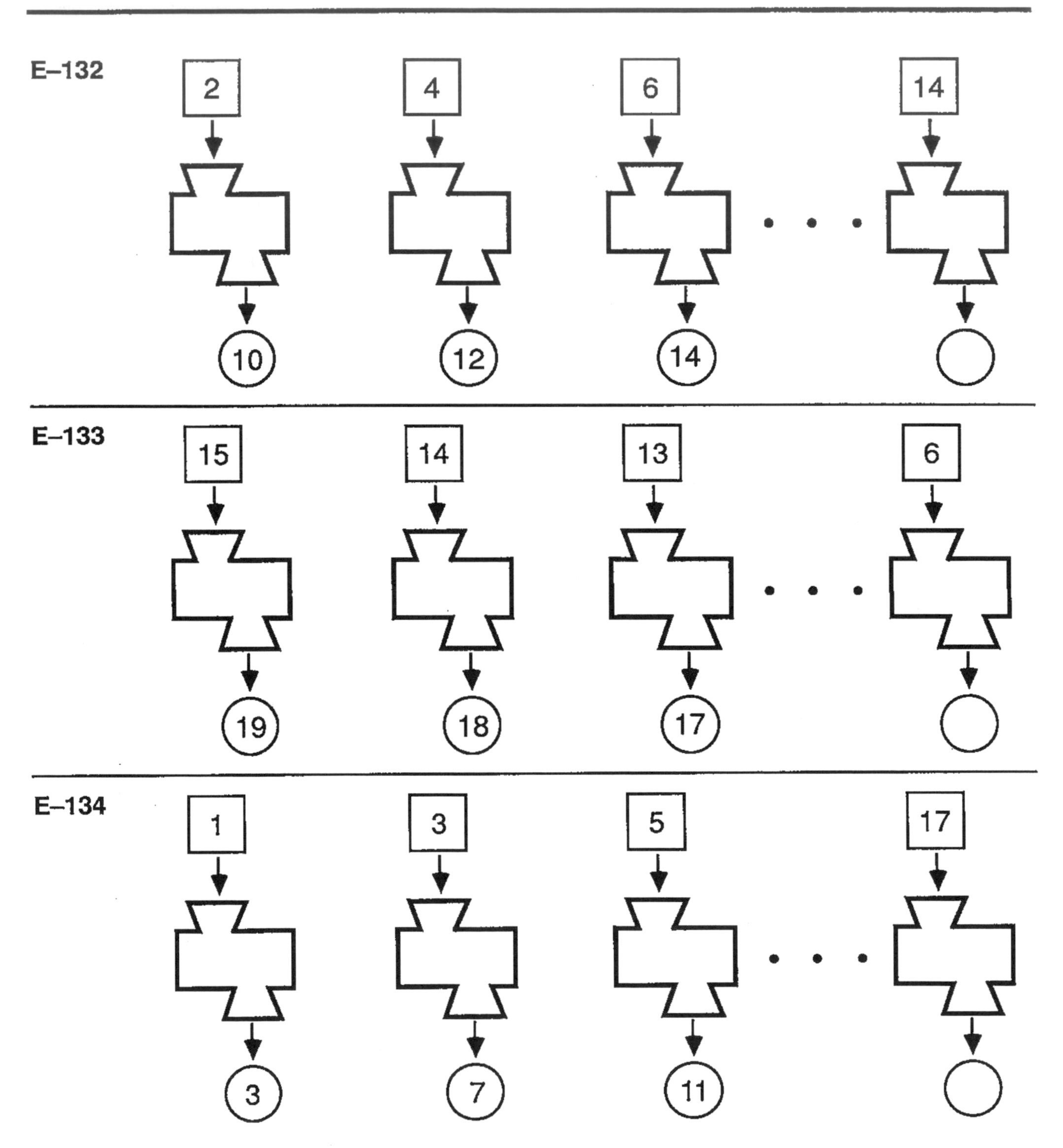

PAIRING NUMBERS

The arrows show that the numbers are paired.
Find out how the numbers are paired.
Fill in the circles with the missing numbers.

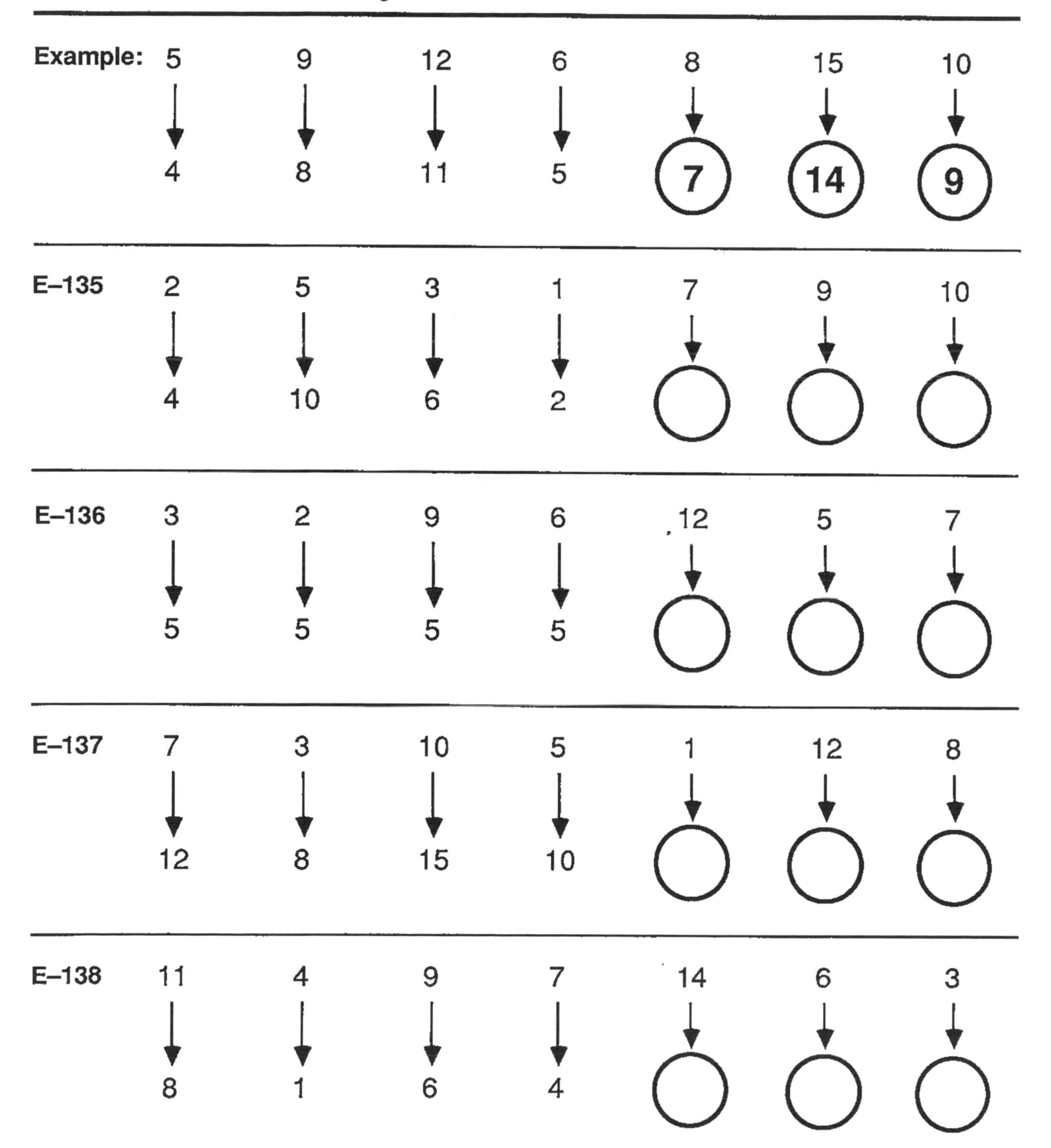

PAIRING NUMBERS

The arrows show that the numbers are paired.
Find out how the numbers are paired.
Fill in the circles with the missing numbers.

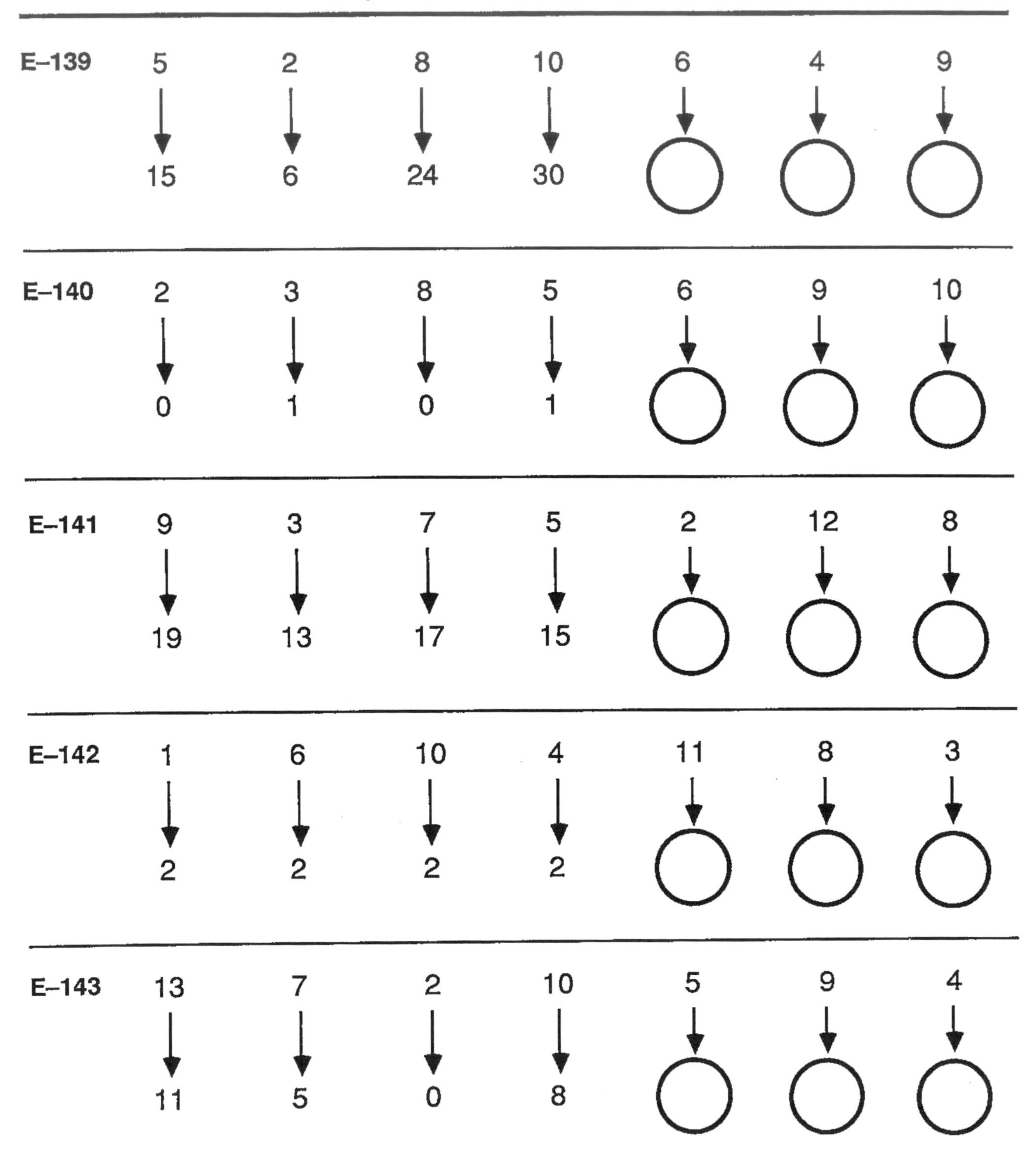

MULTIPLES OF 2, 3, AND 5

Draw a circle around all the multiples of 2.
Draw a square around all the multiples of 3.
Draw a triangle around all the multiples of 5.
Some numbers will have more than one shape around them.

Example:

1	2	3	4	5
6	7	8	9	10
11	12	13	14	15
16	17	18	19	20
21	22	23	24	25
26	27	28	29	30

E–144 Which multiples of 2 are also multiples of 3? ____________________

E–145 Which multiples of 2 are also multiples of 5? ____________________

E–146 Which multiples of 3 are also multiples of 5? ____________________

E–147 Which numbers are multiples of all three numbers? ____________________

MULTIPLES OF 2, 3, AND 5

Example:

Circle all the multiples of 2.

(12)	17	19	(18)
(24)	(8)	9	3
(10)	7	(40)	11

E–148

Circle all the multiples of 3.

9	8	4	7
11	3	12	6
15	10	5	18

E–149

Circle all the multiples of 5.

12	15	8	6
10	22	50	9
35	18	19	52

E–150

Circle all the multiples of 2.

35	22	7	10
8	11	12	2
6	18	13	9

DIVISIBILITY

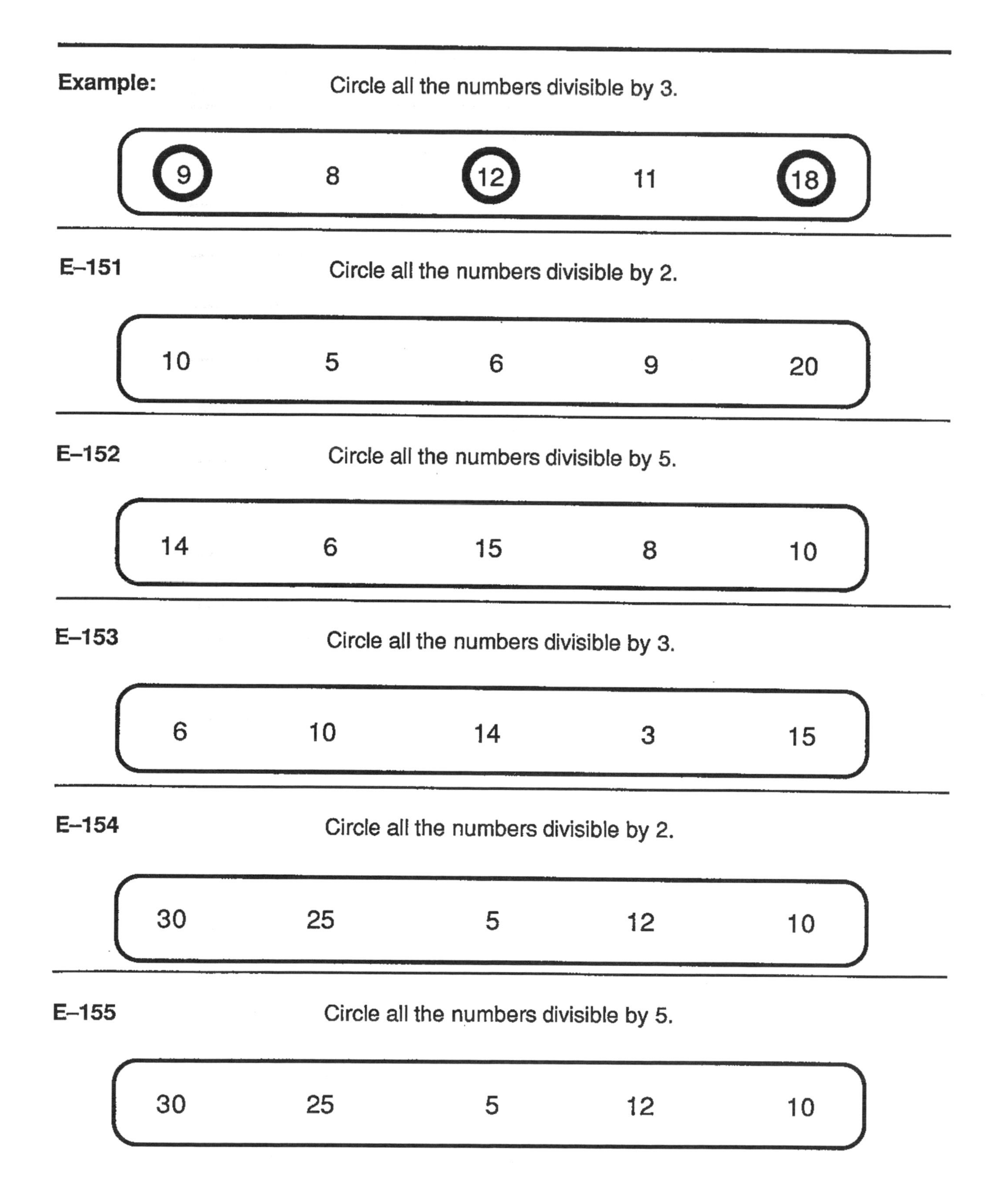

Example: Circle all the numbers divisible by 3.

9	8	12	11	18

E–151 Circle all the numbers divisible by 2.

10	5	6	9	20

E–152 Circle all the numbers divisible by 5.

14	6	15	8	10

E–153 Circle all the numbers divisible by 3.

6	10	14	3	15

E–154 Circle all the numbers divisible by 2.

30	25	5	12	10

E–155 Circle all the numbers divisible by 5.

30	25	5	12	10

DIVISIBILITY

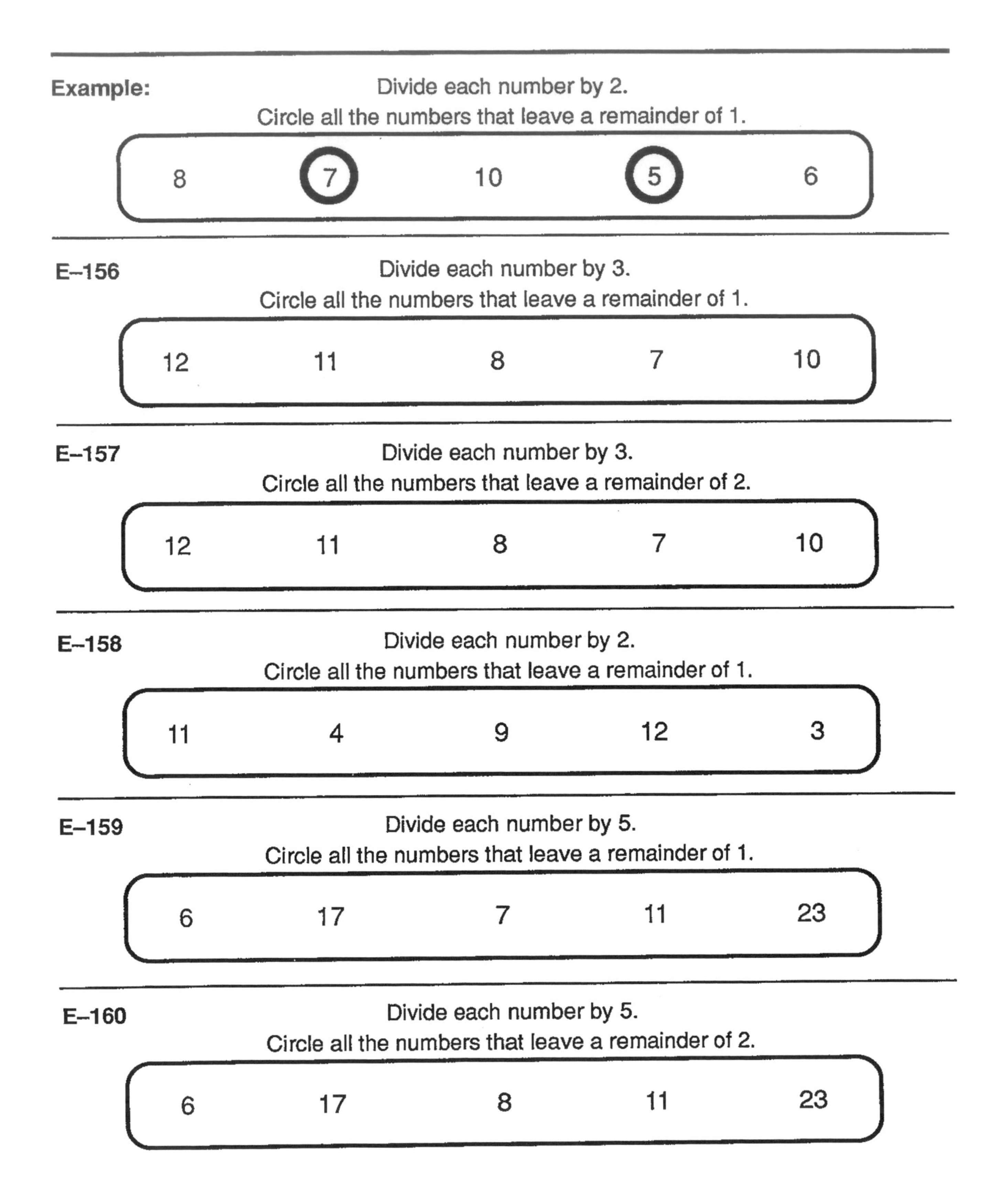

Example: Divide each number by 2.
Circle all the numbers that leave a remainder of 1.

8 (7) 10 (5) 6

E–156 Divide each number by 3.
Circle all the numbers that leave a remainder of 1.

12 11 8 7 10

E–157 Divide each number by 3.
Circle all the numbers that leave a remainder of 2.

12 11 8 7 10

E–158 Divide each number by 2.
Circle all the numbers that leave a remainder of 1.

11 4 9 12 3

E–159 Divide each number by 5.
Circle all the numbers that leave a remainder of 1.

6 17 7 11 23

E–160 Divide each number by 5.
Circle all the numbers that leave a remainder of 2.

6 17 8 11 23

SUMS WITH 1, 2, AND 3

Nine different addition exercises can be made using the numbers 1, 2, and 3.
Write 1, 2, or 3 in the boxes to make the nine different exercises.
Write their sums in the circles.

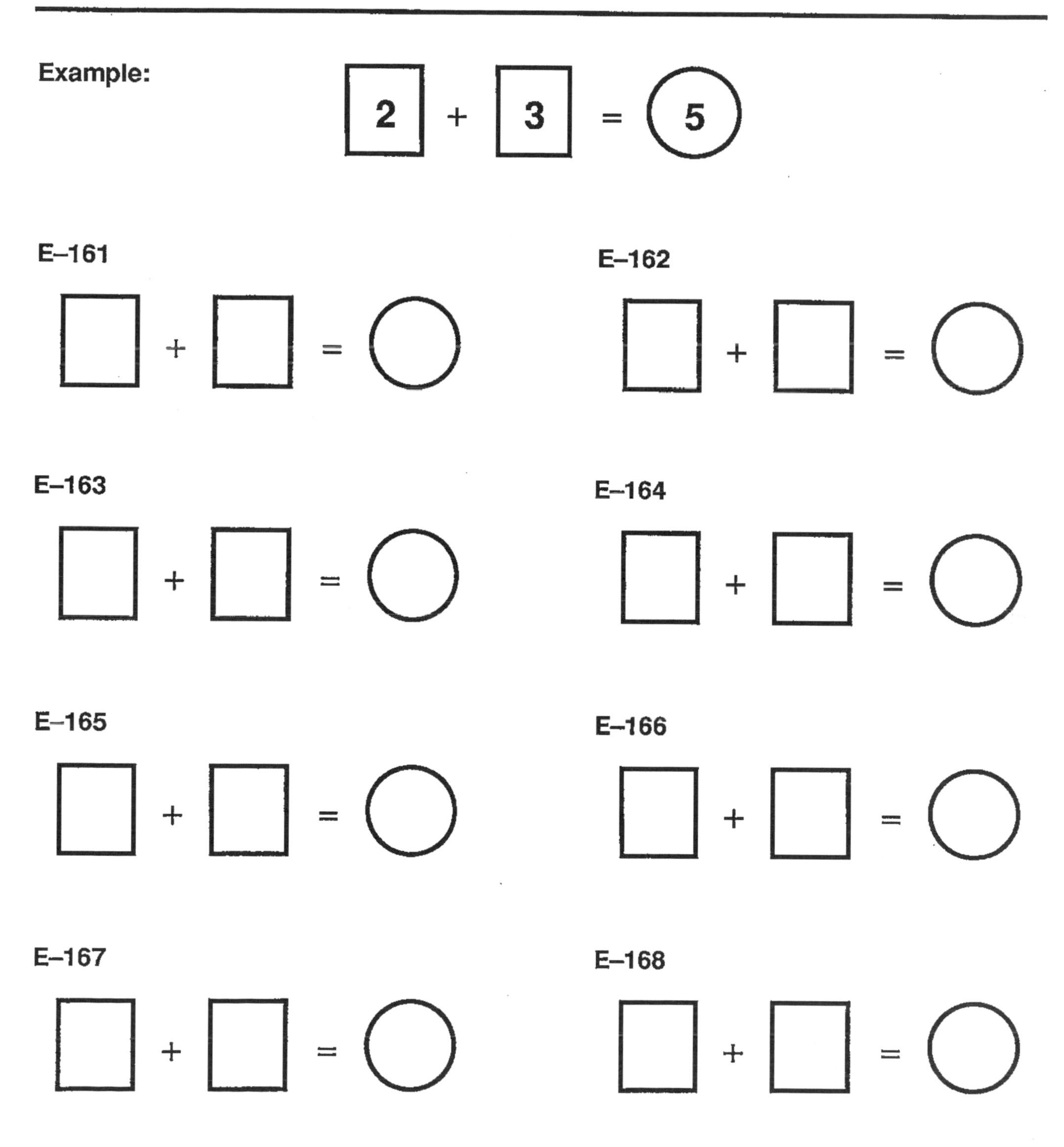

PRODUCTS WITH 2, 3, AND 5

Nine different multiplication exercises can be made using the numbers 2, 3, and 5.
Write 2, 3, or 5 in the boxes to make the nine different exercises.
Write their products in the circles.

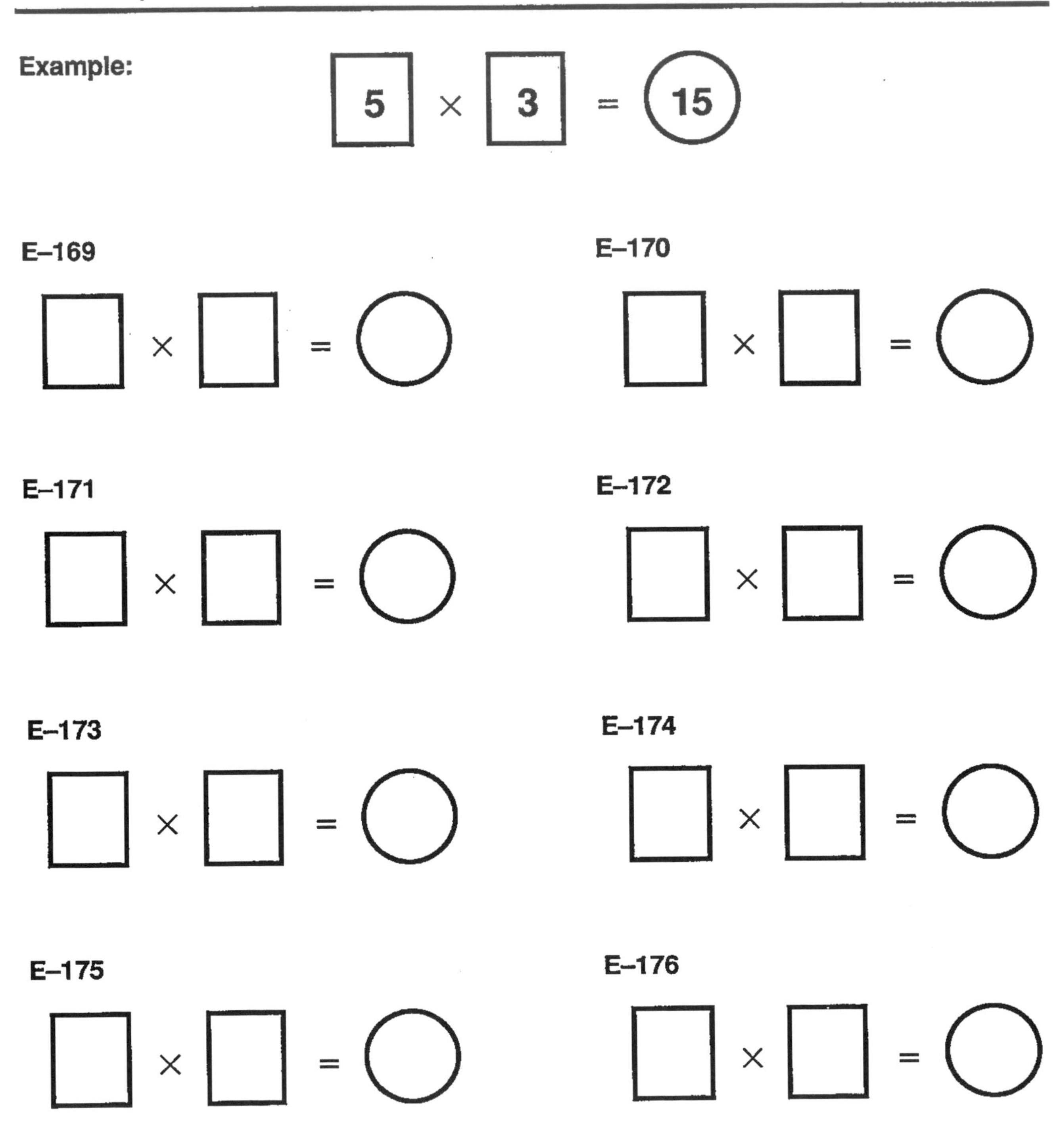

READING TABLES

The table shows the total number of students absent from school during one week.

Day	Number Absent
Monday	35
Tuesday	24
Wednesday	17
Thursday	19
Friday	30

Use the table to answer the following questions.

Example: On what day were most students absent? **Monday**

F–1 How many students were absent on Friday? ____________

F–2 On what day were 24 students absent? ____________

F–3 On what day were the least number absent? ____________

F–4 What was the total number of students absent during the week? ____________

F–5 Were there more students absent on Monday or on Friday? ____________

F–6 Were there fewer students absent on Wednesday or on Thursday? ____________

READING TABLES

The table shows the number of miles between streets and certain places in Old Town.

MILES FROM STREETS TO PLACES

	Taylor School	Hope Theater	City Park	Town Hall
Hope Street	2	0	1	1
Main Street	1	1	2	0
Park Street	1	1	0	2
North Road	4	4	3	5
Elm Street	2	2	1	3

Use the table to answer the following questions.

Example: How many miles is it from Park Street to Town Hall? ____2____

F–7 How many miles is it from Hope Street to City Park? ________

F–8 How many miles is it from North Road to the Hope Theater? ________

F–9 How many miles is Taylor School from Elm Street? ________

F–10 How many miles is City Park from Main Street? ________

F–11 On what street is Town Hall? ________

F–12 On what street is City Park? ________

F–13 Is Main Street or Hope Street further from City Park? ________

F–14 Is Town Hall or Taylor School further from Park Street? ________

COMPLETING A TABLE

An election was held to elect a student leader.
John got 6 votes, Amy got 8 votes, Karen got 4 votes, and Elaine got 11 votes.

Complete the table using the information given above.

	Name of Student	Number of Votes
Example:	Amy	**8**
F–15	Elaine	
F–16	John	
F–17	Karen	

Use the table to answer the following questions.

F–18 How many votes did Karen get? ____________________

F–19 Who got the least number of votes? ____________________

F–20 What was the total number of votes? ____________________

F–21 How many more votes did Amy get than Karen? ____________________

F–22 How many more votes did Elaine get than John? ____________________

F–23 Who won the election? ____________________

COMPLETING A TABLE

The number of students in Mr. Dodd's class that bought lunch on Monday was 20, on Tuesday 23, on Wednesday 19, on Thursday 24, and on Friday 21.
In Ms. Gilman's class there were 16 on Monday, 19 on Tuesday, 20 on Wednesday, 21 on Thursday, and 17 on Friday.

Complete the table using the information given above.

	Day	Mr. Dodd's Class	Ms. Gilman's Class
Example:	Monday	**20**	**16**
F–24	Tuesday		
F–25	Wednesday		
F–26	Thursday		
F–27	Friday		

Use the table to answer the following questions.

F–28 How many students in both classes bought lunch on Wednesday? ____________

F–29 How many students in both classes bought lunch on Friday? ____________

F–30 What was the total number of lunches for the week in Ms. Gilman's class? ____________

F–31 On what day did the largest number of students buy lunch? ____________

F–32 On what day did the students buy the least number of lunches? ____________

CONSTRUCTING A TABLE

Amy, Elaine, and John used a map to find distances from their homes to places in town. From Amy's home it is 1 mile to school, 2 miles to the park, and 3 miles to the theater. From Elaine's home it is 1 mile to the park, 4 miles to school, and 3 miles to the theater. From John's home it is 1 mile to school, 1 mile to the theater, and 5 miles to the park.

Complete the table using the information given above.

		DISTANCE TO		
		Park	Theater	School
F–33	Amy			
F–34	Elaine			
F–35	John			

Use the table to answer the following questions.

F–36 Who lives furthest from the school? ____________________

F–37 Who lives closest to the school? ____________________

F–38 How far is Elaine's home from the theater? ____________________

F–39 How far is the theater from John's home? ____________________

F–40 Who lives further from the park, Amy or Elaine? ____________________

F–41 Who lives closer to the theater, John or Elaine? ____________________

CONSTRUCTING A TABLE

In Mr. Dodd's class 8 students walk to school, 16 come by bus, and 5 come by car.
In Ms. Gilman's class 6 students walk, 8 come by car, and 14 by bus.

Complete the table using the information given above.

HOW STUDENTS COME TO SCHOOL

		Mr. Dodd's Class	Ms. Gilman's Class
F–42	Bus		
F–43	Car		
F–44	Walk		

Use the table to answer the following questions.

F–45 How many students in both classes take the bus? ______________

F–46 Do more students in Mr. Dodd's class or Ms. Gilman's class walk to school? ______________

F–47 How many students are in Ms. Gilman's class? ______________

F–48 How many students are in Mr. Dodd's class? ______________

F–49 How many students in both classes ride to school? ______________

F–50 Do more students in Mr. Dodd's class or Ms. Gilman's class ride to school? ______________

READING GRAPHS

The graph shows the high temperatures for each day during one week.

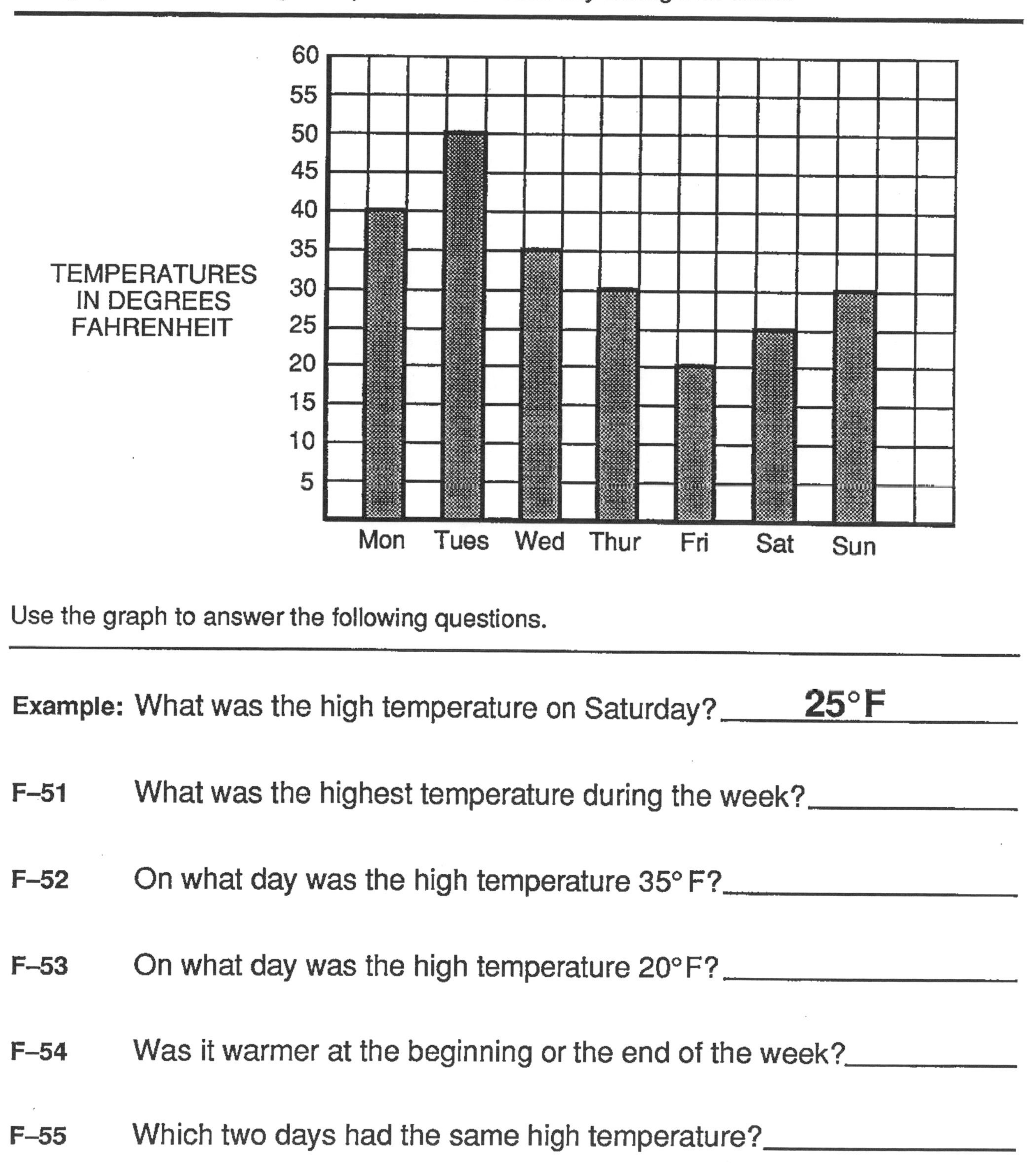

Use the graph to answer the following questions.

Example: What was the high temperature on Saturday? ____25°F____

F–51 What was the highest temperature during the week? ________

F–52 On what day was the high temperature 35° F? ________

F–53 On what day was the high temperature 20° F? ________

F–54 Was it warmer at the beginning or the end of the week? ________

F–55 Which two days had the same high temperature? ________

____

READING GRAPHS

The graph shows the number of hours of sleep for a group of children.

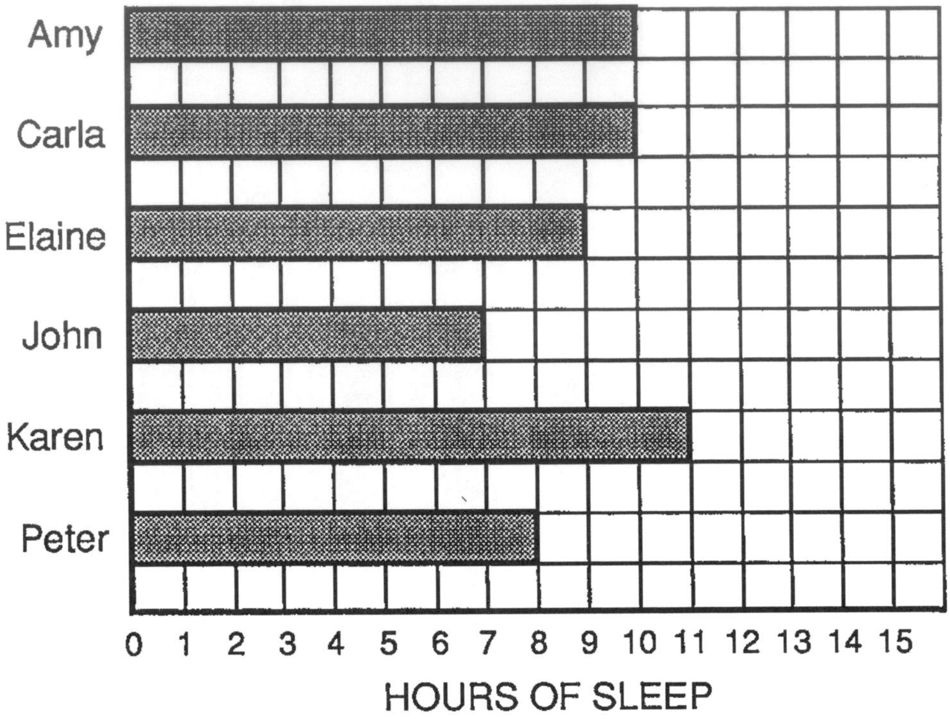

Amy
Carla
Elaine
John
Karen
Peter

0 1 2 3 4 5 6 7 8 9 10 11 12 13 14 15

HOURS OF SLEEP

Use the graph to answer the following questions.

Example: How long did Elaine sleep? ______ **9 hours**

F–56 Who slept the largest number of hours? ______

F–57 Who slept the least number of hours? ______

F–58 Who slept 9 hours? ______

F–59 Which two people slept the same number of hours? ______

F–60 How many more hours did Karen sleep than John? ______

COMPLETING A GRAPH

The height of a plant was measured each week and was written in the table below.

Date	Height in Cm
June 1	2
June 8	2
June 15	4
June 22	6
June 29	10
July 6	16
July 13	18

Use the table to complete the following graph.

F–61

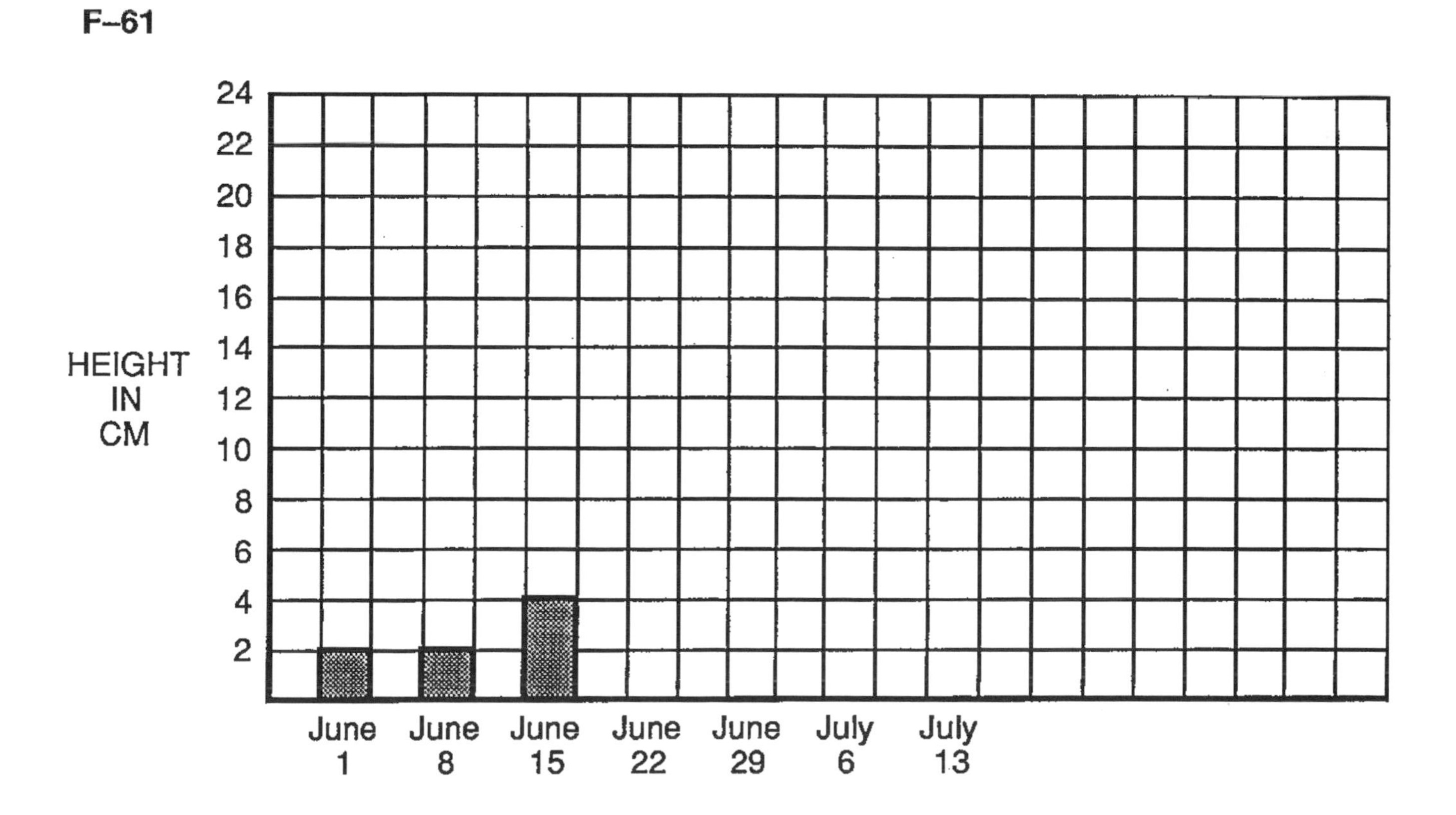

COMPLETING A GRAPH

The height of the plant in the last activity was measured three more times. Enter the following measures on the graph of that activity on the preceding page. The height was 20 cm on July 20, 20 cm on July 27, and 4 cm on August 5.

Use the graph on the preceding page to answer the following questions.

F–62 What was the height of the plant on June 29?________________

F–63 When did the plant measure 18 cm?________________

F–64 What was the height of the plant on July 6?________________

F–65 How much did the plant grow from June 15 to June 29?________________

F–66 How much did the plant grow from June 29 to July 6?________________

F–67 What happened to the plant from June 1 to June 8?________________

F–68 During which week did the plant grow the most?________________

F–69 During which week was the plant the tallest?________________

F–70 What do you think happened to the plant on August 5?________________

____

COMPLETING A GRAPH

In a class election each vote was marked with a √.
Here are the results.

Use the results to complete the following bar graph.

F–71

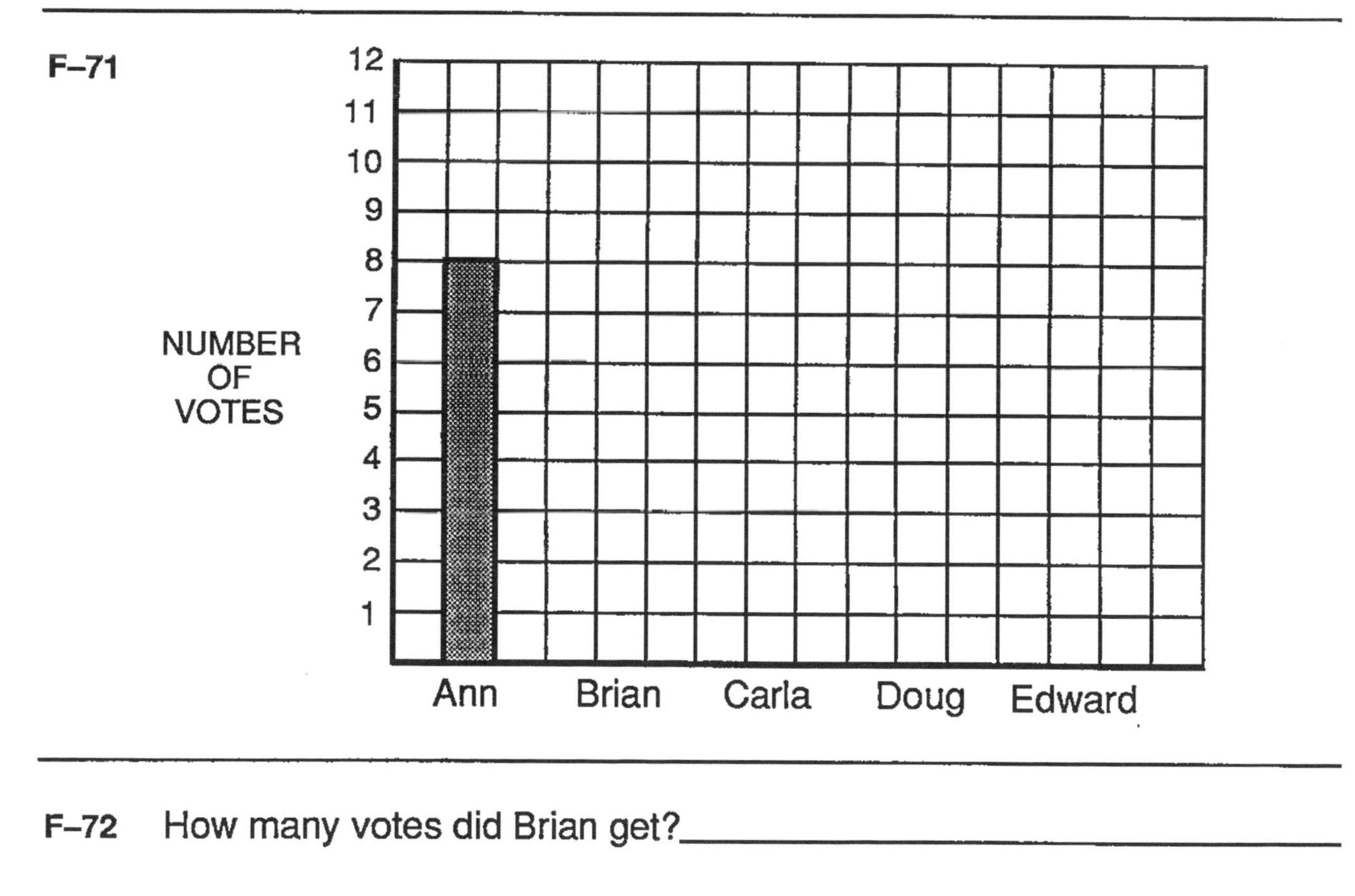

F–72 How many votes did Brian get?________________

F–73 Who won the election?________________

F–74 What was the total number of votes?________________

COMPLETING A GRAPH

The high and low temperatures were recorded for each day of the week.

Day	TEMPERATURE IN FAHRENHEIT	
	High	Low
Monday	72	52
Tuesday	68	48
Wednesday	70	50
Thursday	74	52
Friday	76	56
Saturday	78	60
Sunday	80	68

Use the table to complete the following bar graph.

F–75

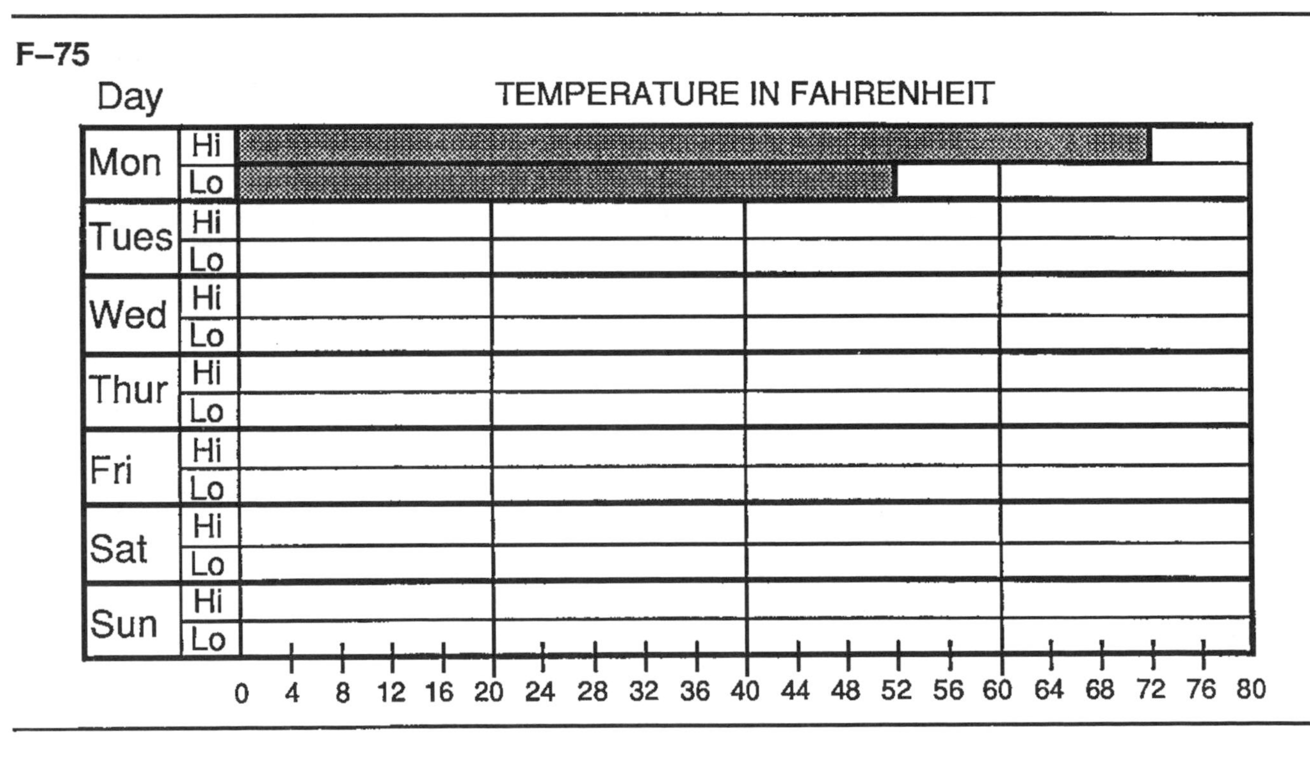

F–76 What was the highest temperature for the week?________________

F–77 What was the lowest temperature for the week?________________

READING CHARTS

Each row in the seating plan is named with a letter.
Each chair is named with a number.

	A	B	C	D	E	F
4		Pat	Sara	Gerry		
3	Marie	Juanita	David		Elise	Debbie
2	Carlos		Chris	Harry	Cindy	Hector
1	Andy	Ann	Richard	Linda	Carol	

Circle the location of each person listed below.

Example: Sara
a. C4 (circled)
b. B3
c. A1

F–78 Elise
a. F2
b. E3
c. D3

F–79 Linda
a. D1
b. D2
c. D3

F–80 Juanita
a. B3
b. C4
c. D3

F–81 Chris
a. A2
b. B2
c. C2

F–82 Hector
a. A4
b. C2
c. F2

LOCATING POSITIONS IN A CHART

Each row in the seating plan is named with a letter.
Each chair is named with a number.

	A	B	C	D	E	F
4		Pat	Sara	Gerry		
3	Marie	Juanita	David		Elise	Debbie
2	Carlos		Chris	Harry	Cindy	Hector
1	Andy	Ann	Richard	Linda	Carol	

Write the location of each person listed below.

Example: Elise E3

F–83 Debbie ____________

F–84 Chris ____________

F–85 Marie ____________

F–86 Gerry ____________

F–87 Ann ____________

F–88 Write the locations of the empty seats in the chart. ____________

F–89 Write the location of the person between Harry and Hector. ____________

F–90 Write the location of the person between Richard and Andy. ____________

F–91 Write the locations of the people in front of Marie. ____________

READING CHARTS

Each row in the seating plan is named with a letter.
Each chair is named with a number.

	A	B	C	D	E	F
4		Pat	Sara	Gerry		
3	Marie	Juanita	David		Elise	Debbie
2	Carlos		Chris	Harry	Cindy	Hector
1	Andy	Ann	Richard	Linda	Carol	

Circle the names of the people seated in the locations in the box.

F–92 C2, E2, D2, F2

Put an X on the names of the people seated in the locations in the box.

F–93 C1, C3, C4, C2

Put a √ on the names of the people seated in the locations in the box.

F–94 C3, E1, B4, D2

Circle the locations in the list below that are empty seats.

F–95

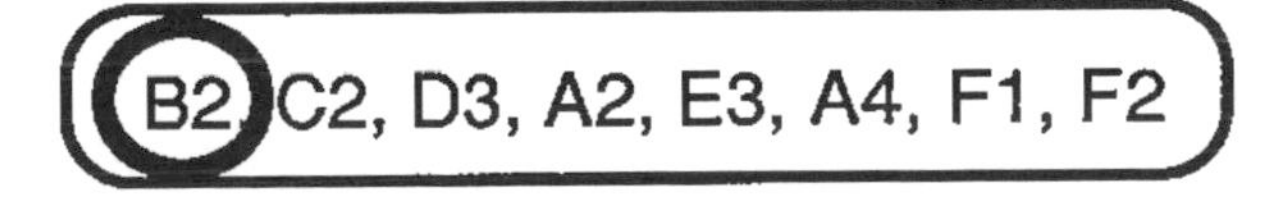

READING CHARTS

Each row in the seating plan is named with a letter.
Each chair is named with a number.

4		Pat	Sara	Gerry		
3	Marie	Juanita	David		Elise	Debbie
2	Carlos		Chris	Harry	Cindy	Hector
1	Andy	Ann	Richard	Linda	Carol	
	A	B	C	D	E	F

Write the name of each person in the seats listed below.

Example: seat D4 Gerry

F–96 seat C3 ____________

F–97 seat B4 ____________

F–98 seat F2 ____________

F–99 seat A2 ____________

F–100 seat B1 ____________

F–101 Write the name of the person seated between C2 and E2. ____________

F–102 Write the name of the person seated between C3 and A3. ____________

F–103 Write the names of the people seated behind E1. ____________

F–104 Write the names of the people seated in front of B4. ____________

LOCATING POSITIONS ON A CHART

Each column in the chart is named with a letter.
Each row in the chart is named with a number.

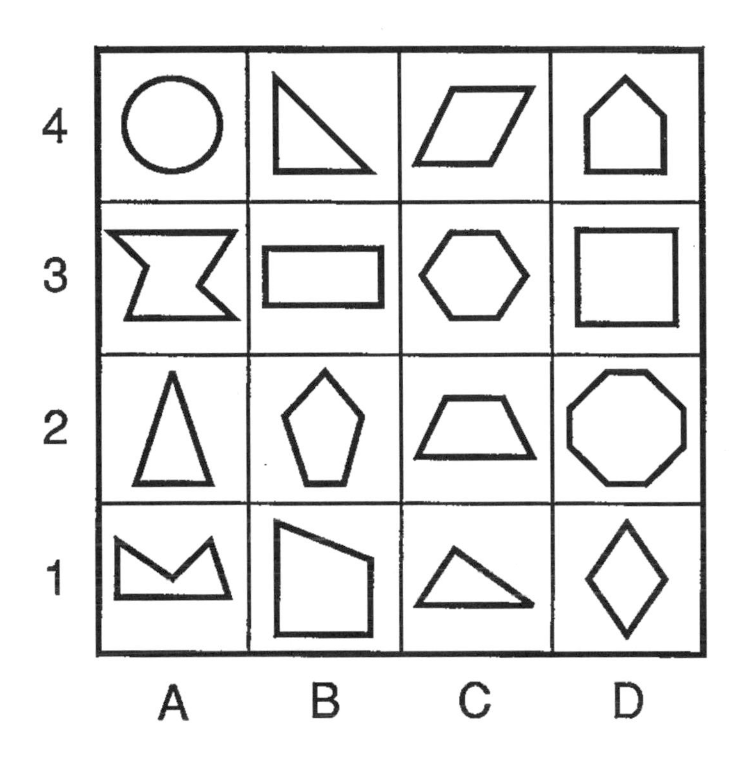

Write the locations of the figures given in the exercises below.

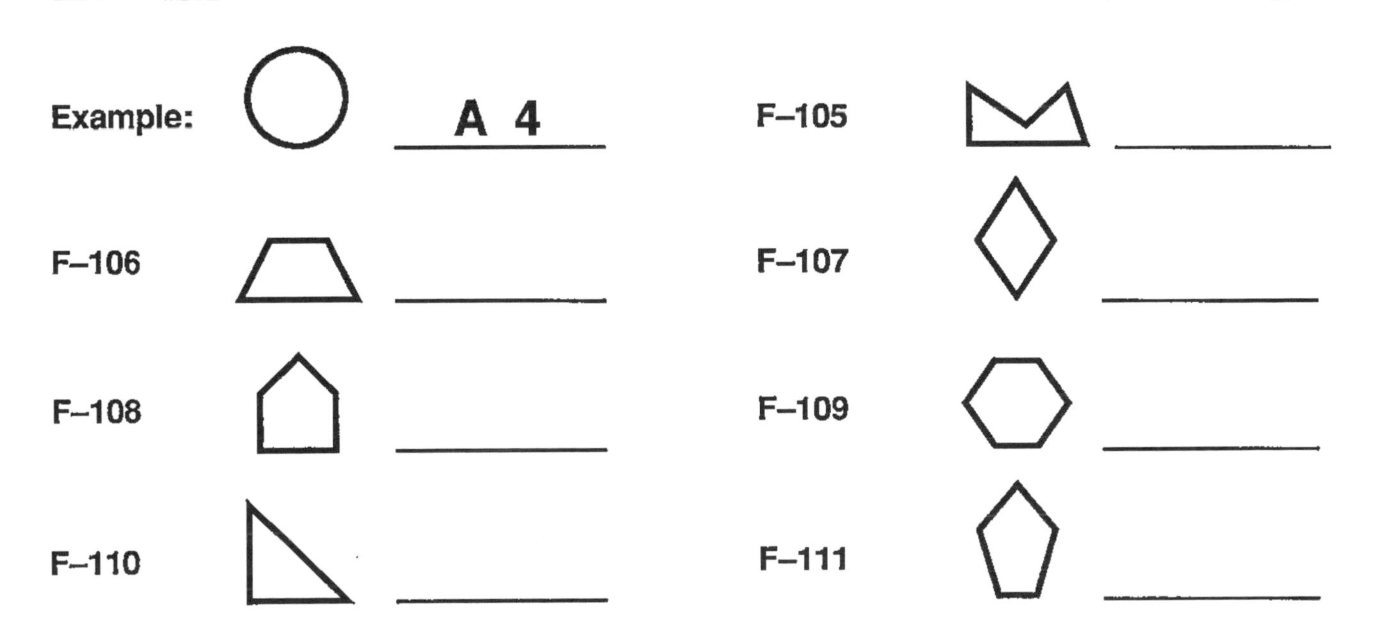

READING CHARTS

Each column in the chart is named with a letter.
Each row in the chart is named with a number.

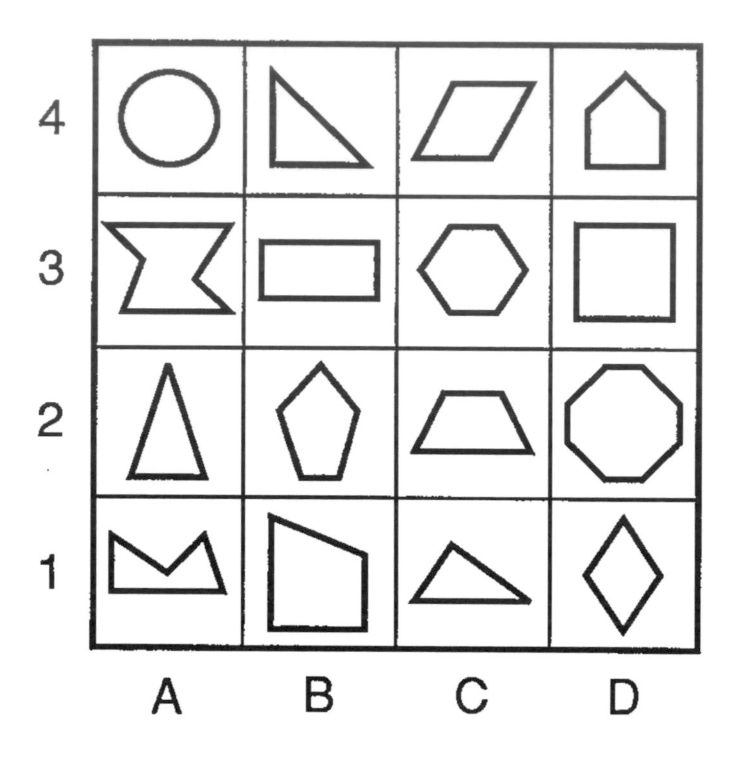

Draw the figures from the chart above next to their locations given below.

Example: B 3 ____________

F–112 D 3 ____________

F–113 A 2 ____________

F–114 C 2 ____________

F–115 A 4 ____________

F–116 C 4 ____________

F–117 D 4 ____________

F–118 B 1 ____________

READING CHARTS

Each column in the chart is named with a letter.
Each row in the chart is named with a number.

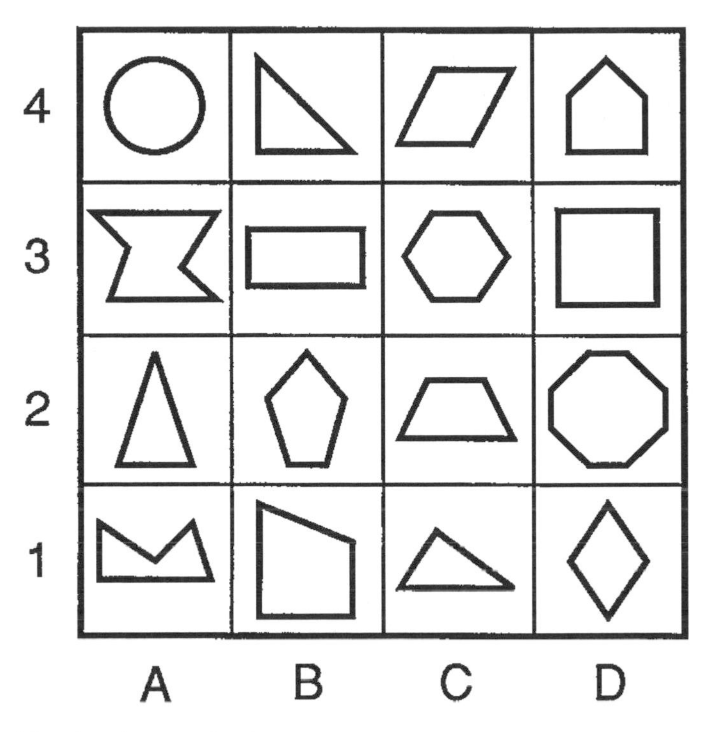

Find the figures listed in the boxes below.
Match the groups of figures with their properties.

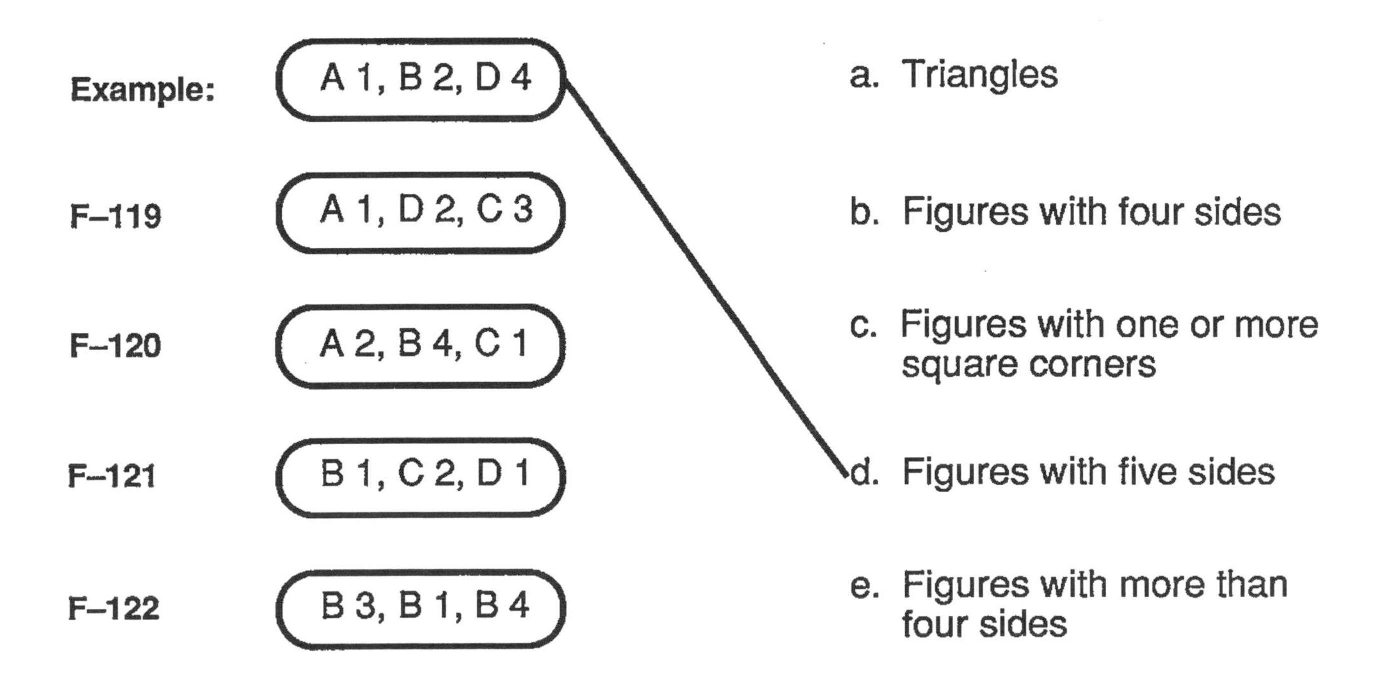

Example: A 1, B 2, D 4

F–119 A 1, D 2, C 3

F–120 A 2, B 4, C 1

F–121 B 1, C 2, D 1

F–122 B 3, B 1, B 4

a. Triangles

b. Figures with four sides

c. Figures with one or more square corners

d. Figures with five sides

e. Figures with more than four sides

READING CHARTS

Each column in the chart is named with a letter.
Each row in the chart is named with a number.

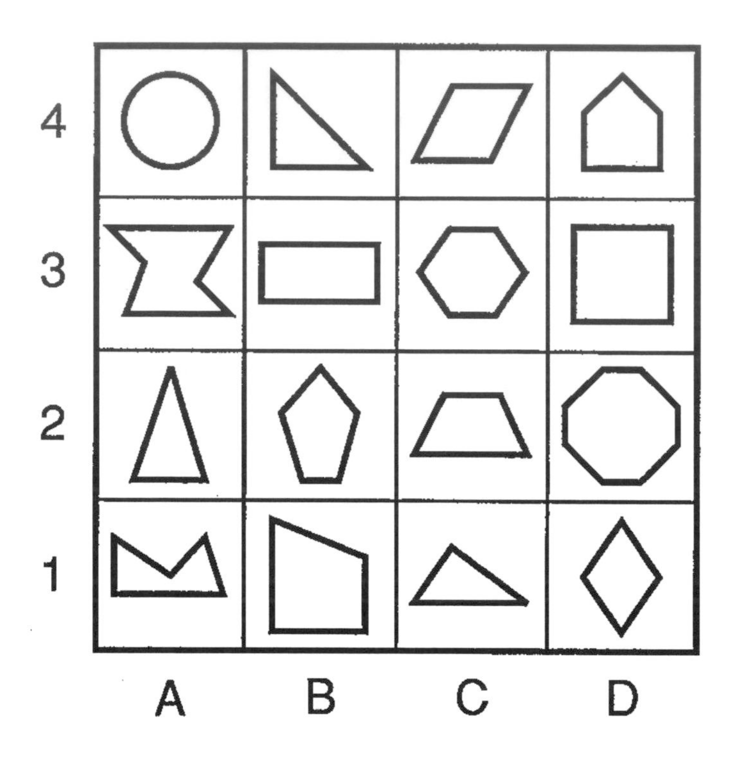

Draw the figures below that are in the following locations on the chart.

Example:	Between B 3 and D 3	**F–123**	Between C 2 and A 2
F–124	Between D 2 and D 4	**F–125**	Between A 3 and A 1
F–126	Below B 2	**F–127**	Above B 2

LOCATING POINTS ON A GRAPH

Each vertical line of the graph is named with a letter.
Each horizontal line of the graph is named with a number.
Put an X on the graph for each point listed in the box.

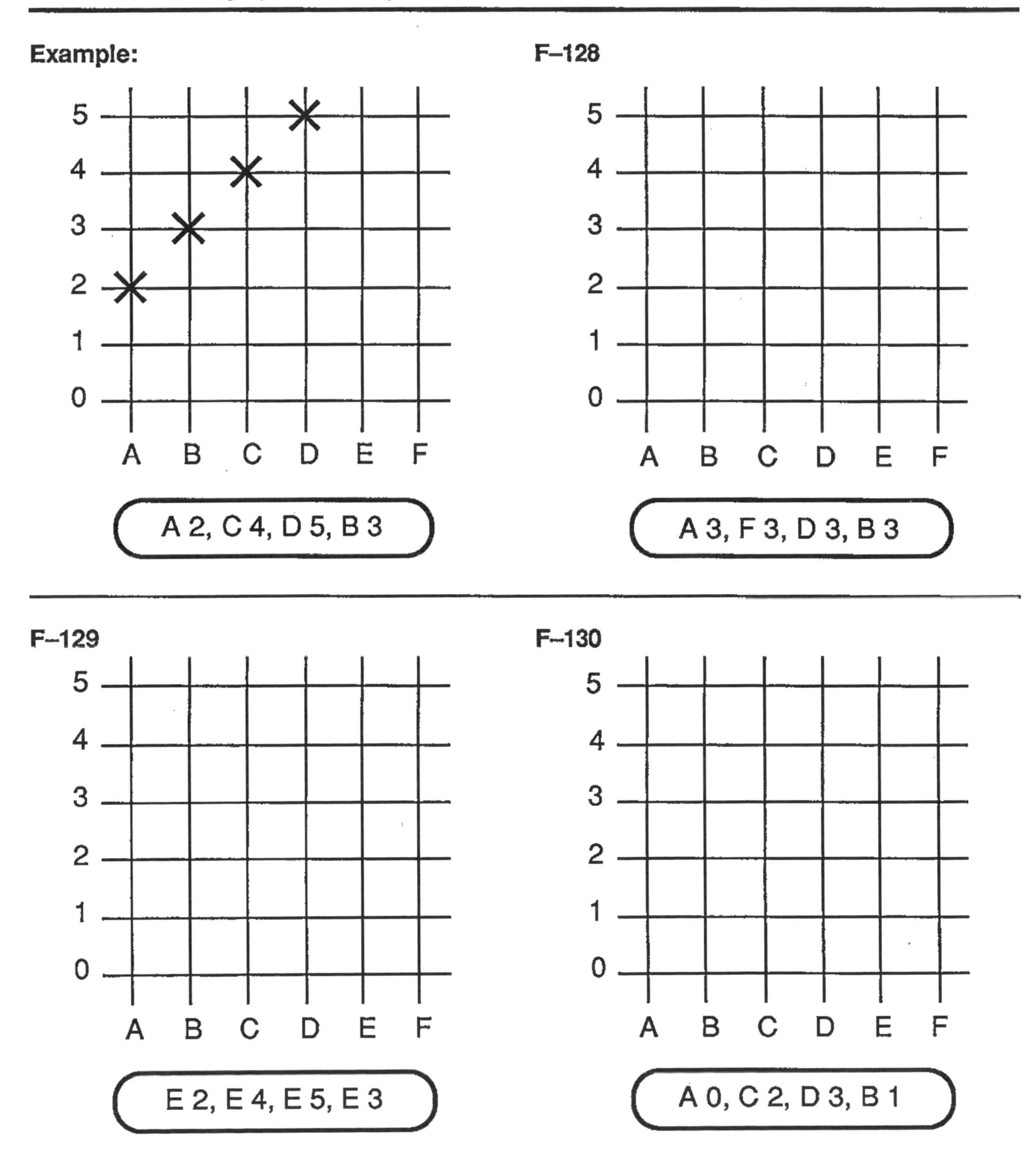

LOCATING POINTS ON A GRAPH

Each vertical line of the graph is named with a letter.
Each horizontal line of the graph is named with a number.
Put an X on the graph for each point listed in the box.

F–131

F–132

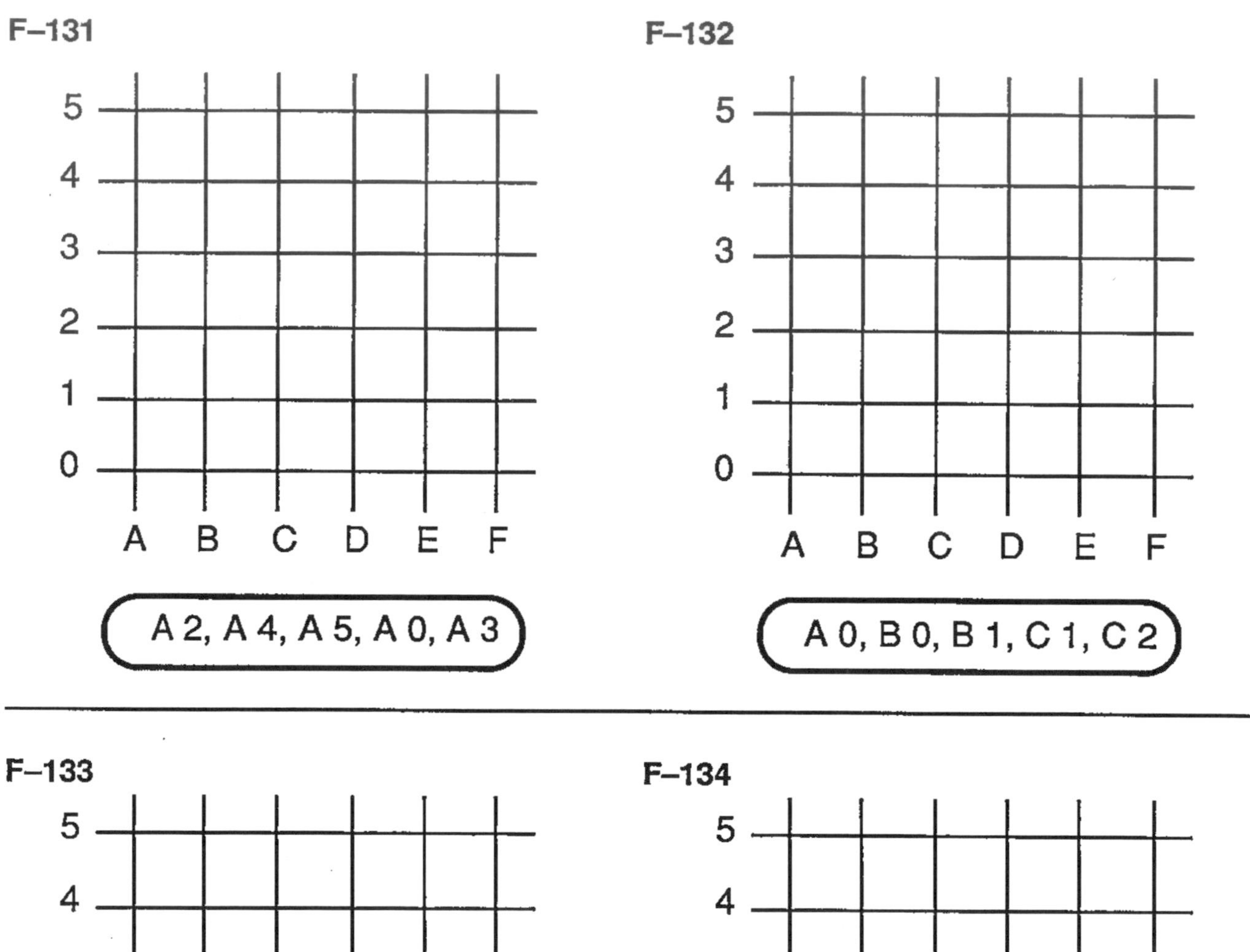

F–133

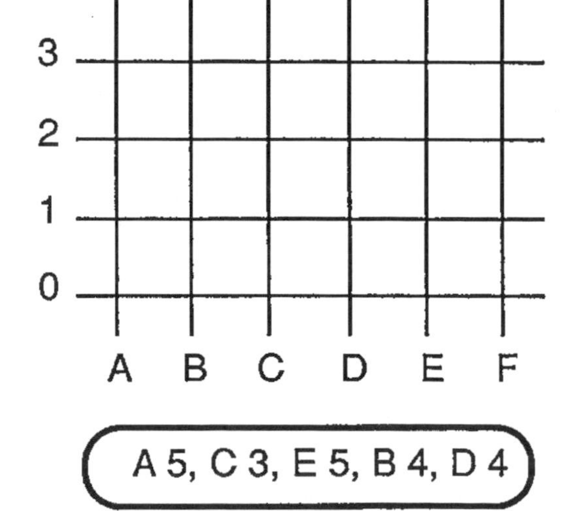

F–134

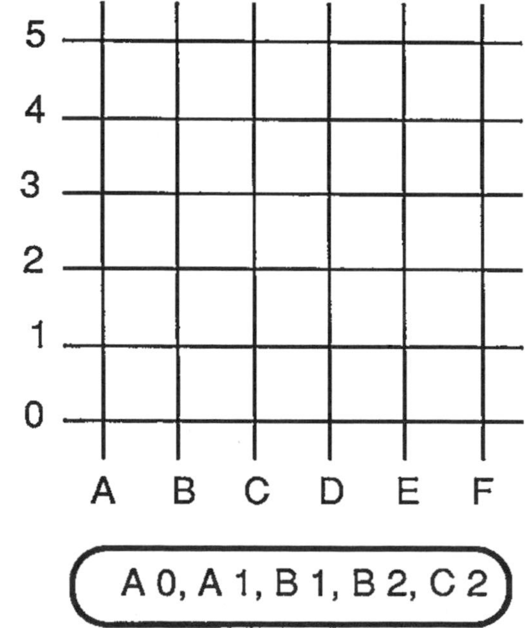

READING GRAPHS

Each vertical line of the graph is named with a letter.
Each horizontal line of the graph is named with a number.
Write the location of each X in the box.

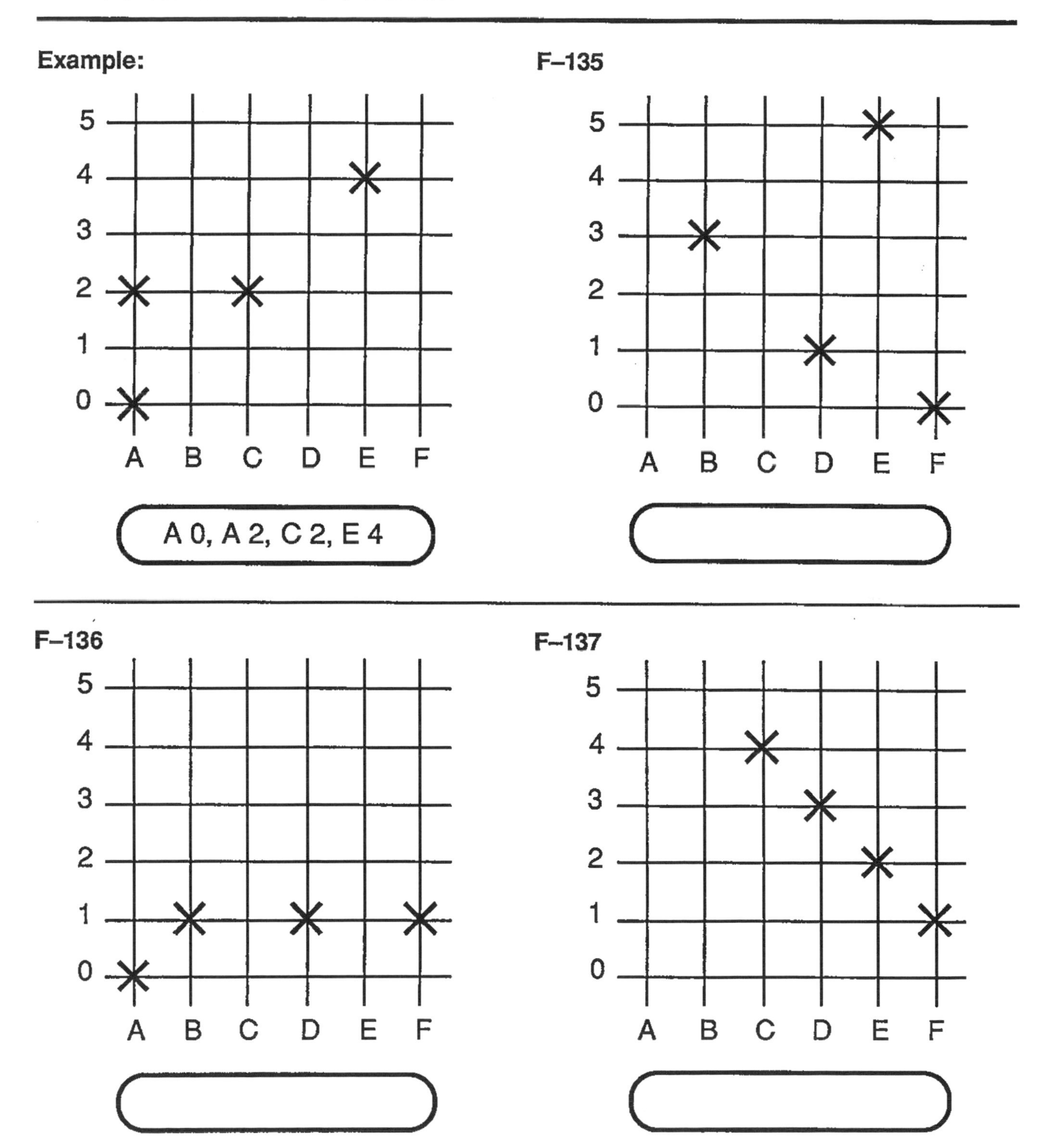

READING GRAPHS

Each vertical line of the graph is named with a letter.
Each horizontal line of the graph is named with a number.
Write the location of each X in the box.

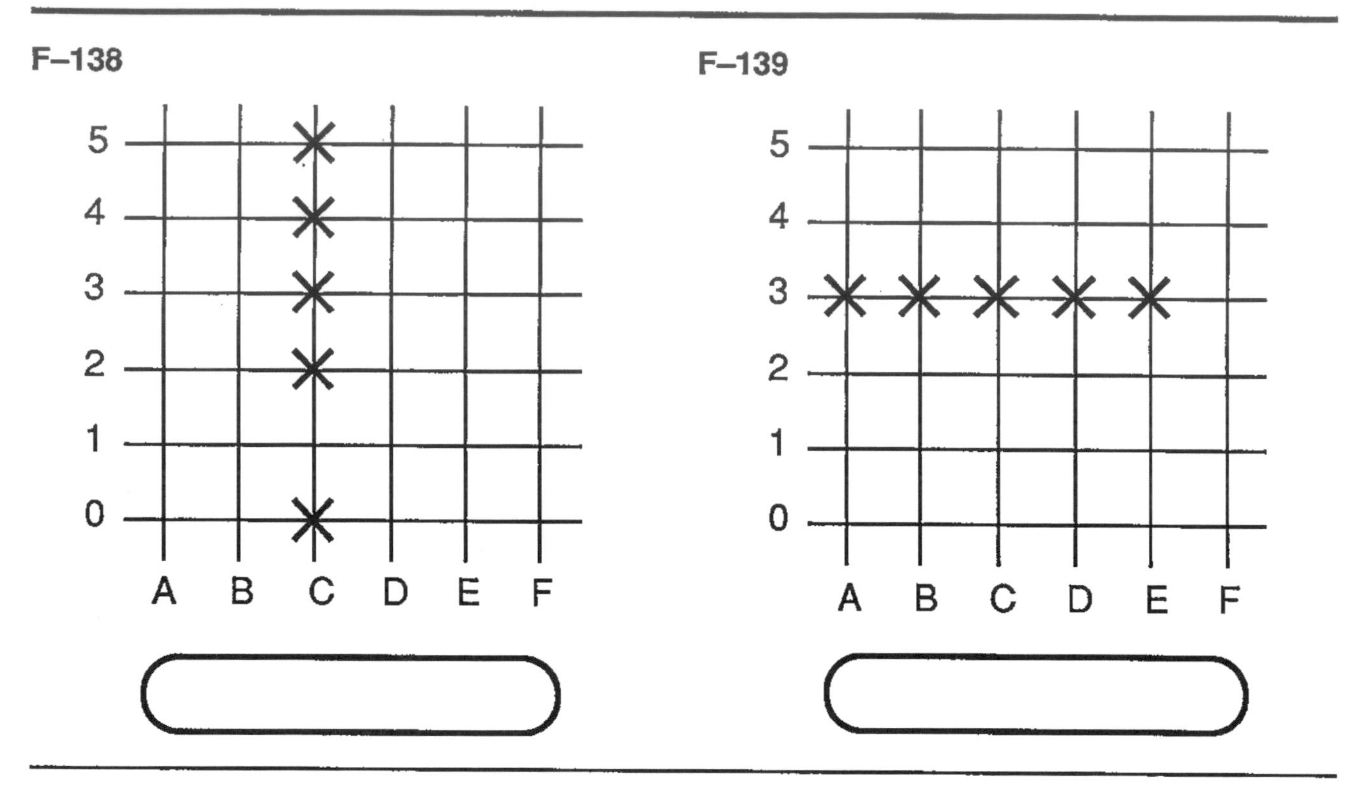

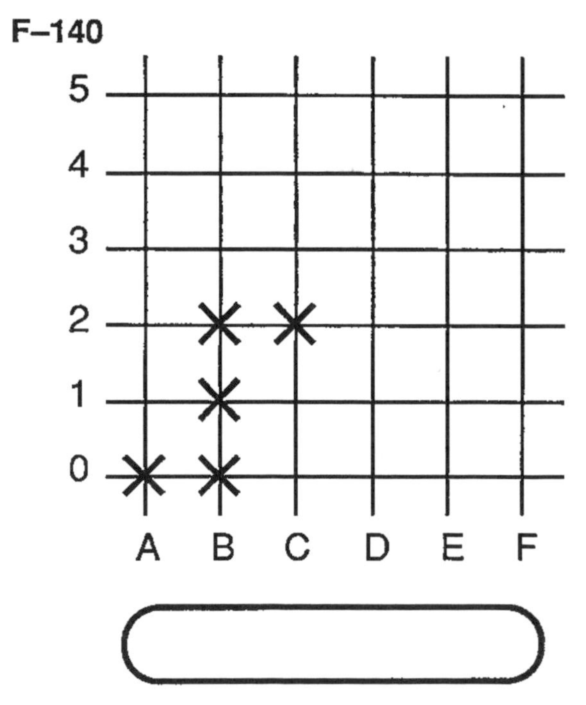

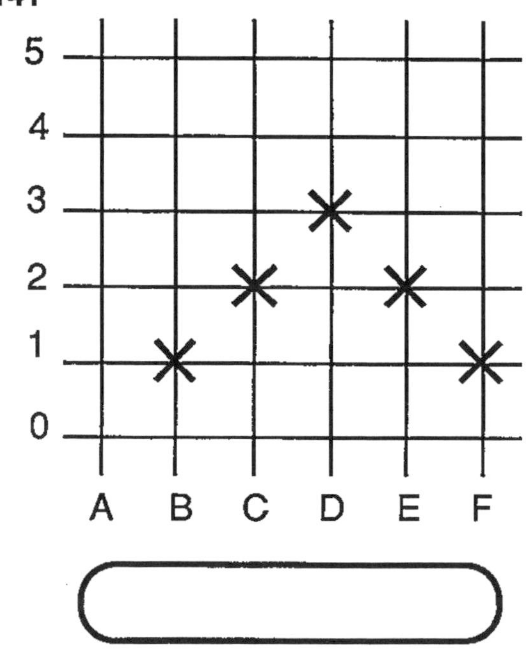

READING GRAPHS

Each vertical line of the graph is named with a letter.
Each horizontal line of the graph is named with a number.
Five points on the graph are connected with a line.
Write the locations of the points that the line connects.

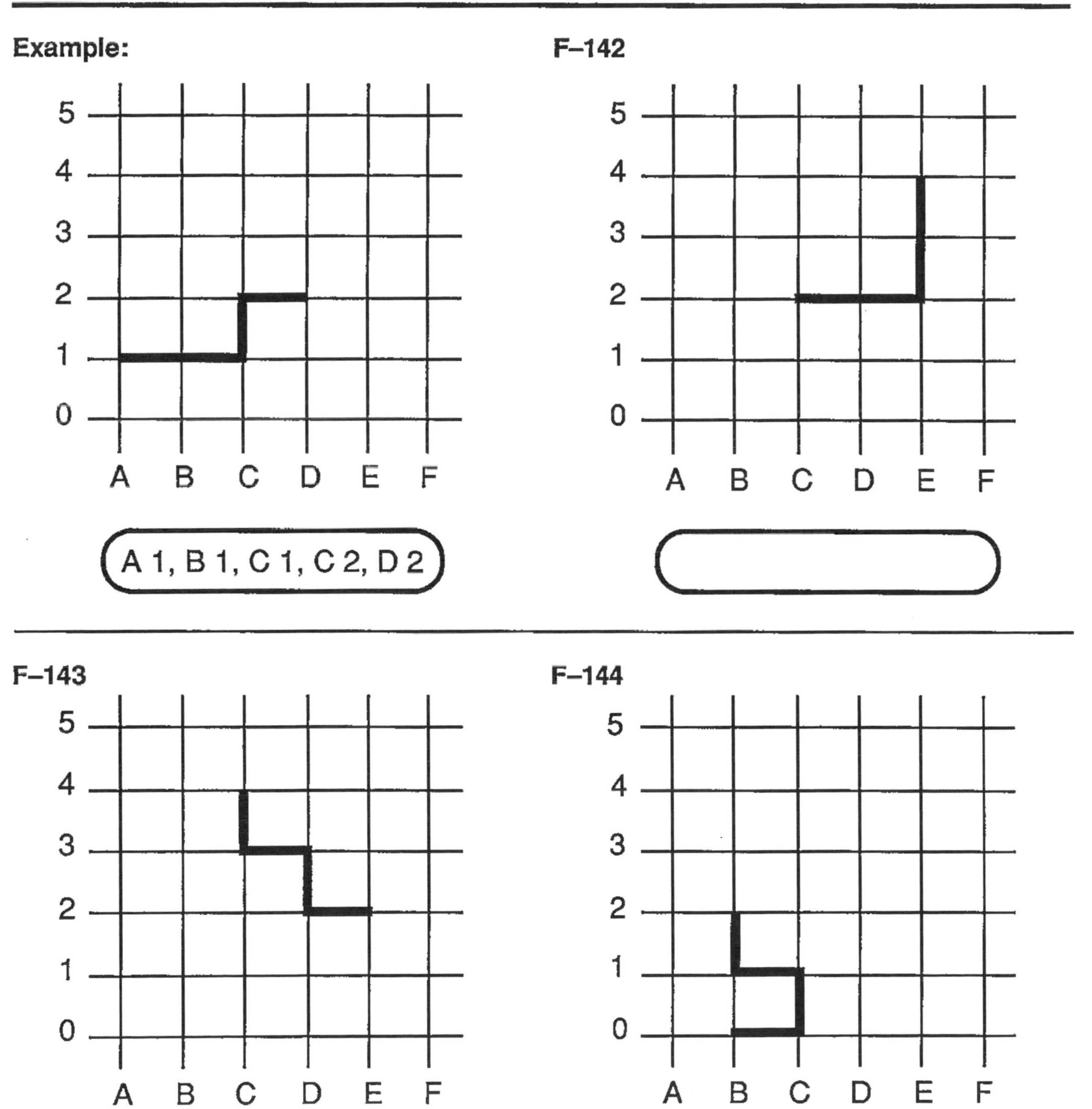

READING GRAPHS

Each vertical line of the graph is named with a letter.
Each horizontal line of the graph is named with a number.
Five points on the graph are connected with a line.
Write the locations of the points that the line connects.

F–145

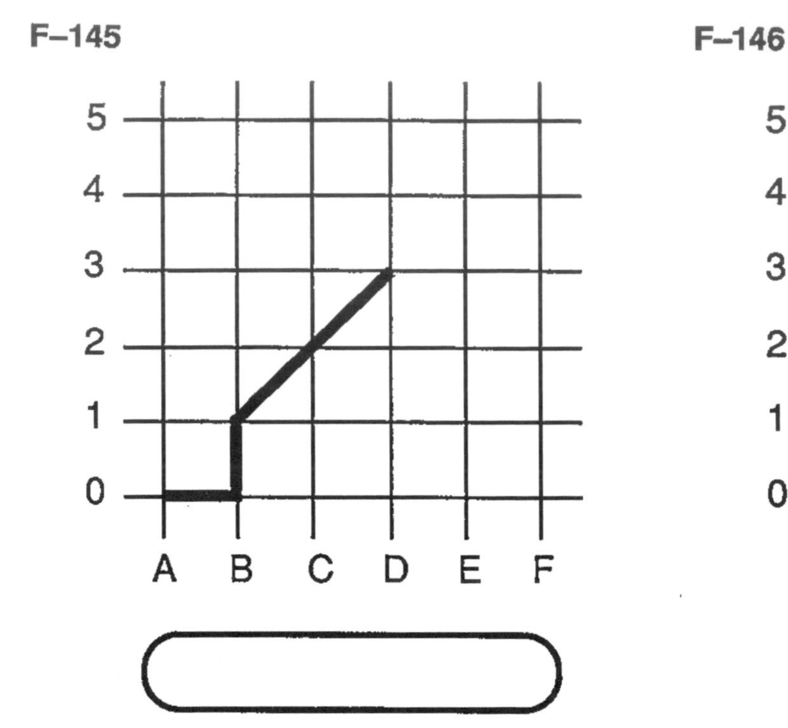

F–146

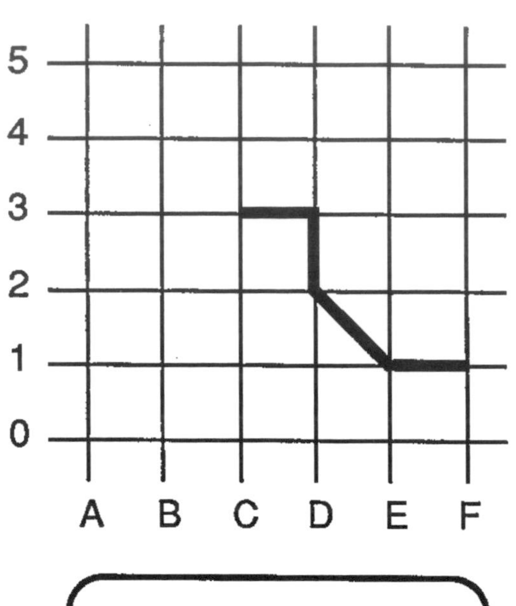

F–147

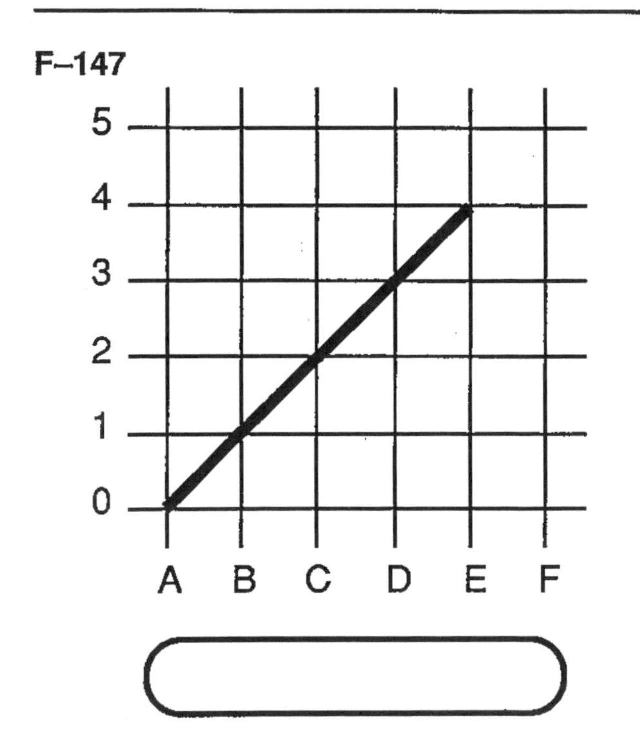

F–148

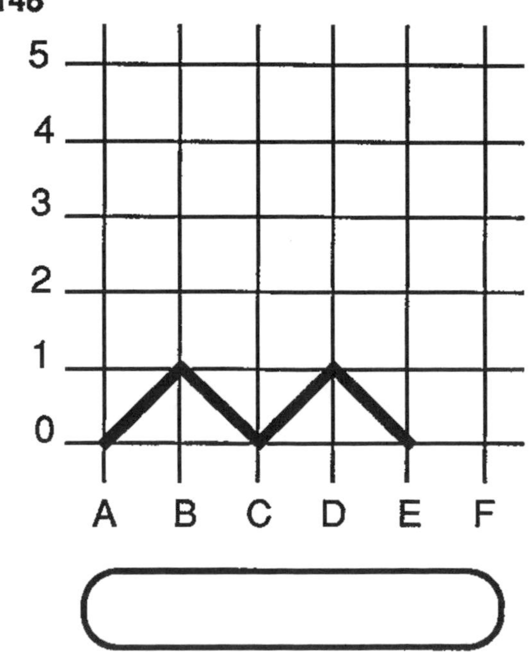

DRAWING GRAPHS

Each vertical line of the graph is named with a letter.
Each horizontal line of the graph is named with a number.
Draw a line to connect the points in the order that they are listed.

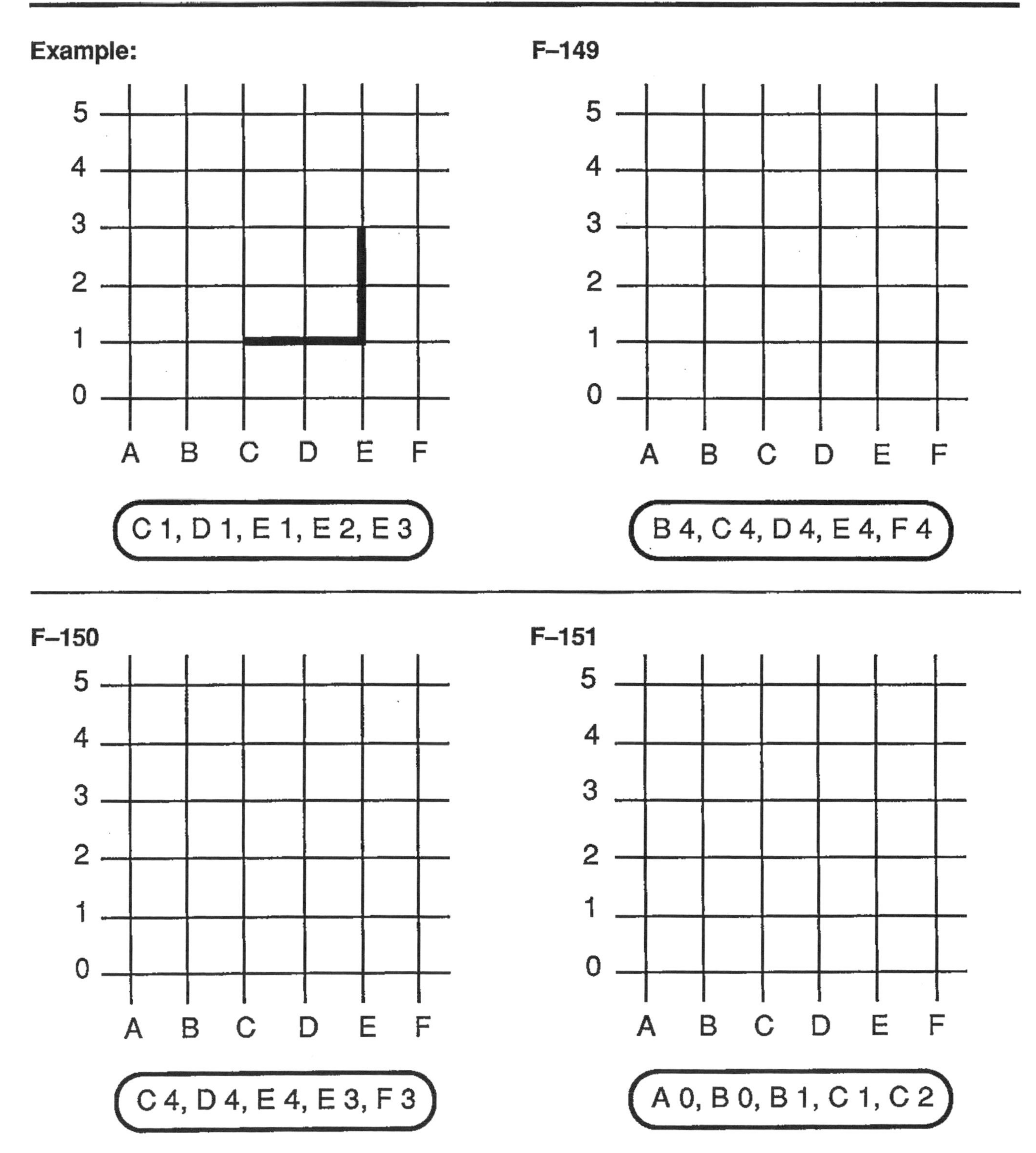

DRAWING GRAPHS

Each vertical line of the graph is named with a letter.
Each horizontal line of the graph is named with a number.
Draw a line to connect the points in the order that they are listed.

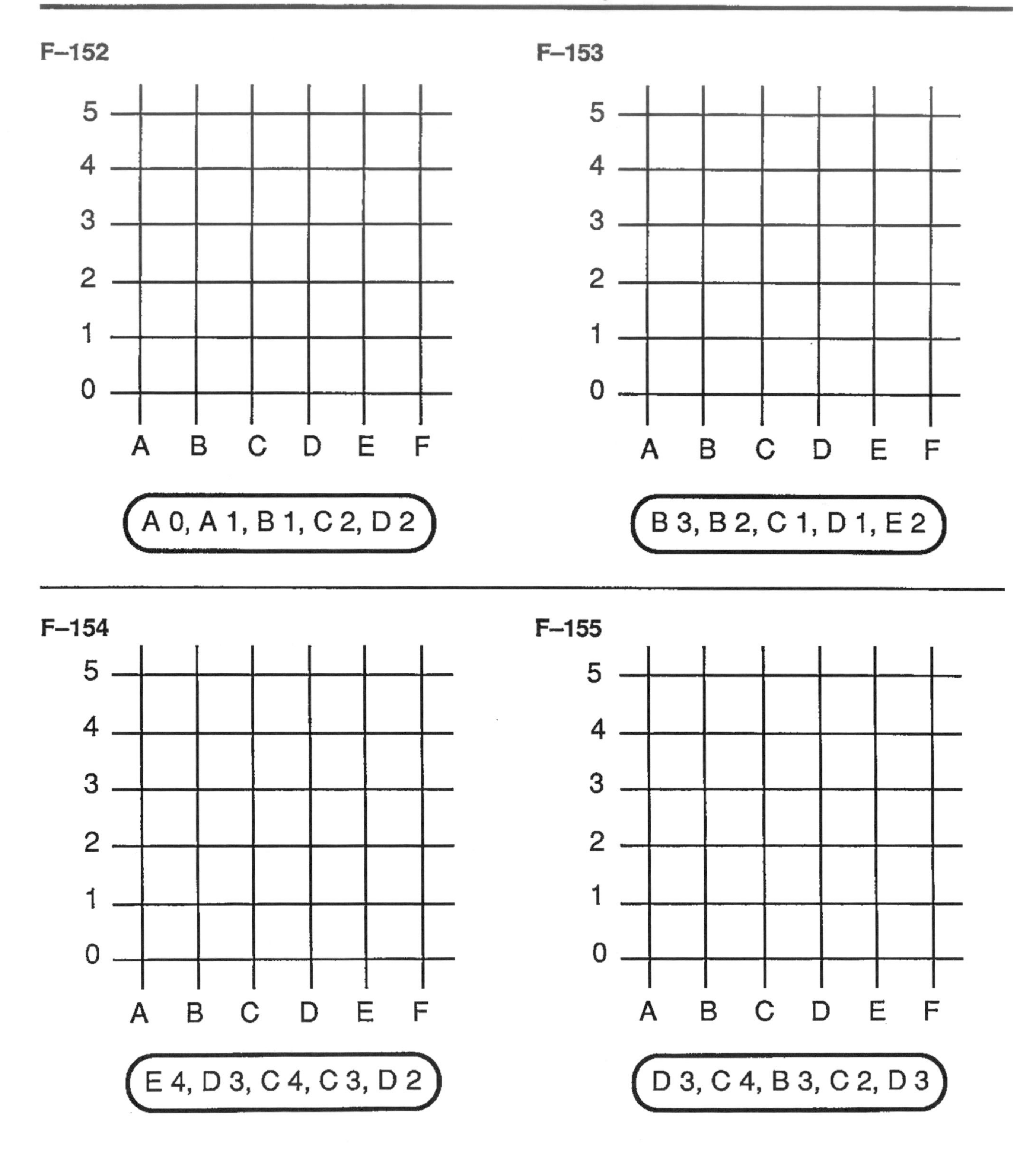

Answers

Page 1
A-1: 5
A-2: 2
A-3: 1
A-4: 6
A-5: 3

Page 2
A-6: 15
A-7: 24
A-8: 6
A-9: 12
A-10: 12

Page 3
A-11: 12
A-12: 4
A-13: 12
A-14: 20
A-15: 8

Page 4
A-16: 9
A-17: 16
A-18: 15
A-19: 15
A-20: 21

Page 5
A-21: 7
A-22: 8
A-23: 9
A-24: 12
A-25: 13

Page 6
A-26: 9
A-27: 3
A-28: 2
A-29: 6
A-30: 10

Page 7
A-31: h, 9
A-32: t, 4
A-33: j, 5
A-34: r, s, t, 7
A-35: n, o, p, q, r, 9
A-36: v, w, x, 7
A-37: a, d, 5

Page 8
A-38: t, u, v, 5
A-39: e, f, g, h, i, 8
A-40: c, d, e, f, 6
A-41: t, u, v, w, 7
A-42: d, e, f, g, i, 6
A-43: l, m, n, o, 5
A-44: p, q, r, s, 5
A-45: f, g, h, i, j, l, 7

Page 9
A-46: f, g, h, i, 8
A-47: s, t, u, 7
A-48: o, p, q, r, s, 8
A-49: m, n, o, p, q, r, 9

Page 10
A-50: 5
A-51: 10
A-52: 10
A-53: 26
A-54: 24
A-55: 24
A-56: 22

Page 11
A-57: 3, 4; 5
A-58: 9, 10, 11; 6
A-59: 10, 11; 4
A-60: 13, 14, 15; 6
A-61: 25, 26; 5
A-62: 37, 38; 5
A-63: 51, 52, 53, 54; 6

Page 12
A-64: 7, 8; 5
A-65: 12, 13, 14; 6
A-66: 21, 22, 23, 24; 6
A-67: 32, 33, 35, 36, 37; 7
A-68: 14, 15, 16; 6
A-69: 27, 28, 29; 6
A-70: 17, 18, 20, 21; 5
A-71: 10, 9; 6

Page 13
A-72: 6, 7, 8; 7
A-73: 14, 15, 16, 17; 8
A-74: 32, 33, 34, 35, 36, 37; 9
A-75: 52, 53, 54, 55, 56, 57; 9

Page 14
A-76: 6
A-77: 17
A-78: 25
A-79: 15
A-80: 9
A-81: 20

Page 15
A-82: 20, 21, 22
A-83: 19, 20, 21, 22
A-84: 54, 55, 56
A-85: 93, 94, 95, 96
A-86: 67, 68, 69
A-87: 9, 10, 11, 12
A-88: 32, 33, 34, 35

Page 16
A-89: 10, 9, 8
A-90: 17, 16, 15
A-91: 90, 89, 88, 87
A-92: 31, 30, 29
A-93: 39, 38, 37, 36
A-94: 7, 6, 5
A-95: 57, 56, 55, 54
A-96: 60, 59, 58

Page 17
A-97: 5, 7, 9
A-98: 83, 86, 87
A-99: 18, 20, 21
A-100: 56, 57, 60, 61
A-101: 11, 12, 16
A-102: 29, 31, 32, 34
A-103: 15, 16, 18, 19

Page 18
A-104: 95, 94, 90, 89
A-105: 83, 86, 87, 89
A-106: 21, 20
A-107: 16, 14, 12
A-108: 8, 7, 6, 3
A-109: 9, 7, 5, 4
A-110: 45, 46, 49, 50, 51
A-111: 71, 70, 69, 67, 66

Page 19
A-112: 8, 10, 12, 14
A-113: 15, 18, 21
A-114: 20, 25, 30, 35
A-115: 32, 34, 36
A-116: 70, 80, 90
A-117: 45, 50, 55, 60
A-118: 39, 42, 45, 48

Page 20
A-119: 6, 15
A-120: 15, 20, 30, 35
A-121: 15, 20, 25, 35
A-122: 4, 8, 12
A-123: 17, 18, 20, 21
A-124: 18, 12, 8
A-125: 45, 40, 30, 25

Page 21
A-126: b. 30
A-127: c. 67
A-128: b. 4
A-129: b. 7

Page 22
A-130: 46
A-131: 21
A-132: 33
A-133: 49
A-134: 21
A-135: 6
A-136: 64

Page 23 Shade the following rectangles:
A-137
A-139
A-142

Page 24 Shade the following rectangles:
A-145
A-147
A-149
A-150

Page 25
A-151: Set B
A-152: Set B
A-153: Set B

Page 26
A-154: Set B
A-155: Set A
A-156: Set B
A-157: Set A

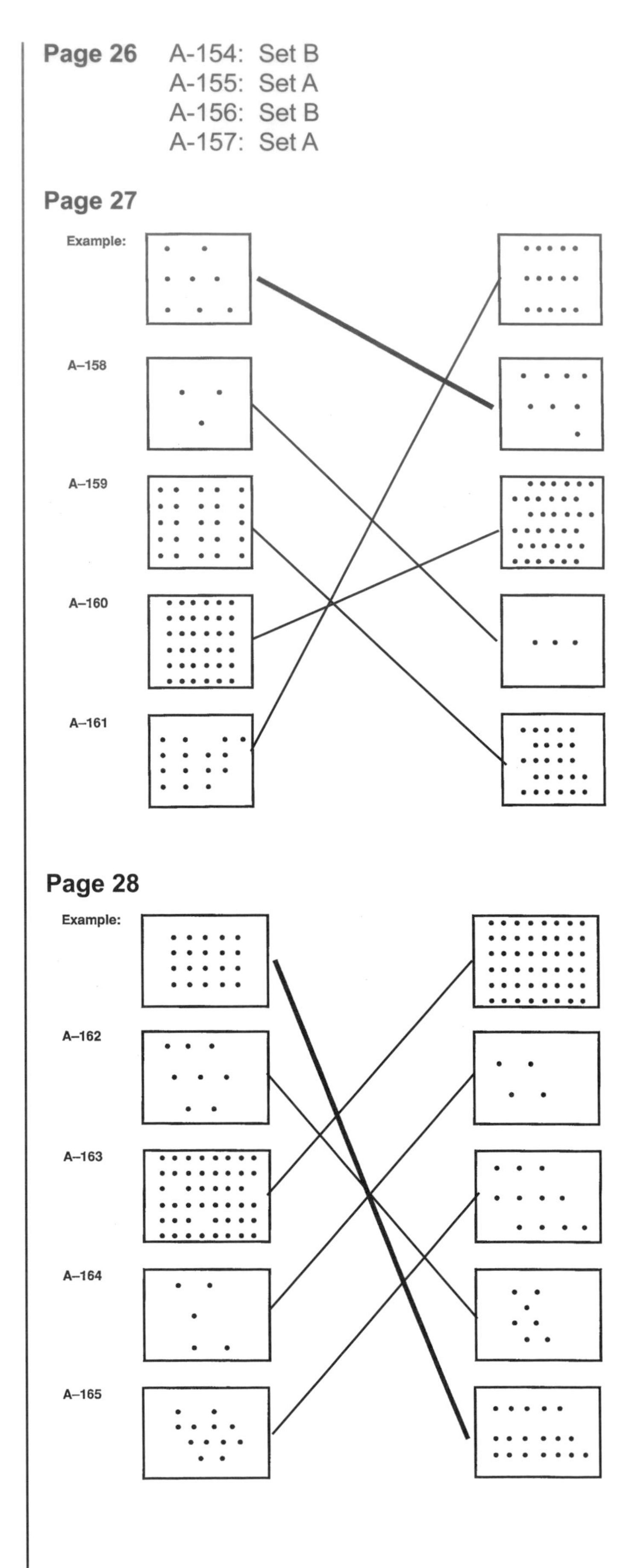

Page 29 A-166: 1, 4 A-167: 3, 4 A-168: 4, 8 A-169: 3, 8 A-170: 4, 8

Page 30 A-171: 1, 4 A-172: 3, 4 A-173: 2, 4 A-174: 8, 16 A-175: 8, 16 A-176: 6, 16

Page 31 A-177: Less A-178: More A-179: More A-180: Less A-181: More

Page 32 A-182: More A-183: Less A-184: More A-185: Less A-186: More

Page 33 A-187: 6, 7, 8, 9 A-188: 11, 12, 13, 14, 15, 16 A-189: 19, 20, 21, 24, 25 A-190: 31, 32, 34, 35

Page 34 A-191: 5, 6, 7, 11, 12 A-192: 18, 19, 20, 24, 25 A-193: 18, 19, 20, 21, 22 A-194: 33, 34, 35, 36, 37 A-195: 51, 52, 53, 54, 56, 57, 58

Page 35 A-196: 29 A-197: 11 A-198: 7 A-199: 36

Page 36 A-200: 37 A-201: 65 A-202: 5 A-203: 22

Page 37 A-204: 3, 5, 6, 10 A-205: 9, 12, 13, 15 A-206: 11, 12, 15, 16

Page 38 A-207: 3, 7, 9, 12 A-208: 5, 10, 12, 15 A-209: 10, 12, 17, 24 A-210: 32, 34, 36, 40

Page 39 A-211: c. 7 A-212: b. 21 A-213: a. 21 A-214: c. 58 A-215: d. 60

Page 40 A-216: c. 33, d. 40 A-217: b. 43, d. 6 A-218: a. 50 A-219: a. 34 A-220: c. 34

Page 41 A-221: 5 A-222: 11 A-223: 8 A-224: 14 A-225: 27

Page 42 A-226: 4 A-227: 12 A-228: 16 A-229: 7 A-230: 25 A-231: 61

Page 43 A-232: 10, 20, 12, 16, 13, X on 20 A-233: 11, 20, 4, 9, 6, X on 20 A-234: 15, 12, 32, 20, 41, X on 41 A-235: 90, 70, 80, 60, X on 90 A-236: 28, 36, 42, 25, X on 42

Page 44 A-237: 4, 5, 0, 7, X on 0 A-238: 9, 12, 14, 10, 8, 0, X on 0 A-239: 29, 32, 20, 19, X on 19 A-240: 35, 60, 75, 55, 70, 65, X on 35 A-241: 44, 39, 27, 40, X on 27

Page 45 A-242: 6, 5, 4 A-243: 7, 6, 6, 7 A-244: 9, 7, 6, 10 A-245: 12, 14, 13 A-246: 28, 30, 27, 31

Page 46 A-247: 14, 15 A-248: 16, 14, 17 A-249: 25 A-250: 25, 30, 20 A-251: 68, 59 A-252: 39, 43, 41, 35

Page 47

Page 48

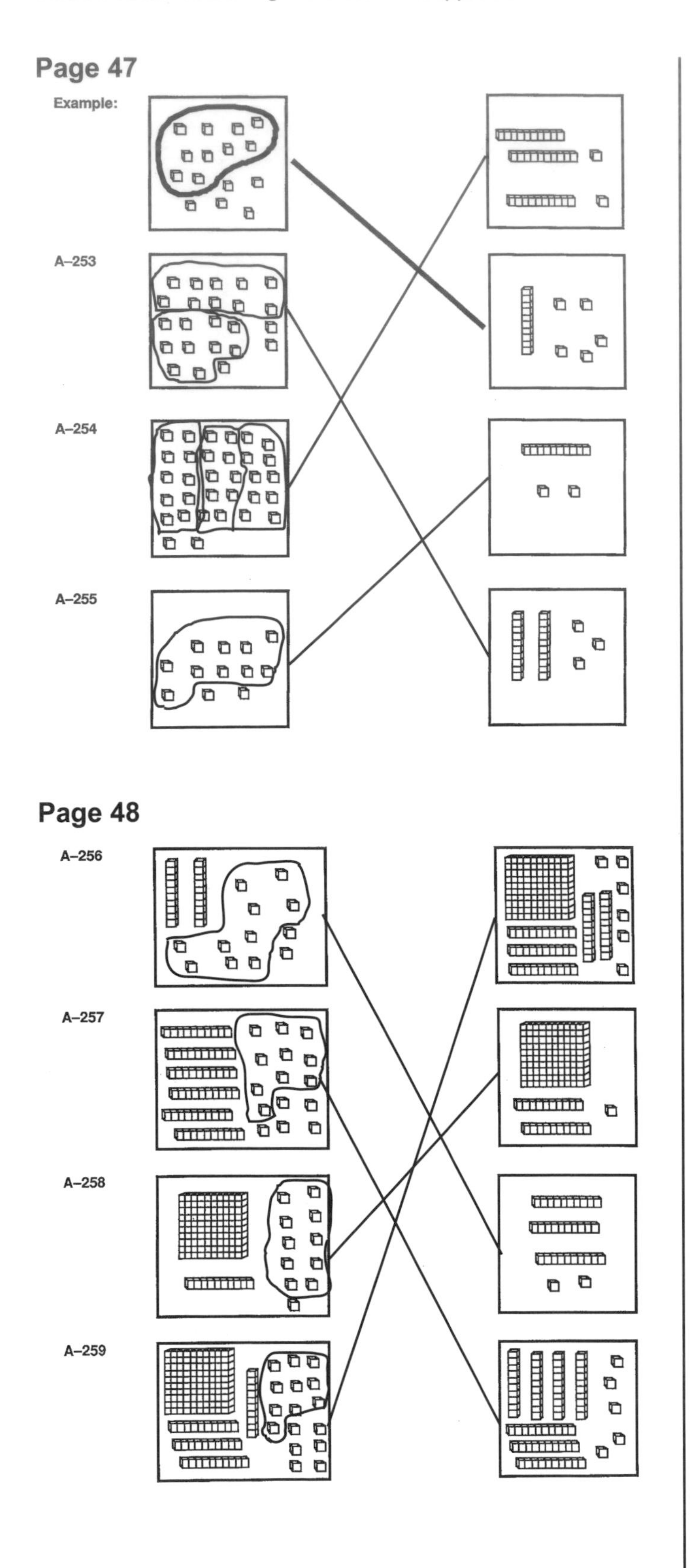

Page 49

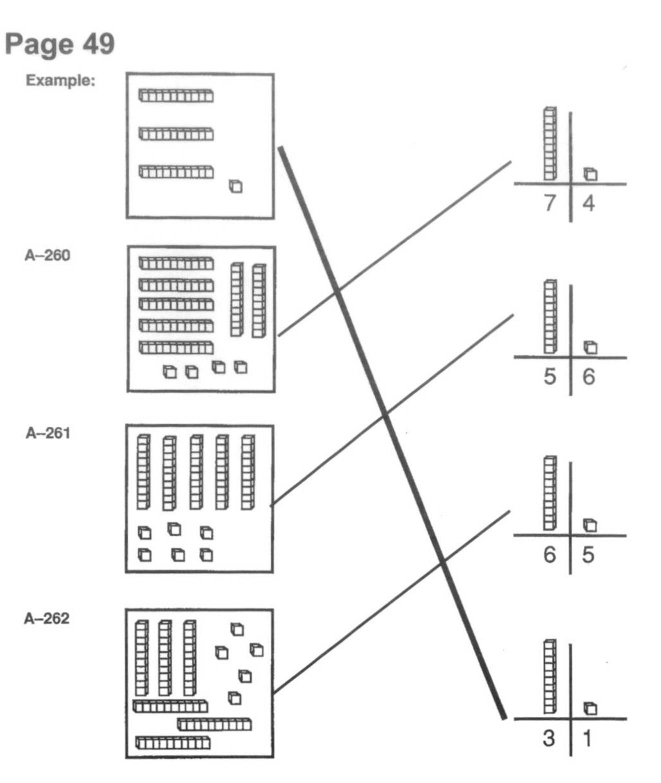

Page 50

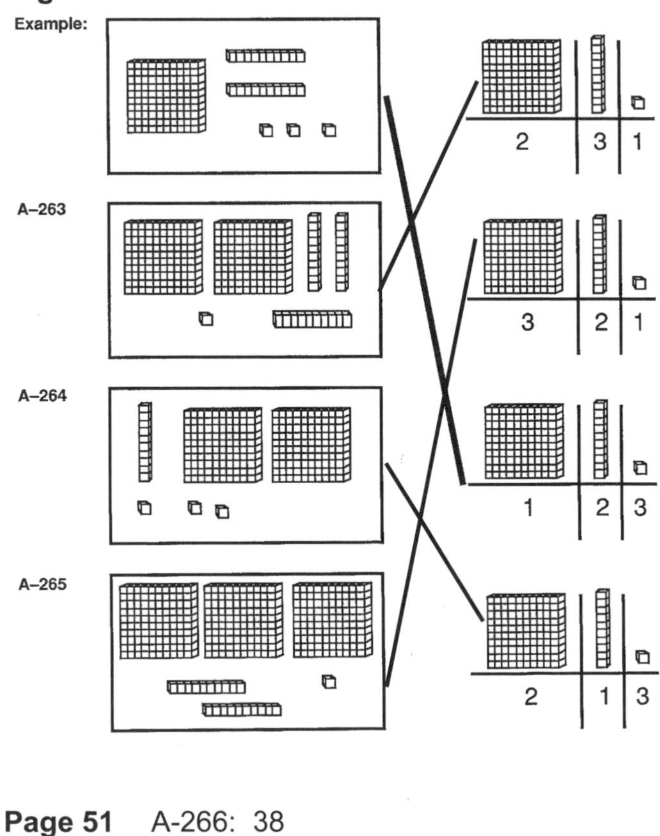

Page 51

A-266: 38
A-267: 53
A-268: 41

Page 52 A-269: 153
A-270: 156
A-271: 150

Page 53 A-272: 78
A-273: 62
A-274: 26

Page 54 A-275: 235
A-276: 143
A-277: 207
A-278: 130

Page 55

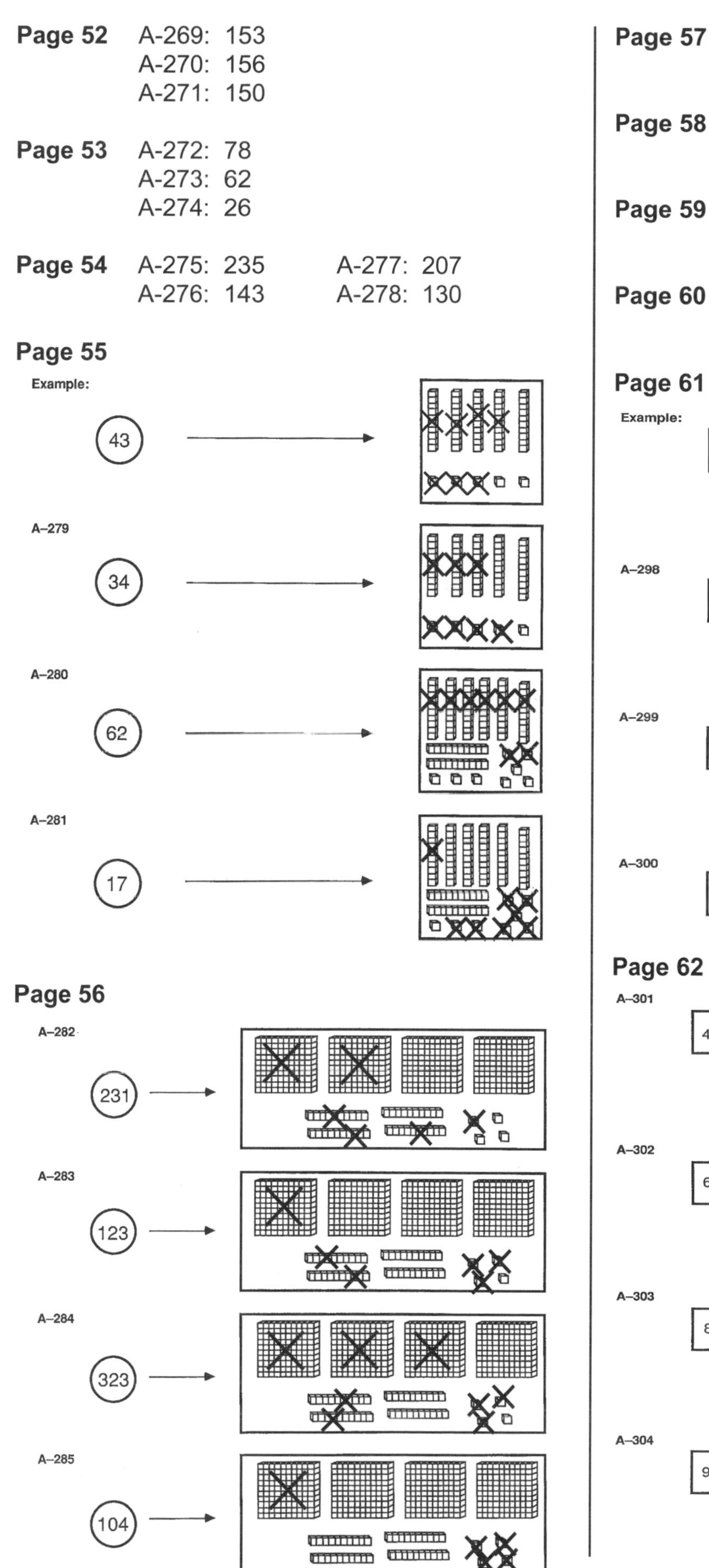

Page 57 A-286: 62
A-287: 94
A-288: 39

Page 58 A-289: 359
A-290: 489
A-291: 637

Page 59 A-292: a. 57
A-293: a. 53
A-294: a. 75

Page 60 A-295: c. 123
A-296: a. 439
A-297: c. 762

Page 61

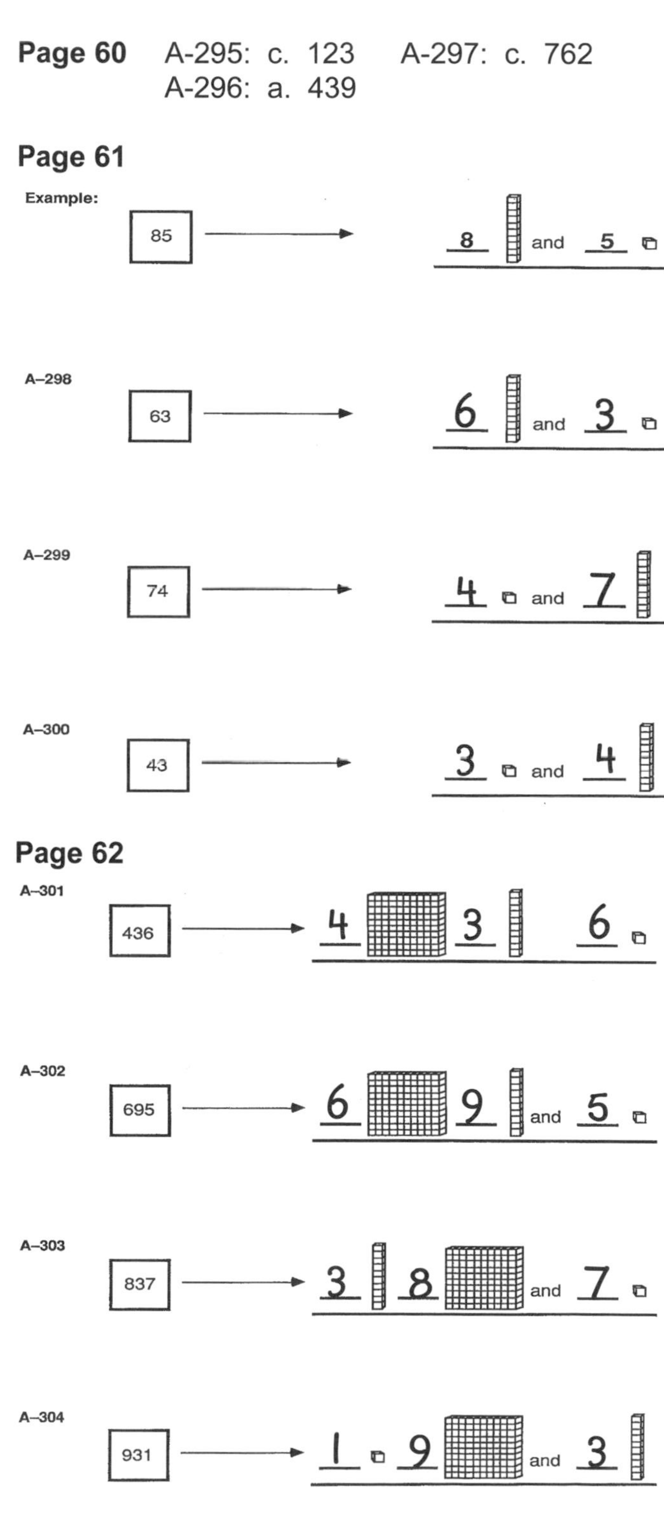

Page 63 Shade the following rectangles: B-2, B-4, B-6, B-7

Page 64 Shade the following rectangles: B-8, B-10, B-12, B-14

Page 65 Shade the following rectangles: B-16, B-17, B-20

Page 66 Shade the following rectangles: B-23, B-25, B-28

Page 67 Shade the following rectangles: B-32, B-34

Page 68 Shade the following rectangles: B-37, B-39, B-40

Page 69

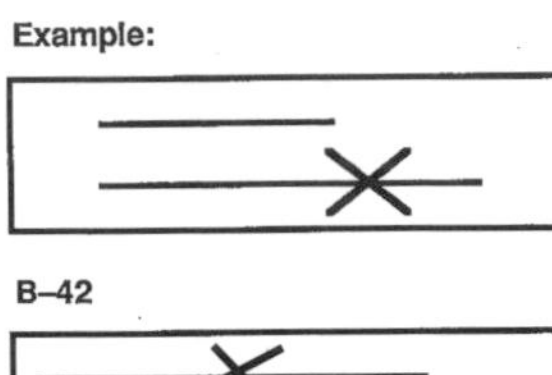

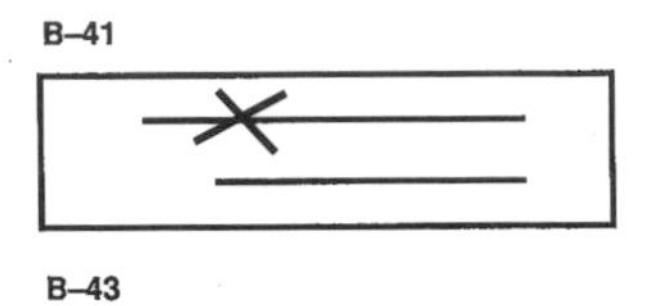

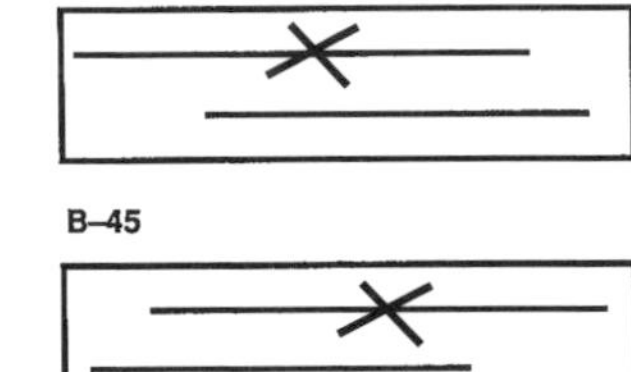

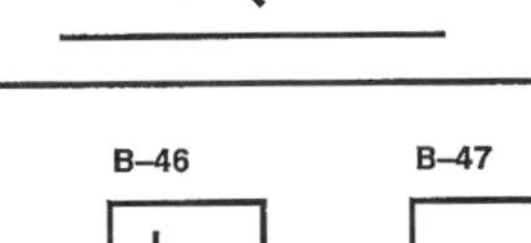

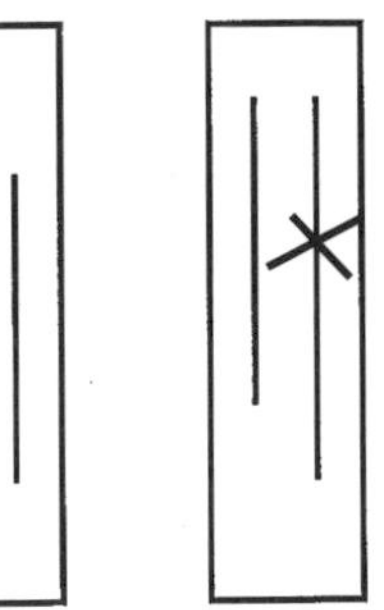

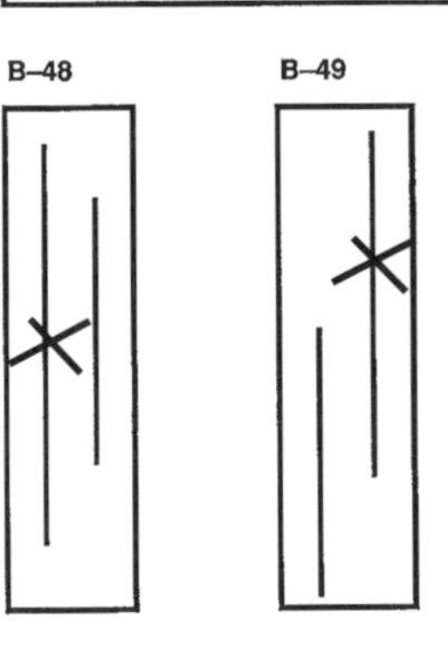

Page 70

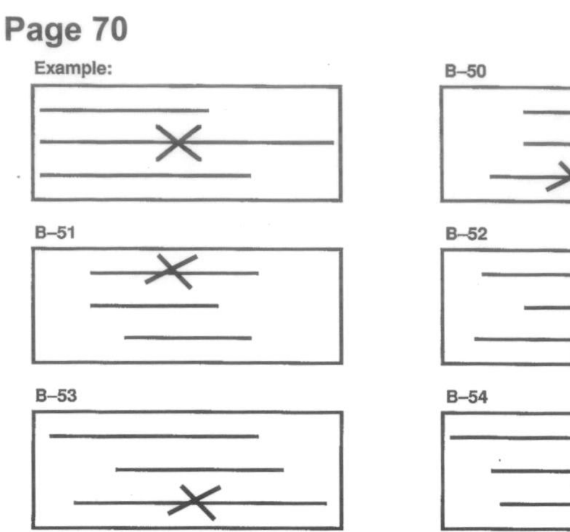

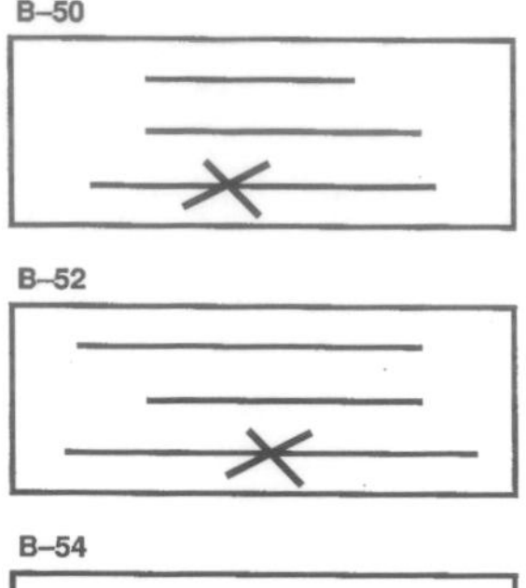

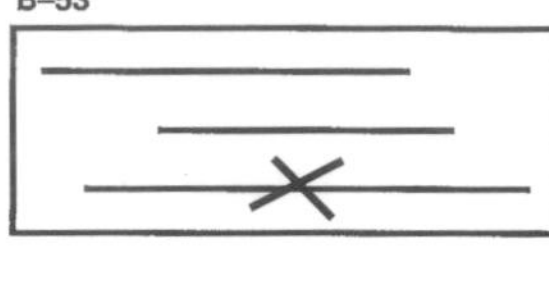

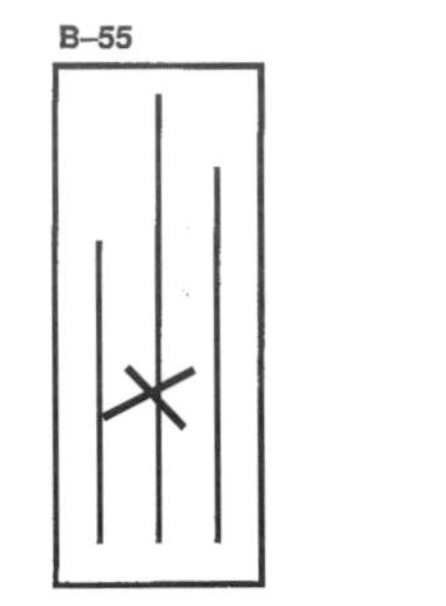

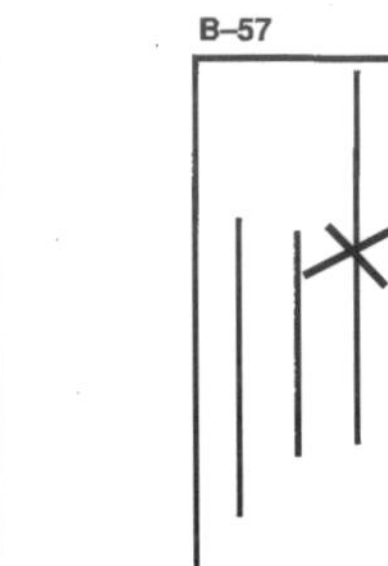

Page 71

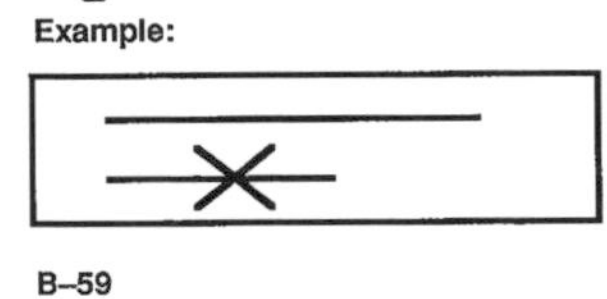

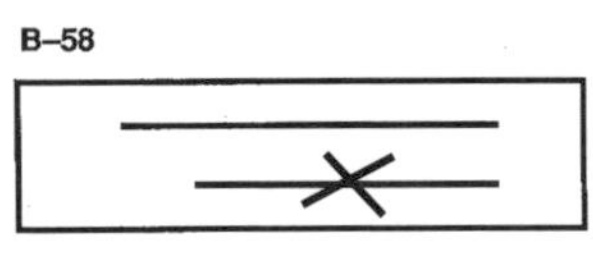

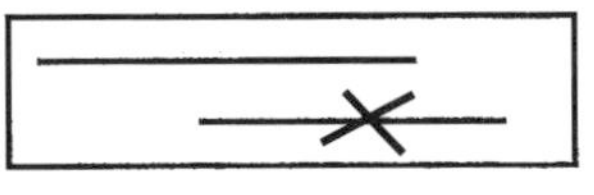

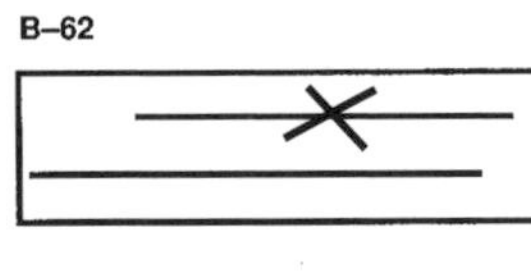

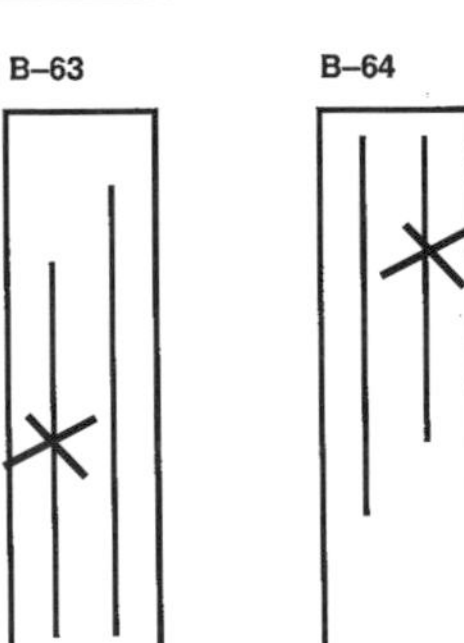

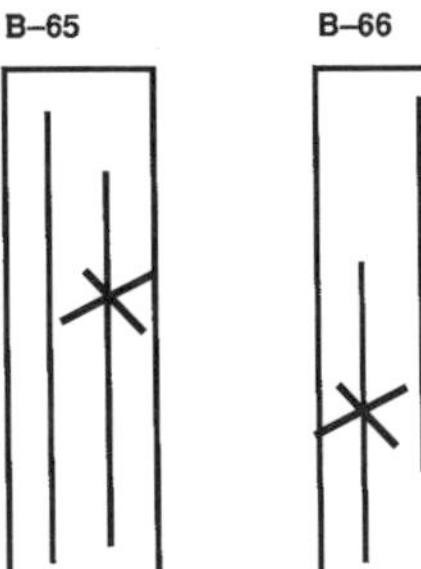

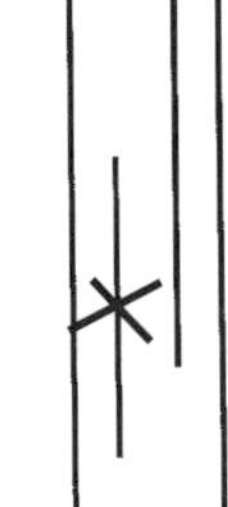

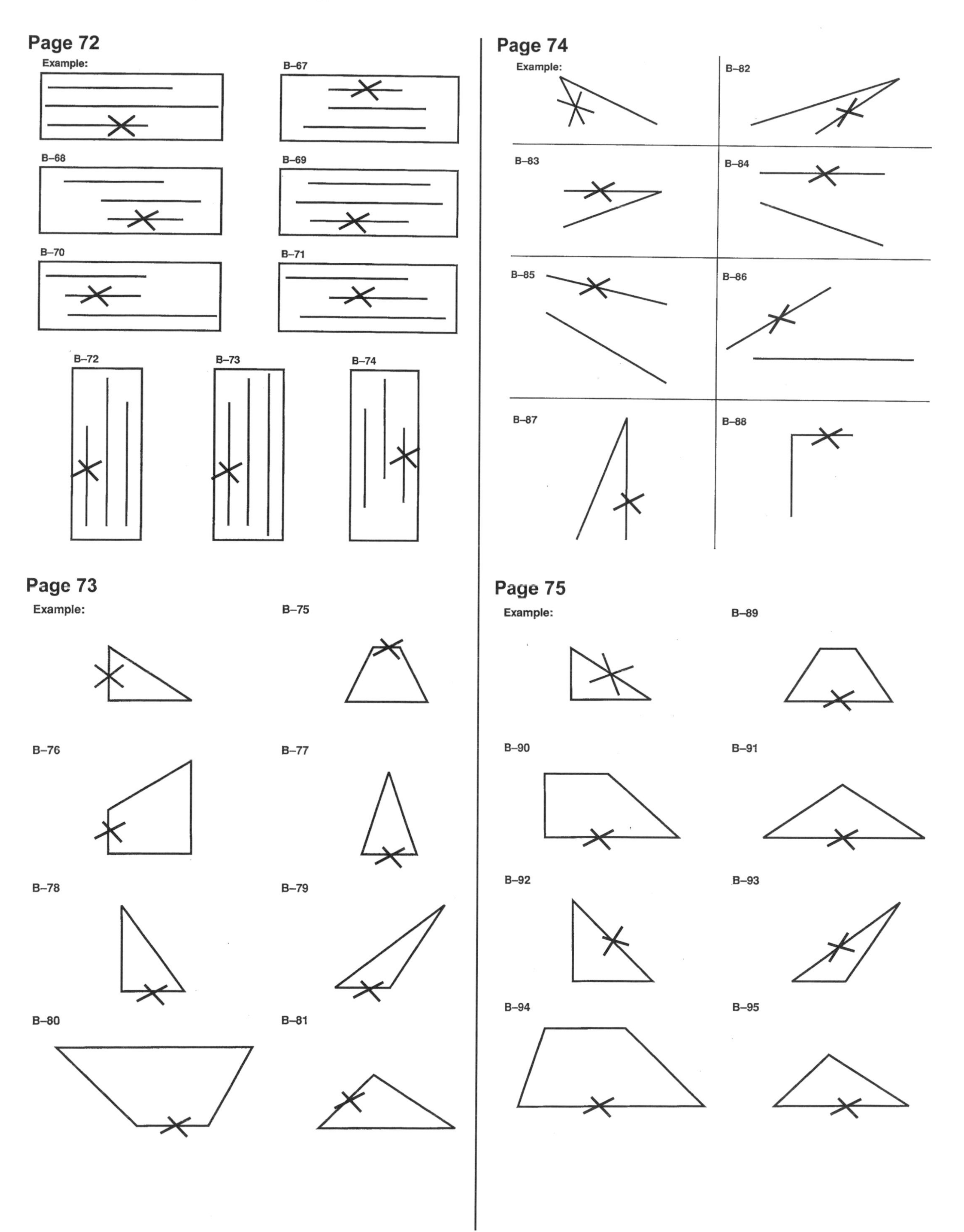
Page 72
Example:
B–67
B–68
B–69
B–70
B–71
B–72
B–73
B–74
Page 73
Example:
B–75
B–76
B–77
B–78
B–79
B–80
B–81
Page 74
Example:
B–82
B–83
B–84
B–85
B–86
B–87
B–88
Page 75
Example:
B–89
B–90
B–91
B–92
B–93
B–94
B–95

Page 76

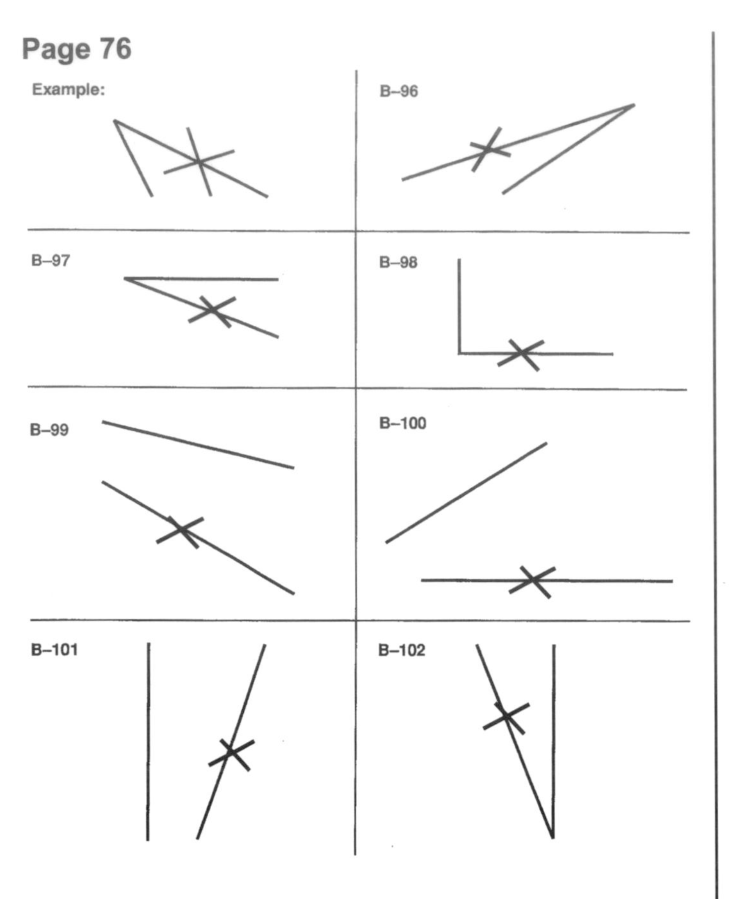

Page 77 Put an X on the following shapes:
B-107, B-108, B-109

Page 78 Put an X on the following shapes:
B-112, B-113, B-114, B-116

Page 79 Put an X on the following shapes:
B-117, B-120, B-121

Page 80 Put an X on the following shapes:
B-125, B-128, B-129

Page 81 Put an X on the following shapes:
B-131: c
B-132: b
B-133: c

Page 82

Example:

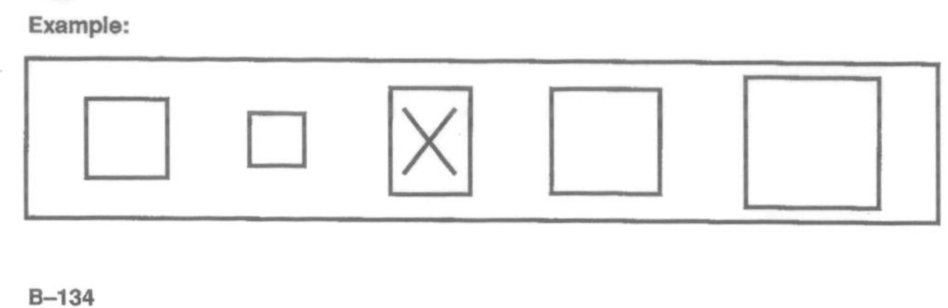

B–134

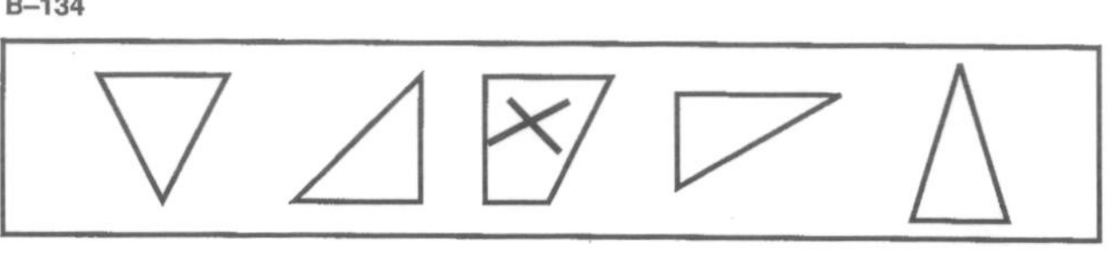

B–135

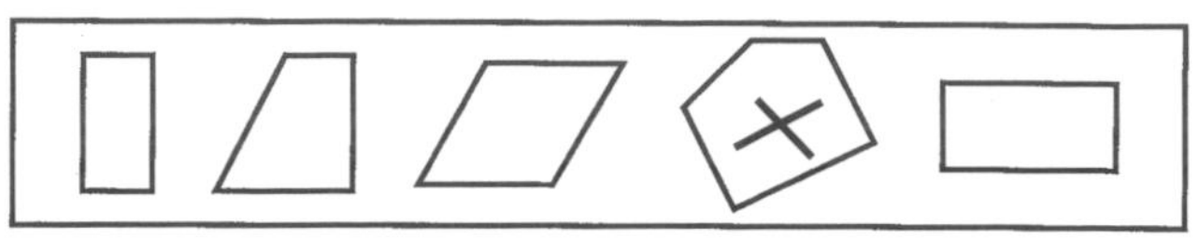

B–136

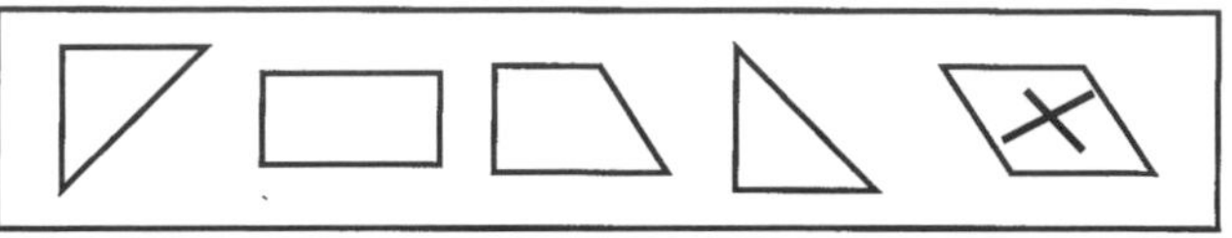

Page 83

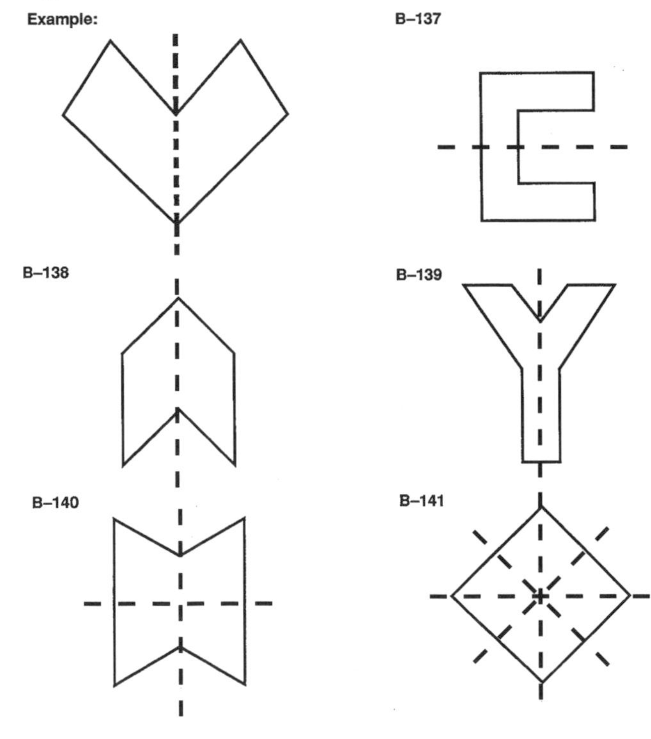

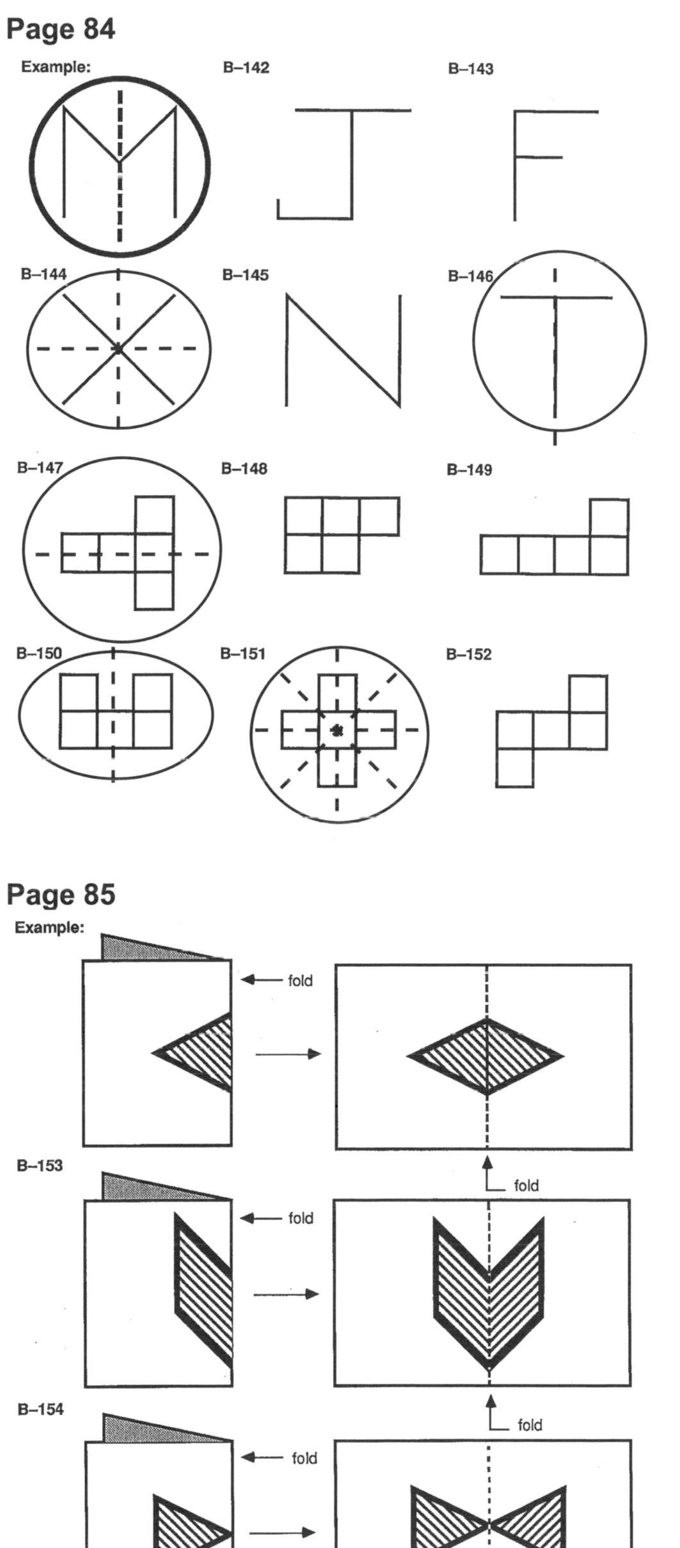
Page 84
Example:
B–142
B–143
B–144
B–145
B–146
B–147
B–148
B–149
B–150
B–151
B–152
Page 85
Example:
fold
fold
B–153
fold
fold
B–154
fold
fold

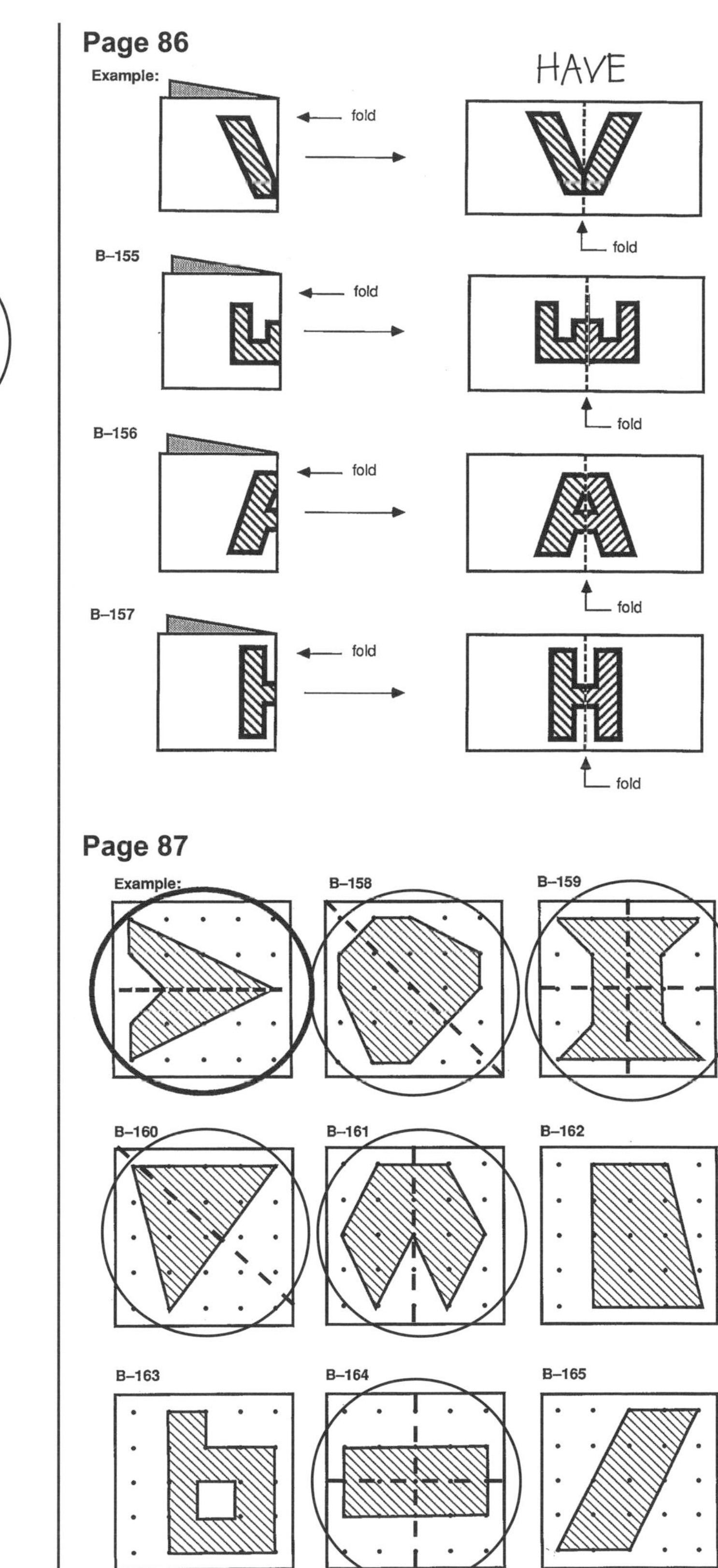
Page 86
Example:
HAVE
fold
fold
B–155
fold
fold
B–156
fold
fold
B–157
fold
fold
Page 87
Example:
B–158
B–159
B–160
B–161
B–162
B–163
B–164
B–165

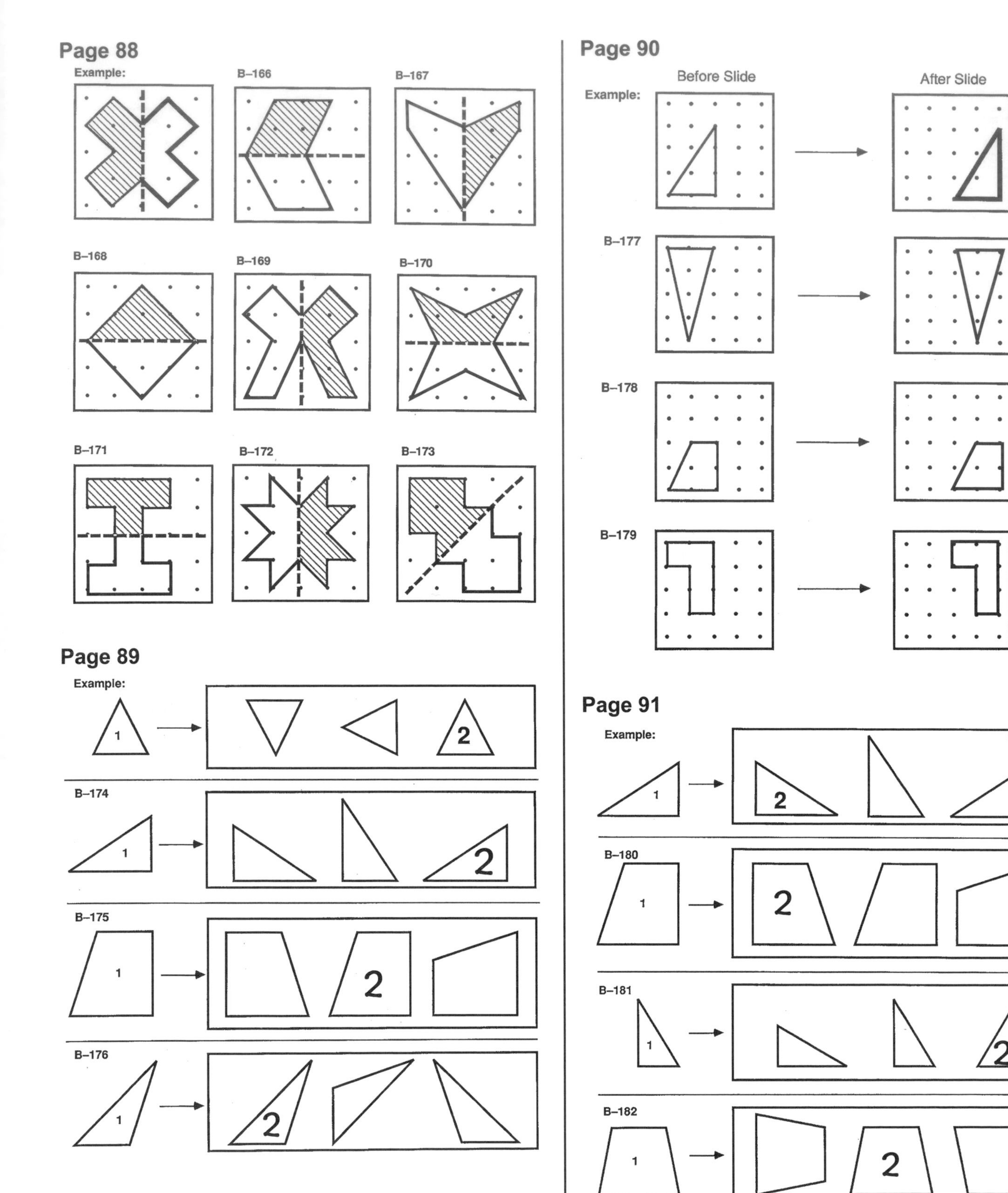
Page 88
Example:
B–166
B–167
B–168
B–169
B–170
B–171
B–172
B–173
Page 89
Example:
1
2
B–174
1
2
B–175
1
2
B–176
1
2
Page 90
Before Slide
After Slide
Example:
B–177
B–178
B–179
Page 91
Example:
1
2
B–180
1
2
B–181
1
2
B–182
1
2

Page 92

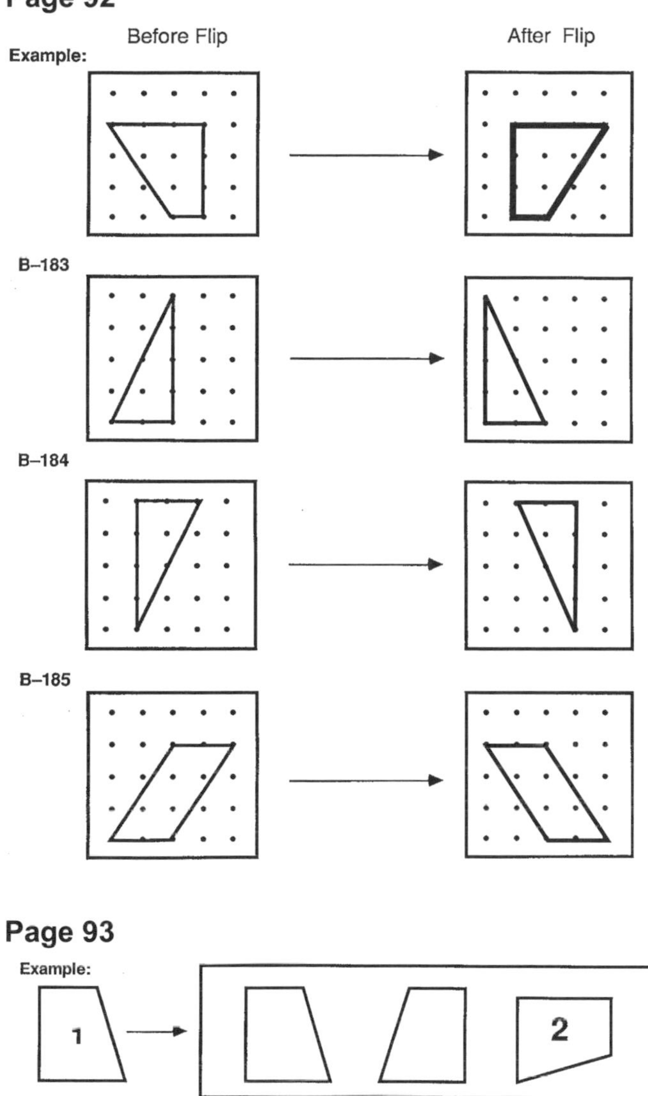

Page 93

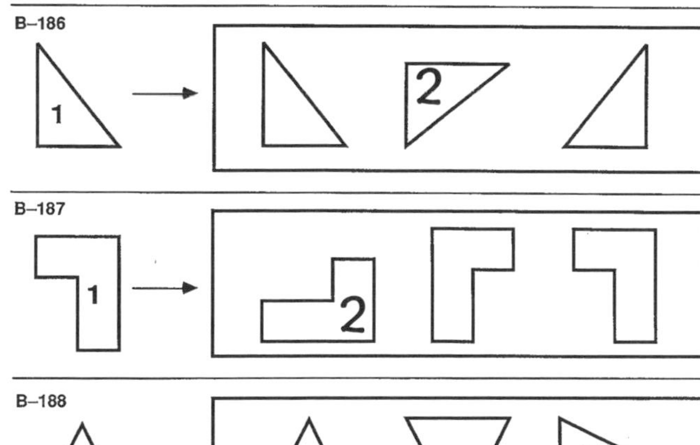

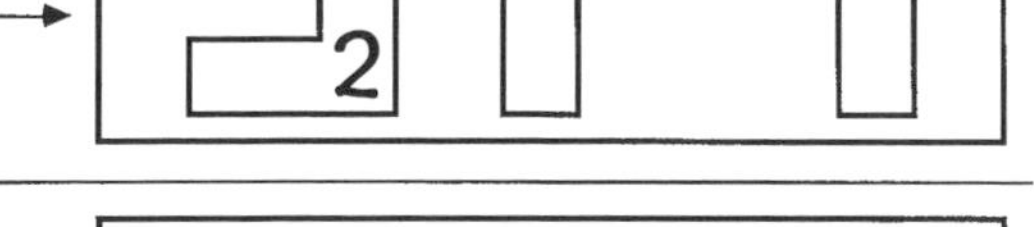

Page 94

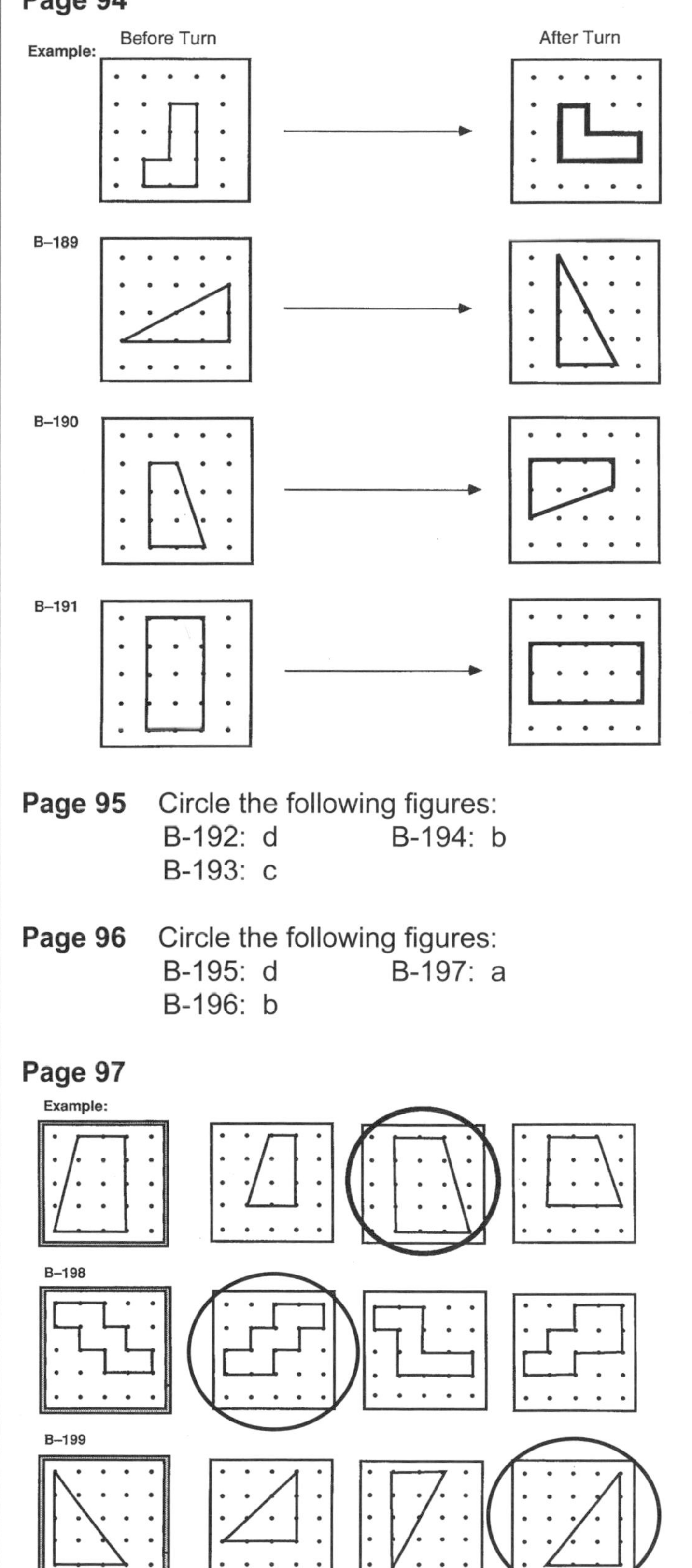

Page 95 Circle the following figures:
B-192: d B-194: b
B-193: c

Page 96 Circle the following figures:
B-195: d B-197: a
B-196: b

Page 97

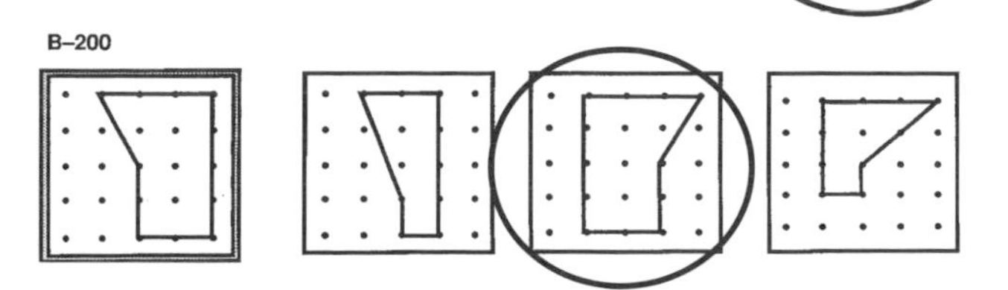

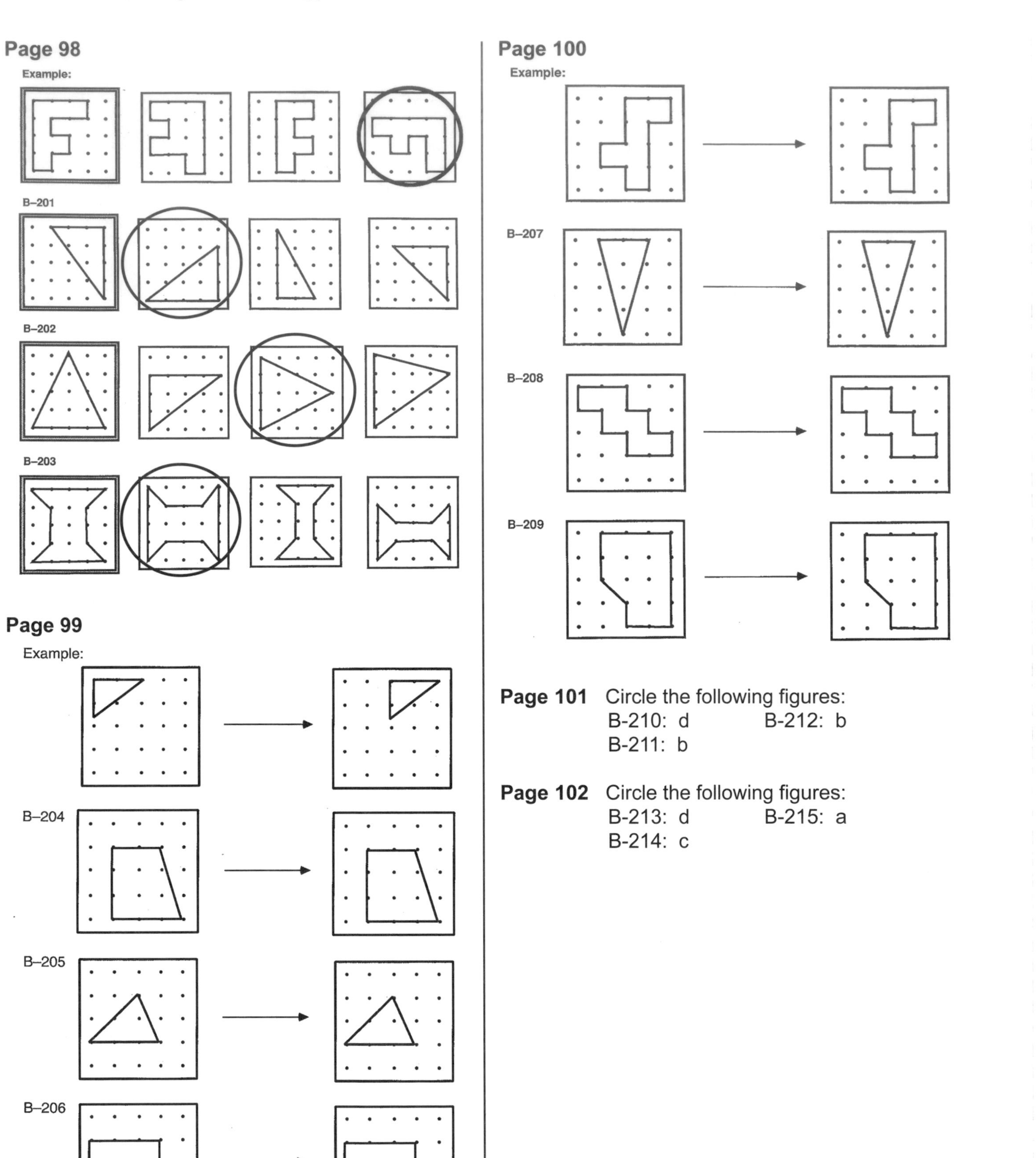

Page 101 Circle the following figures:
B-210: d
B-211: b
B-212: b

Page 102 Circle the following figures:
B-213: d
B-214: c
B-215: a

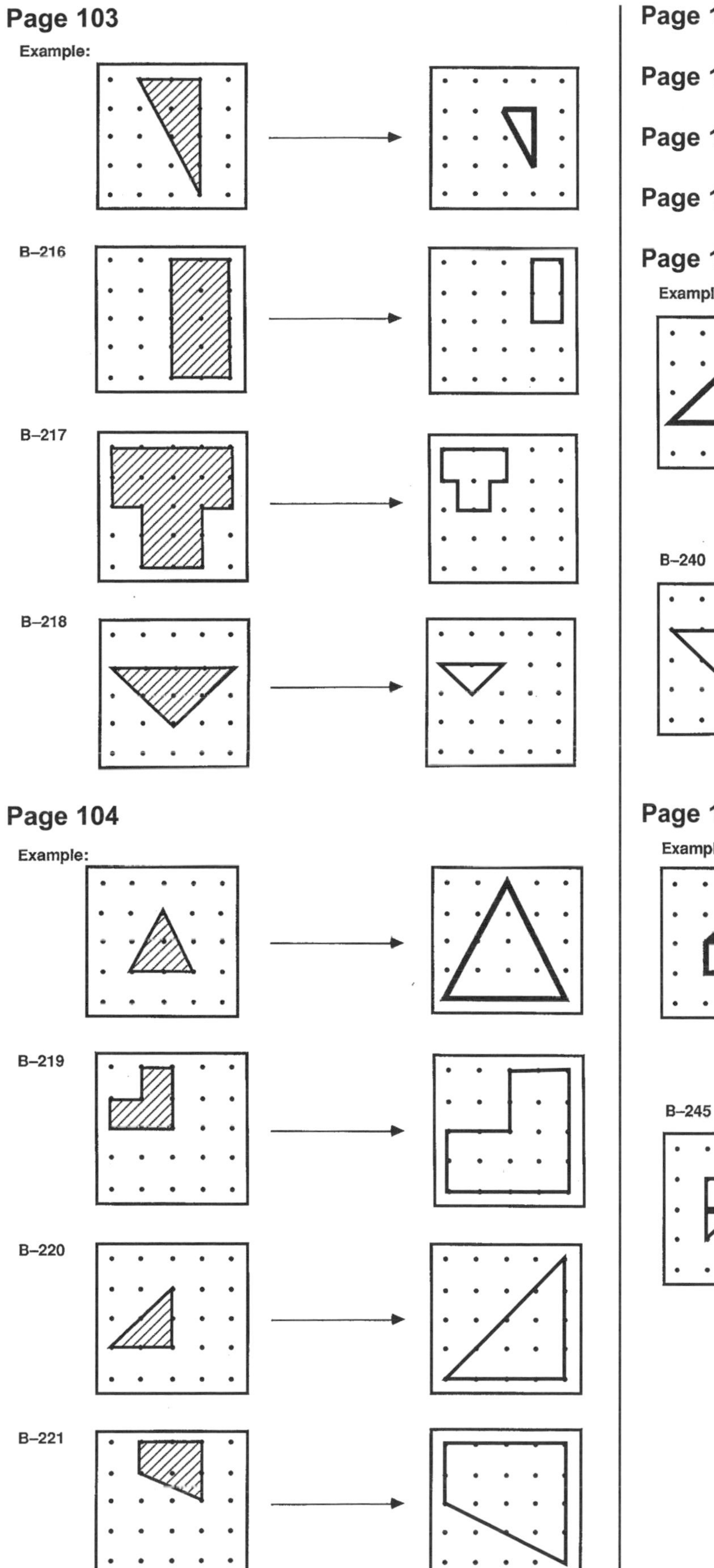

Page 105 Put an X on: B-224

Page 106 Put an X on: B-227

Page 107 Put an X on: B-229, B-230

Page 108 Put an X on: B-233, B-234, B-235

Page 109

Example:

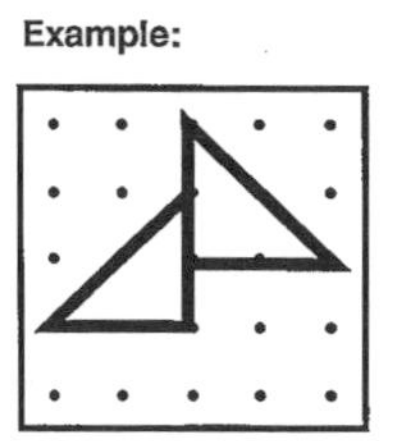

B–238

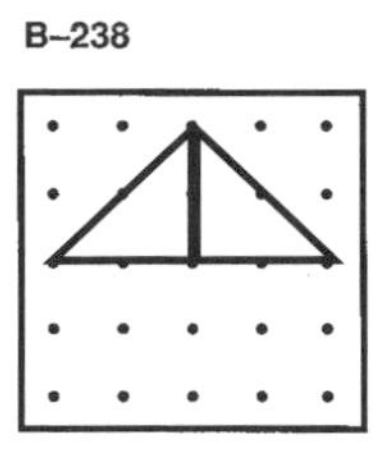

B–239

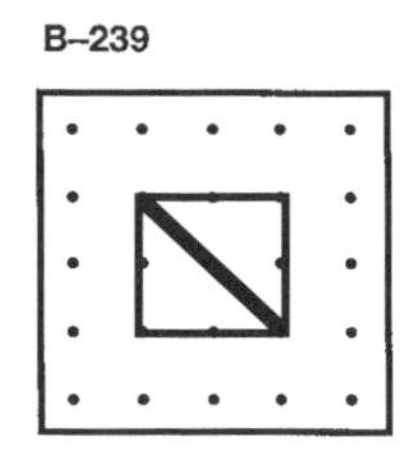

B–240

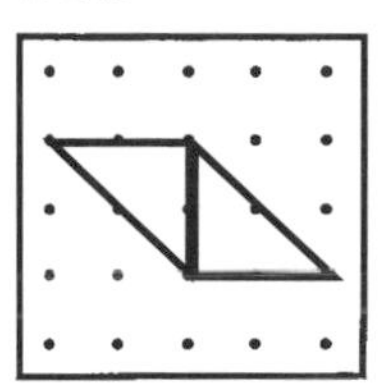

B–241

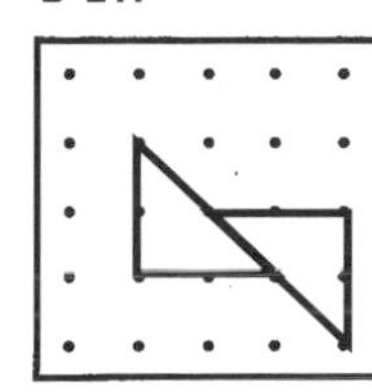

B–242

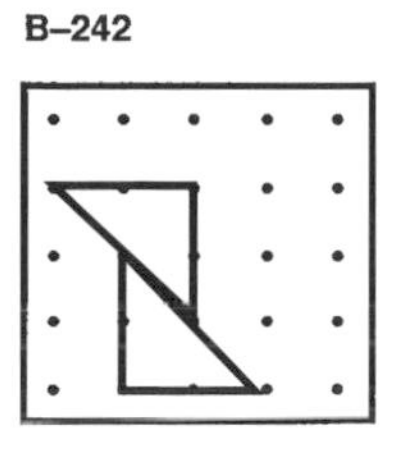

Page 110

Example:

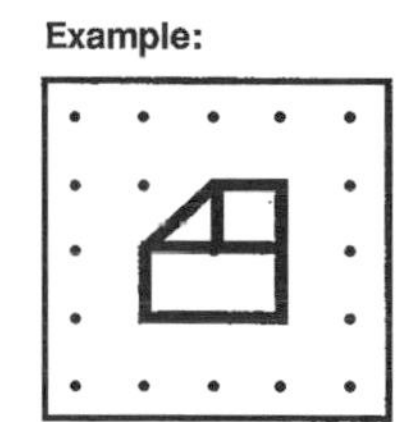

B–243

B–244

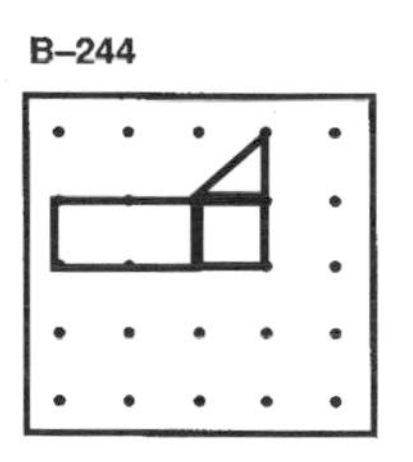

B–245

B–246

B–247

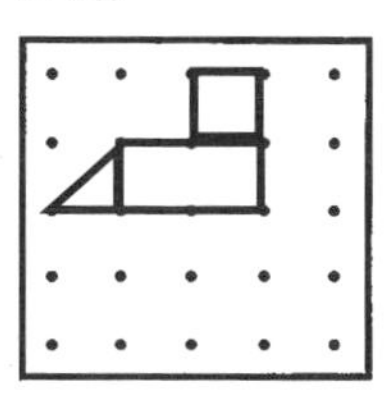

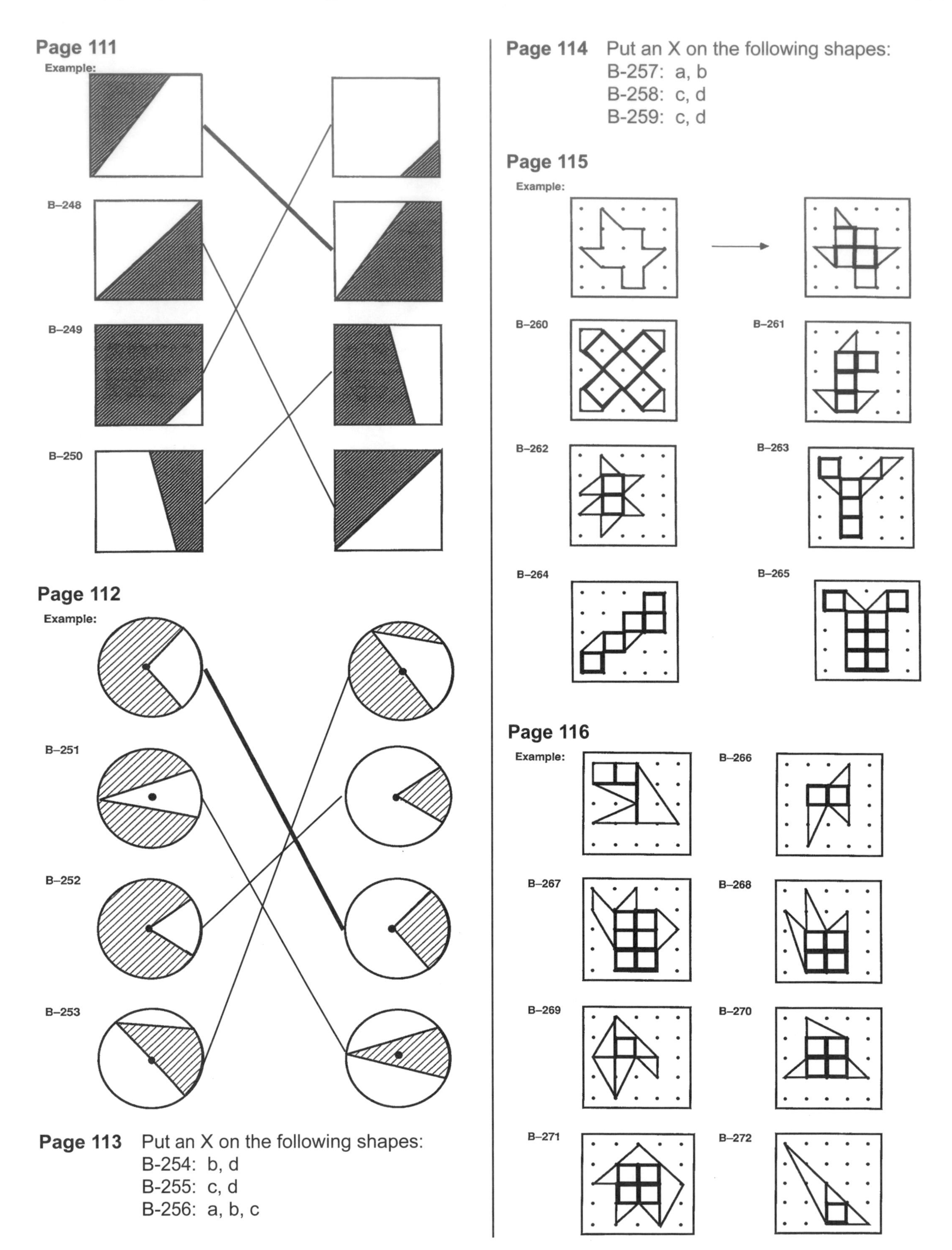
Page 111
Example:
B–248
B–249
B–250
Page 112
Example:
B–251
B–252
B–253
Page 113 Put an X on the following shapes:
B-254: b, d
B-255: c, d
B-256: a, b, c
Page 114 Put an X on the following shapes:
B-257: a, b
B-258: c, d
B-259: c, d
Page 115
Example:
B–260
B–261
B–262
B–263
B–264
B–265
Page 116
Example:
B–266
B–267
B–268
B–269
B–270
B–271
B–272

Page 117

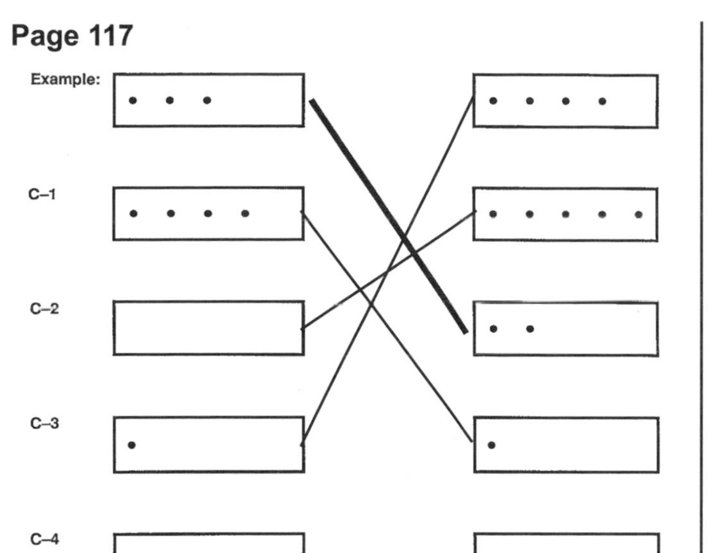

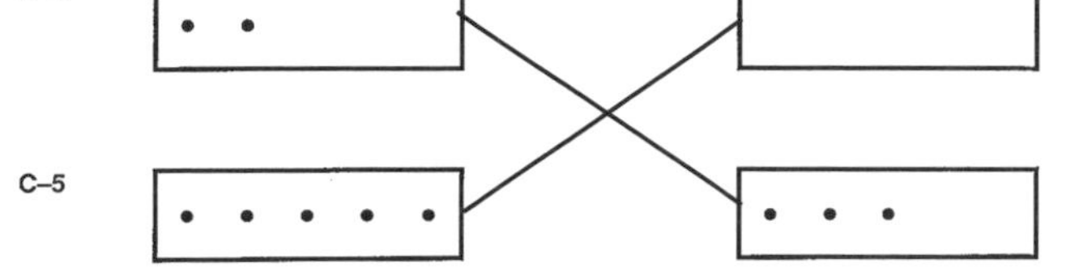

Page 118

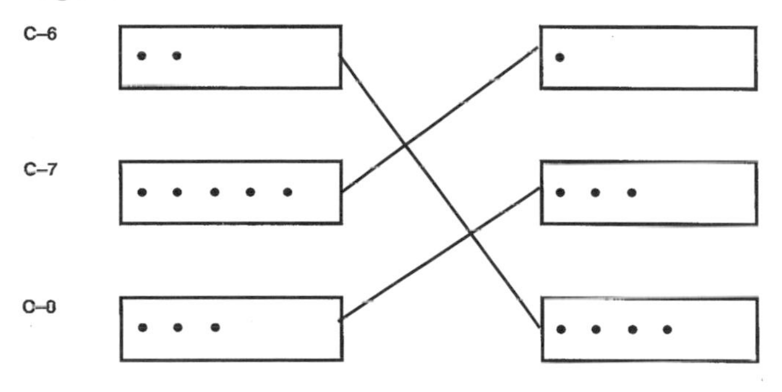

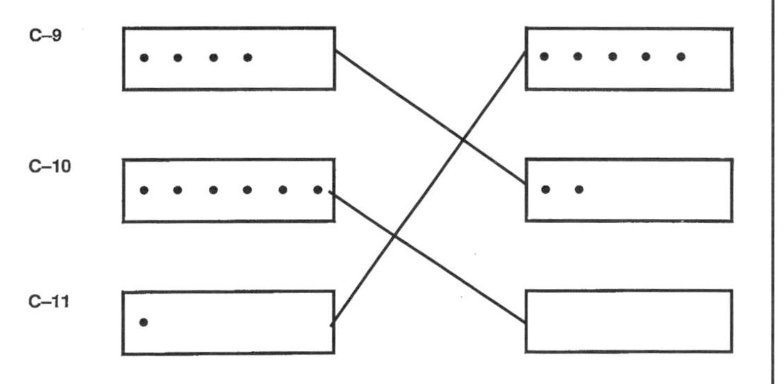

Page 119

C–12

C–13

C–14

C–15

C–16

C–17

Page 120

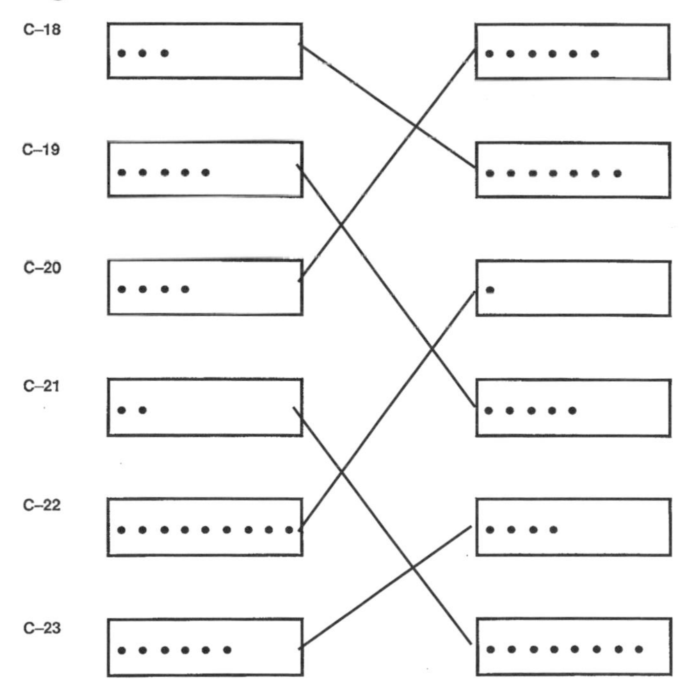

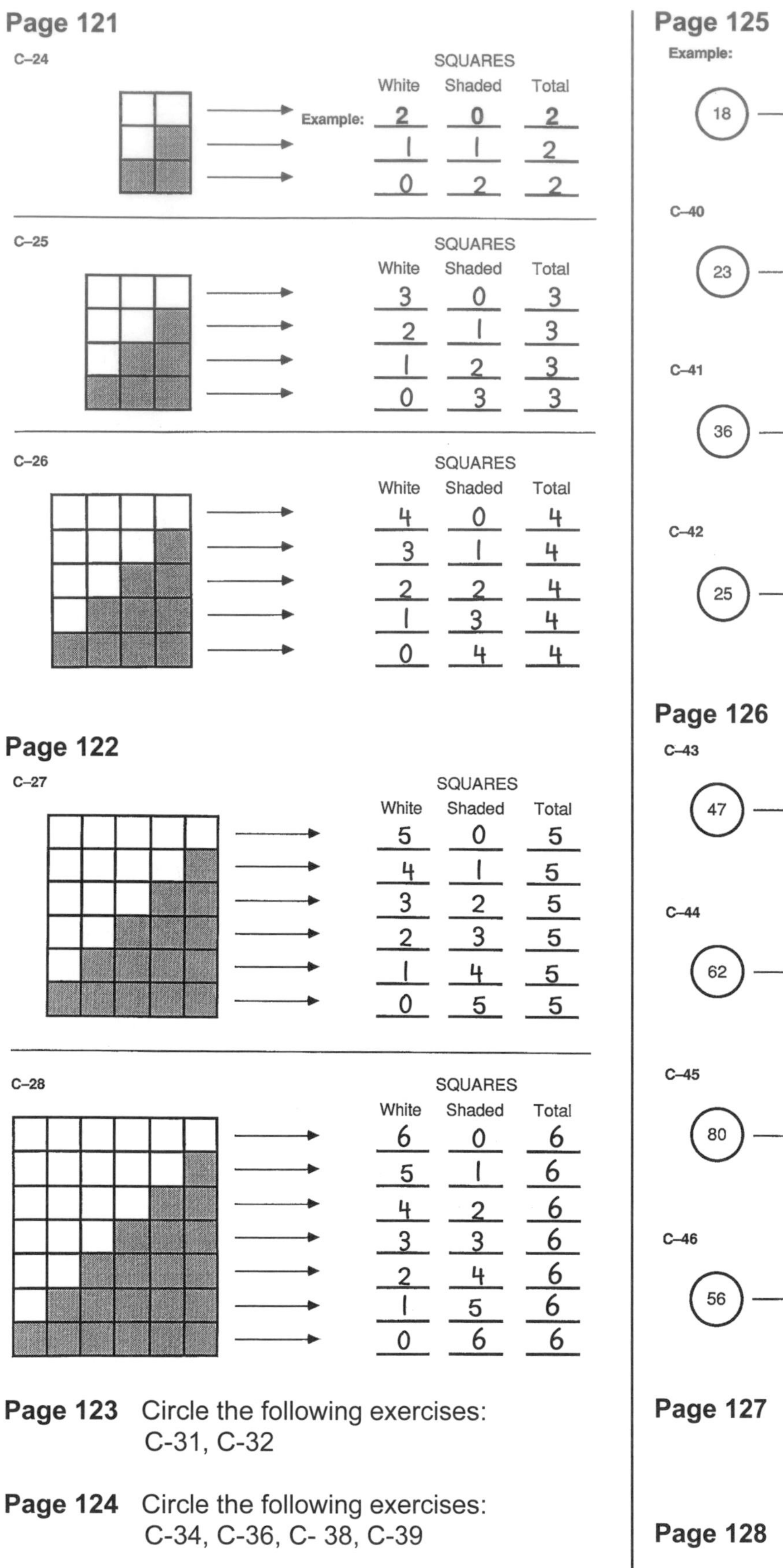

Page 121

C–24

	SQUARES	
White	Shaded	Total
Example: 2	0	2
1	1	2
0	2	2

C–25

	SQUARES	
White	Shaded	Total
3	0	3
2	1	3
1	2	3
0	3	3

C–26

	SQUARES	
White	Shaded	Total
4	0	4
3	1	4
2	2	4
1	3	4
0	4	4

Page 122

C–27

	SQUARES	
White	Shaded	Total
5	0	5
4	1	5
3	2	5
2	3	5
1	4	5
0	5	5

C–28

	SQUARES	
White	Shaded	Total
6	0	6
5	1	6
4	2	6
3	3	6
2	4	6
1	5	6
0	6	6

Page 123 Circle the following exercises: C-31, C-32

Page 124 Circle the following exercises: C-34, C-36, C- 38, C-39

Page 125

Example:

18 →

C–40

23 →

C–41

36 →

C–42

25 →

Page 126

C–43

47 →

C–44

62 →

C–45

80 →

C–46

56 →

Page 127

C-47: 2 + 3 = 5
C-48: 5 + 0 = 5
C-49: 1 + 4 = 5
C-50: 3 + 2 = 5
C-51: 0 + 5 = 5

Page 128

C-52: 2 + 4 = 6
C-53: 3 + 3 = 6
C-54: 1 + 5 = 6
C-55: 4 + 2 = 6
C-56: 0 + 6 = 6
C-57: 5 + 1 = 6

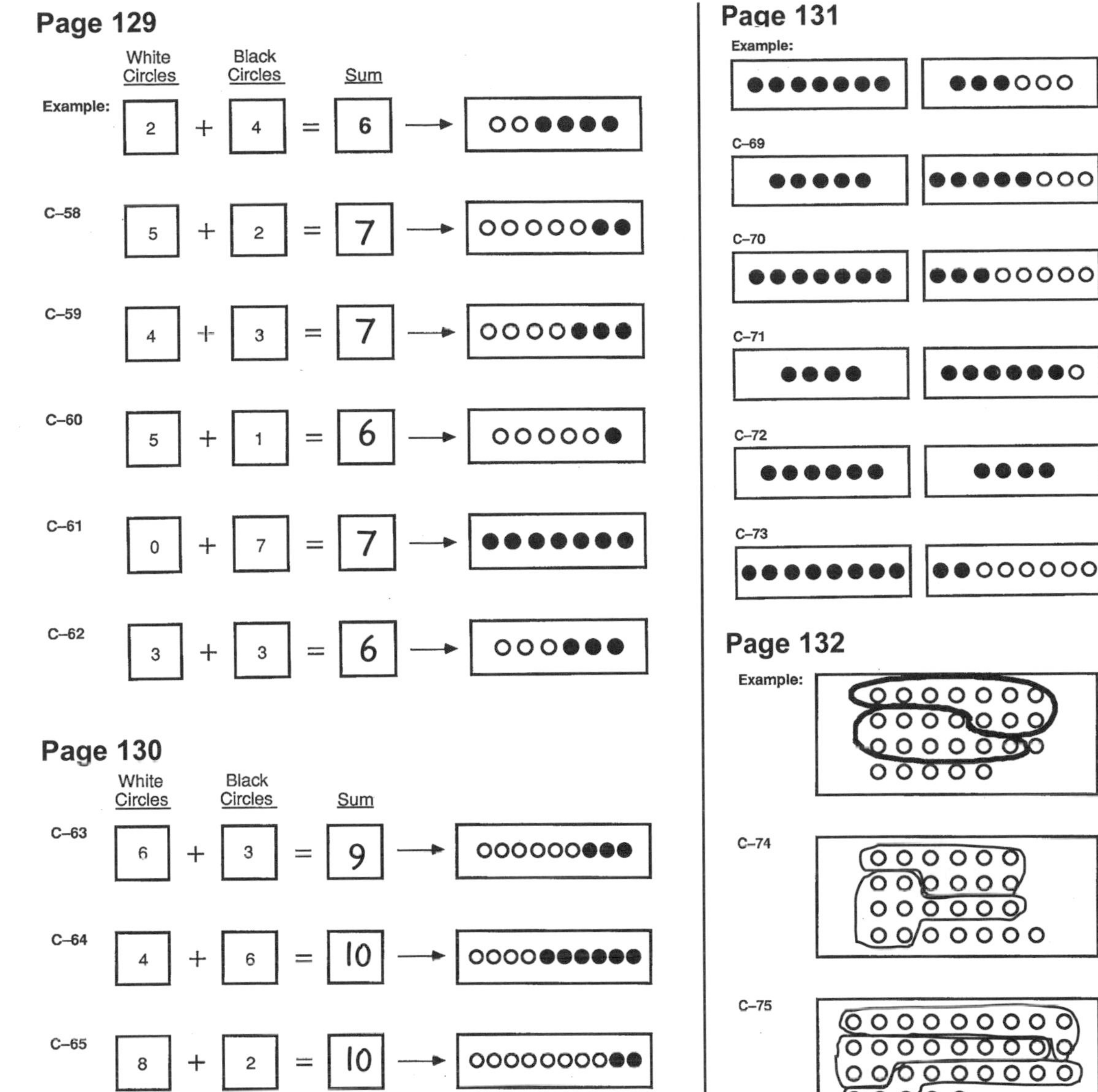

Page 129

	White Circles		Black Circles		Sum
Example:	2	+	4	=	6
C–58	5	+	2	=	7
C–59	4	+	3	=	7
C–60	5	+	1	=	6
C–61	0	+	7	=	7
C–62	3	+	3	=	6

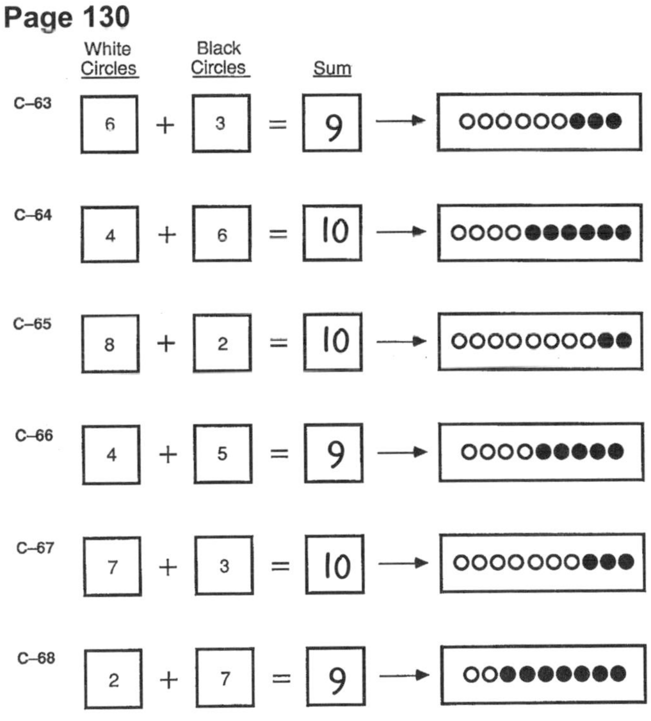

Page 130

	White Circles		Black Circles		Sum
C–63	6	+	3	=	9
C–64	4	+	6	=	10
C–65	8	+	2	=	10
C–66	4	+	5	=	9
C–67	7	+	3	=	10
C–68	2	+	7	=	9

Page 131

	Tens	Ones
Example:	1	3
C–69	1	3
C–70	1	5
C–71	1	1
C–72	1	0
C–73	1	6

Page 132

	Tens	Ones
Example:	2	6
C–74	2	5
C–75	3	2
C–76	2	9

Page 133

C-77: 3 + 6
C-78: 8 + 8, 7 + 9
C-79: 9 + 2, 5 + 6
C-80: 8 + 4
C-81: 2 + 6, 7 + 1
C-82: 9 + 9
C-83: 9 + 6, 6 + 9

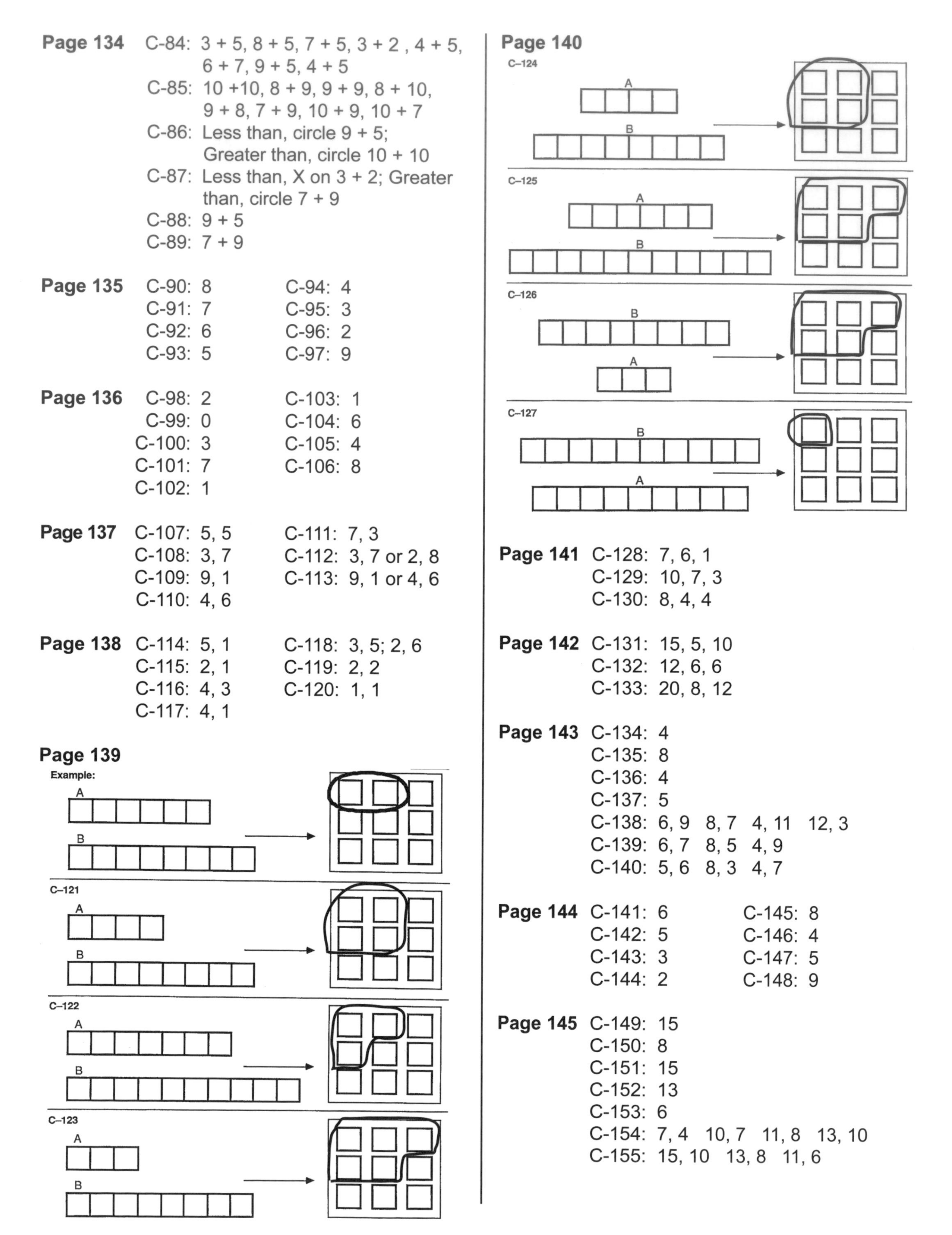

Page 134
C-84: 3 + 5, 8 + 5, 7 + 5, 3 + 2 , 4 + 5, 6 + 7, 9 + 5, 4 + 5
C-85: 10 +10, 8 + 9, 9 + 9, 8 + 10, 9 + 8, 7 + 9, 10 + 9, 10 + 7
C-86: Less than, circle 9 + 5; Greater than, circle 10 + 10
C-87: Less than, X on 3 + 2; Greater than, circle 7 + 9
C-88: 9 + 5
C-89: 7 + 9

Page 135
C-90: 8
C-91: 7
C-92: 6
C-93: 5
C-94: 4
C-95: 3
C-96: 2
C-97: 9

Page 136
C-98: 2
C-99: 0
C-100: 3
C-101: 7
C-102: 1
C-103: 1
C-104: 6
C-105: 4
C-106: 8

Page 137
C-107: 5, 5
C-108: 3, 7
C-109: 9, 1
C-110: 4, 6
C-111: 7, 3
C-112: 3, 7 or 2, 8
C-113: 9, 1 or 4, 6

Page 138
C-114: 5, 1
C-115: 2, 1
C-116: 4, 3
C-117: 4, 1
C-118: 3, 5; 2, 6
C-119: 2, 2
C-120: 1, 1

Page 139

Page 140

Page 141
C-128: 7, 6, 1
C-129: 10, 7, 3
C-130: 8, 4, 4

Page 142
C-131: 15, 5, 10
C-132: 12, 6, 6
C-133: 20, 8, 12

Page 143
C-134: 4
C-135: 8
C-136: 4
C-137: 5
C-138: 6, 9 8, 7 4, 11 12, 3
C-139: 6, 7 8, 5 4, 9
C-140: 5, 6 8, 3 4, 7

Page 144
C-141: 6
C-142: 5
C-143: 3
C-144: 2
C-145: 8
C-146: 4
C-147: 5
C-148: 9

Page 145
C-149: 15
C-150: 8
C-151: 15
C-152: 13
C-153: 6
C-154: 7, 4 10, 7 11, 8 13, 10
C-155: 15, 10 13, 8 11, 6

Page 146 C-156: 7
C-157: 10
C-158: 17
C-159: 10
C-160: 9
C-161: 10
C-162: 5
C-163: 16

Page 147 C-164: 12 - 7
C-165: 12 - 4, 16 - 8
C-166: 12 - 9, 7 - 4
C-167: 15 - 8
C-168: 14 - 9
C-169: 15 - 9, 12 - 6
C-170: 13 - 9

Page 148 C-171: 15 - 7, 18 - 9, 13 - 5, 13 - 7, 14 - 9, 16 - 9, 14 - 7, 12 - 5
C-172: 16 - 3, 17 - 3, 18 - 6, 17 - 6, 16 - 2, 18 - 4, 17 - 2, 15 - 3
C-173: Less than, circle 18 - 9; Greater than, circle 17 - 2
C-174: Less than, X on 14 - 9; Greater than, X on 17 - 6
C-175: 18 - 9
C-176: 17 - 6

Page 149

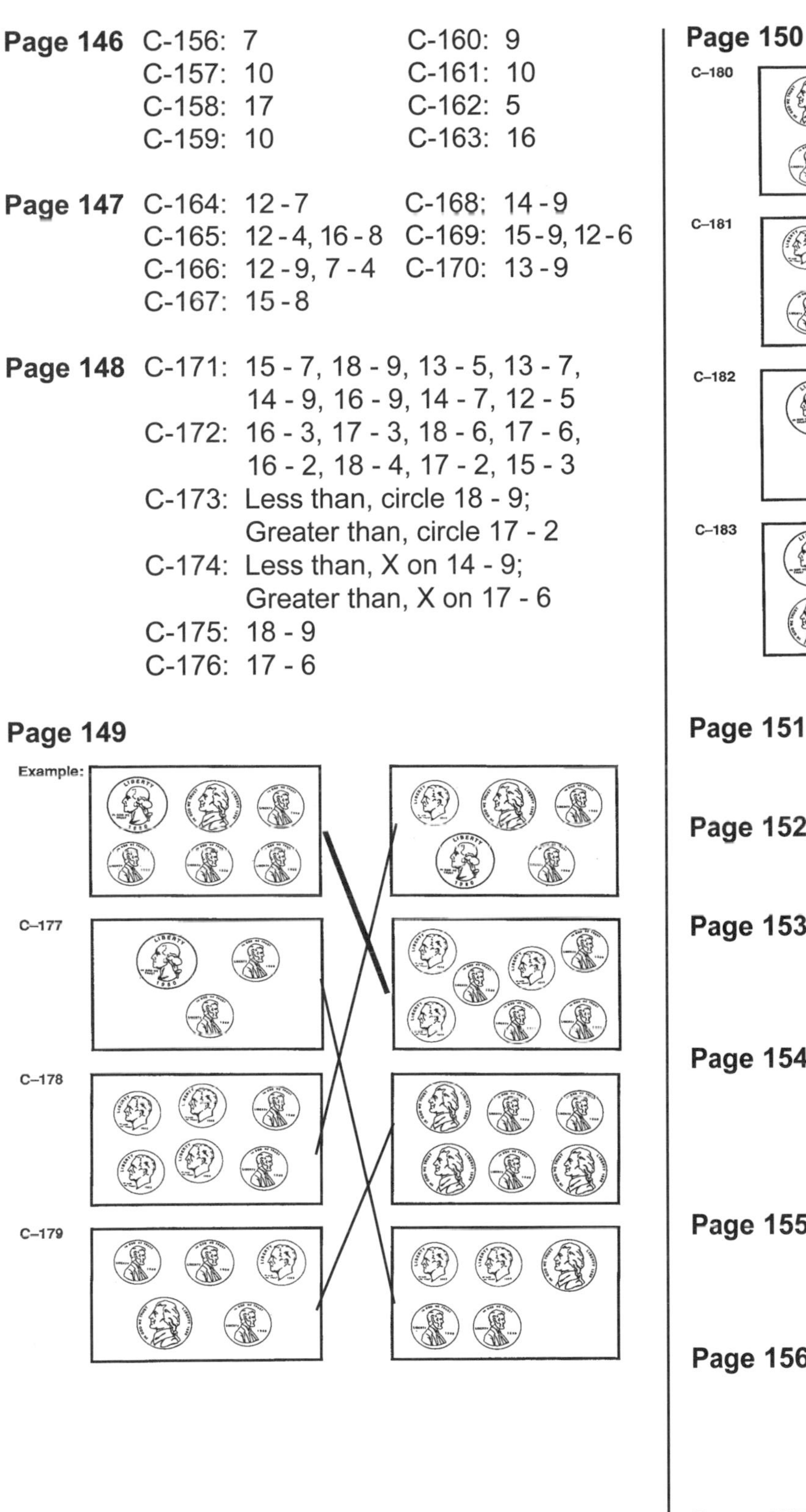

Page 150

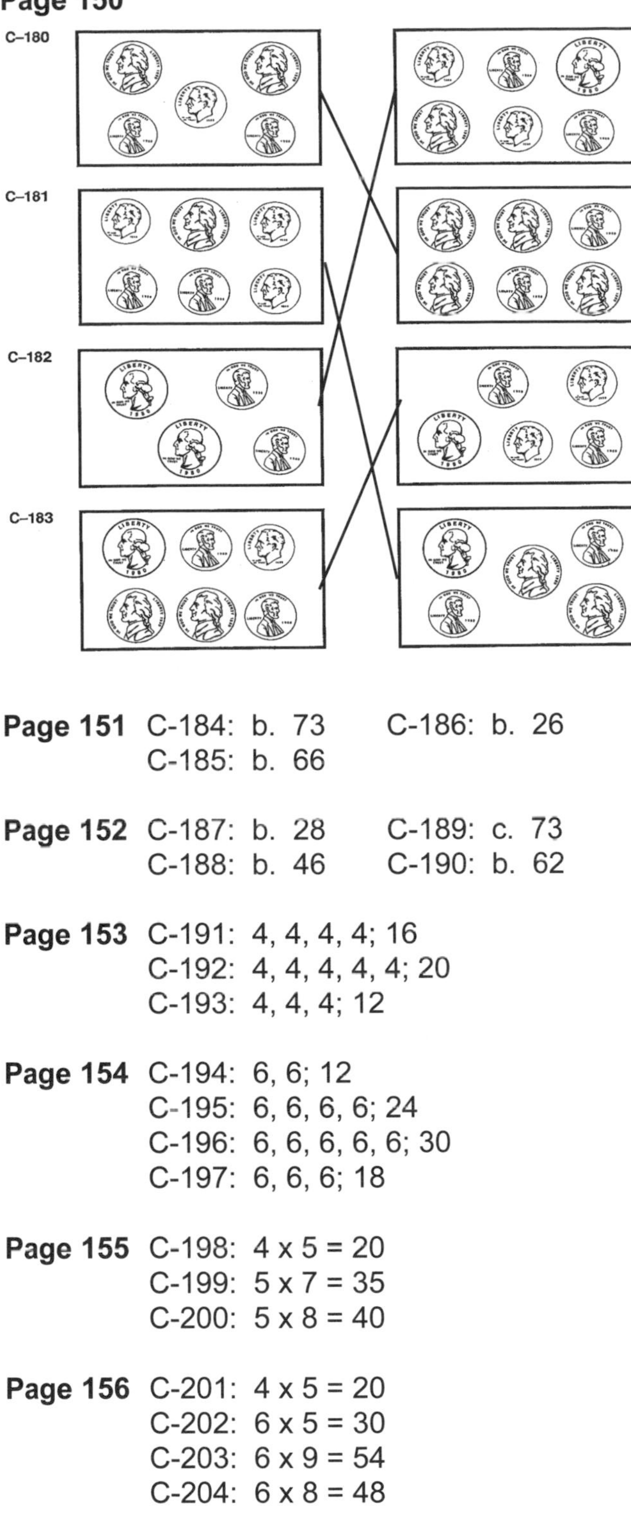

Page 151 C-184: b. 73
C-185: b. 66
C-186: b. 26

Page 152 C-187: b. 28
C-188: b. 46
C-189: c. 73
C-190: b. 62

Page 153 C-191: 4, 4, 4, 4; 16
C-192: 4, 4, 4, 4, 4; 20
C-193: 4, 4, 4; 12

Page 154 C-194: 6, 6; 12
C-195: 6, 6, 6, 6; 24
C-196: 6, 6, 6, 6, 6; 30
C-197: 6, 6, 6; 18

Page 155 C-198: 4 x 5 = 20
C-199: 5 x 7 = 35
C-200: 5 x 8 = 40

Page 156 C-201: 4 x 5 = 20
C-202: 6 x 5 = 30
C-203: 6 x 9 = 54
C-204: 6 x 8 = 48

Page 157 C-205: 4 x 3, 2 x 6
C-206: 5 x 9
C-207: 9 x 4, 6 x 6
C-208: 8 x 2, 4 x 4
C-209: 5 x 6
C-210: 6 x 3, 2 x 9
C-211: 6 x 4, 3 x 8

Page 158
C-212: 2 x 8, 3 x 5, 6 x 3, 4 x 4, 4 x 8, 4 x 9, 9 x 3, 5 x 5
C-213: 7 x 8, 7 x 9, 8 x 9, 8 x 8, 7 x 7, 9 x 9, 6 x 7, 6 x 9
C-214: Less than, circle 4 x 9; Greater than, circle 9 x 9
C-215: Less than, X on 3 x 5; Greater than, X on 6 x 7
C-216: 4 x 9
C-217: 6 x 7

Page 159
C-218: 5
C-219: 9
C-220: 4
C-221: 9
C-222: 7
C-223: 3
C-224: 6
C-225: 7
C-226: 8

Page 160
C-227: 8
C-228: 10
C-229: 5
C-230: 7
C-231: 1
C-232: 1
C-233: 4
C-234: 2, 2; 4, 1
C-235: 9
C-236: 3, 3; 9, 1

Page 161
C-237: 2 + 3 = 5
C-238: 9 - 2 = 7
C-239: 3 - 2 = 1*
C-240: 9 x 8 = 72
C-241: 2 x 3 = 6
*Six other answers are possible.

Page 162
C-242: 10 + 8 = 18
C-243: 2 + 3 = 5
C-244: 10 - 2 = 8
C-245: 3 - 2 = 1*
C-246: 10 x 8 = 80
C-247: 2 x 3 = 6
*Five other answers are possible.

Page 163
C-248: 18 - 9
C-249: 12 - 4
C-250: 20 ÷ 4
C-251: 6 + 3

Page 164
C-252: 4 - 2
C-253: 12 + 6
C-254: 50 x 3
C-255: 12 ÷ 4
C-256: 5 x 10

Page 165
C-257: 10
C-258: 20
C-259: 20
C-260: 50
C-261: 80
C-262: 10
C-263: 30

Page 166
C-264: 10
C-265: 60
C-266: 50
C-267: 20
C-268: 90
C-269: 100
C-270: 400
C-271: 700
C-272: 400
C-273: 600

Page 167
C-274: 41, 40, 39, 43, 37, 42, 38, 44
C-275: 52, 46, 53, 50, 47, 51, 48, 49

Page 168
C-276: 3 + 6, 4 + 9, 9 + 5, 6 + 8, 8 + 2, 5 + 7, 7 + 4, 6 + 6, 9 + 2, 7 + 7 6 + 7, 5 + 8
C-277: 10 + 7, 11 + 10, 8 + 9, 7 + 9, 6 + 10, 9 + 10, 8 + 8, 9 + 9

Page 169
C-278: 16, 160
C-279: 36, 360
C-280: 30, 300
C-281: 8, 800
C-282: 28, 2800
C-283: 900
C-284: 720
C-285: 3500
C-286: 4800

Page 170
C-287: 50, 300
C-288: 70, 560
C-289: 40, 280
C-290: 20, 180
C-291: 60, 240

Page 171
D-1: b. 3
D-2: c. 2
D-3: a. 4
D-4: a. 2
D-5: b. 2
D-6: a. 3
D-7: c. 1

Page 172
D-8: a. 7
D-9: c. 4
D-10: b. 8
D-11: c. 1
D-12: a. 5
D-13: b. 2
D-14: c. 0

Page 173
D-15: 11
D-16: 8
D-17: 9
D-18: 17
D-19: 15

Page 174
D-20: 17
D-21: 12
D-22: 16
D-23: 14
D-24: 18

Page 175
D-25: 10, X
D-26: 10, X
D-27: 9
D-28: 10, X
D-29: 11

Page 176
D-30: 9
D-31: 8, X
D-32: 8, X
D-33: 8, X
D-34: 7

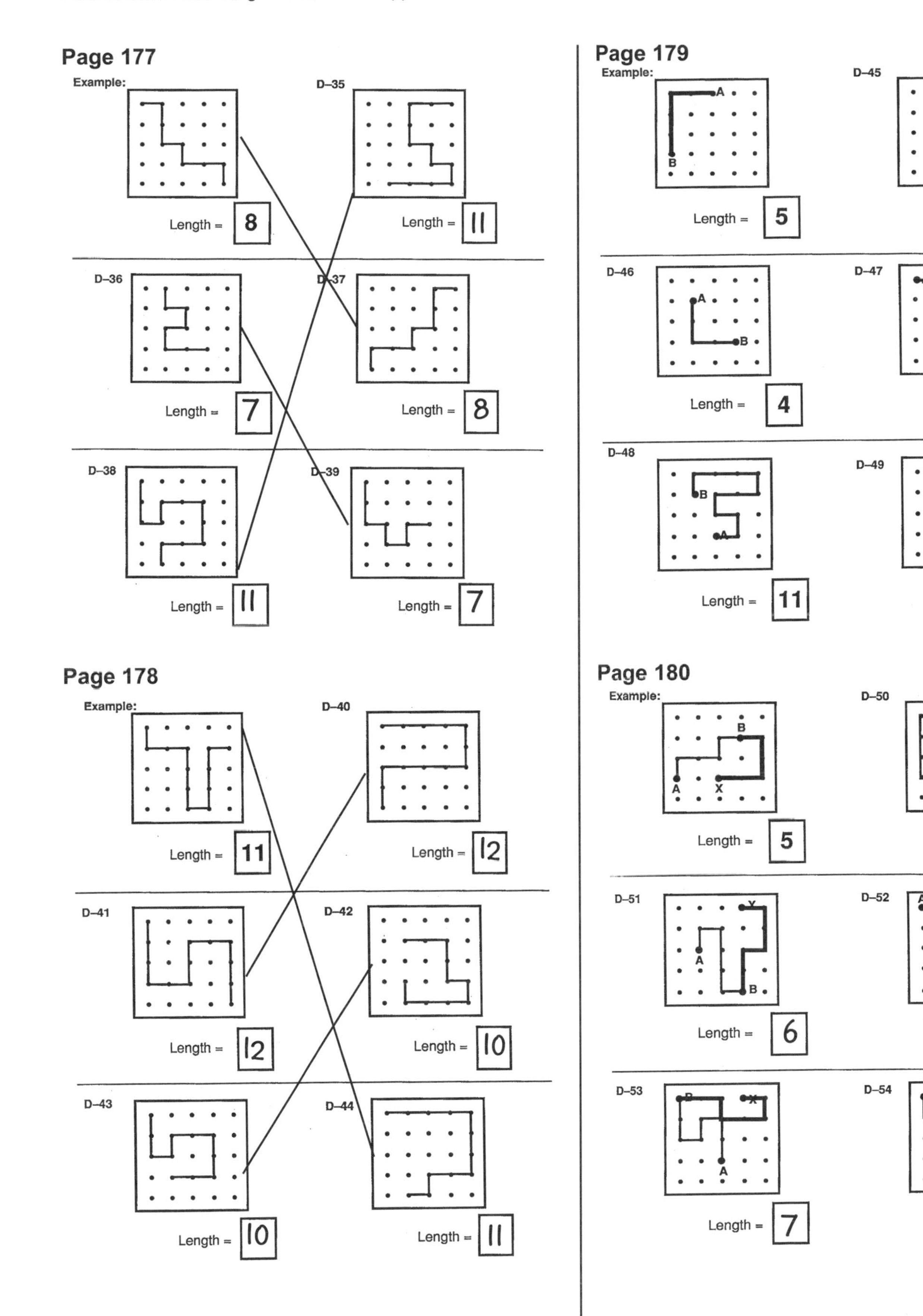
Page 177
Example:
Length = 8
D–35
Length = 11
D–36
Length = 7
D–37
Length = 8
D–38
Length = 11
D–39
Length = 7
Page 178
Example:
Length = 11
D–40
Length = 12
D–41
Length = 12
D–42
Length = 10
D–43
Length = 10
D–44
Length = 11
Page 179
Example:
A
B
Length = 5
D–45
A
B
Length = 7
D–46
A
B
Length = 4
D–47
A
B
Length = 8
D–48
B
A
Length = 11
D–49
A
B
Length = 9
Page 180
Example:
B
A
X
Length = 5
D–50
A
X
B
Length = 5
D–51
X
A
B
Length = 6
D–52
A
X
B
Length = 8
D–53
B
X
A
Length = 7
D–54
X
A
B
Length = 10

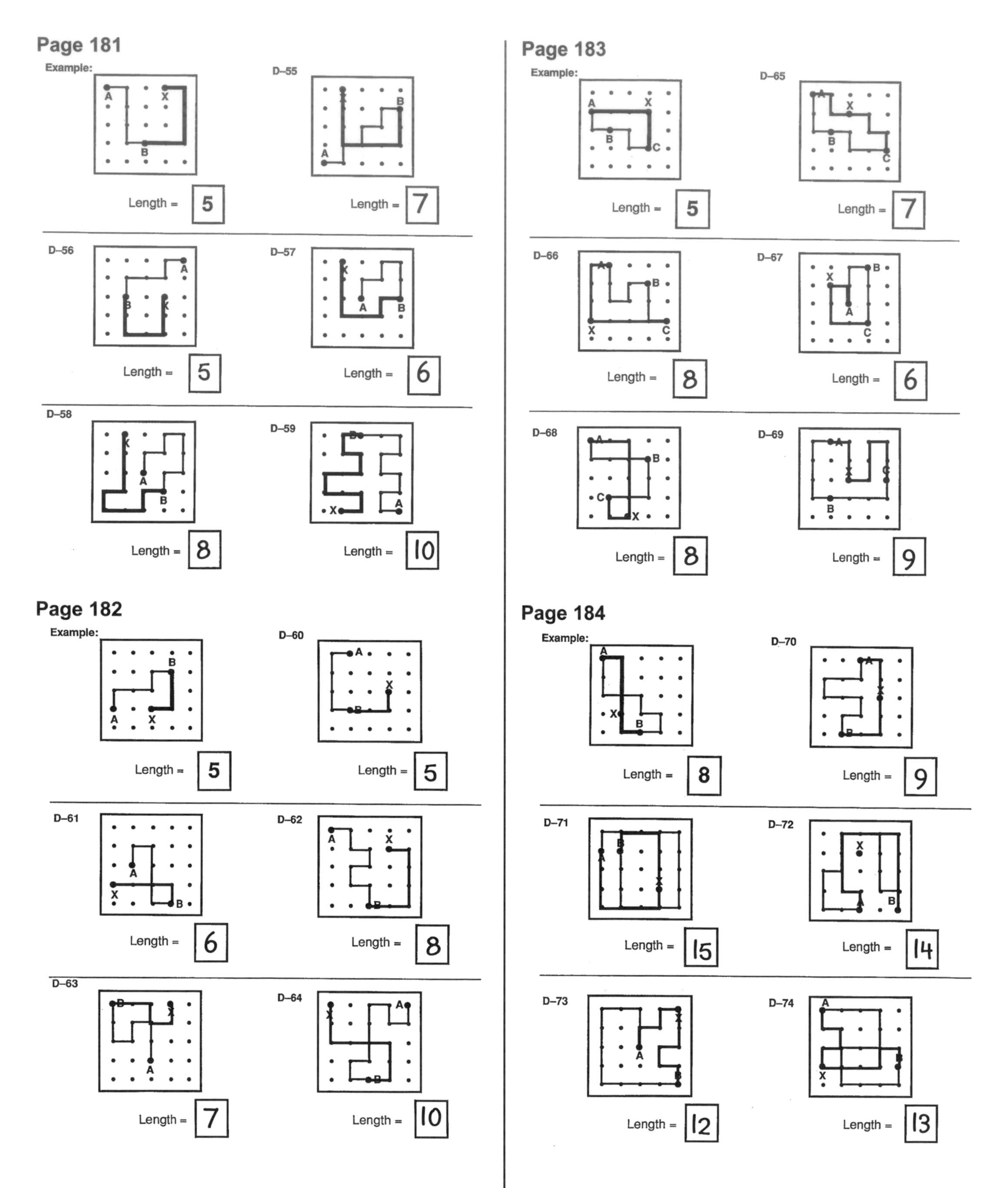
Page 181
Example:
Length = 5
D–55
Length = 7
D–56
Length = 5
D–57
Length = 6
D–58
Length = 8
D–59
Length = 10
Page 182
Example:
Length = 5
D–60
Length = 5
D–61
Length = 6
D–62
Length = 8
D–63
Length = 7
D–64
Length = 10
Page 183
Example:
Length = 5
D–65
Length = 7
D–66
Length = 8
D–67
Length = 6
D–68
Length = 8
D–69
Length = 9
Page 184
Example:
Length = 8
D–70
Length = 9
D–71
Length = 15
D–72
Length = 14
D–73
Length = 12
D–74
Length = 13

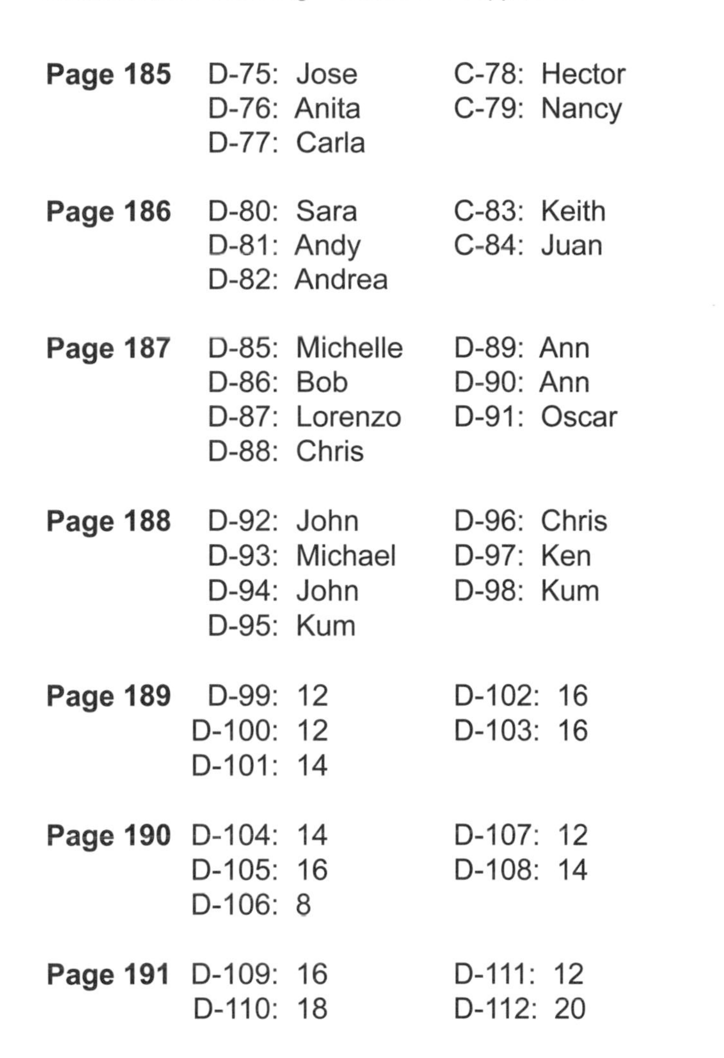

Page 185 D-75: Jose; D-76: Anita; D-77: Carla; C-78: Hector; C-79: Nancy

Page 186 D-80: Sara; D-81: Andy; D-82: Andrea; C-83: Keith; C-84: Juan

Page 187 D-85: Michelle; D-86: Bob; D-87: Lorenzo; D-88: Chris; D-89: Ann; D-90: Ann; D-91: Oscar

Page 188 D-92: John; D-93: Michael; D-94: John; D-95: Kum; D-96: Chris; D-97: Ken; D-98: Kum

Page 189 D-99: 12; D-100: 12; D-101: 14; D-102: 16; D-103: 16

Page 190 D-104: 14; D-105: 16; D-106: 8; D-107: 12; D-108: 14

Page 191 D-109: 16; D-110: 18; D-111: 12; D-112: 20

Page 192

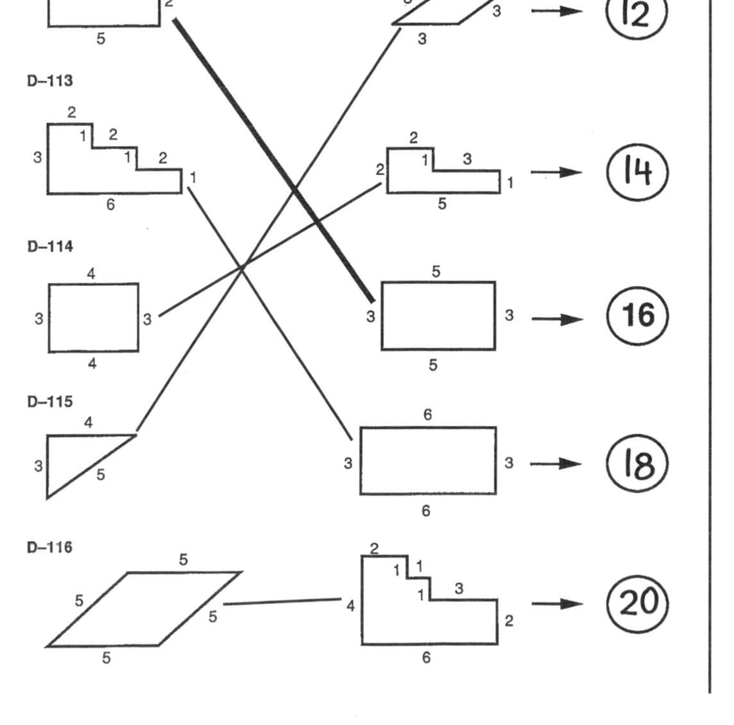

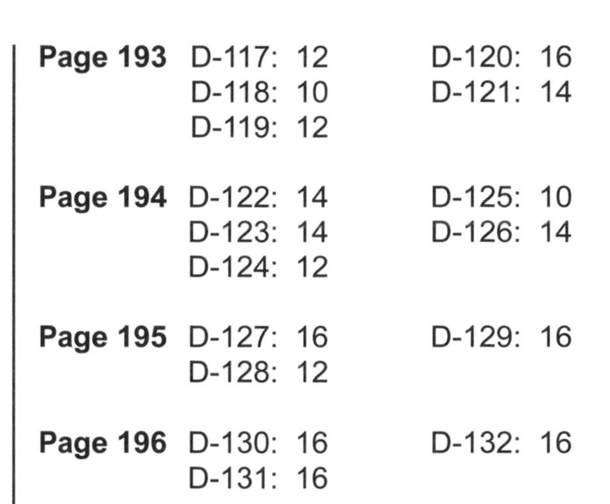

Page 193 D-117: 12; D-118: 10; D-119: 12; D-120: 16; D-121: 14

Page 194 D-122: 14; D-123: 14; D-124: 12; D-125: 10; D-126: 14

Page 195 D-127: 16; D-128: 12; D-129: 16

Page 196 D-130: 16; D-131: 16; D-132: 16

Page 197

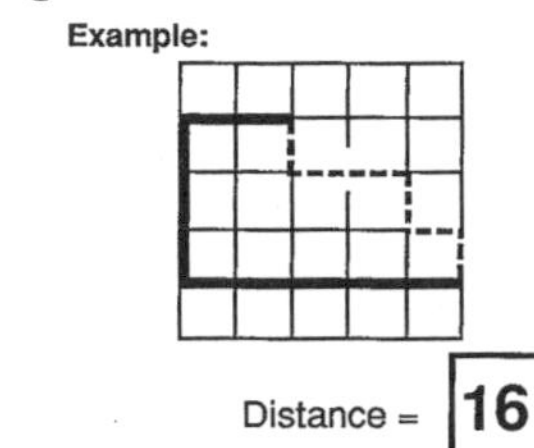

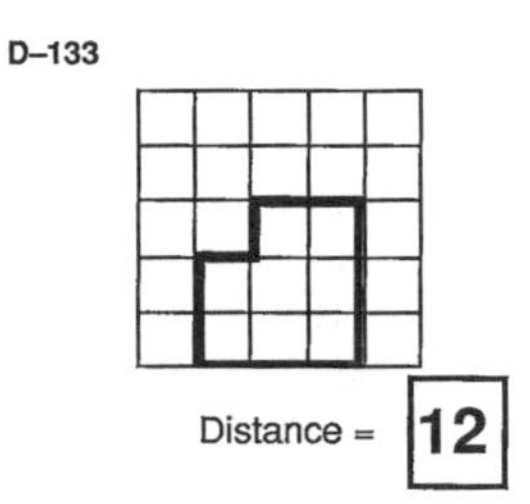

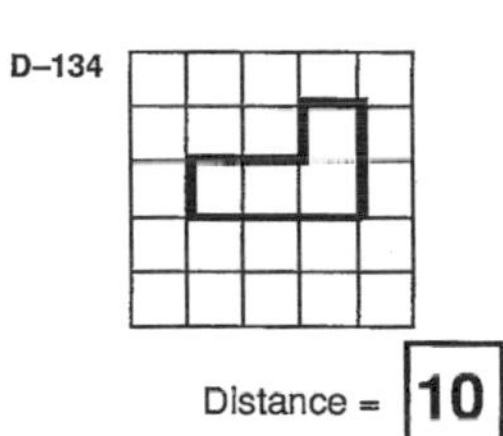

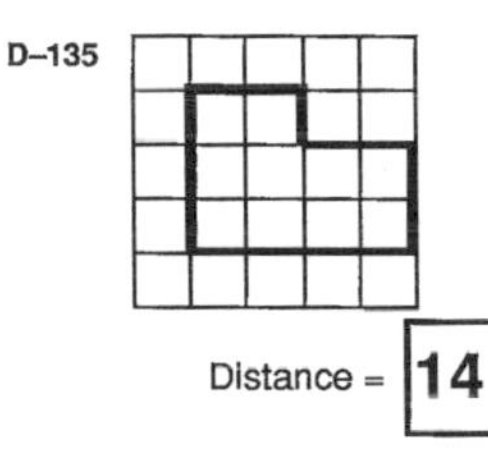

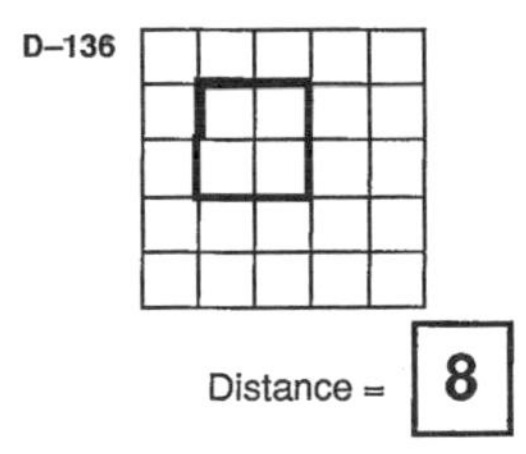

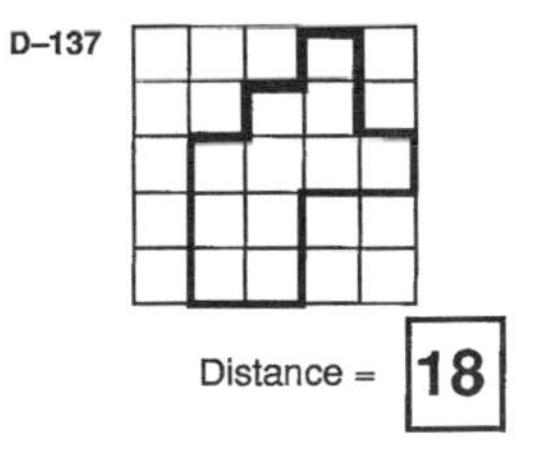

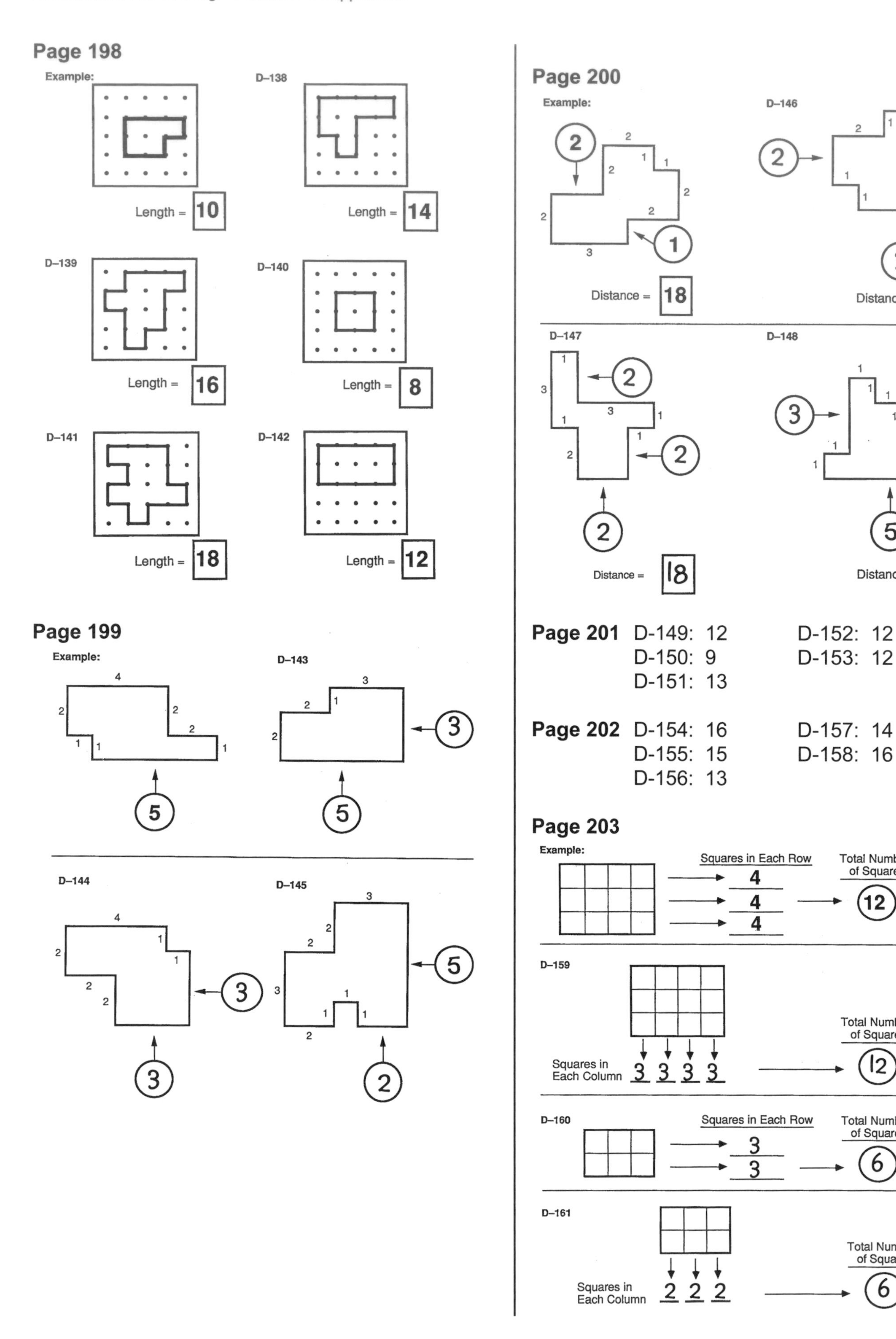

Page 198
Example:
Length = 10
D–138
Length = 14
D–139
Length = 16
D–140
Length = 8
D–141
Length = 18
D–142
Length = 12
Page 199
Example:
D–143
D–144
D–145
Page 200
Example:
Distance = 18
D–146
Distance = 18
D–147
Distance = 18
D–148
Distance = 18
Page 201 D-149: 12 D-152: 12
D-150: 9 D-153: 12
D-151: 13
Page 202 D-154: 16 D-157: 14
D-155: 15 D-158: 16
D-156: 13
Page 203
Example:
Squares in Each Row
Total Number of Squares
4
4
4
12
D–159
Total Number of Squares
Squares in Each Column 3 3 3 3
12
D–160
Squares in Each Row
Total Number of Squares
3
3
6
D–161
Total Number of Squares
Squares in Each Column 2 2 2
6

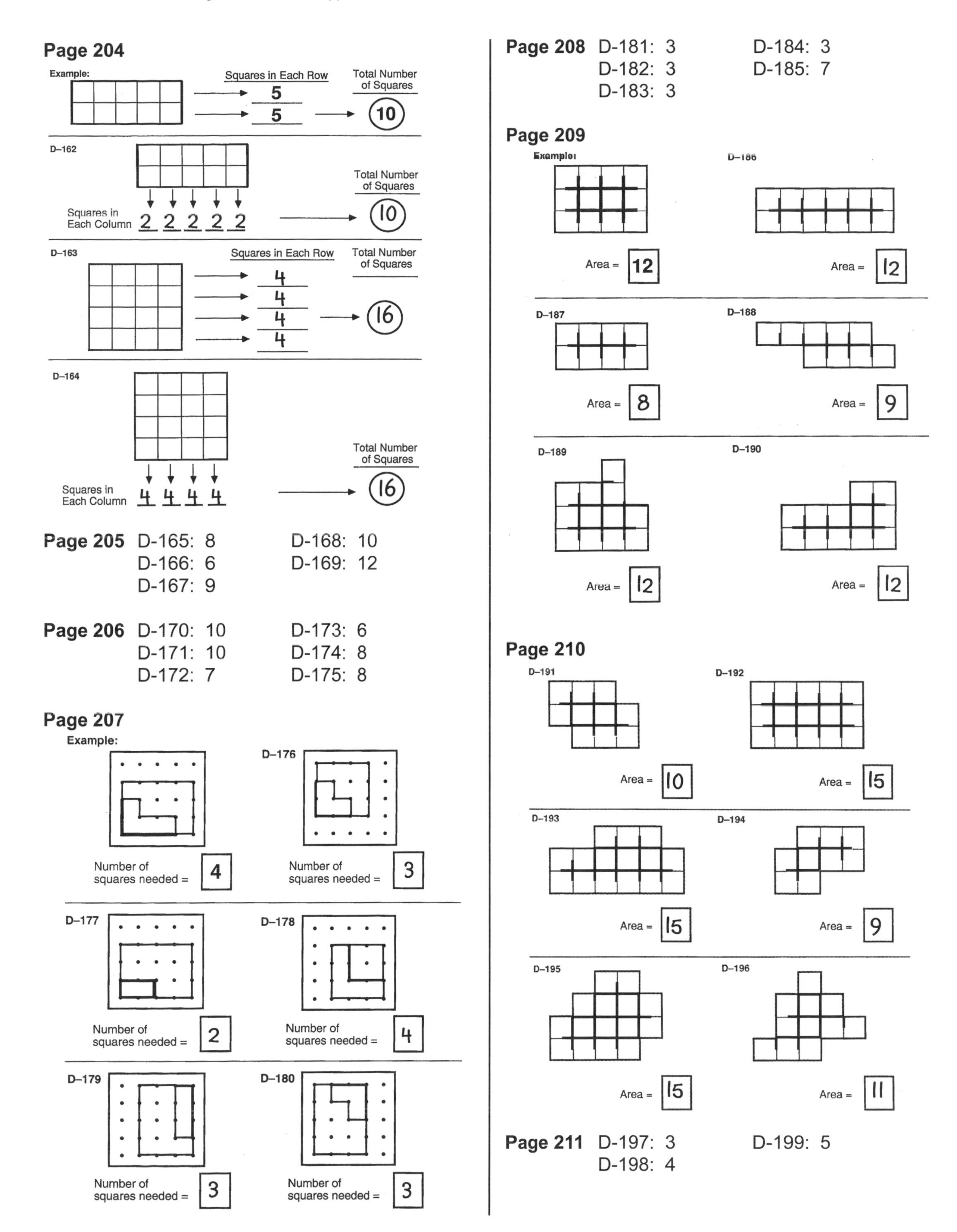
Page 204
Example:
Squares in Each Row
5
5
Total Number of Squares
10
D–162
Total Number of Squares
Squares in Each Column 2 2 2 2 2
10
D–163
Squares in Each Row
Total Number of Squares
4
4
4
4
16
D–164
Total Number of Squares
Squares in Each Column 4 4 4 4
16
Page 205 D-165: 8 D-166: 6 D-167: 9 D-168: 10 D-169: 12
Page 206 D-170: 10 D-171: 10 D-172: 7 D-173: 6 D-174: 8 D-175: 8
Page 207
Example:
Number of squares needed = 4
D–176
Number of squares needed = 3
D–177
Number of squares needed = 2
D–178
Number of squares needed = 4
D–179
Number of squares needed = 3
D–180
Number of squares needed = 3
Page 208 D-181: 3 D-182: 3 D-183: 3 D-184: 3 D-185: 7
Page 209
Example:
Area = 12
D–186
Area = 12
D–187
Area = 8
D–188
Area = 9
D–189
Area = 12
D–190
Area = 12
Page 210
D–191
Area = 10
D–192
Area = 15
D–193
Area = 15
D–194
Area = 9
D–195
Area = 15
D–196
Area = 11
Page 211 D-197: 3 D-198: 4 D-199: 5

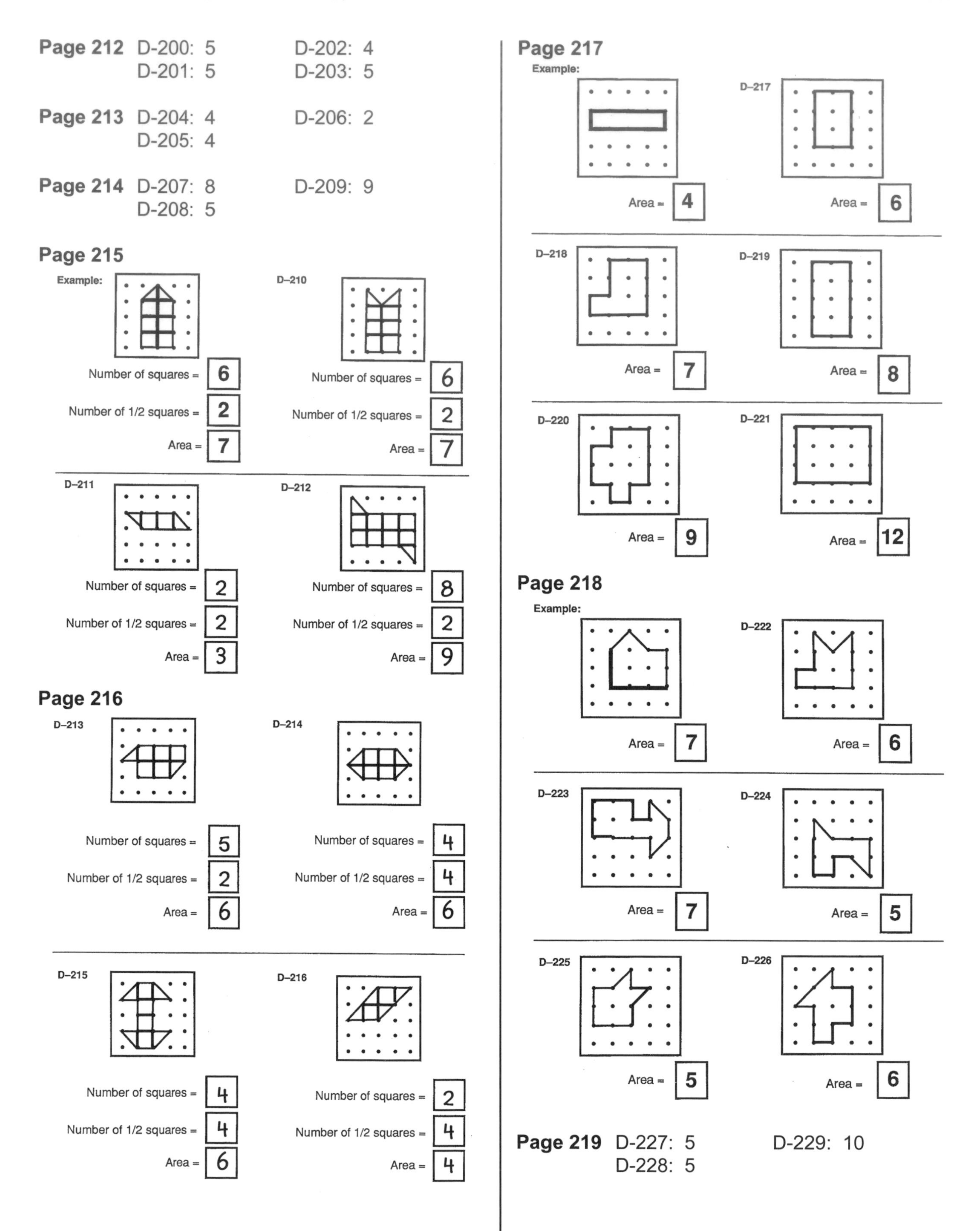

Page 212 D-200: 5 D-201: 5 D-202: 4 D-203: 5

Page 213 D-204: 4 D-205: 4 D-206: 2

Page 214 D-207: 8 D-208: 5 D-209: 9

Page 215

Example: Number of squares = 6; Number of 1/2 squares = 2; Area = 7

D-210: Number of squares = 6; Number of 1/2 squares = 2; Area = 7

D-211: Number of squares = 2; Number of 1/2 squares = 2; Area = 3

D-212: Number of squares = 8; Number of 1/2 squares = 2; Area = 9

Page 216

D-213: Number of squares = 5; Number of 1/2 squares = 2; Area = 6

D-214: Number of squares = 4; Number of 1/2 squares = 4; Area = 6

D-215: Number of squares = 4; Number of 1/2 squares = 4; Area = 6

D-216: Number of squares = 2; Number of 1/2 squares = 4; Area = 4

Page 217

Example: Area = 4

D-217: Area = 6

D-218: Area = 7

D-219: Area = 8

D-220: Area = 9

D-221: Area = 12

Page 218

Example: Area = 7

D-222: Area = 6

D-223: Area = 7

D-224: Area = 5

D-225: Area = 5

D-226: Area = 6

Page 219 D-227: 5 D-228: 5 D-229: 10

Page 220

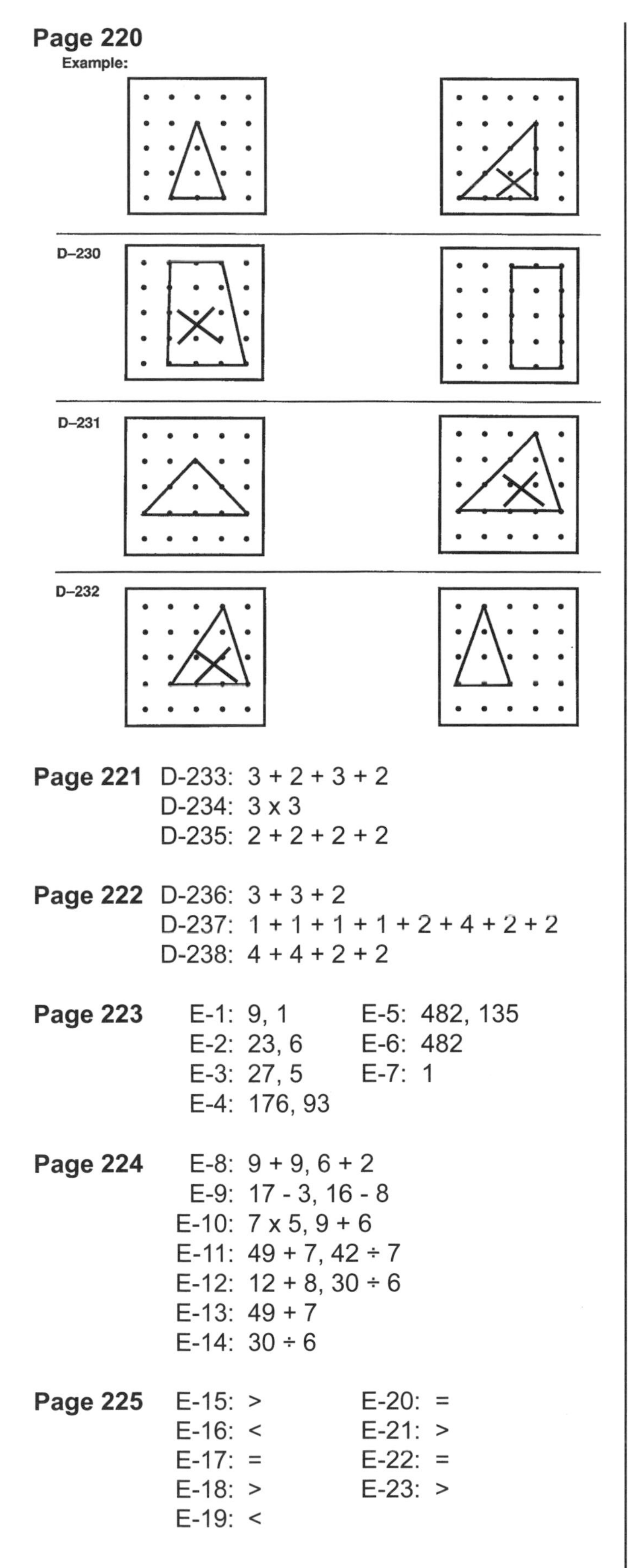

Page 221
D-233: 3 + 2 + 3 + 2
D-234: 3 x 3
D-235: 2 + 2 + 2 + 2

Page 222
D-236: 3 + 3 + 2
D-237: 1 + 1 + 1 + 1 + 2 + 4 + 2 + 2
D-238: 4 + 4 + 2 + 2

Page 223
E-1: 9, 1
E-2: 23, 6
E-3: 27, 5
E-4: 176, 93
E-5: 482, 135
E-6: 482
E-7: 1

Page 224
E-8: 9 + 9, 6 + 2
E-9: 17 - 3, 16 - 8
E-10: 7 x 5, 9 + 6
E-11: 49 + 7, 42 ÷ 7
E-12: 12 + 8, 30 ÷ 6
E-13: 49 + 7
E-14: 30 ÷ 6

Page 225
E-15: >
E-16: <
E-17: =
E-18: >
E-19: <
E-20: =
E-21: >
E-22: =
E-23: >

Page 226
E-24: a. 46
E-25: b. 23 + 22
E-26: c. 16 + 18
E-27: c. 15 +14
E-28: a. 6 x 7
E-29: b. 9
E-30: b. 15
E-31: b. 9
E-32: a. 13 + 13

Page 227
E-33: 25, 34
E-34: 19, 23, 6
E-35: 8
E-36: 11, 9
E-37: 19, 15
E-38: 36
E-39: 15, 20, 35

Page 228
E-40: 3, 8, 8
E-41: 5, 5, 17
E-42: 8, 12, 16
E-43: 11, 16, 23
E-44: 35, 21, 13
E-45: 9, 7, 7
E-46: 36, 40, 40

Page 229
E-47: 6 x 5 > 25
E-48: 9 + 8 > 15
E-49: 18 - 7 < 18
E-50: 16 + 12 = 28
E-51: 14 < 13 + 3
E-52: 17 - 7 > 7
E-53: 50 > 50 - 32

Page 230

Example:	3 + 4	<	12	E–54	5 + 6	=	11
	3 + 4	>	5		5 + 7	>	11
	3 + 4	=	7		5 × 7	>	11
E–55	9 × 9	>	18	E–56	4	<	12 – 6
	9 + 9	=	18		7	>	12 – 6
	9 – 9	<	18		5	<	12 – 6
E–57	20	=	13 + 7	E–58	19 + 7	<	27
	20	=	7 + 13		8 + 19	=	27
	20	>	13 – 7		18 + 19	>	27
E–59	23 + 23	<	60	E–60	90	>	43 + 43
	37 + 15	<	60		90	>	43 × 2
	15 × 4	=	60		90	>	43 – 43

Page 231
E-61: 9
E-62: 10, 8
E-63: 0
E-64: 4, 8
E-65: 5
E-66: 13, 10
E-67: 3, 4

Page 232
E-68: 2, 3, 6
E-69: 73, 83
E-70: 2, 3
E-71: 0, 2
E-72: 7
E-73: 10, 12, 16
E-74: 17, 19
E-75: 6, 16, 24

Page 233
E-76: -
E-77: x
E-78: x
E-79: ÷
E-80: -
E-81: ÷
E-82: ÷

Page 234
E-83: x
E-84: +, x
E-85: +, -, x
E-86: +, x
E-87: ÷
E-88: ÷
E-89: -
E-90: x
E-91: x

Page 235
E-92: b. 8, 9 c. 9, 9
E-93: a. 6, 7 b. 6, 6
E-94: d: 17, 8
E-95: b. 63, 7
E-96: a. 7, 7

Page 236

Example:
a. 3, 4 → 8 + 5 > 7 + 5
b. 5, 5
c. 3, 5 → 8 + 3 < 7 + 5

E–97
a. 9, 2 → 9 × 9 > 2 + 9
b. 2, 9 → 2 × 9 = 9 + 9
c. 0, 3

E–98
a. 24, 3 → 24 ÷ 3 > 18 ÷ 3
b. 18, 3
c. 6, 6 → 6 ÷ 3 < 18 ÷ 6

E–99
a. 23, 23 → 12 + 23 = 23 + 12
b. 5, 12
c. 12, 5 → 12 + 12 > 5 + 12

E–100
a. 24, 48 → 54 – 24 > 54 – 48
b. 48, 24 → 54 – 48 < 54 – 24
c. 24, 24

Page 237
E-101: b. 16, 19, 22, 25
E-102: a. 1, 5, 1, 6
E-103: c. 25, 20, 15, 10
E-104: c. 10, 9, 12, 11

Page 238
E-105: c. 1, 5, 9, 13
E-106: a. 6, 9, 12, 15
E-107: b. 40, 35, 30, 25
E-108: c. 2, 5, 8, 11

Page 239
E-109: 14, 19, 34
E-110: 21, 19, 17
E-111: 35, 40, 60, 65
E-112: 2, 6, 8
E-113: 10, 13, 16
E-114: 38, 35, 23, 20
E-115: 9, 15, 21, 27

Page 240
E-116: a. 55, 60, 65, 70
E-117: c. 19, 21, 23, 25
E-118: c. 30, 32, 34, 36
E-119: a. 34, 39, 44, 49

Page 241
E-120: 9
E-121: 8

Page 242
E-122: 9
E-123: 4
E-124: 3

Page 243
E-125: X on 9
E-126: X on 13

Page 244
E-127: X on 2
E-128: X on 16
E-129: X on 34

Page 245
E-130: 20
E-131: 7

Page 246
E-132: 22
E-133: 10
E-134: 35

Page 247
E-135: 14, 18, 20
E-136: 5, 5, 5
E-137: 6, 17, 13
E-138: 11, 3, 0

Page 248
E-139: 18, 12, 27
E-140: 0, 1, 0
E-141: 12, 22, 18
E-142: 2, 2, 2
E-143: 3, 7, 2

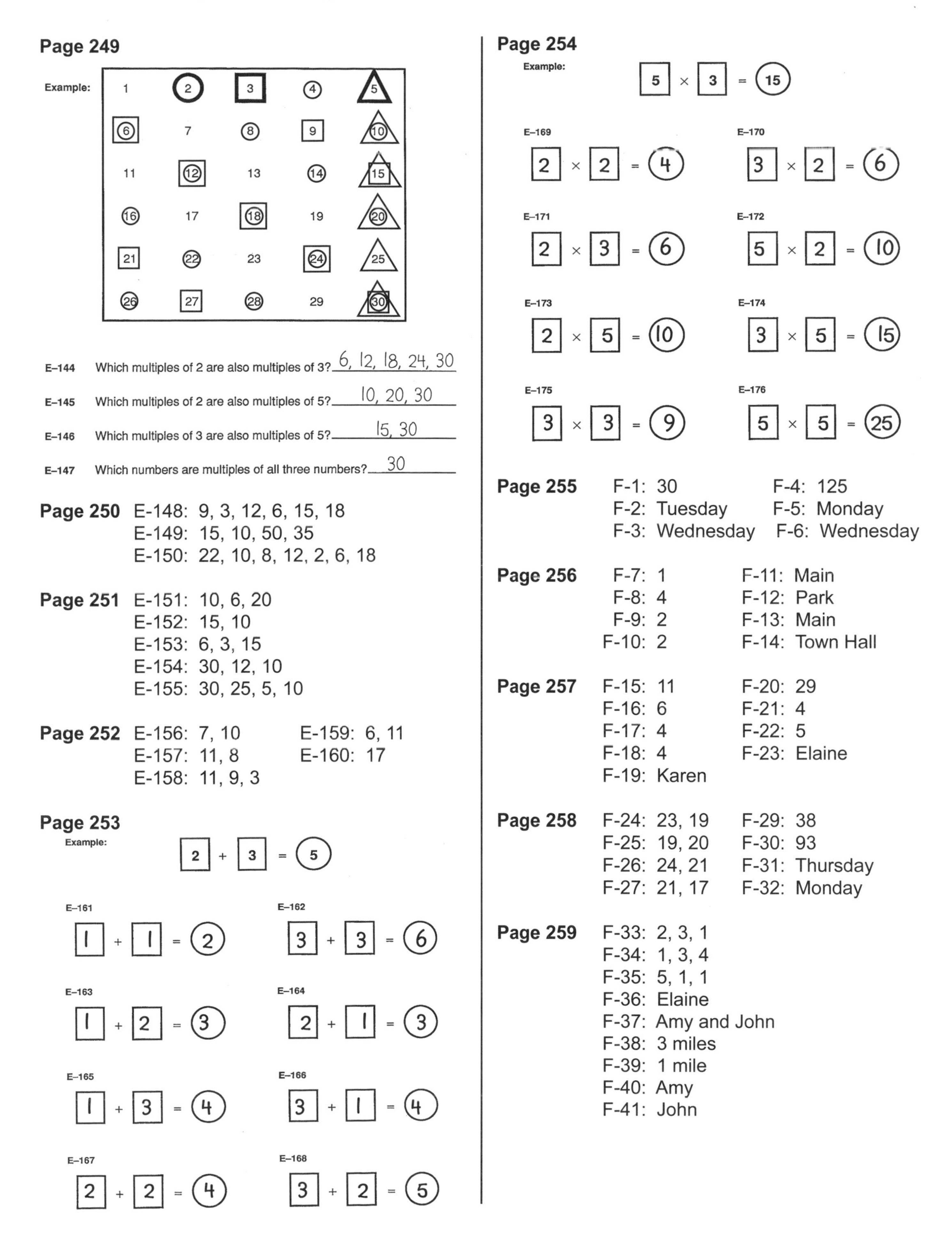

Page 249

Example:

1	2	3	4	5
6	7	8	9	10
11	12	13	14	15
16	17	18	19	20
21	22	23	24	25
26	27	28	29	30

E–144 Which multiples of 2 are also multiples of 3? 6, 12, 18, 24, 30

E–145 Which multiples of 2 are also multiples of 5? 10, 20, 30

E–146 Which multiples of 3 are also multiples of 5? 15, 30

E–147 Which numbers are multiples of all three numbers? 30

Page 250

E-148: 9, 3, 12, 6, 15, 18
E-149: 15, 10, 50, 35
E-150: 22, 10, 8, 12, 2, 6, 18

Page 251

E-151: 10, 6, 20
E-152: 15, 10
E-153: 6, 3, 15
E-154: 30, 12, 10
E-155: 30, 25, 5, 10

Page 252

E-156: 7, 10
E-157: 11, 8
E-158: 11, 9, 3
E-159: 6, 11
E-160: 17

Page 253

Example: 2 + 3 = 5

E–161: 1 + 1 = 2
E–162: 3 + 3 = 6
E–163: 1 + 2 = 3
E–164: 2 + 1 = 3
E–165: 1 + 3 = 4
E–166: 3 + 1 = 4
E–167: 2 + 2 = 4
E–168: 3 + 2 = 5

Page 254

Example: 5 × 3 = 15

E–169: 2 × 2 = 4
E–170: 3 × 2 = 6
E–171: 2 × 3 = 6
E–172: 5 × 2 = 10
E–173: 2 × 5 = 10
E–174: 3 × 5 = 15
E–175: 3 × 3 = 9
E–176: 5 × 5 = 25

Page 255

F-1: 30
F-2: Tuesday
F-3: Wednesday
F-4: 125
F-5: Monday
F-6: Wednesday

Page 256

F-7: 1
F-8: 4
F-9: 2
F-10: 2
F-11: Main
F-12: Park
F-13: Main
F-14: Town Hall

Page 257

F-15: 11
F-16: 6
F-17: 4
F-18: 4
F-19: Karen
F-20: 29
F-21: 4
F-22: 5
F-23: Elaine

Page 258

F-24: 23, 19
F-25: 19, 20
F-26: 24, 21
F-27: 21, 17
F-29: 38
F-30: 93
F-31: Thursday
F-32: Monday

Page 259

F-33: 2, 3, 1
F-34: 1, 3, 4
F-35: 5, 1, 1
F-36: Elaine
F-37: Amy and John
F-38: 3 miles
F-39: 1 mile
F-40: Amy
F-41: John

Page 260
F-42: 16, 14
F-43: 5, 8
F-44: 8, 6
F-45: 30
F-46: Mr. Dodd's
F-47: 28
F-48: 29
F-49: 43
F-50: Ms. Gilman's

Page 261
F-51: 50°F
F-52: Wednesday
F-53: Friday
F-54: beginning
F-55: Thursday, Sunday

Page 262
F-56: Karen
F-57: John
F-58: Elaine
F-59: Amy, Carla
F-60: 4 hours

Page 263

Date	Height in Cm
June 1	2
June 8	2
June 15	4
June 22	6
June 29	10
July 6	16
July 13	18

Use the table to complete the following graph.

F–61

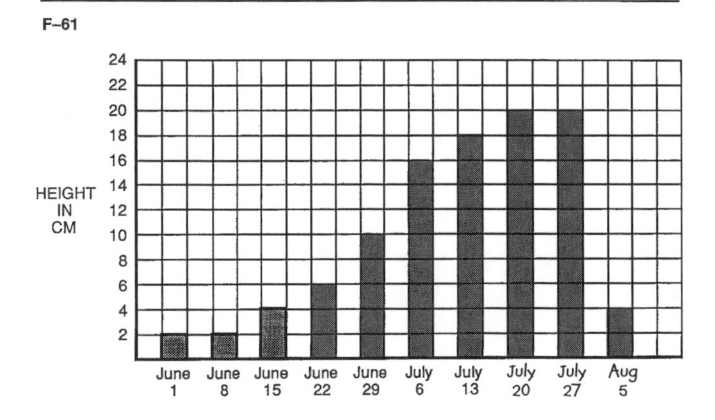

Page 264
F-62: 10 cm
F-63: July 13
F-64: 16 cm
F-65: 6 cm
F-66: 6 cm
F-67: It stayed the same height.
F-68: June 29 - July 6
F-69: July 20 - July 27
F-70: Maybe it was cut or died.

Page 265

Ann ✓✓✓✓✓✓✓✓
Carla ✓✓✓✓✓
Edward ✓✓✓✓✓✓✓✓✓
Brian ✓✓✓✓✓✓
Doug ✓✓✓✓

Use the results to complete the following bar graph.

F–71

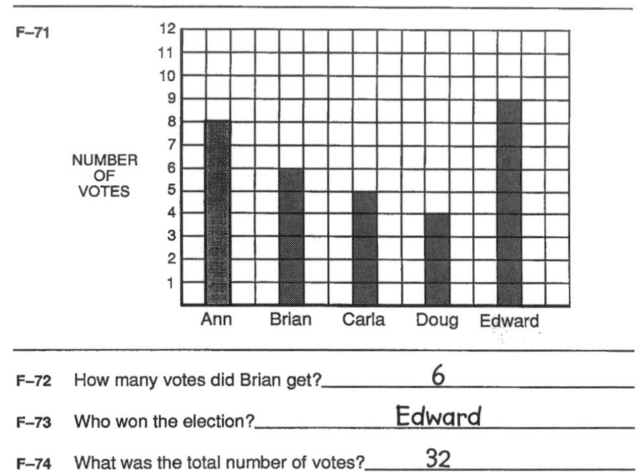

F–72 How many votes did Brian get? 6
F–73 Who won the election? Edward
F–74 What was the total number of votes? 32

Page 266

Day	TEMPERATURE IN FAHRENHEIT	
	High	Low
Monday	72	52
Tuesday	68	48
Wednesday	70	50
Thursday	74	52
Friday	76	56
Saturday	78	60
Sunday	80	68

Use the table to complete the following bar graph.

F–75

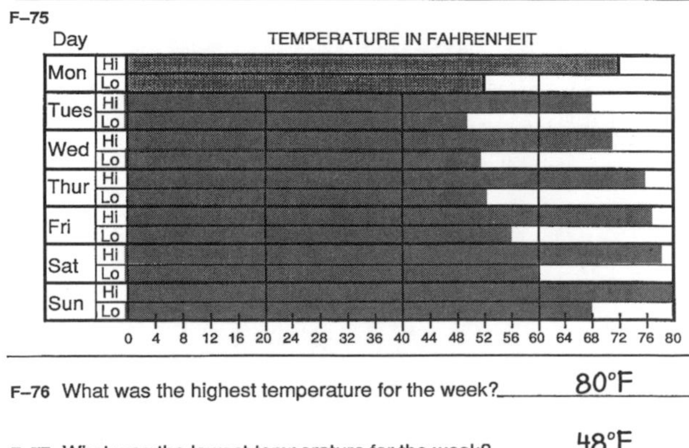

F–76 What was the highest temperature for the week? 80°F
F–77 What was the lowest temperature for the week? 48°F

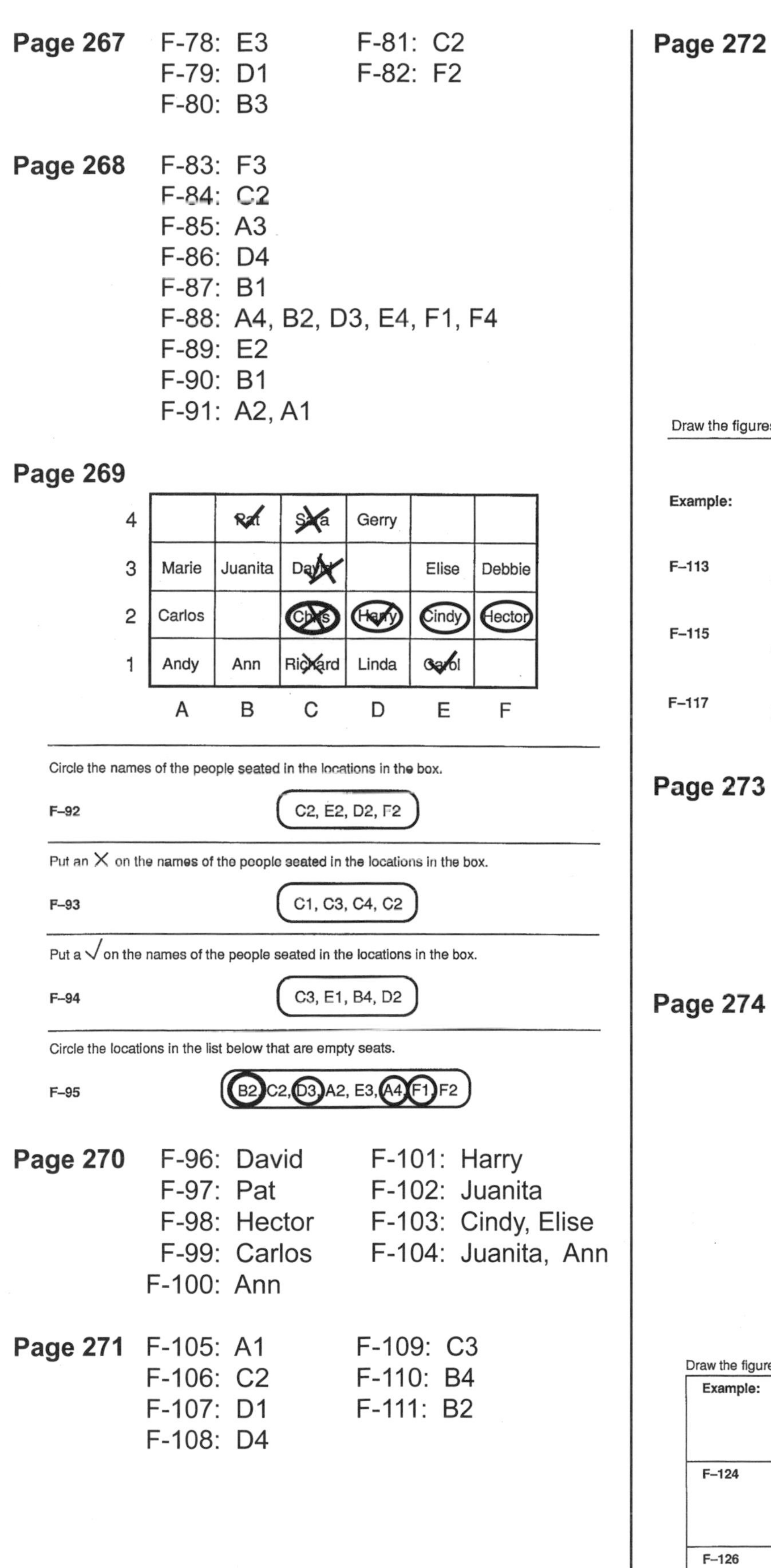

Page 267
F-78: E3
F-79: D1
F-80: B3
F-81: C2
F-82: F2

Page 268
F-83: F3
F-84: C2
F-85: A3
F-86: D4
F-87: B1
F-88: A4, B2, D3, E4, F1, F4
F-89: E2
F-90: B1
F-91: A2, A1

Page 269

	A	B	C	D	E	F
4		Pat	Sara	Gerry		
3	Marie	Juanita	David		Elise	Debbie
2	Carlos		Chris	Harry	Cindy	Hector
1	Andy	Ann	Richard	Linda	Carol	

Circle the names of the people seated in the locations in the box.

F-92 C2, E2, D2, F2

Put an X on the names of the people seated in the locations in the box.

F-93 C1, C3, C4, C2

Put a √ on the names of the people seated in the locations in the box.

F-94 C3, E1, B4, D2

Circle the locations in the list below that are empty seats.

F-95 B2, C2, D3, A2, E3, A4, F1, F2

Page 270
F-96: David
F-97: Pat
F-98: Hector
F-99: Carlos
F-100: Ann
F-101: Harry
F-102: Juanita
F-103: Cindy, Elise
F-104: Juanita, Ann

Page 271
F-105: A1
F-106: C2
F-107: D1
F-108: D4
F-109: C3
F-110: B4
F-111: B2

Page 272

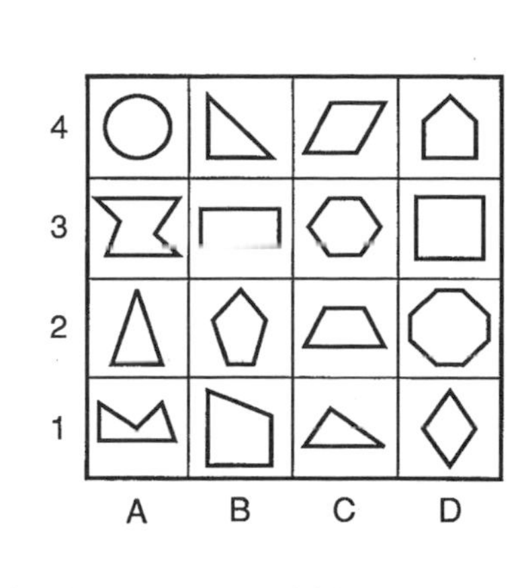

Draw the figures from the chart above next to their locations given below.

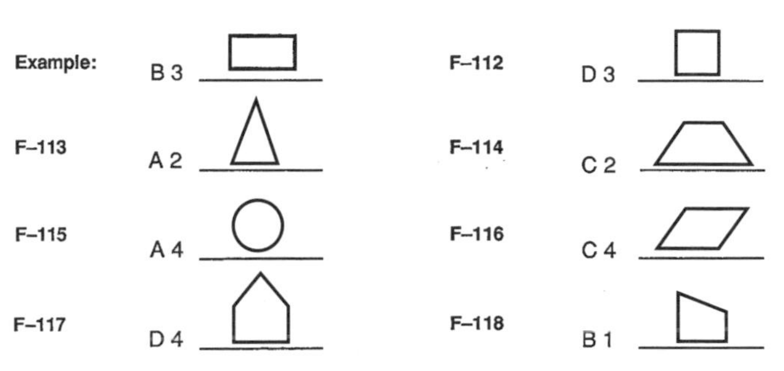

Page 273
F-119: e. Figures with more than four sides.
F-120: a. Triangles
F-121: b. Figures with four sides.
F-122: c. Figures with one or more square corners.

Page 274

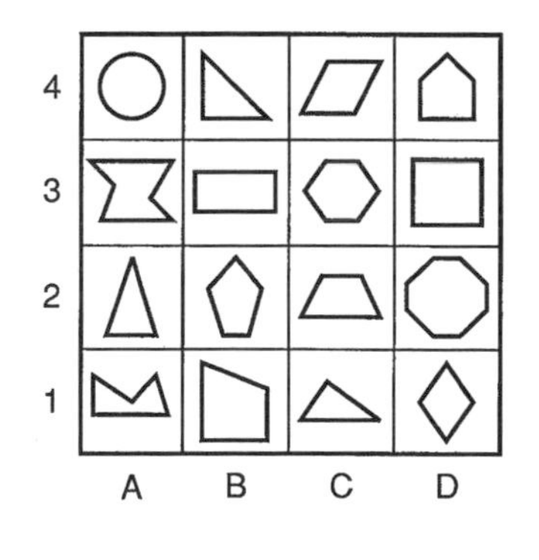

Draw the figures below that are in the following locations on the chart.

Example: Between B 3 and D 3	**F-123** Between C 2 and A 2
F-124 Between D 2 and D 4	**F-125** Between A 3 and A 1
F-126 Below B 2	**F-127** Above B 2

Page 275

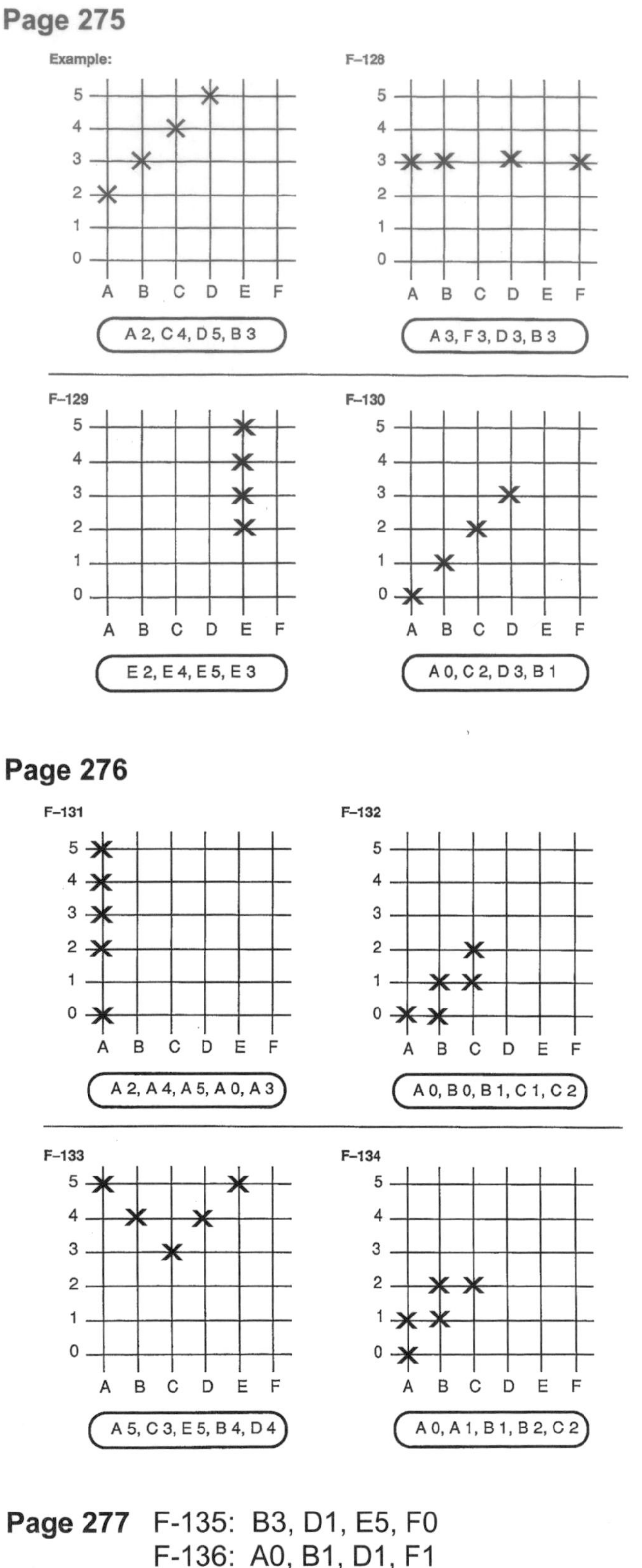

Page 277 F-135: B3, D1, E5, F0
F-136: A0, B1, D1, F1
F-137: C4, D3, E2, F1

Page 278 F-138: C0, C2, C3, C4, C5
F-139: A3, B3, C3, D3, E3
F-140: A0, B0, B1, B2, C2
F-141: B1, C2, D3, E2, F1

Page 279 F-142: C2, D2, E2, E3, E4
F-143: C4, C3, D3, D2, E2
F-144: B0, C0, C1, B1, B2

Page 280 F-145: A0, B0, B1, C2, D3
F-146: C3, D3, D2, E1, F1
F-147: A0, B1, C2, D3, E4
F-148: A0, B1, C0, D1, E0

Page 281

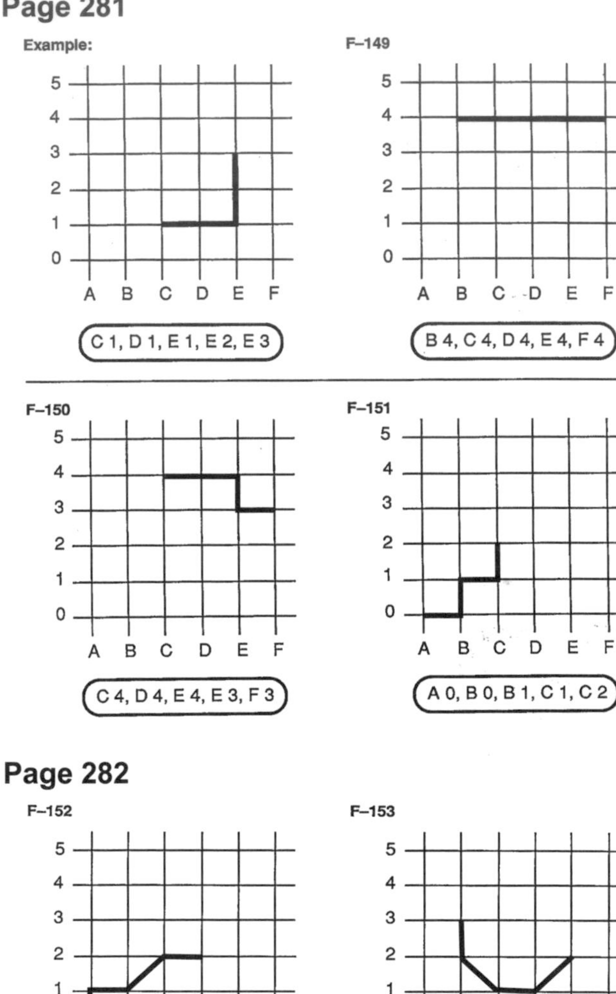

Page 282

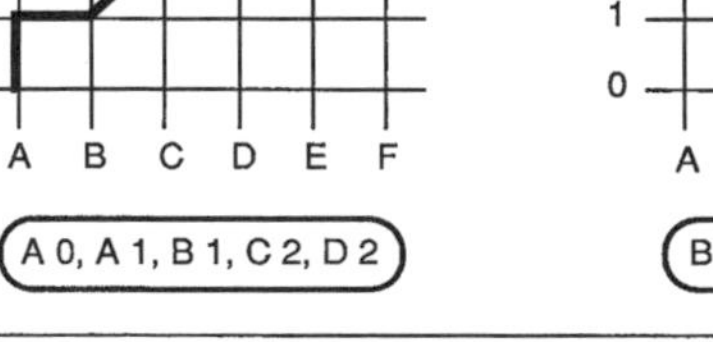

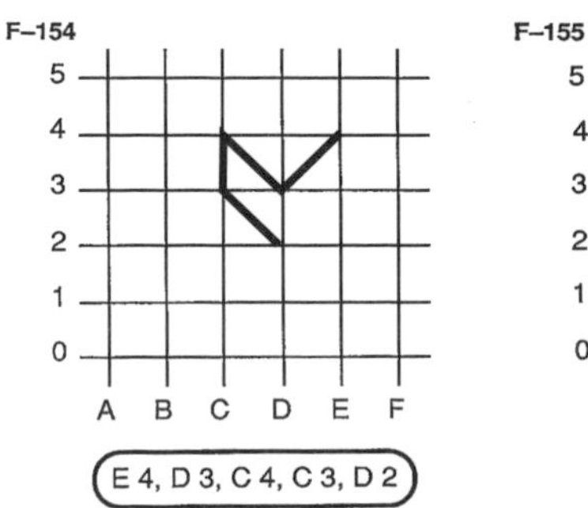

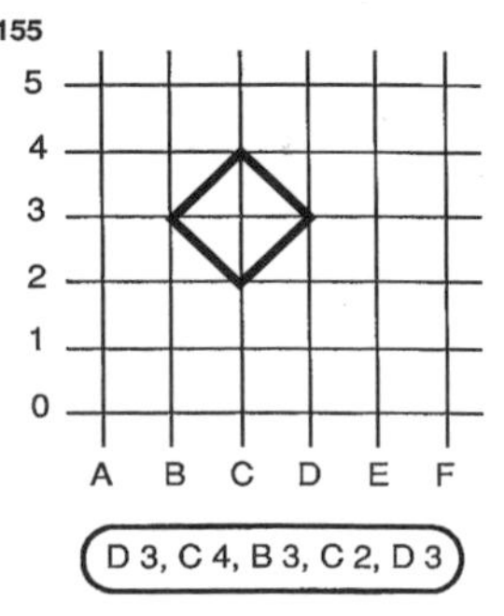